Current Aspects of
BIOCHEMICAL ENERGETICS

Fritz Lipmann Dedicatory Volume

FRITZ LIPMANN

Current Aspects of
BIOCHEMICAL ENERGETICS

Fritz Lipmann Dedicatory Volume

Edited by

NATHAN O. KAPLAN
Graduate Department of Biochemistry
Brandeis University
Waltham, Massachusetts

and

EUGENE P. KENNEDY
Department of Biological Chemistry
Harvard University Medical School
Boston, Massachusetts

ACADEMIC PRESS   *New York • London • 1966*

ACADEMIC PRESS, INC.
111 Fifth Avenue, New York, New York 10003

United Kingdom Edition published by
ACADEMIC PRESS, INC. (LONDON) LTD.
Berkeley Square House, London W.1

LIBRARY OF CONGRESS CATALOG CARD NUMBER: 66-29877

Second Printing, 1969

PRINTED IN THE UNITED STATES OF AMERICA

List of Contributors

Numbers in parentheses indicate the pages on which the authors' contributions begin.

Charles M. Allen, Jr. (401), Department of Chemistry, Harvard University, Cambridge, Massachusetts

James Baddiley (371), Department of Organic Chemistry, The University, Newcastle upon Tyne, England

H. A. Barker (97), Biochemistry Department, University of California, Berkeley, California

H. Chantrenne (33), Faculté de Sciences, Université Libre de Bruxelle, Brussels, Belgium

Carl F. Cori (127), Department of Biological Chemistry, Washington University School of Medicine, St. Louis, Missouri

Michael Doudoroff (385), Department of Bacteriology and Immunology, University of California, Berkeley, California

V. A. Engelhardt (213), Institute of Molecular Biology, Academy of Sciences, Moscow, U. S. S. R.

G. Gottschalk (97), Biochemistry Department, University of California, Berkeley, California

Helene Graetz (111), Institut für Biochemie der Deutschen Akademie der Wissenschaften zu Berlin, Berlin-Buch, Germany

John D. Gregory (257), The Rockefeller University, New York, New York

W. Z. Hassid (351), Department of Biochemistry, University of California, Berkeley, California

Katsumi Hata (315), Laboratory of Organic Chemistry and Enzymology, Fordham University, Bronx, New York

Richard S. Hayward (227), Argonne Cancer Research Hospital and the Department of Biochemistry, University of Chicago, Chicago, Illinois

Ernst Helmreich (127), Department of Biological Chemistry, Washington University School of Medicine, St. Louis, Missouri

H. Hilz (413), Physiologisch-Chemisches Institut der Universität Hamburg, Hamburg, Germany

Mahlon B. Hoagland (199), Department of Bacteriology and Immunology, Harvard Medical School, Boston, Massachusetts

Rollin D. Hotchkiss (237), The Rockefeller University, New York, New York

Akio Iwashima (343), Biochemical Institute, Kyoto Prefectural University of Medicine, Kyoto, Japan

William P. Jencks (273), Graduate Department of Biochemistry, Brandeis University, Waltham, Massachusetts

Mary Ellen Jones (401), Graduate Department of Biochemistry, Brandeis University, Waltham, Massachusetts[1]

Herman M. Kalckar (1), Biochemical Research Laboratory, Massachusetts General Hospital and Harvard Medical School, Boston, Massachusetts

Nathan O. Kaplan (447), Graduate Department of Biochemistry, Brandeis University, Waltham, Massachusetts

Simon Karpatkin (127), Department of Biological Chemistry, Washington University School of Medicine, St. Louis, Missouri[2]

Eugene P. Kennedy (433), Department of Biological Chemistry, Harvard University Medical School, Boston, Massachusetts

Berma M. Kinsey (331), Division of Biochemistry, Department of Biology, Massachusetts Institute of Technology, Cambridge, Massachusetts

L. L. Kisselev (213), Institute of Molecular Biology, Academy of Sciences, Moscow, U. S. S. R.

M. Kittler (83), Physiologisch-Chemisches Institut der Universität Hamburg, Hamburg, Germany

H. A. Krebs (83), Department of Biochemistry, University of Oxford, Oxford, England

---

[1] Present address: Department of Biochemistry, School of Medicine, University of North Carolina, Chapel Hill, North Carolina.

[2] Present address: Department of Medicine, New York University Medical School, New York, New York.

P. *Langen* (111), Institut für Biochemie der Deutschen Akademie der Wissenschafen zu Berlin, Berlin-Buch, Germany

Jean Legault-Demare (227), Argonne Cancer Research Hospital and the Department of Biochemistry, University of Chicago, Chicago, Illinois[3]

K. *Lohmann* (111), Institut für Biochemie der Deutschen Akademie der Wissenschaften zu Berlin, Berlin-Buch, Germany

W. F. *Loomis* (173), Graduate Department of Biochemistry, Brandeis University, Waltham, Massachusetts

David Nachmansohn (145), Departments of Biochemistry and Neurology, College of Physicians and Surgeons, Columbia University, New York, New York

Yoshitsugu Nose (343), Biochemical Institute, Kyoto Prefectural University of Medicine, Kyoto, Japan

F. F. *Nord* (315), Laboratory for Organic Chemistry and Enzymology, Fordham University, Bronx, New York

G. *David Novelli* (183), Biology Division, Oak Ridge National Laboratory, Oak Ridge, Tennessee

Jane Harting Park (299), Department of Physiology, Vanderbilt University Medical School, Nashville, Tennessee

Gertrude E. Perlmann (265), The Rockefeller University, New York, New York

Rudolph A. Peters (77), Department of Biochemistry, University of Cambridge, Cambridge, England

Elliott Richelson (401), Graduate Department of Biochemistry, Brandeis University, Waltham, Massachusetts[4]

P. W. *Robbins* (331), Division of Biochemistry, Department of Biology, Massachusetts Institute of Technology, Cambridge, Massachusetts

---

[3] Present address: Institut du Radium, Facultes des Sciences, Orsay (Essonne), France.

[4] Present address: School of Medicine, The Johns Hopkins University, Baltimore, Maryland.

R. Seifert (413), Physiologisch-Chemisches Institut der Universität Hamburg, Hamburg, Germany

Morris Soodak (459), Graduate Department of Biochemistry, Brandeis University, Waltham, Massachusetts

E. R. Stadtman (39), National Institutes of Health, Bethesda, Maryland

Albert Szent-Györgyi (63), Institute for Muscle Research, Marine Biological Laboratory, Woods Hole, Massachusetts

C. B. van Niel (9), Hopkins Marine Station of Stanford University, Pacific Grove, California

George Wald (27), Harvard University, Cambridge, Massachusetts

Otto Warburg (103), Max-Planck-Institut for Cell Physiology, Berlin-Dahlem, Germany

Samuel B. Weiss (227), Argonne Cancer Research Hospital and the Department of Biochemistry, University of Chicago, Chicago, Illinois

Preface

The extraordinary development of biology in the mid-twentieth century constitutes a remarkable chapter in the history of science. On the occasion of the one-hundredth anniversary of the founding of the National Academy of Sciences of the United States, Theodosius Dobzhansky pointed out . . . "that despite the unprecedented advances in the physical sciences and the technologies based on them, which we have witnessed, our time may stand in the history of science partly, if not mainly, for major advances in the study of life."

Fritz Lipmann is one of the few who may be regarded as the founders of modern biology. His contributions to biochemistry at the experimental level have ranged from intermediary metabolism (most notably the discovery of coenzyme A) to the biosynthesis of proteins. However, in view of the extraordinary impact of his formulation of the chemical basis of bioenergetics, his contributions to the point of view which dominates present-day biochemistry must be regarded as no less far reaching. The appearance in 1941 of his paper "Metabolic Generation and Utilization of Phosphate Bond Energy" (*Advan. Enzymol.* 1, 99) signaled the beginning of a new era in biochemistry. With characteristic simplicity and insight, in this paper Lipmann laid the theoretical groundwork for the development of our knowledge of the energetics of biosynthetic reactions and an appreciation of the relationship of exergonic to endergonic processes occurring in living cells.

Needless to say, the ideas set out in the 1941 review have been triumphantly vindicated and extended. It has seemed fitting to some of Lipmann's friends and former colleagues to dedicate this volume to him to mark the twenty-fifth anniversary of the publication of this germinal paper, and in recognition of his many other contributions to fundamental biochemistry. It is a token also of the warmth of our friendship and esteem for Fritz Lipmann.

NATHAN O. KAPLAN
EUGENE P. KENNEDY

October, 1966

Contents

Lipmann and the "Squiggle"

Herman M. Kalckar

Thirty years ago in Copenhagen Fritz Lipmann and Einar Lundsgaard sparked my interest in phosphorylation. My main interest had been turned toward the monumental work carried out by a novel type of cell physiologist, typified by personalities like Otto Meyerhof and Otto Warburg from the "Kaiser-Wilhelm-Institut," Gustav Embden at the University of Frankfurt am Main, and more than anyone else, Fritz Lipmann, who at that time was doing research at the Biological Institute of the Carlsberg Foundation. Lipmann acquainted me not only with German scientific literature, but also with important work which appeared in English and American periodicals. I recall especially articles by R. A. Peters, H. G. Wood (part of his thesis), Marjorie Stephenson, and R. R. Williams. This was of importance to me, because unlike Lipmann, I had at that time very little appreciation of work done outside continental Europe, except that of the Cori's, who then were doing the most imaginative work on phosphorylation in the entire Western hemisphere. I knew that the Cori's were in St. Louis and that "St. Louis, Mo." was part of the United States ("Forenede Stater"); but otherwise, like any reasonably cultivated Copenhagener, my knowledge extended only as far as realizing that St. Louis was a city mentioned somewhere in Mark Twain's "Life on the Mississippi." When I asked Lipmann about St. Louis, and especially what "Mo" stood for, Lipmann, who had been in New York a year with P. A. Levene and whom I therefore considered a source of knowledge about the States, pondered a little bit about "Mo," and said in a contemplative way, "Mo—Mo—that must be Montana!" (It is now 25 years since I became a "Missourian," with my draft board located in St. Louis; it is needless to stress that there were stronger bonds drawing me to St. Louis—among them phosphate bonds!)

1

Back in 1937, I was muddling through a dissertation supposedly spelling out the new type of cell physiology. I must have bothered Lipmann with many trivial experiments (he did not hesitate to say "trivial"), but once presented with the phenomenon, "respiration obligatory for phosphorylation," he said quietly, "I would forget all your other theories." I did indeed and spent some exciting years experimenting with the Krebs tricarboxylic acid cycle and oxidative phosphorylation in tissue dispersions of kidney cortex from rats and rabbits. I discussed thermodynamics and "energetic coupling" of phosphorylation and oxidation with the three big L's of Copenhagen (or rather four): Linderstrøm-Lang, Lipmann, and Lundsgaard.

These years constituted a proper setting for my application to the Rockefeller Foundation to go to Cal Tech and spend a year in Henry Borsook's department. Borsook, Lang, and Lipmann were all oriented very early toward problems of protein synthesis. Yet, in California in 1939, no one cared very much about phosphorylation and I was therefore zealous to preach the "gospel of phosphorylation." Being within the orbit of the great G. N. Lewis school of thermodynamics, I stayed carefully away from "frivolous" thermodynamic expressions, even years later. (I have rarely said "phosphate bond energy" without a quotation mark.) I volunteered for Hugh Huffmann's so-called "crematory" where one was supposed to obtain the ΔH of combustion of benzoic acid or naphthalene (in the form of neat tablets) with a precision within eight decimal places. (I never got farther than six and I never advanced to the point of doing Huffmann's elegant heat capacity measurements.)

Concerning the succeeding years in St. Louis and New York I shall just mention that it was in a way thanks to St. Louis I forgot to pursue oxidative phosphorylation. I decided that Carl and Gerty Cori could really teach me some exciting new things about enzymes and together with Sidney Colowick I had much fun drinking from the well of "phosphosphoryl enzymes" and phosphoric acid (including Coca Cola).

THE "~P"; TWENTY-FIFTH ANNIVERSARY

I am pleased that the editors of this volume, commemorating the 25th anniversary of Lipmann's pioneering article on phosphate bond energy, have asked me to comment on this event. I cannot believe that the famous "squiggle", "~," is not more than 25 years old, being as classic today as a Greek letter. It originated right here at "Mass General" (1), where Lipmann had found his new scientific home (thanks to Walter Bauer and

"Pete" Churchill) and where he also did the work for which he received the Nobel Prize.

With the discovery of acetyl phosphate (2) and Negelein and Brömel's "R-diphosphoglyceric acid" (3) which Lipmann, in analogy to his own acetyl phosphate, called "phosphoglycerylphosphate" (1), the time had arrived when someone had to formulate the theoretical aspects of these discoveries. In 1941 Lipmann decided that in order to make physiologists and biochemists aware of the new problem it would be necessary to express the gospel of phosphorylation in a clever slang: "phosphate bond energy," "energy-rich bond" or "~," "group potential"!—and to disregard the purity and austerity of classic thermodynamics. We all know that this article in *Advances in Enzymology* and some of the succeeding works [cf. (4)] have had an enormous impact over the years, and now it has even prompted this impressive 25-year anniversary volume. If the 1941 article did not create an acute storm among biochemists at the time it appeared, this can be partly attributed to the fact that molecular biology in the U.S.A. was centered around a novel invention, the use of isotopes in intact organisms. In 1941, who could believe in the biological significance of the phenomenon acetyl phosphate? I can still hear Lipmann exclaim passionately, "Of course energy cannot come from acetate—it *must* come from acetyl."

This acetyl phosphate with the Janus face, being active phosphate as well as active acetate, could be a fitting symbol for research at "Mass. General" for the next 15 years, culminating with the active amino acids and the Hoagland-Zamecnik amino acid transfer RNase's.[*]

The most sophisticated part of the 1941 Lipmann review, to my mind, was the elegant analysis of the possible basis for the high "phosphate bond energy" of phosphopyruvate as compared with phosphoglycerate. My Pasadena education in the Cal Tech "crematorium" helped me greatly to follow and see the scope of this highly sophisticated and profound treatise.

The 1941 review in *Advances in Enzymology* initiated a renaissance for the pioneering ideas of Meyerhof and Lundsgaard. The idea of "high-energy phosphate," i.e., the existence of phosphoryl esters having a high ΔH of hydrolysis, stemmed originally from Meyerhof and Lohmann in 1927 (5). Their experiments dealing with heat production brought about

---

[*] Abbreviations used in this chapter: RNA, ribonucleic acid; RNase, ribonuclease; ATP, adenosine triphosphate; ATPase, adenosinetriphosphatase; ADP, adenosine diphosphate; CoA, coenzyme A; UDP, uridine diphosphate.

by glycolysis in muscle were published a few months after the discovery of phosphocreatine by Fiske and Subarrow. Meyerhof and Lohmann's computations showed a release of heat from an unknown source present in intact muscle but not in muscle dispersions. Since phosphocreatine breaks down in minced muscle, the unaccounted source of heat observed in intact muscle was ascribed to the splitting of phosphocreatine, present in large amounts in muscle.

The formulation of a coupling between phosphorylation and fermentation became possible in 1930 thanks to the experiments by Lundsgaard who was able to show that rephosphorylation of creatine is sustained by glycolysis (6). During the same year, Engelhardt found that phosphorylation in red cells could be sustained better by oxidation than by glycolysis (7). In 1931 Lundsgaard (8) showed that in an iodoacetate-poisoned muscle, phosphocreatine levels could be kept up for some time during mechanical work if conditions for oxygen uptake were facilitated. The compulsory coupling between cell respiration and phosphorylation (oxidative phosphorylation) was formulated in the late 1930's (9).

Many of these important observations did not attract much attention at that time, except for a small group of cell physiologists. This may be attributed to the lack of appreciation of the importance of phosphorylation in cellular physiology in most leading biochemical and physiological circles at that time. It was not uncommon to consider phosphocreatine and ATP as nice "cellular buffers" and phosphorylation as an artifact found in broken cells, a queer and insensitive argument which disregarded the fact that many of the clearest experiments on phosphocreatine splitting were done on intact cells, not to speak of the observations of ^{32}P turnover in intact cells. Yet this argument prevailed for a surprisingly long time.

However, Lipmann's forceful and imaginative formulation of phosphorylations exerted an ever-increasing influence among the young generation of biochemists. Phosphorylation was soon to become generally recognized as an essential process of the living cell.

Many new ideas originated around 1941. Engelhardt advanced the idea of mechanochemistry from his observations of the "plasticizing" effect of ATP on myosin filaments (10). At the same time he found that myosin catalyzes the dephosphorylation of ATP. Engelhardt proposed that muscle ATPase was identical with myosin (11). The experiments by Engelhardt and Ljubimowa (10) occupied my own mind a good deal too. I made an attempt to interpret the supposed identity between myosin and ATPase in a somewhat different direction, namely, phosphorylation. In

an article for the transactions of the Cambridge Philosophical Society
(12) I proposed that myosin ATPase operates in two steps, the first of
which is a phosphorylation of myosin by ATP, thus trying to tie in the
role of ATP splitting in contraction or relaxation, a ghost of the ~ P.
Some years later, a related phosphorylation theory was proposed and
discussed on a more quantitative basis by Riseman and Kirkwood (13).
The observations by Koshland and his group (14) show that the issue is
still rumbling.

Developments in a different direction were, however, in the making in
1942. Albert Szent-Györgyi and his group (15), who also pioneered the
idea of "mechanochemistry," had demonstrated the formation of actomyosin and the effect of ATP on this system. Among their many observations, the crucial importance of divalent cations for the effect of ATP
on actomyosin (and the stoichiometrical relations) was a most con-
spicuous feature. In general, Szent-Györgyi put more emphasis on the
"anatomy" of the ATP molecule as a whole (metal-ATP chelate) than on
the possible utilization of the high-energy phosphate bond in the molecule in trying to explain the effect of ATP on the contractile system. The
splitting of ATP therefore may not play a direct role in the thermodynamics of contraction and thus in one sense appears wasteful. However, in muscular contraction waste of energy should not be the first
concern, anyhow, compared with the problem of not wasting time. If
ATP is needed for the contraction process, but must be whittled down
to ADP before the relaxation phase can ensue, a quick destruction of one
of the pyrophosphate bonds seems inevitable in order to bring about a
proper modulation of muscle function. In any event, Lipmann never
wasted time on dogmatic arguments. He always felt free, and still does,
to embrace new imaginative work and incorporate it into his thinking;
it is therefore not surprising that he took the Szent-Györgyi creations to
his heart. It blossomed years later when Setsuro Ebashi came to the Lipmann laboratory and got Lipmann actively involved in the biochemistry
of relaxation (16). I believe that this work appeared 30 years after Lipmann's previous active encounter with muscle structure (17) which was
part of his dissertation.

In the meantime, the new ideas generated by the discovery of acetyl
phosphate and acetyl-CoA and Kornberg's discovery of adenylation (18)
came to play a leading role in the work by the Hoagland-Zamecnik group
on the mechanism of protein synthesis. In turn, the discoveries by the
latter group of the transfer RNA population (19) brought Lipmann into
a new adventurous land—that of the genetic code.

THE "SUPER ~ P"

It seems that nature exploits the principle of "~ P" in biosynthetic pathways to an extent that was not anticipated until the discovery of key compounds like Leloir's UDP-glucose (20) or Kornberg's phosphoribosyl pyrophosphate (21). It had previously been shown that enzymatic synthesis of glycogen proceeds very well with α-glucose 1-phosphate as the glucosyl donor (22) and likewise that nucleoside biosynthesis also proceeds readily using α-ribose 1-phosphate or α-deoxyribose 1-phosphate (23). In either instance, more than 80% of the 1-ester undergoes conversion.

It seems indeed like an "overkill" to make glycogen by a mechanism which pushes the reaction more that 99% toward polymer synthesis instead of the 80% obtained if glucose 1-phosphate and inorganic phosphate were present in equimolar amounts. Yet, Robbins and Lipmann (24) showed in a particularly convincing way that in muscle the latter system, although highly active in the reverse process, does not contribute anything to glycogen synthesis. This has also turned out to be the case with the biosynthesis of a variety of polysaccharides in microorganisms.

OXIDATIVE PHOSPHORYLATION AND ATPASE'S

I have forgotten to mention that Lipmann also showed active interest in the field of oxidative phosphorylation and photophosphorylation. In 1948 Loomis and Lipmann (25) showed that dinitrophenol abolishes oxidative phosphorylation without inhibition of oxidation. The same year Kennedy and Lehninger (26) demonstrated that the mitochondrion is the seat of oxidative phosphorylation. These two important observations revealed features which were vastly different from those encountered in fermentative phosphorylation.

It has been customary to ascribe the splitting of ATP by adenosine-triphosphatase as an energy-yielding reaction which can be used to drive ions across a membrane against a gradient. However, Mitchell's interesting suggestion (27) that the oxygen cytochrome system releases OH^- or $H_2O_3^-$ ions on one side of the membrane and the dehydrogenase system (starting with succinate) releases H^+ ions on the opposite side ("Chemiosmosis") would pave the way for an alternative and perhaps more appealing formulation of mitochondrial phosphorylation. The polarity and structure of a membrane containing an operating respiratory chain might well suffice to create a powerful ion potential which in turn could be used for formation of $\sim$ P. The Mitchell theory might also explain another curious phenomenon in oxidative phosphorylation.

The oxygen of inorganic phosphate is able to undergo a rapid exchange with the OH^- of water, provided intact mitochondria are performing oxidative phosphorylation (28). This important but rather puzzling observation can be explained if one assumes that the trapped H^+ drives OH^- out of orthophosphate creating an electrophilic "phosphoryl" group.

If the phosphoryl group is located close to a nucleophilic acceptor like adenosine diphosphate, perhaps embedded in a membrane ATPase, formation of ATP would ensue. The reverse reaction, ATP splitting, releasing phosphoryl which picks up $^{18}OH^-$ from the medium, might in fact directly contribute to raise the potential again. Mitchell and Moyle have been able to support this thesis recently (29). Moreover, Jagendorf and Uribe (30) have recently been able to demonstrate ATP generation in chloroplasts in the dark by acid-base transition. This observation seems also in harmony with the chemiosmotic phosphorylation mechanism. As can be seen, chemiosmotic phosphorylation is quite a different type of coupling than that discovered in fermentation; perhaps it is also more differentiated.

Splitting of $\sim$ P may not always be poised against other group potentials. It is worth pointing out that in the 1941 review Lipmann takes into consideration that splitting of ATP, although wasteful, may well serve as a regulatory process rather than in a thermodynamic capacity. Timing and control may in many cases demand a higher priority over simple economy from the point of view of cellular thermodynamics. Under usual conditions there is presumably an excess of flow of "$\sim$ P," largely due to an ingeniously constructed system of oxidative phosphorylation. The living cell or organism seems in many ways like an "affluent society."

REFERENCES

1. Lipmann, F. *Advan. Enzymol.* **1**, 99.
2. Lipmann, F. *J. Biol. Chem.* **134**, 463 (1940).
3. Negelein, E., and Brömel, H. *Biochem. Z.* **303**, 132 (1939).
4. Lipmann, F. Attempts at the formulation of some basic biochemical questions. *In* "Currents in Biochemical Research" (D. E. Green, ed.) p. 241. Wiley (Interscience), New York, 1956. Lipmann, F., *Advan. Enzymol.*, **6**, 231 (1946).
5. Meyerhof, O., and Lohmann, K. *Naturwiss.* **15**, 670 (1927); Meyerhof, O., and Suranyi, J. *Biochem. Z.* **191**, 106 (1927).
6. Lundsgaard, E. *Biochem. Z.* **227**, 51 (1930).
7. Engelhardt, W. A. *Biochem. Z.* **227**, 16 (1930).

8. Lundsgaard, E. *Harvey Lectures, Ser.* 33 (*1937-1938*) p. 65 (1938).
9. Kalckar, H. M. Fosforyleringsprocesser i dyrisk vaev, Diss., Nyt Nordisk Forlag. Arnold Busck, Copenhagen, 1938.
10. Engelhardt, W. A., and Ljubimova, M. N. *Nature* 144, 668 (1939).
11. Engelhardt, W. A. (P. Talalay, trans.). *Yale J. Biol. Med.* 15, 21 (1942).
12. Kalckar, H. M. *Biol. Rev. Cambridge Phil. Soc.* 17, 28 (1942).
13. Riseman, J., and Kirkwood, J. G. *J. Am. Chem. Soc.* 70, 2820 (1948).
14. Koshland, D. E., Jr., and Levy, H. M. Evidence for an intermediate in ATP hydrolysis by myosin. *In* "Biochemistry of Muscle Contraction" (J. Gergeley, ed.) p. 87. Little, Brown, Boston, Massachusetts, 1964.
15. Szent-Györgyi, A. "Studies for the Institute of Medical Chemistry," Univ. of Szeged. Karger, Basel. (1942).
16. Ebashi, S., and Lipmann, F. *J. Cell Biol.* 14, 389 (1962).
17. Lipmann, F., and Meyerhof, O. *Biochem. Z.* 227, 84 (1930).
18. Kornberg, A. *J. Biol. Chem.* 182, 779 (1950).
19. Hoagland, M. B., Zamecnik, P. C., and Stephenson, M. L. *Biochim. Biophys. Acta* 24, 215 (1957).
20. Caputto, R., Leloir, L. F., Cardini, C. E., and Paladini, A. C. *J. Biol. Chem.* 184, 333 (1950); Leloir, L. F., Olavarria, J. M., Goldemberg, S. H., and Carminatti, H. *Arch. Biochem. Biophys.* 81, 508 (1959).
21. Kornberg, A. *J. Biol. Chem.* 182, 779 (1950).
22. Cori, G. T., Cori, C. F., and Schmidt, G. *J. Biol. Chem.* 129, 629 (1939).
23. Kalckar, H. M. *Federation Proc.* 4, 248 (1945); Kalckar, H. M. *Harvey Lectures, Ser.* 45 (*1949-1950*) p. 11 (1952).
24. Robbins, P. W., Traut, R. R., and Lipmann, F. *Proc. Natl. Acad. Sci. U.S.* 45, 6 (1959).
25. Loomis, W. F., and Lipmann, F. *J. Biol. Chem.* 173, 807 (1948).
26. Kennedy, E. P., and Lehninger, A. L. *J. Biol. Chem.* 179, 957 (1949).
27. Mitchell, P. *Nature* 191, 133 (1961).
28. Cohn, M. A study of oxidative phosphorylation with inorganic phosphate labeled with oxygen-18. *In* "Phosphorus Metabolism" (W. B. McElroy and B. Glass, eds.), Vol. I, p. 374. Johns Hopkins Press, Baltimore, Maryland, 1951.
29. Mitchell, P., and Moyle, J. *Nature* 208, 147 (1965).
30. Jagendorf, A. T., and Uribe, E. *Proc. Natl. Acad. Sci. U.S.* 55, 170 (1966).

Lipmann's Concept of the Metabolic Generation and Utilization of Phosphate Bond Energy: A Historical Appreciation

C. B. van Niel

ALCOHOLIC FERMENTATION AND ITS PHYSIOLOGICAL SIGNIFICANCE: THE PROBLEM OF BIOLOGICAL ENERGY SUPPLY

Nearly a century ago Pasteur, after having considerably expanded the earlier studies of Cagniard-Latour, Kützing, and Schwann, strongly supported their conclusions that the phenomenon of alcoholic fermentation is invariably associated with the presence of yeast and that yeast should be considered as the causal agent of the fermentation. This was violently contested by a number of chemists, particularly Liebig, who flatly stated that "one should recognize once and for all that causes cannot be seen with a microscope."

This controversy has often been regarded as a clash between the basically divergent "vitalistic" and "mechanistic" viewpoints. It may, however, be more judicious to look upon the opposition to Pasteur's claim as the result of an apprehension that acceptance of the latter would hamper the development of an interpretation of fermentation in chemical terms. Admittedly, the verdict that "causes cannot be seen with a microscope" was an obvious exaggeration; causal relations can always be formulated at different levels of understanding, and it is one of the chief characteristics of science that it strives toward an increasingly refined and comprehensive definition of such relations. Pasteur did not deny the possibility that alcoholic fermentation might eventually be understood as a chemical mechanism. But in the 1870's there

9

was no immediate prospect of achieving this; hence he contented himself with stating that "fermentation is a correlative of yeast growth" and "the consequence of life in the absence of air."

In the present context it is of particular significance that Pasteur also assigned a special function to fermentation; it served to supply the energy for growth and maintenance of the integrity of a living organism, the yeast cell, and thus represented the physiological equivalent of respiration, or, less equivocally, of biological oxidation. What exactly was meant by "energy supply" could not then be specified; and it remained vague until Lipmann launched his concept of the metabolic generation and utilization of phosphate bond energy, 25 years ago.

CELL-FREE FERMENTATION AND THE CHEMISTRY OF ALCOHOLIC FERMENTATION: 1897–1933

About two decades after the above-mentioned studies by Pasteur, Buchner and Hahn accidentally discovered that the cell-free juice of ground-up yeast can induce an alcoholic fermentation of sugar, which opened the way to much subsequent work on the chemical mechanism of the process. It soon led to the discovery by Harden of a diffusible, heat-stable entity, the "coenzyme," which somehow participated in the fermentation, and to the famous equation of Harden and Young (1906):

$$2C_6H_{12}O_6 + 2HPO_4^{--} \rightarrow 2CO_2 + 2C_2H_5OH + C_6H_{10}O_4(PO_4^{--})_2 + 2H_2O$$

This equation implied that the esterification of hexose represented an integral part of the fermentation mechanism.

In the meantime other approaches, particularly the "trapping procedures" of Neuberg, in which intermediate products arising during the fermentation could be sidetracked and obtained in sufficient quantity for isolation and characterization, further aided in the attempts to interpret fermentation in a chemically intelligible manner. Based upon these advances, Kluyver and co-workers developed the concept that fermentation is the result of a series of simple, consecutive step reactions, each one representing an inter- or intramolecular transfer of two hydrogen atoms, and that this applies equally to other metabolic processes (Kluyver, 1930, 1931; Kluyver and Donker, 1926). Moreover, the then still mysterious involvement of phosphorylations also seemed amenable to a rational interpretation. It was postulated that the introduction of a single phosphate group, with its polar properties, into a hexose molecule renders the latter preeminently fit to be split into two moieties, triose phosphate and free triose, the triose being the actual substrate for the hydrogen transfer reactions. Harden and Young's hexose diphosphate was thus considered as a mere side product, resulting from the temporary accumulation of triose phosphate and its condensation to hexose diphosphate (Kluyver and Struyk, 1926). Chemically this interpretation made good sense because it obviated the need to account for the curious implication of the Harden and Young equation that the esterification of one hexose molecule could somehow induce another hexose molecule to undergo a decomposition to CO_2 and ethanol. At the end of the 1920's the "hexose monophosphate theory" was therefore generally accepted; it held sway until 1933.

ENERGETIC COUPLING

While these developments had shown that fermentations and biological oxidations can be explained in terms of chemically intelligible reactions, they contributed little to a better understanding of Pasteur's concept of their physiological function. In their preoccupation with the details of the chemical mechanism, the biochemists almost seemed to lose sight of this aspect, whose importance had been reemphasized by Max Rubner (1913) in his extensive treatise on the physiology of yeast during alcoholic fermentation. This study, based on calorimetric measurements, was a sequel to Rubner's earlier work which had led him to formulate his theory of caloric equivalence of various foodstuffs. The new experiments clearly showed that, in the absence of air, the conversion of sugar to CO_2 and ethanol by yeast must represent the sole source of energy available for growth; and this very fact had not found expression in the studies with cell-free extracts. Furthermore, Rubner stressed the fact that the activity of such extracts was no more than a very small fraction of that of an equivalent mass of intact cells and therefore expressed the opinion that experiments with cell-free preparations were inherently inadequate to advance our understanding of the problem of energy provision. Not until the mid-1940's could cell-free extracts be prepared with activities closely approximating those of whole cells; and at that time the mechanism of energy provision had been essentially clarified.

Nevertheless, this problem had not been altogether dismissed. It was recognized in the sharp distinction made between catabolism and anabolism (breakdown of substrate and synthesis of cell material; or, in the pithy German terms, Betriebs- and Baustoffwechsel), the former sup-

plying the energy required by the latter. This was indicated by representing catabolism and anabolism as energetically coupled reactions:

$$\left\{ \begin{array}{l} \text{Part of substrate} \xrightarrow{\text{catabolism}} \text{end (waste) products} + \text{energy } (E') \\[2ex] \text{Part of substrate} + \text{energy } (E'') \xrightarrow{\text{anabolism}} \text{assimilation products} \end{array} \right.$$

in which E' must be equal to or greater than E''. Particularly in the case
of microorganisms that can grow in a medium composed of minerals
and a single, simple organic compound, the need for this distinction
seemed evident because the conversion of the medium components
into the large variety of complex cellular constituents can obviously
occur only if a supply of free energy is available.

But the concept of energetic coupling still begged the question of a
mechanism, and Kluyver (1924), influenced by the work of Rubner,
called attention to this fundamental problem by asking whether the
physical chemists knew of similar cases of coupled reactions in inanimate systems and "whether they would have fundamental objections
to the occurrence of such energetic coupling."

During the next few years Kluyver came to realize that certain fermentations could provide a clue to the solution of this problem. In alcoholic fermentation ethanol and glycerol are formed from sugar; in the
butyric acid fermentation butyric acid and butanol can be produced
from three-carbon compounds, such as triose and glycerol. But these
fermentations are exergonic and represent the sole source of energy
available to the causative organisms. Nevertheless, the products in question are clearly more reduced than is the substrate and some of them
must be formed by condensation reactions. Now, these two features are
equally characteristic of the products of anabolism and are responsible
for the energy requirement. Since it had been found possible to account
for the formation of the fermentation products by invoking a series of
chemically intelligible step reactions, all of which are exergonic, it log-
ically followed that assimilatory processes might also proceed by comparable mechanisms.

At first sight this may seem to conflict with the fact that ordinarily the
product of a biosynthetic reaction has a free energy content greater
than that of an equal weight of the substrate from which it is formed.
But the conflict is more apparent than real. The synthesis of butyric
acid in the fermentation by that name was assumed to result from a
condensation of two molecules of acetaldehyde, formed as an interme-

diate product in the decomposition of a three-carbon precursor, pyruvic acid, along with CO_2. The crucial point is that the free energy of CO_2 is zero, so that more than two-thirds of the total free energy of the three-carbon compound can be retained in the two-carbon moiety, whose chemical potential may thus be raised to a higher level. This implies that this two-carbon moiety can be converted to assimilation products in spontaneous (exergonic) reactions.

These considerations permitted a new formulation of the relationship between catabolism and anabolism, which took the form of a simple scheme:

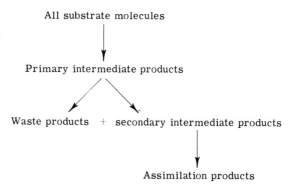

All substrate molecules

Primary intermediate products

Waste products + secondary intermediate products

Assimilation products

It implies that there exists a common *material* link between the two aspects of metabolism and that the secondary intermediate products are the genuine building blocks for exergonic synthetic processes.

Hence this concept provided an intelligible mechanism for energetic coupling (Kluyver and Donker, 1926; Kluyver, 1930, 1931). In a later contribution from Kluyver's laboratory (Giesberger, 1936) it was argued that biological oxidations similarly served to produce intermediate products with a high chemical potential from the substrate molecules, by gradual transformations involving the elimination of CO_2. Here the term "chip respiration" was introduced to indicate that the substrate oxidation served to generate the true building blocks for biosyntheses.

It is clear that Kluyver's ideas contain the essence of current interpretations of the mechanism of energetic coupling. But they lacked precision, and the particular substances that were postulated as the key intermediate products for exergonic syntheses failed to behave as expected. Hence they remained little more than a first approximation without satisfactory experimental support.

BIOCHEMICAL DEVELOPMENTS: 1930–1939

Meanwhile, developments in the early 1930's led to advances in other directions. With extracts of muscle tissue, Embden and Meyerhof with their co-workers showed that the conversion of sugar to lactic acid (glycolysis) proceeded by way of step reactions involving a large diversity of phosphorylated compounds: hexose monophosphates and diphosphates, phosphoglyceraldehyde, dihydroxyacetone phosphate, glycerophosphate, 2- and 3-phosphoglyceric acid, and phosphoenolpyruvate. The same substances were also encountered in comparable studies on the mechanism of alcoholic fermentation with cell-free extracts of yeast.

Furthermore, a new hexose monophosphate, glucose 1-phosphate, was found to be formed from either glycogen or starch and inorganic phosphate by enzyme extracts of muscle and potato, respectively (Cori and Cori, 1936, 1937; Hanes, 1940a,b), whereas the enzymatic formation of hexose diphosphate from hexose and from glucose 1-phosphate was shown to require adenosine triphosphate (ATP) as phosphate donor (Meyerhof, 1935; Parnas and Ostern, 1935; Colowick and Kalckar, 1943).

These findings made it necessary to abandon the "hexose monophosphate theory." Hexose diphosphate now had to be considered as a primary intermediate product in the lactic acid and alcoholic fermentations, rather than as a substance produced in a side reaction as a result of abnormal experimental conditions. Although the metabolic significance of the various phosphorylated compounds was not apparent at the time, other contributions held out a promise that this, too, would eventually be elucidated.

The first such inkling came from Lundsgaard's discovery in 1930 that muscle tissue can continue to contract in the presence of iodoacetate in concentrations that completely block glycolysis (Lundsgaard, 1930). This implied that the concept of a direct connection between contraction and lactic acid formation, evolved mainly from the studies of A. V. Hill and Otto Meyerhof (Meyerhof, 1930) on the energetics of the two processes, needed modification. It was also established that the contraction of iodoacetate-poisoned muscle was accompanied by the dephosphorylation of creatine phosphate and ATP, whereas rephosphorylation occurred under conditions where the normal catabolic activities— glycolysis in the absence of air or, aerobically, oxidation of lactic acid —could proceed. The dephosphorylations, being strongly exergonic processes, can provide the energy for contraction; conversely, the resynthesis of creatine phosphate and ATP from the split products is possible only if energy is supplied, and it was clear that this could be done by glycolysis or by the oxidation of lactate. Thus attention was once again focused on the mechanism of energetic coupling.

The first important contribution to this problem was provided by the studies of Parnas *et al.* (1934) and Lohmann and Meyerhof (1934), who established that the enzymatic conversion of phosphoglyceric to pyruvic acid, by way of phosphoenolpyruvate, proceeded only in the presence of a special phosphate acceptor, adenylic acid (AMP) or adenosine diphosphate (ADP), which was phosphorylated to ATP. This led Parnas (1937, 1940) to formulate a "phosphate cycle," in which the utilization of ATP for the initial phosphorylation of hexose is counterbalanced by the regeneration of ATP in the course of the subsequent reactions leading to the formation of lactic acid:

$$C_6H_{12}O_6 + ATP \rightarrow C_6H_{10}O_4(OPO_3{}^{--})_2 + AMP + 2H_2O \tag{1}$$

$$C_6H_{10}O_4(OPO_3{}^{--})_2 \rightarrow 2C_3H_5O_2(OPO_3{}^{--}) \tag{2}$$

$$2C_3H_5O_2(OPO_3{}^{--}) + 2H_2O \rightarrow 2C_3H_5O_3(OPO_3{}^{--}) + 4H \tag{3}$$

$$2C_3H_5O_3(OPO_3{}^{--}) \rightarrow 2C_3H_3O_2(OPO_3{}^{--}) + 2H_2O \tag{4}$$

$$2C_3H_3O_2(OPO_3{}^{--}) + 2H_2O + AMP \rightarrow 2C_3H_4O_3 + ATP \tag{5}$$

$$2C_3H_4O_3 + 4H \rightarrow 2C_3H_6O_3 \tag{6}$$

In this manner a material link was established between the degradation of fructose diphosphate and the formation of ATP. Although it represented a large step forward, this formulation was not yet altogether satisfactory because it failed to account for a net synthesis of ATP and creatine phosphate by muscle tissue during glycolysis.

The next significant advances came from the studies of Lipmann (1939*a,b*) and Negelein and Brömel (1939*a,b*). In his masterly review of the mechanisms of lactic acid and alcoholic fermentations, Meyerhof (1937) had stated that the only difference between these two processes lies in the fate of the common intermediate product, pyruvic acid. In alcoholic fermentation this substance is decarboxylated to CO_2 and acetaldehyde, the latter acting as hydrogen acceptor for the reoxidation of a reduced coenzyme, whereas in glycolysis pyruvic acid itself must fulfill this function because it cannot be decarboxylated by the lactic acid-producing cells. It was an eminently satisfactory picture; yet in the same year the studies of Krebs (1937) showed that it could not be entirely correct. Krebs had found that *Streptococcus lactis,* a typical lactic acid bacterium that converts sugar quantitatively to lactic acid, can cause a fermentation of pyruvate to CO_2, acetic and lactic acids, according to the equation:

$$2C_3H_4O_3 + H_2O \rightarrow CO_2 + C_2H_4O_2 + C_3H_6O_3$$

Now, the formation of equimolar amounts of CO_2 and acetic acid obviously meant that the lactic acid bacteria can, in fact, decarboxylate pyruvic acid. This posed the problem why CO_2 and two-carbon compounds are not found among the products of the fermentation of sugar by these organisms.

A similar problem had been encountered earlier in studies on the metabolism of the propionic acid bacteria (van Niel, 1928). These organisms ferment sugars, lactate, and pyruvate to CO_2, acetate, and propionate. The formation of CO_2 and a two-carbon compound in a 1:1 ratio from pyruvate naturally suggested a decarboxylation of this substrate. But this implied that all of the acetaldehyde produced would have to be oxidized to acetate and that this should be coupled with a reaction in which propionate is formed as the only reduction product. It was further shown that added acetaldehyde can be reduced to ethanol by the propionic acid bacteria, so that the complete absence of this substance among the fermentation products normally encountered seemed incompatible with the decomposition of pyruvate by a simple decarboxylation. As a way out of this difficulty it was therefore postulated that pyruvic acid would undergo a combined oxidation-decarboxylation, yielding, CO_2 and acetic acid in the observed ratio, while an appropriate hydrogen acceptor would be reduced to propionic acid. The oxidation was depicted as a dehydrogenation following the primary addition of H_2O to the carbonyl group of pyruvic acid:

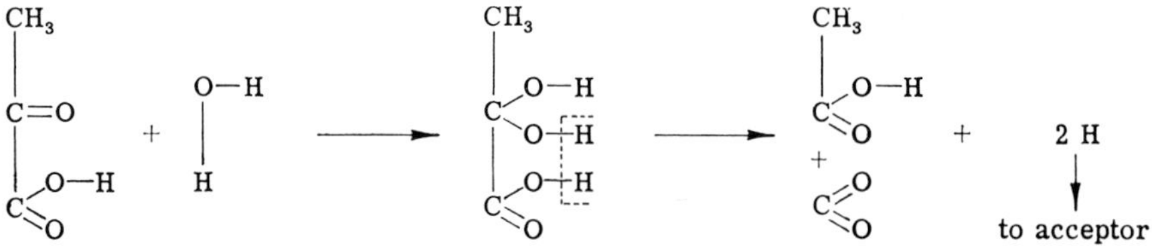

It is clear that such a reaction would also account for the results of Krebs' experiments with S. *lactis*, where the pyruvate could act both as substrate for an oxidative decarboxylation and as hydrogen acceptor.

ACETYL PHOSPHATE AND PHOSPHOGLYCERYL PHOSPHATE

Two years after Krebs' contribution, Lipmann (1939a,b) studied the decomposition of pyruvate by another lactic acid bacterium, *Lactobacillus delbrückii*, in the presence of O_2 as hydrogen acceptor. This led to the discovery that the oxidation of pyruvate requires the presence of inorganic phosphate and yields, in addition to CO_2, acetyl phosphate. Its formation was explained by postulating a primary addition of phosphate instead of H_2O to the carbonyl group of pyruvate; the oxidation of the phosphorylated product then produces acetyl phosphate instead of acetic acid:

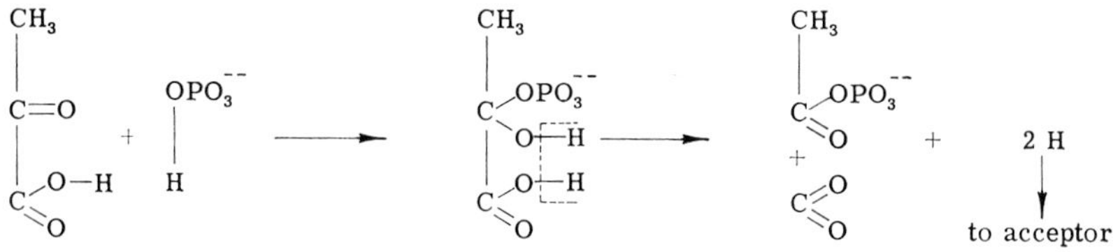

This seemingly trivial modification of the earlier postulated mechanism had far-reaching consequences; it became the basis on which Lipmann, 25 years ago, constructed his general theory of the generation and utilization of phosphate bond energy. It is noteworthy that in the same year Kalckar (1941) published an extensive paper on the nature of energetic coupling in biological syntheses in which very similar ideas were expressed.

THE HIGH-ENERGY BOND AND THE PRESERVATION OF BOND ENERGY

Acetyl phosphate is a mixed acid anhydride, an unstable and hence reactive compound, whose phosphate group can be readily transferred, in a spontaneous reaction, to ADP with the production of ATP. A comparable substance was found by Negelein and Brömel (1939a,b) during a study of the enzymatic oxidation of phosphoglyceraldehyde. This, too, requires the presence of inorganic phosphate and yields, instead of 3-phosphoglyceric acid, 1,3-diphosphoglycerate, more appropriately designated as phosphoglyceryl phosphate by Lipmann (1941). It is another mixed acid anhydride that can act as phosphate donor for the production of ATP from ADP. As a result of the Negelein-Brömel discovery, Eq. (3) of the phosphate cycle as formulated by Parnas could now be replaced by a series of three consecutive step reactions:

$$2C_3H_5O_2(OPO_3{}^{--}) + 2HOPO_3{}^{--} \rightarrow 2C_3H_6O_2(OPO_3{}^{--})_2 \qquad (3a)$$

$$2C_3H_6O_2(OPO_3{}^{--})_2 \rightarrow 2C_3H_4O_2(OPO_3{}^{--})_2 + 4H \qquad (3b)$$

$$2C_3H_4O_2(OPO_3{}^{--})_2 + 2ADP \rightarrow 2C_3H_5O_3(OPO_3{}^{--}) + 2ATP \qquad (3c)$$

In consequence, glycolysis was seen to be accompanied by a net synthesis of ATP, thus providing the energy needed for muscular contraction.

Meanwhile Kalckar (1938) had found that ATP can also be generated during the oxidation of various substrates by animal tissues. Since that time intensive studies have been devoted to unraveling the detailed mechanism of this "oxidative phosphorylation," but this still remains unresolved (see, e.g., Ernster and Lee, 1964; Sanadi, 1965). It therefore stands in sharp contrast to the readily understandable mechanism by which the labile phosphate groups are generated during the formation of acetyl phosphate and phosphoglyceryl phosphate. As Lipmann (1941) pointed out, the addition of phosphate to the carbonyl groups of pyruvate and phosphoglyceraldehyde does not involve a significant entropy change and can thus be achieved in a spontaneous reaction. But the oxidation of the phosphorylated carbonyl groups leaves the phosphate moiety dangling in an unstable position; it has become reactive and can be used for the phosphorylation of ADP. Expressed in a different manner, a large fraction of the decrease in free energy that would be released as heat during the oxidation of pyruvate or 3-phosphoglyceraldehyde is retained in one of the oxidation products of the phosphorylated compounds; and this "stored" energy can then be used to drive energy-requiring cellular activities.

The crucial element of Lipmann's concept is the principle of the preservation of bond energy. It had long been recognized that there are two classes of organophosphate compounds, which differ markedly in their relative stability; this is also reflected by the amount of heat liberated during their hydrolysis. In the case of phosphate esters this is approximately 3000 cal per mole, whereas for substances such as ADP, ATP, creatine phosphate, and arginine phosphate, phosphoenolpyruvate, acetyl phosphate, and phosphoglyceryl phosphate it is of the order of magnitude of 10,000 cal per mole. By virtue of the presence of a high-energy phosphate group, for which Lipmann introduced the designation $\sim$ P, the latter group is thus characterized by a higher chemical potential than the former.

Available experimental evidence, amplified by thermodynamic calculations, led Lipmann to propose that phosphate groups should be freely transferable among compounds belonging to the same class. This idea of the preservation of bond energy accounted for the reversible enzymatic reactions of some polysaccharides (glycogen, starch) with inorganic phosphate to form glucose 1-phosphate, by phosphorolysis instead of hydrolysis, providing a mechanism for the preservation of ester bond energy. A corresponding kind of reaction was soon afterward discovered by Kagan *et al.* (1942) and by Doudoroff and co-workers (Doudoroff, 1943; Doudoroff *et al.*, 1943) in studies on the metabolism of sucrose by some bacteria, enzyme extracts of which were shown to catalyze the reversible reaction:

$$\text{Sucrose} + \text{HOPO}_3^{--} \rightleftarrows \text{glucose 1-phosphate} + \text{fructose}$$

thus permitting the first enzymatic synthesis of sucrose from hexose units.

Other examples of the preservation of ester bond energy are the direct enzymatic syntheses of dextran (Hehre, 1941, 1943; Hehre and Sugg, 1942; Stacey, 1942) and levan (Beijerinck, 1912; Ashner *et al.*, 1942; Hestrin *et al.*, 1943) from sucrose. If these reactions are represented by the equations:

$$n\text{Glucosido-fructoside} \rightarrow (\text{glucosan})_n + n\text{fructose}$$
$$\text{dextran}$$

and

$$n\text{Fructosido-glucoside} \rightarrow (\text{fructosan})_n + n\text{glucose}$$
$$\text{levan}$$

the analogy with the synthesis of glycogen or starch by phosphorylase:

$$n\text{Glucosido-1-phosphate} \rightarrow (\text{glucosan})_n + n\text{H}_3\text{PO}_4$$
$$\text{glycogen,}$$
$$\text{starch}$$

is obvious (Leibowitz and Hestrin, 1945).

Metabolically of far greater general significance are, however, those reactions in which the energy of the high-energy phosphate bond is preserved by transfer of the $\sim$ P group from appropriate donors to acceptors, as in the case of the synthesis of ATP from ADP and phosphoenolpyruvate, phosphoglyceryl phosphate, or acetyl phosphate; and of creatine phosphate and arginine phosphate from ATP and creatine or arginine. It is these processes that permitted a formulation of energetic coupling in metabolism in chemical terms: the degradation of substrates proceeds by way of reactions in which part of the free energy change is retained in the form of $\sim$ P bonds. Thus, the dependence of mechanical work, such as muscular contraction, on metabolism becomes readily understandable because the latter generates ATP, creatine phosphate, and arginine phosphate.

UTILIZATION OF BOND ENERGY FOR MECHANICAL WORK

It also seemed reasonable to invoke an essentially similar mechanism to account for the locomotion of flagellated microorganisms, especially after Weibull (1948–1951; Astbury et al., 1955) had shown that bacterial flagella are composed of contractile protein. On this basis Links (1955) proposed an interpretation of the chemotactic and phototactic responses of algae and bacteria as the result of abrupt, temporary changes in the rate of metabolic ATP formation. This idea fitted in with the well-established production of ATP during oxidative metabolism and with the discovery that ATP is also generated by chromatophores of photosynthetic bacteria (Frenkel, 1954) and by chloroplasts of green plants (Arnon et al., 1954) upon exposure to light, a process that has become known as photophosphorylation. It should, however, be mentioned that the hypothesis proposed by Links has been criticized by Clayton (1958), who considers it an oversimplification.

The concept of a close association of flagellar locomotion and utilization of high-energy phosphate bonds has received support from the studies of Hoffman-Berling (1955), which showed that isolated flagella of sperm and trypanosomes rhythmically contract when suspended in an ATP-containing medium; of Tibbs (1957), who demonstrated adenosinetriphosphatase (ATPase) activity of flagella of *Polytoma;* and of Sherris et al. (1957), later extended by Shoesmith and Sherris (1960). The last-mentioned papers deal with observations on the motility of a strictly aerobic pseudomonad. Like other obligatorily aerobic bacteria, it soon ceases to move in the absence of oxygen; but it remains motile if it is supplied with arginine or citrulline, which are anaerobically converted to ornithine with the production of ATP.

UTILIZATION OF BOND ENERGY FOR CHEMICAL WORK

Since the coupling of metabolic activities and the performance of mechanical work had thus been rendered chemically intelligible, we must now consider the implications of Lipmann's grand generalization for a better understanding of the nature of energetic coupling between degradative and biosynthetic processes. Can this coupling also be explained on the basis of high-energy bond formation, and, if so, in what manner?

The answer to these questions can again be found in Lipmann's epoch-making paper (1941). It is derived from a consideration of the properties of acetyl phosphate. Lipmann pointed out that this substance resembles acetyl chloride, another mixed acid anhydride with a high-energy bond, and commonly used by chemists as an effective acetylating agent. Applying this experience to acetyl phosphate, it was evident that its high-energy bond causes not only the phosphate group, but also the acetyl moiety, to be endowed with special activity, so that acetyl phosphate can function either as a phosphate or as an acetyl donor. In the latter case the bond energy is used to permit addition of the acetyl group to other molecular species in spontaneous enzymatic reactions in which acetate itself cannot participate. And because, in accordance with the concept of the preservation of bond energy, ATP can be used for the enzymatic synthesis of acetyl phosphate from ATP and acetate, it follows that this reaction results in the activation of acetate.

The same principle applies to other compounds requiring activation in order to prepare them for participation in spontaneous biosynthetic reactions, so that the metabolic generation of ATP can be viewed as providing a general mechanism for the coupling of energy-yielding and energy-requiring processes.

ATP AND GROWTH

In this connection the results of some experiments in which the cell yields of microorganisms grown in various media have been determined deserve to be mentioned. As early as 1951, DeMoss and colleagues (1951) had observed that homofermentative lactic acid bacteria produce a larger cell crop per mole of sugar fermented than does the heterofermentative *Leuconostoc mesenteroides*. They inferred from this result that the latter organism derives less utilizable energy from the fermentation of a unit amount of substrate than do the homofermentative lactic acid bacteria. Later, Sokatch and Gunsalus (1957) found that the cell yield of the homofermentative *Streptococcus faecalis* grown in a gluconate medium is approximately the same as that obtained in an equimolar glucose medium. Hence, gluconate appeared to be roughly equivalent to glucose as an energy source for this organism. This led them to conclude: "Measurements of the total cell crops with increasing equimolar amounts of glucose and gluconate should furnish an indication of the net amount of energetic coupling—presumably by phosphorylation—during fermentation of the oxidized (aldonic acid) substrate, as compared with glucose" (Sokatch and Gunsalus, 1957, pp. 454-455).

The studies of Bauchop and Elsden (1960) provided a more direct support for the contention that the amount of ATP produced in different fermentations does, in fact, determine the extent to which biosynthetic reactions can proceed. Because the ATP yields of the alcoholic and lactic acid fermentations by way of the Embden-Meyerhof-Parnas mechanisms had been clearly established as two moles per mole of hexose fermented, they first grew yeast and homofermentative lactic acid bacteria in media with sugar as the limiting factor and determined the quantity of cells produced. The results showed that, per unit amount of sugar fermented, this is practically the same for both organisms; calculated on the basis of ATP formation, it amounts to about 10 gm dry weight of cell material per mole of ATP.

In order to test further the correspondence between cell yield and ATP formation, they grew the homofermentative S. faecalis in sugar media supplemented with arginine, which this bacterium can decompose with the generation of one mole of ATP per mole of arginine. Under these conditions the cell yield was found to be increased over that obtained in an arginine-free medium and again by an amount of 10 gm per mole.

Another striking confirmation of the close relation between cell yield and ATP formation was furnished by experiments with Pseudomonas lindneri. This bacterium ferments glucose mainly to CO_2 and ethanol, not by way of the Embden-Meyerhof-Parnas mechanism, but via the Entner-Doudoroff pathway which, in contrast to the former, yields only one mole of ATP per mole of sugar fermented. Accordingly, the cell crop of P. lindneri per gram of sugar turned out to be only one-half that obtained with yeast.

These results support the view that the amount of metabolically generated ATP is a measure of the biosynthetic activities of a cell. As the yield of the former in various catabolic reactions and the ATP requirements for diverse syntheses become more accurately known, it will become possible to compute the cell crops of microorganisms obtainable under specified conditions, as has been pointed out by Gunsalus and Shuster (1961). Conversely, determinations of growth at the expense of various substrates may provide a simple means of estimating the ATP yields of the catabolic processes involved in their decomposition.

While the quantity of available ATP can determine the extent of biosynthetic processes, their rate should also be a function of the rate of ATP formation. This permits a logical interpretation of the fact that some photosynthetic bacteria, which can grow at the expense of the same oxidizable substrate either aerobically in darkness or anaerobically in light, grow faster under the latter conditions, as observed by Burlant et al. (1965) for Rhodopseudomonas capsulatus and by Gherna

(1965) for *Rhodomicrobium vannielii*. At first sight this may seem to conflict with the results of measurements of substrate oxidation by photosynthetic bacteria, which have shown that at sufficiently high light intensities the rate of these oxidations is the same in light and in darkness (van Niel, 1949, 1952). But in darkness ATP is formed only by oxidative phosphorylation, whereas in light cyclic or noncyclic photophosphorylation provides an additional source of ATP. If the growth rate in darkness were limited by the rate of ATP generation, then this auxiliary mechanism for ATP production would have the effect of accelerating growth in light.

The ideas which Lipmann expressed 25 years ago lifted Kluyver's earlier concept that catabolic processes yield the genuine building blocks for spontaneous biosyntheses to a new level of comprehension. For the first time the exact nature of such building blocks could be more precisely defined, so that it became possible to demonstrate their effectiveness as substrates for enzyme-mediated syntheses *in vitro*.

ENVOY

This is not the place to discuss the subsequent developments which have clarified the various mechanisms involved in the activation of different types of compounds in ever greater detail. Suffice it to say that they have gradually increased our insight into the chemical mechanisms of biosyntheses to the point where it has become possible to interpret even the transcription of the genetic code in a chemically intelligible manner. The result has been the accumulation of an impressive body of information which eloquently testifies to the fundamental significance of Lipmann's concept of the metabolic generation and preservation of bond energy. It is now generally and most concisely expressed in the statement that the high-energy phosphate bond represents the common currency for the transfer of energy between the various activities of living organisms.

REFERENCES

Arnon, D. I., Whatley, F. R., and Allen, M. B. (1954). *J. Am. Chem. Soc.* **76**, 6324.

Ashner, M., Avineri-Shapiro, S., and Hestrin, S. (1942). *Nature* **149**, 527.

Astbury, W. T., Beighton, E., and Weibull, C. (1955). *Symp. Soc. Exptl. Biol.* **9**, 282.

Bauchop, T., and Elsden, S. R. (1960). *J. Gen. Microbiol.* **23**, 457.

Beijerinck, M. W. (1912). *Folia Microbiol.* (*Delft*) **1**, 377.

Burlant, L., Datta, P., and Gest, H. (1965). *Science* **148**, 1353.

Clayton, R. K. (1958). *Arch. Mikrobiol.* **29**, 189.

Colowick, S. P., and Kalckar, H. M. (1943). *J. Biol. Chem.* **148**, 117.

Cori, C. F., and Cori, G. T. (1936). *Proc. Soc. Exptl. Biol. Med.* **34**, 702.

Cori, C. F., and Cori, G. T. (1937). *Proc. Soc. Exptl. Biol. Med.* **36**, 119.

DeMoss, R. D., Bard, R. C., and Gunsalus, I. C. (1951). *J. Bacteriol.* **62**, 499.

Doudoroff, M. (1943). *J. Biol. Chem.* **151**, 351.

Doudoroff, M., Kaplan, N., and Hassid, W. Z. (1943). *J. Biol. Chem.* **148**, 67.

Ernster, L., and Lee, C.-P. (1964). *Ann. Rev. Biochem.* **33**, 729.

Frenkel, A. (1954). *J. Am. Chem. Soc.* **76**, 5568.

Gherna, R. (1965). Personal communication.

Giesberger, G. (1936). "Beiträge zur Kenntnis der Gattung *Spirillum* Ehbg. mit besonderer Berücksichtigung der Atmungsprozesse bei den Vertretern dieser Gattung." Ph.D. Dissertation, Utrecht University; 134 pp. W. D. Meinema, Delft.

Gunsalus, I. C., and Shuster, C. W. (1961). *In* "The Bacteria" (I. C. Gunsalus and R. Y. Stanier, eds.), Vol. II, pp. 1-57. Academic Press, New York.

Hanes, C. (1940*a*). *Proc. Roy. Soc. (London)* **B128**, 421.

Hanes, C. (1940*b*). *Proc. Roy. Soc. (London)* **B129**, 174.

Harden, A., and Young, W. J. (1906). *Proc. Roy. Soc. (London)* **B77**, 405.

Hehre, E. (1941). *Science* **93**, 237.

Hehre, E. (1943). *Proc. Soc. Exptl. Biol. Med.* **54**, 240.

Hehre, E., and Sugg, G. (1942). *J. Exptl. Med.* **75**, 339.

Hestrin, S., Avineri-Shapiro, S., and Ashner, M. (1943). *Biochem. J.* **37**, 450.

Hoffman-Berling, H. (1955). *Biochim. Biophys. Acta* **16**, 146.

Kagan, B., Lyatker, S., and Tszafman, E. (1942). *Biokhimiya* **7**, 92.

Kalckar, H. M. (1938). "Fosforyleringsprocesser i dyrisk vaev," 138 pp. Nyt Nordisk Forlag Arnold Busck, Copenhagen.

Kalckar, H. M. (1941). *Chem. Rev.* **28**, 71.

Kamp, A. F., La Rivière, J. W. M., and Verhoeven, W., eds. (1959). "Albert Jan Kluyver, His Life and Work." 567 pp. North-Holland Publ., Amsterdam.

Kluyver, A. J. (1924). *Chem. Weekblad* **21**, 266; an English translation of this paper can be found in Kamp *et al.* (1959), pp. 186-210.

Kluyver, A. J. (1930). *Arch. Mikrobiol.* **1**, 181.

Kluyver, A. J. (1931). "The Chemical Activities of Micro-Organisms," 109 pp. Univ. London Press, London.

Kluyver, A. J., and Donker, H. J. L. (1926). *Chemie Zelle Gewebe* **13**, 134; also in Kamp *et al.* (1959), pp. 210-267.

Kluyver, A. J., and Struyk, A. P. (1926). *Koninkl. Ned. Akad. Wetenschapp. Proc.* **29**, 322.

Krebs, H. A. (1937). *Biochem. J.* **31**, 661.

Leibowitz, J., and Hestrin, S. (1945). *Advan. Enzymol.* **5**, 87.

Links, J. (1955). "Onderzoekingen met *Polytoma uvella.*" Ph.D. Dissertation Leiden University, 153 pp. Uitgeverij Excelsior, The Hague.

Lipmann, F. (1939*a*). *Nature* **143**, 281.

Lipmann, F. (1939*b*). *Cold Spring Harbor Symp. Quant. Biol.* **7**, 248.

Lipmann, F. (1941). *Advan. Enzymol.* **1**, 99.

Lohmann, K., and Meyerhof, O. (1934). *Biochem. Z.* **273**, 60.

Lundsgaard, E. (1930). *Biochem. Z.* **217**, 162.

Meyerhof, O. (1930). "Die chemischen Vorgänge im Muskel," 350 pp. Springer, Berlin.

Meyerhof, O. (1935). *Naturwissenschaften* 23, 850.

Meyerhof, O. (1937). *Ergeb. Physiol. Biol. Chem. Exptl. Pharmakol.* 39, 10.

Negelein, E., and Brömel, H. (1939a). *Biochem. Z.* 300, 255.

Negelein, E., and Brömel, H. (1939b). *Biochem. Z.* 303, 132.

Parnas, J. K. (1937). *Ergeb. Enzymforsch.* 6, 57.

Parnas, J. K. (1940). *In* "Handbuch der Enzymologie" (F. F. Nord and R. Weidenhagen, eds.), Vol. II, pp. 902-967. Akad. Verlagsges., Leipzig.

Parnas, J. K., and Ostern, P. (1935). *Biochem. Z.* 279, 94.

Parnas, J. K., Ostern, P., and Mann, T. (1934). *Biochem. Z.* 272, 64.

Rubner, M. (1913). "Die Ernährungsphysiologie der Hefezelle bei alkoholischer Gährung," 396 pp. Veit, Leipzig.

Sanadi, D. R. (1965). *Ann. Rev. Biochem.* 34, 21.

Sherris, J. C., Preston, N. W., and Shoesmith, J. G. (1957). *J. Gen. Microbiol.* 16, 86.

Shoesmith, J. G., and Sherris, J. C. (1960). *J. Gen. Microbiol.* 22, 10.

Sokatch, J. T., and Gunsalus, I. C. (1957). *J. Bacteriol.* 73, 452.

Stacey, M. (1942). *Nature* 149, 639.

Tibbs, J. (1957). *Biochim. Biophys. Acta* 23, 275.

van Niel, C. B. (1928). "The Propionic Acid Bacteria," 187 pp. Boissevain, Haarlem.

van Niel, C. B. (1949). *In* "Photosynthesis in Plants" (J. Franck and W. E. Loomis, eds.), pp. 437-495. Iowa State Coll. Press, Ames, Iowa.

van Niel, C. B. (1952). *In* "The Enzymes" (J. B. Sumner and K. Myrbäck, eds.), Vol. 2, pp. 1074-1088. Academic Press, New York.

Weibull, C. (1948). *Biochim. Biophys. Acta* 2, 351.

Weibull, C. (1949). *Biochim. Biophys. Acta* 3, 378.

Weibull, C. (1950). *Acta Chem. Scand.* 4, 268.

Weibull, C. (1951). *Acta Chem. Scand.* 5, 529.

On the Nature of Cellular Respiration

George Wald

Teaching, before it grows too repetitive, is better education for the teacher than the student. It draws one out of a special field into the subject as a whole; but more than that, it forces one beyond the facts that are the raw material of knowledge to its fabric. Facts come and go; they are learned only to be forgotten. The job of teaching is to weave them into a coherent structure, tied at so many points to other things the student knows that it becomes an irrevocable part of him. In weaving that fabric, however, one occasionally encounters curious obstacles, places where the information that is offered doesn't hang together. I should like here to discuss such a situation, one that happily, as it worked itself out, I could talk over with Fritz Lipmann, who at that time still lived in Boston; and he added, as will appear, important elements to the story.

Everyone knows—at least everyone is taught—that glucose is consumed in cellular respiration according to the equation:

$$C_6H_{12}O_6 + 6O_2 \longrightarrow 6CO_2 + 6H_2O \qquad (\Delta H = 672 \text{ kcal/mole})$$

Everyone knows also that this process can yield 36–40 high-energy phosphate bonds in the form of adenosine triphosphate (ATP). Thirty-six of those ATP bonds come in the course of burning $12H_2$ to water; each pair of H atoms passed up through the cytochrome system and burned yields 3ATP. We do not yet know the mechanism by which the ATP is formed, but we have a fair idea which steps in the chain of hydrogen and electron transport are coupled with ATP formation.

Now for the question: Where in that equation above are $12H_2$? Obviously there are only 12H. Half the hydrogens are missing. Where do they come from?

They come from the splitting of water. This process is commonly associated with photosynthesis, where the energy for it is supplied by light. As a "dark" process, however, it is also an intrinsic part of cellular respiration. Half the hydrogen burned in respiration comes from water. The equation above is wrong; the correct equation is

$$C_6H_{12}O_6 + 6H_2O + 6O_2 \longrightarrow 6CO_2 + 12H_2O \qquad (\Delta H = 672 \text{ kcal/mole})$$

If this were algebra rather than biochemistry, adding $6H_2O$ to each side of the equation would be meaningless. But it is biochemistry; and the $6H_2O$ is all-important, not only as an expression of the basic mechanism of respiration, but because it accounts for half the production of ATP.

When I talked this over with Lipmann, he put it in a particularly striking way, that I have ever since taught my students. Recognizing that in cellular respiration a molecule of water is added for each C in sugar, one can rearrange the formulas as follows:

$$C_6H_{12}O_6 \cdot 6H_2O = 6CO_2 \cdot 12H_2$$

This is the essence of the respiratory process. The object of all that goes on in cellular respiration up to the cytochrome system is to carry out this rearrangement, liberating $6CO_2$ by decarboxylation, and making $12H_2$ available for combustion to water.

There is another point of interest in this correct equation for respiration, with the extra $6H_2O$ added to both sides. In that form it is just the reverse of van Niel's corrected equation for photosynthesis. The traditional way of writing the over-all equation for photosynthesis, still dominant in the textbooks, is

$$6CO_2 + 6H_2O \xrightarrow{\text{light}} C_6H_{12}O_6 + 6O_2$$

Many years ago, however, van Niel showed that the general over-all equation for photosynthesis in bacteria, algae, and higher plants is

$$6CO_2 + 12H_2A \xrightarrow{\text{light}} C_6H_{12}O_6 + 6H_2O + 12A$$

in which A can be O, S, an organic molecule, or nothing. Green plants present a special variant of this equation in which A = O. The correct equation for their photosynthesis is therefore

$$6CO_2 + 12H_2O \xrightarrow{\text{light}} C_6H_{12}O_6 + 6H_2O + 6O_2$$

or expressed more conveniently in terms of unit carbohydrate (CH_2O),

$$CO_2 + 2H_2O \xrightarrow{\text{light}} (CH_2O) + H_2O + O_2$$

Again the addition of H_2O to each side of the unit equation is no empty formalism. On the contrary, it states fundamental relationships that are concealed by the earlier equation. It shows the source of the *four* H atoms (or four electrons) that must be moved to reduce each molecule of CO_2, a process that requires at least *four* photons. It expresses also the realization that all the oxygen emitted in photosynthesis comes out of water; and since that is so, to form O_2 requires $2H_2O$.

To return to respiration: the need to add a molecule of water for each unit of carbohydrate metabolized can be put in another way. The product, CO_2, has twice as much O per carbon as (CH_2O); and with rare exceptions the only way to add O biochemically is to add water and remove hydrogen.

That in itself is profoundly significant. Organisms seem to have begun life on this planet in the virtual absence of oxygen and had to endure this condition until they themselves put oxygen into the atmosphere as a by-product of photosynthesis. Perhaps for this reason almost all biological oxidations are anaerobic. They are dehydrogenations rather than combustions. The mechanisms of energy metabolism seem to have developed in the sequence: fermentation, hexose monophosphate cycle, photophosphorylation, photosynthesis—all typically anaerobic processes. When as a result of photosynthesis oxygen finally became available, organisms already skillful at dehydrogenation learned to perform one combustion, that of hydrogen; and with almost negligible exceptions, that is the way it has remained.

An industrial analogy may help to make this plain. Coal can be burned in oxygen to CO_2, as in a furnace. This is the aerobic way of going about its combustion. Alternatively, if steam is blown over white hot coke or anthracite, the carbon abstracts an atom of oxygen from the water, yielding as product the inflammable mixture of carbon monoxide and hydrogen known as *water gas*. This can be burned in oxygen to carbon dioxide and water; but alternatively, if it is passed with superheated steam over a catalyst such as iron oxide, the CO abstracts another O out of water to form a mixture of CO_2 and hydrogen; this is the cheapest way to make industrial hydrogen. Finally, the hydrogen can be burned in oxygen to water (Table I).

Glucose, the principal metabolite for energy production in organisms, has the same elementary composition as water gas. Like water gas, a unit of carbohydrate (CH_2O) could be burned with one molecule of oxygen to yield CO_2 and H_2O. That is not, however, what happens in respiration. Instead the carbohydrate is used to split water according to the equation, $(CH_2O) + H_2O \longrightarrow CO_2 + 2H_2$, a disguised equation of preparatory glycolysis, in which carbohydrate plays just the role that carbon monoxide does in the industrial production of hydrogen. This is then followed by the combustion of hydrogen, $2H_2 + O_2 \longrightarrow 2H_2O$, the fundamental equation of respiration (Table I).

TABLE I

COMPARISON OF AN INDUSTRIAL SYSTEM WITH A BIOLOGICAL SYSTEM

Industrial hydrogen from coal	ΔH (kcal per mole)
(a) $C + H_2O \longrightarrow CO + H_2$ (water gas)	$-$ 29.1 (endothermic)
(b) $CO + H_2O \longrightarrow CO_2 + H_2$	$+$ 9.8
(c) $2H_2 + O_2 \longrightarrow 2H_2O$	$+116.2$
Net: $C + O_2 \longrightarrow CO_2$	$+$ 96.9

Carbon cycle in organisms	ΔH (kcal per mole)
Photosynthesis:	
(a') $CO_2 + H_2O \xrightarrow{\text{light}} (CH_2O) + O_2$	-111.7
Respiration:	
(b') $(CH_2O) + H_2O \longrightarrow CO_2 + 2H_2$	$-$ 4.5
(c') $2H_2 + O_2 \longrightarrow 2H_2O$	$+116.2$
Net: $CH_2O + O_2 \longrightarrow CO_2 + H_2O$	$+$ 111.7

Carbohydrate is essentially a solid, water-soluble, metabolizable form of water gas. Water gas has a heat of combustion of 126.3 kcal per mole; a unit of carbohydrate (CH_2O) has a heat of combustion of 111.7 kcal per mole. The difference is the price organisms pay to bring water gas into a form in which they can handle it.

[This is poorly said. These heats of combustion disregard differences of state and say nothing of the useful work to be derived (ΔF). Water gas used as fuel in a heat engine would rarely yield more than 20% of the energy of combustion as useful work; whereas the six ATP's provided by the cold metabolic combustion of a unit of carbohydrate represent about 40% of the total energy change. Depending upon how the ATP is used, there are further losses of energy as heat; yet the organism comes out pretty well in this comparison.]

Where is the water added? When glucose is the metabolite, the $6H_2O$ are added in the following three steps (per half-glucose):

$$3\text{-Phosphoglyceraldehyde} \longrightarrow 3\text{-phosphoglyceric acid} \qquad (1)$$

$$\text{Pyruvic acid} \longrightarrow \text{acetic acid} \qquad (2)$$

$$\text{Fumaric acid} \longrightarrow \text{malic acid} \qquad (3)$$

Of these, the first two represent only a *net* addition of water. In step (1) the actual mechanism involves adding initially a cysteine-SH residue of the enzyme, phosphoglyceraldehyde dehydrogenase, to the aldehyde group. Then, this is *phosphorylized* off after removing 2H. The resulting high-energy carboxy phosphate linkage then transfers phosphate to adenosine diphosphate (ADP) to yield ATP. It is only in this last process that the over-all change from the aldehyde to the acid is completed, *as though* it had involved the sequence:

$$RHC{=}O + H_2O \xrightarrow{} RC(OH)_2 \xrightarrow{-2H} RCOOH$$

Similarly step (2) takes a quite different course from the simple addition of water. Here in a complicated reaction the full mechanism of which is not yet clear, pyruvic acid by oxidative decarboxylation yields acetyl coenzyme A (CoA). What has been added to the carbonyl group is not H_2O, but HS—CoA. Normally also the acetyl CoA is not hydrolyzed, but the acetyl group is transferred into another organic linkage, for example, to oxalacetic acid to yield citric acid. In the latter reaction a water molecule is added, its hydrogen going to the radical —SCoA to reconstitute CoA—SH, its hydroxyl group going into the citric acid.

In steps (1) and (2) therefore it is a carbonyl group (—C=O) that ends by drawing an oxygen out of water, becoming in the process a carboxyl group (—COOH) and liberating hydrogen, in close analogy to the way in which CO draws an oxygen out of water to yield $CO_2 + H_2$ in the industrial production of hydrogen. In step (3) however, a double bond between two carbon atoms performs the same role—as is also true in the water-splitting step in the β-oxidation of fatty acids.

The hexose monophosphate (HMP) cycle presents an exactly similar situation. Each turn of the cycle completely oxidizes the equivalent of a triose molecule, according to the over-all equation:

$$2 \text{ glucose 6-phosphate} + 3\,H_2O \longrightarrow \text{fructose 6-phosphate}$$
$$+ \text{ glyceraldehyde 3-phosphate} + 3\,CO_2 + 6\,H_2$$

The net change here is:

$$C_3H_6O_3 + 3\,H_2O \longrightarrow 3\,CO_2 + 6\,H_2$$

Once again a molecule of water has been added for each carbon atom metabolized. It enters at the point at which glucose 6-phosphate loses 2H on the one-carbon to form 6-phosphogluconolactone, the latter being hydrolyzed with H_2O to 6-phosphogluconic acid. The $6H_2$ made available in the HMP cycle are from nicotinamide adenine dinucleotide phosphate (TPN). They can be transferred to nicotinamide adenine dinucleotide (DPN) and burned through the cytochrome system; that is why the HMP cycle is often regarded as an alternative mechanism of respiration. The cycle functions in this way, however, only when frustrated. When performing its proper function the HMP cycle is an anaerobic system for providing hydrogen on TPN to be used in metabolic reductions.

That brings me to another conversation with Lipmann. All of us tend to associate degradative metabolism with oxidations and synthetic metabolism conversely with reductions. In parallel, we tend to associate energy production with oxidations and the utilization of energy with reductions.

Of course it is really just the other way around. Work must be done to remove a hydrogen atom or an electron from an organic molecule, i.e., to oxidize it; and conversely an H or an electron falling into organic linkage, i.e., a reduction, yields energy. In the oxido-reductions that actually occur in metabolism, rather than these partial steps, we habitually fasten our attention on the wrong member. The work of oxidation is performed by the reduction; and over and above that, the reduction yields enough extra energy to provide for all the manifestations of life.

That is what Lipmann said to me in conversation; and then, because he was afraid he had not said it clearly enough, he wrote me a note about it next morning: "My point is as follows (and it is an important point): to remove hydrogen from a compound like lactic acid, the O/R potential of which is far above the hydrogen potential, another system is needed the affinity of which is higher for hydrogen than that of the lactic-pyruvic system, e.g., oxygen. The great gain through the $O + 2H \longrightarrow H_2O$ reaction is used partly, so to say, to rip the hydrogen from the lactate. If you have free hydrogen—and a suitable catalyst—pyruvate will capture the hydrogen to form lactate + free energy. The removal of two hydrogens from lactate is expensive; the reaction pyruvate $+ 2H \longrightarrow$ lactate + energy is irreversible.

"An important consequence of all this talk is that the gain of energy, or where energy can be taken off in a biological system for any purposes, is where the hydrogen falls into the new linkage, and not where it is taken off."

Those conversations with Lipmann—how I miss them!

For the 25th Anniversary of ~ P

H. Chantrenne

Last summer, I found old copybooks in the attic of my father's house. Two of them contained notes I took in 1938–1939 when I was studying biochemistry. Browsing through these old papers, I read with amusement a comment written in angry handwriting on the side of a page: "Is this biochemistry? This is the chemistry of death and decay. We want to understand growth, i.e. synthesis. Hydrolysis cannot do the job!"

Biochemistry in 1938 looked somewhat depressing to a student eager to learn about the processes of life. It had barely emerged from the period of inventory and classification by which all sciences begin. Textbooks contained long lists of body constituents, the functions of which were often unknown, a classification of enzymes, the structures of which were completely obscure, and a description of many enzymatic reactions between which there was little connection. Most known enzymatic reactions were steps in the hydrolysis or in the oxidation of body constituents; none explained their formation. Textbooks often displayed schemes of synthesis based on organic chemistry; except for a few notable cases, such "paper" chemistry was utterly irrelevant, as we know today.

The isolation of several crystallized hydrolytic enzymes was one of the achievements of the 1930's. The chapter on hydrolases was extensive and usually concluded with the suggestion that hydrolases probably catalyze synthesis reactions as well. Some reversal of hydrolysis was indeed shown to occur *in vitro* under special conditions. The need of energy for synthesis was only mentioned—if at all—in vague remarks; for instance, it was often advanced that the *heat* generated by the oxidation of foodstuff might serve to force endothermic syntheses. Elementary considerations of thermodynamics were indeed alien to the majority of biochemists. Only a few laboratories had been concerned with the

33

equilibrium of enzymatic hydrolysis and were clearly conscious of the difficulties presented by uphill reactions.

The energy problem, however, had long been recognized in photosynthesis and in muscular contraction. Here the absorption of light or the output of mechanical work made it obvious. As early as 1930, Meyerhof, Parnas, Lundsgaard, and a few others were deeply concerned with this problem. The hydrolysis of creatine phosphate was shown to release a large amount of heat. Since creatine phosphate was known to split during muscular work and in the absence of carbohydrate breakdown the muscle stopped working as soon as creatine phosphate was exhausted, these workers realized that the energy of glycolysis is somehow stored in creatine phosphate and eventually changed into mechanical work. It was also recognized that the formation of creatine phosphate is connected to energy-yielding oxidoreduction processes, but even these latter reactions were not well known yet. In 1938, the Krebs cycle was received as a somewhat disturbing hypothesis. The scheme of glycolysis was not completed until 1939, when the two dehydrogenases were crystallized by Warburg's group, and the fundamental oxidoreduction obtained *in vitro*. As a result, the equilibrium of triose phosphate oxidation by cozymase was shown to depend on phosphate concentration and the product of oxidation was found to be "1,3-diphosphoglyceric" acid (phosphoglyceryl phosphate).

A comparable observation was made by Lipmann for the oxidation of pyruvate in bacterial extracts. This oxidation also depends on phosphate concentration and one of the end products is acetyl phosphate.

The recognition that in these oxidations phosphate is not a mere activator, that it is a reactant, that it does participate in the reaction since it influences the oxidation-reduction equilibrium, that it is linked in the process to the oxidized group, was the clue toward understanding energy conservation in biological systems. This must have been realized at the time by several biochemists. But it was Lipmann's role to explore the idea most thoroughly, to appreciate its significance, to generalize it, and to expound clearly the principles of coupling. He did this in a paper (Lipmann, 1941) which, after 25 years, remains a guide for continuing research as well as a milestone in biochemistry. Lipmann presented the new concepts so simply that everyone was able to grasp them and soon to take them as obvious; they immediately became classic.

Estimation of the free energy from phosphoenolpyruvate and carboxyl phosphate splitting indeed showed how the cell creates phosphate groups of high chemical potential, comparable in this respect to that of creatine phosphate. A large amount of energy is stored in such compounds; this energy can be released as heat when the compounds are hydrolyzed. The cell taps energy from spontaneous exergonic reactions exactly as an engineer draws energy from falling water. The engineer blocks the waterfall and provides a roundabout path through which water can flow only if it pushes the turbine. In the same way, the life process avoided producing any catalyst which would allow triose phosphate to be oxidized into phosphoglyceric acid directly. Instead, it managed to develop an enzyme which permits the oxidation to proceed only together with the fixation of a phosphate group on the reaction product. This detour results in the conservation of part of the energy in the created phosphate bond. Just as in mechanical arts, conservation of part of the energy is achieved by elaborating a structurally organized system, which controls the dissipation of energy and orients it toward useful purposes. The need for establishing a roundabout process if energy is to be tapped thus justifies the incredible pathway of glycolysis. Passage through hexose phosphates, for instance, makes sense: it is part of the trick by which energy will be preserved. Conservation of the energy of respiration or photosynthesis in the same way justifies the complexities of the electron transfer chains. "In all cells a tendency exists to convert the major part of available oxidation reduction energy into phosphate bond energy" (Lipmann, 1941).

What becomes of this stored energy?

Comparison of the free energy of various phosphoric groups proved essential; it immediately showed which phosphorylations could possibly occur and which ones would never take place whatever catalyst was present. The scale of phosphate bond energy was intrinsically similar to the familiar scale of oxidoreduction potential. It showed the direction of flow of phosphate groups, just as oxidoreduction potentials indicate the direction of flow of electrons. The scale of phosphate bond energy was a new element of irreversibility, a new arrow in biochemical processes.

The somewhat arbitrary—if amply justified—distinction between high- and low-energy phosphate bonds had a didactic importance; it simplified the picture, because it established a qualitative difference between the two classes. It was easy to visualize the free reversible exchange of phosphate groups within one class, as contrasted with the irreversible flow of phosphate from a high-energy donor to an acceptor, which resulted in the formation of a low-energy bond, the energy difference being dissipated. It became clear that hydrolysis of a bond is a wasteful process, irreversible in effect. In muscle it is not the hydrolysis of creatine phosphate which provides energy to the muscle machinery; the phosphate group must be transferred to some acceptor. Hydrolysis generates much heat, but no work, and can just help in removing a final product.

If the cell manages to convert energy into phosphate bonds and thus possesses an ideal system for making all kinds of phosphate esters, what else can it do? Can the cell use phosphate energy for forcing other types of endergonic syntheses? Can the phosphate bond energy be changed into other types of bonds, can it be used for other syntheses beside phosphorylation? The bridge between the phosphate bond and other types of bonds was provided by acetyl phosphate, which Lipmann himself had discovered. This is the mixed anhydride of phosphoric and acetic acid and its phosphate bond is energy-rich. Obviously, Lipmann thought it must be a high-potential acetyl compound, a probable acetyl donor, high on the scale of acetyl bond energy. The cell might use it for acetylation purposes just as the organic chemist uses acetic anhydride or acetyl chloride. Connection between the two chains is provided by an intermediate partaking of the two, through which the energy can be fed into the pool of high-energy acetyl compounds.

The idea of acetyl transfer was but an extension of the idea of phosphoryl transfer. It contained the same concept of oriented transfer from high-energy compounds to acceptors, thus providing an explanation for acetylation of alcohols or amines.

The sketches illustrating this concept—acetylation of choline by acetyl phosphate, acylation of glycerol by phosphoric anhydrides of fatty acids, peptide synthesis from aminoacyl phosphates—may be regarded as opening the field of biosynthesis. They were the first hypothetical schemes to imply the real principle of all biosyntheses and of their connection with phosphorylation.

Transfer of groups, in the direction imposed by group potential, is indeed the fundamental rule. All the biosyntheses analyzed at present (and we now know essentially how all types of cell constituents are made) illustrate the principles expounded in Lipmann's paper of 1941. To the small list that was then suggested—phosphate, acetyl, amino, methyl, and carbamyl—we can now add many more: pyrophosphoryl, sulfuryl, a large variety of acyl groups, with formyl as a remarkable case, aminoacyl, osidyl, nucleotidyl compounds, and among the most versatile energy-rich bonds the acyl thioesters with Lipmann's coenzyme A as the most characteristic representative.

Lipmann's analysis of the generation and utilization of phosphate bond energy pulled research on biosynthesis away from sidetracks and blind alleys and pointed to the right path. Labeled compounds helped to do the rest.

Biochemistry is no longer the chemistry of death and decay; it is the chemistry of the living cell, with its essentially irreversible, oriented processes admirably organized and controlled.

When looking back on past accomplishments, one often feels slightly sad. But we need not be; we are indeed commemorating an accomplishment which marked the beginning in a new field of research. We can now fully appreciate the influence Lipmann's ideas had in shaping present-day biochemistry; we realize how much Lipmann's group contributed experimentally to the later discoveries of the pathways of biosynthesis. Moreover, we can rejoice that once again these workers are progressing with remarkable success toward a new frontier of biosynthesis, solving the riddles of the expression of structural information.

I wish to express to Dr. F. Lipmann the gratitude and the admiration of all those who were privileged to work with him. They are proud of their master.

REFERENCE

Lipmann, F. Advan. Enzymol. 1, 99 (1941).

Some Considerations of the Energy Metabolism of Anaerobic Bacteria

E. R. Stadtman

INTRODUCTION

Ever since the pioneering discovery of Harden and Young that glucose dissimilation proceeds by way of phosphorylated intermediates, biochemists have concerned themselves with the biosynthesis and transformation of phosphorylated metabolites and the significant role that these play in the energetics of specific enzymatic processes and in the over-all energy metabolism of living organisms. But perhaps no single effort has had as much impact on the subsequent thinking and experimental progress in the area of bioenergetics as did the searching report of Fritz Lipmann (1941) on "Metabolic Generation and Utilization of Phosphate Bond Energy" which appropriately appeared in the first volume of *Advances in Enzymology,* a quarter of a century ago. In this classic paper, Lipmann formulated with lucid simplicity the basic mechanisms and thermodynamics that underlie the derivation of useful chemical energy from metabolic processes and the mechanisms by which this chemical energy can be stored, transferred, and ultimately utilized for essential biosynthetic purposes. These concepts captured the imagination of many biochemists and stimulated a flurry of intensive research on specific enzyme systems that could be used as models to support and extend the basic ideas that were so clearly outlined in Lipmann's report. The result has been very rewarding. Much information is now available on a number of key metabolic systems; new kinds of energy-yielding processes have been discovered and the detailed mechanisms by which the energy is utilized for specific biosynthetic reactions have been delineated, as, for example, those involved in the synthesis of fatty acids, peptides, and carbohydrates. These studies have confirmed, in essential details, the Lipmann concept.

During the past 15 years, the activities of our own laboratory have been concerned with the energy metabolism of anaerobic organisms and this research has, to a large measure, derived stimulus from Lipmann's basic concepts. Our interest in anaerobic metabolism was provoked by the consideration that, unlike aerobic organisms, which can derive most of their metabolic energy by coupling phosphate esterification with terminal steps in the transfer of electrons to molecular oxygen, the energy metabolism of anaerobes is restricted to fermentative processes in which terminal respiration is excluded as a source of energy. As a consequence, the anaerobic dissimilation of fermentable substrates must be geared to the generation of critical intermediates which, according to Lipmann's terminology, are characterized by having high "group potentials" and are therefore capable of undergoing group substitution reactions in which the potential chemical energy is utilized for the synthesis of adenosine triphosphate (ATP) or is consumed in specific biosynthetic processes. This concept is well supported by studies of anaerobic glycolysis showing that two steps (i.e., the oxidation of 3-phosphoglyceraldehyde to 1,3-diphosphoglycerate and the conversion of 2-phosphoglyceric acid to phosphoenolpyruvate) result in the synthesis of so-called "energy-rich" phosphate esters from which ATP can be obtained. It is significant that those anaerobic organisms whose carbohydrate metabolism is restricted to alcoholic or lactic acid fermentations via the glycolytic pathway depend on diphosphoglycerate and phosphoenolpyruvate as the exclusive sources of ATP needed for growth and cellular metabolism (Gunsalus and Shuster, 1961).

Extension of the concept that "energy-rich" intermediates are formed in the dissimilation of fermentable substrates by obligate anaerobes leads to interesting predictions when one considers the large number and varieties of compounds that can serve as sole carbon and energy sources for anaerobic growth. It can be anticipated that the fermentation of certain of these compounds may lead to the formation of new kinds of activated intermediates that are functional in biosynthetic reactions and at the same time may serve as final links in the synthesis of ATP.

Prompted by these considerations we have undertaken a series of studies on the intermediary reactions of several anaerobic fermentations that offered unique opportunities to investigate some specific biochemical processes.

In some instances these studies have led to the identification of those reactions in which "energy-rich" intermediates are produced. They have led also to the discovery of some basic mechanisms by which the energy of such intermediates can be transferred or consumed in specific biosynthetic processes or utilized for the synthesis of ATP. On the other hand, examination of these fermentations discloses the fact that, in some instances, the amount of growth supported by a specific fermentative process is significantly greater than that which can be accounted for on the basis of "energy-rich" compound formation in the established pathways of substrate dissimilation. One is therefore left with the obvious conclusion that the energy available for the growth of anaerobic microorganisms is not necessarily restricted to the generation of substrate-level "energy-rich" intermediates, as has been generally assumed. Energy might also be provided by other, as yet unrecognized sources, possibly by mechanisms comparable to those found in aerobic metabolism where a major source of energy is derived from the coupling of electron transport to ATP synthesis.

It is the purpose of the present discussion to summarize some of the earlier work on the synthesis and energy metabolism of acyl coenzyme A (CoA) intermediates in *Clostridium kluyveri* and to draw attention to studies on this and several other organisms that point to the existence of as yet unidentified biologically significant energy-yielding processes.

THE ENERGY METABOLISM OF *CLOSTRIDIUM KLUYVERI*

Earlier studies (Barker, 1937; Bornstein and Barker, 1948) showed that the over-all fermentation of ethanol and acetate by *C. kluyveri* leads to the formation of variable amounts of butyrate and caproate and small amounts of molecular hydrogen. For the present discussion, however, it is permissible and also desirable, for the sake of clarity, to consider the fermentation as a homofermentative process in which one mole of acetate and one mole of ethanol are converted to butyrate according to Eq. (1).

$$C_2H_5OH + CH_3COO^- \rightarrow CH_3CH_2CH_2COO^- + H_2O \qquad (1)$$

It is inappropriate here to discuss in detail the studies of Barker and his students which established the mechanism of this over-all fermentation. This work and the prominent role that it played in elucidation of the mechanism of fatty acid oxidation and the metabolism of acetyl CoA have been thoroughly reviewed (Barker, 1951, 1956; Lynen and Decker, 1957; Stadtman, 1954).

Suffice it to say that the conversion of ethanol and acetate to butyrate involves the following sequence of reactions:[*]

$$C_2H_5OH + DPN^+ \leftrightharpoons DPNH + H^+ + CH_3CHO \tag{2}$$

$$CH_3CHO + DPN^+ + CoASH \leftrightharpoons CH_3COSCoA + DPNH + H^+ \tag{3}$$

$$2CH_3COSCoA \leftrightharpoons CH_3COCH_2COSCoA + CoASH \tag{4}$$

$$CH_3COCH_2COSCoA + DPNH + H^+ \leftrightharpoons CH_3CHOHCH_2COSCoA + DPN^+ \tag{5}$$

$$CH_3CHOHCH_2COSCoA \leftrightharpoons CH_3CH{=}CHCOSCoA + H_2O \tag{6}$$

$$CH_3CH{=}CHCOSCoA + DPNH + H^+ \leftrightharpoons CH_3CH_2CH_2COSCoA + DPN^+ \tag{7}$$

$$CH_3CH_2CH_2COSCoA + CH_3COO^- \leftrightharpoons CH_3CH_2CH_2COO^- + CH_3COSCoA \tag{8}$$

Sum 2–8: $C_2H_5OH + CH_3COO^- \rightarrow CH_3CH_2CH_2COO^- + H_2O$ (1)

For the reasons discussed above it was anticipated that the fermentation of ethanol and acetate would lead to the formation of an "energy-rich" intermediate that could be used directly for the synthesis of ATP. Examination of the fermentation mechanism shows that only one step, i.e., the oxidation of acetaldehyde to acetyl CoA [Eq. (3)], gives rise to an "energy-rich" compound. Whereas the "energy-rich" nature of acetyl CoA had been established by earlier studies (Stadtman *et al.*, 1951; Stern *et al.*, 1951 Stadtman, 1952), it was possible from a detailed analysis of Eq. (3) to obtain a reliable estimate of the free energy of hydrolysis of acetyl CoA. Thus, from the equilibrium constant of Eq. (3), it could be calculated that the standard free energy change $\Delta F'$ is -4.0 kcal (Burton and Stadtman, 1953).[†] This is to be compared with a calculated $\Delta F'$ of -12.0 kcal for the DPN-linked oxidation of acetaldehyde to acetate [Eq. (9)].[**]

As is shown below, the difference in standard free energy changes between Eqs. (9) and (3) [sum of Eq. (9) and the reverse of Eq. (3)] is

[*] In this Chapter DPN is used for nicotinamide adenine dinucleotide.

[†] The following abbreviations are used: $\Delta F°$, increment in free energy under standard conditions, which are 25°C, 1.0 atmosphere pressure, and concentrations of all solutes are 1.0 molal; $\Delta F'$ is identical with $\Delta F°$ except H^+ is 10^{-7} M. $\Delta F°f$ and $\Delta F'f$ refer to free energies of formation under standard conditions and under standard conditions except at pH 7.0, respectively.

[**] The $\Delta F'$ for Eq. (9) is calculated from thermal data for the oxidation of acetaldehyde to acetate and H_2 (Kaplan, 1951) and from the standard potential for the oxidation of DPNH to DPN as estimated by Burton and Wilson (1953).

≈ -8.0 kcal which represents the free energy of hydrolysis of acetyl CoA [Eq. (10)].

$$CH_3CHO + H_2O + DPN^+ \leftrightarrows DPNH + CH_3COO^- + 2H^+ \qquad \Delta F' = -12.0 \text{ kcal}$$
$$\text{(9)}$$

$$CH_3COSCoA + DPNH + H^+ \leftrightarrows CH_3CHO + DPN^+ + CoASH \qquad \Delta F' = +4.0 \text{ kcal}$$
$$\text{(3)}$$

$$Sum: CH_3COSCoA + H_2O \leftrightarrows CH_3COO^- + CoASH + H^+ \qquad \Delta F' = -8.0 \text{ kcal}$$
$$\text{(10)}$$

The standard free energy change associated with the hydrolysis of the thiolester bond is therefore essentially the same as that associated with the hydrolysis of the pyrophosphate bonds of ATP and justifies the designation of acyl CoA derivatives as "energy-rich" compounds in the same thermodynamic sense as ATP or adenosine diphosphate (ADP) are considered "energy-rich" compounds.

A consideration of Eqs. (3) and (9) illustrates an important principle that was emphasized by Lipmann (1941); namely, that the substitution of phosphate (or in this instance CoASH) for water in certain key reactions leads to the synthesis of ester derivatives rather than the free acids and that this affords a basic mechanism by which metabolic energy that would otherwise be lost as heat may be conserved. In the present instance, the substitution of CoASH for water in the oxidation of acetaldehyde leads to the synthesis of acetyl CoA [Eq. (3)] rather than acetate [Eq. (9)], and consequently, about 8.0 out of the 12.0 kcal that are potentially available from the oxidation of the aldehyde group to a carboxyl group are conserved in a chemically useful form.

Equation (3) constitutes the only obvious mechanism by which metabolic energy derived from ethanol oxidation by *C. kluyveri* may be conserved in a chemically useful form. However, to be of general significance in energy metabolism, the potential hydrolysis energy of acetyl CoA must be made available for biosynthetic reactions, especially for the synthesis of ATP which is the more immediate source of energy for biosynthesis. In *C. kluyveri* the synthesis of ATP from CoA is achieved by the coupling of two group substitution reactions as follows:*

$$\text{Acetyl CoA} + P_i \leftrightarrows \text{acetyl-P} + \text{CoA} \qquad \Delta F = +2.5 \text{ kcal} \quad (11)$$

$$\text{Acetyl-P} + \text{ADP} \leftrightarrows \text{acetate} + \text{ATP} \qquad \Delta F = -2.5 \text{ kcal} \quad (12)$$

$$Sum: \text{Acetyl CoA} + P_i + \text{ADP} \leftrightarrows \text{acetate} + \text{CoA} + \text{ATP} \qquad \Delta F = 0 \quad (13)$$

* P_i, inorganic phosphate; acetyl-P, acetyl phosphate.

Equation (11), which is catalyzed by phosphotransacetylase (Stadtman *et al.*, 1957; Stadtman, 1952), may be regarded as an acetyl group transfer reaction that involves the substitution of a phosphoryl group for the CoA thioalkyl group of acetyl CoA. Equation (12), on the other hand, is catalyzed by acetate kinase (Lipmann, 1944; Stadtman and Barker, 1950; Rose, 1955); this may be regarded as a phosphoryl group transfer reaction which involves substitution of ADP for the acetyl moiety of acetyl-P. The net result of these two coupled group substitution reactions is given by Eq. (13) which shows that the esterification of ADP by orthophosphate is accomplished at the expense of acetyl CoA decomposition to acetate and CoA. We see then that, in effect, the synthesis of ATP is achieved by a mechanism in which the energy that would be lost by the hydrolysis of acetyl CoA is transferred by means of group substitution reactions, first to form acetyl-P and then to form ATP. Reactions (11), (12), and (13) thus illustrate an important principle that was enunciated by Lipmann in his 1941 report; namely, that the transfer of metabolic energy is mediated by group transfer reactions (i.e., by group substitution reactions). Lipmann pointed out further that the thermodynamic capacity of various compounds to undergo group transfer reactions (i.e., their "group potential") is related to their standard free energy of hydrolysis. He also noted that in compounds such as acetyl-P the standard free energy of hydrolysis is not only an index of the *phosphoryl-group potential*, but is an index of the *acetyl-group potential* as well. Accordingly it is not surprising that acetyl-P is on the one hand a good phosphoryl donor, as in Eq. (12), and on the other hand a good acetyl donor, as is illustrated by the reverse of Eq. (11). By analogy an "energy-rich" compound such as acetyl CoA would be expected to have both high acetyl-group potential and high *thiol-alkyl-group potential* and should serve either as an acetyl donor or as a thiolalkyl donor. It is therefore understandable that enzymes catalyzing both kinds of energy transfer reactions could be demonstrated in cell-free extracts of *C. kluyveri*. The significance of these enzymes in the energy metabolism of *C. kluyveri* is discussed below.

THE ACETYL TRANSFER FUNCTION OF ACETYL CoA

The Acetylation of Orthophosphate

The acetyl transfer function of acetyl CoA is clearly illustrated by Eq. (11), as has already been described. This reaction is of historical importance because it was among the first CoA-dependent reactions to be recognized (Stadtman *et al.*, 1951), and a detailed study of it has contributed significantly to a knowledge of the mechanism of CoA action and the thermodynamics of acyl CoA derivatives.

From the standpoint of bioenergetics, Eq. (11) is of particular significance in the energy metabolism of anaerobic bacteria since acetyl CoA is a common metabolite in the fermentation of most substrates and in some instances probably represents the only metabolic energy available for growth. As noted above, the utilization of acetyl CoA for the synthesis of ATP involves Eq. (11) and (12) which together constitute one basic mechanism for the conversion of metabolic thiolester energy into the more generally useful form of ATP.

For certain biosynthetic processes, the reverse of Eq. (11) (i.e., the synthesis of acetyl CoA from acetyl-P) may have importance in those organisms in which acetyl-P rather than acetyl CoA is the primary "energy-rich" product of substrate dissimilation, as, for example, in the oxidation of pyruvate by *Lactobacillus delbruckii* (Lipmann, 1939) or in the phosphorolytic cleavage of xylulose-5-P by *Lactobacillus pentosus* (Heath *et al.*, 1958). In these instances the utilization of acetyl-P for the synthesis of acetyl CoA by Eq. (11) provides a more direct means of utilizing the acetyl moiety in biosynthetic reactions.

Thioltransacetylation

In the course of studies on the mechanism of action of phosphotransacetylase it was discovered incidentally (Stadtman, 1952) that cell-free extracts of *C. kluyveri* contain a family of enzymes that catalyze thioltransacetylation reactions of the type described by Eq. (14).

$$\text{Acetyl-SCoA} + \text{RSH} \rightarrow \text{acetyl-SR} + \text{CoASH} \tag{14}$$

Thus, 2-mercaptoethanol, hydrogen sulfide, glutathione, lipoic acid, and other mercaptans are able to serve as acetyl group acceptors (Brady and Stadtman, 1954). Although precise equilibrium measurements have not been made for Eq. (14), it involves the decomposition and formation of homologous derivatives and therefore should occur with relatively little change in free energy. With the possible exception of the reaction with lipoic acid, which has been shown in other organisms to be involved in α-ketoacid oxidation, it seems unlikely that the reactions with the particular mercaptans tested are of physiological significance. It is believed that the capacities of the mercaptans to serve as acetyl acceptors are merely the manifestations of substrate nonspecificity that is characteristic of these enzymes, whose normal function remains to be discovered.

One possibility deserving consideration is that these enzymes catalyze transacylation between various acyl CoA derivatives and the sulfhydryl groups of enzymes involved in acyl CoA-linked reactions. This possibility seems all the more probable in view of the studies in Vagelos' laboratory showing that enzymes of *C. kluyveri* and *Escherichia coli* catalyze trans-acylations between acetyl CoA (and malonyl CoA) and the pantetheine sulfhydryl group of the acyl carrier protein (ACP) [Eq. (17)] (Alberts *et al.*, 1964). As Vagelos and his associates have demonstrated, the latter reactions constitute the first steps in the conversion of acetyl CoA and malonyl CoA to long-chain fatty acids in these organisms (Vagelos, 1964). Detailed studies of the mechanism of these acyl transfer reactions indicate that they probably involve two consecutive thioltransacylation reactions [Eqs. (15) and (16)] in which thioacyl enzyme derivatives are common

$$\text{Acyl-SCoA} + \text{E-SH} \rightleftharpoons \text{acyl-SE} + \text{CoASH} \tag{15}$$

$$\text{Acyl-SE} + \text{ACP-SH} \rightleftharpoons \text{acyl-SACP} + \text{E-SH} \tag{16}$$

$$\textit{Sum: } \text{Acyl-SCoA} + \text{ACP-SH} \rightleftharpoons \text{acyl-SACP} + \text{CoASH} \tag{17}$$

intermediates. These studies focus attention on the significance of thiol-acyl enzyme intermediates in acyl group transfer reactions and on the importance of thioltransacylation as a basic mechanism by which the transfer of acyl groups can be mediated without a loss of *group potential*.

The Acetylation of Imidazole

During investigations on the oxidation of butyrate to acetyl CoA in the presence of imidazole buffer, an enzyme-catalyzed transfer of the acetyl group of acetyl CoA to imidazole was observed [Eq. (18)] (Stadtman,

$$\text{Acetyl-SCoA} + \text{imidazole} \rightleftharpoons \text{N-acetylimidazole} + \text{CoASH} \tag{18}$$

1954). From equilibrium measurements it could be determined that the $\Delta F°$ for Eq. (18) is about $+ 5.3$ kcal. The $\Delta F°$ for hydrolysis of acetyl-imidazole is therefore about 13.0 kcal, which means that its "acetyl group potential" is greater than that of most other biological intermediates thus far recognized. Whereas this reaction calls attention to the potential role of imidazole derivatives in the biological transfer of acyl groups, its precise role, if any, in the intermediary metabolism of *C. kluyveri* remains to be explained. As with the thioltransacylases discussed above, and the HCN acetylase to be described below, it is tempting to believe that the acetylation of imidazole by acetyl CoA is an expression of the lack of specificity of an enzyme which has another physiologically important catalytic function. However, in contrast to some of the thioltrans-acetylases, imidazole acetylase is characterized by high substrate specificity; thus far none of a large number of imidazole derivatives nor of various other heterocyclic nitrogen compounds tested will replace free imidazole as an acetyl acceptor in Eq. (18). The possibility remains that an imidazole group of a histidine residue present at the catalytically active site of some enzyme involved in acetyl CoA metabolism is the normal acetyl acceptor for this enzyme. Considered in the broader sense, Eq. (18) illustrates a new type of biological energy transfer reaction that may be fundamental in mechanisms of enzyme action, especially those concerned with the conservation of energy that is associated with substrate dissimilation.

The Acetylation of Hydrogen Cyanide

Another curious example of transacetylation at the high-energy level is the acetylation of HCN by acetyl CoA [Eq. (19)]. The discovery of this reaction was incidental to studies in which HCN was added to reaction mixtures in an effort to trap acetoacetate formed as a transient intermediate in the oxidation of butyrate to acetyl CoA by extracts of *C. kluyveri*. Contrary to expectation, neither acetyl CoA nor the cyanohydrin derivative of acetoacetate accumulated. Instead the amino groups of amino acids and proteins, that were present in the crude enzyme preparation, became acetylated (Stadtman *et al.*, 1952). A detailed study of this phenomenon disclosed the presence in cell-free extracts of *C. kluyveri* of an enzyme that catalyzes the substitution of HCN for the CoA moiety of acetyl CoA according to Eq. (19) (Eggerer *et al.*, 1962). The accumu-

$$CH_3COSCoA + HCN \overset{\text{HCN acetylase}}{\underset{}{\rightleftarrows}} CH_3COCN + CoASH \qquad (19)$$

$$CH_3COCN + RNH_2 \overset{\text{nonenzymatic}}{\longrightarrow} CH_3CONHR + HCN \qquad (20)$$

$$Sum: CH_3COSCoA + RNH_2 \longrightarrow CH_3CONHR + CoASH \qquad (21)$$

lation of N-acetyl amino acids and N-acetylated protein [Eq. (21)] is attributed to the extremely rapid spontaneous reaction of acetyl cyanide with free amino groups [Eq. (20)] (Eggerer *et al.*, 1962). In the absence of amino acceptors, the acetyl cyanide is almost instantly hydrolyzed. Because of the extreme lability of acetyl cyanide the equilibrium constant for Eq. (19), and hence the free energy of hydrolysis of acetyl cyanide, could not be determined. Nevertheless, the extreme lability of acetyl cyanide to hydrolysis is suggestive of a high "group potential." This conclusion is substantiated by the fact that acetyl cyanide is able to undergo rapid nonenzymatic exchange reactions with mercaptans to form acetyl thiolester derivatives [Eq. (21)] (Eggerer *et al.*,

$$CH_3COCN + RSH \rightleftharpoons CH_3COSR + HCN \qquad (22)$$

1962). Since HCN is not a normal metabolite it is obvious that Eq. (19) per se is of no physiological significance; nevertheless, the reaction makes us aware of a new kind of energy transfer process at the energy-rich level. The fact that it is catalyzed by a specific enzyme present in extracts of *C. kluyveri* suggests that an analogous reaction in which HCN is replaced by an as yet unidentified biologically active counterpart may be important in the mediation of acyl group transfer involving acyl CoA derivatives.

The Synthesis of Acetoacetyl CoA

Whereas early tracer experiments offered substantial proof that the synthesis of acetoacetate involves the condensation of two carbon compounds at the oxidation level of acetate, Lipmann (1946) called attention to the fact that the conversion of acetate to acetoacetate is a strongly endergonic process and could not be expected to occur readily under normal physiological conditions. He pointed out that acetoacetate synthesis would be facilitated by the substitution of an activated derivative such as acetyl-P for acetate in the coupling reaction. This prediction was confirmed, in principle, with the demonstration that acetoacetate synthesis involves the coupling of two equivalents of acetyl CoA (Stadtman *et al.*, 1951a) to form acetoacetyl CoA [Eq. (4)]. This reaction constitutes the first step uniquely concerned with synthesis of butyrate by *C. kluyveri*. Whereas Eq. (4) is still strongly endergonic ($\Delta F° \approx + 6.0$ kcal), substitution of acetyl CoA for acetate in the coupling reaction overcomes an otherwise almost insurmountable energy barrier ($\Delta F° \approx + 14.0$ kcal) and permits the reaction to occur readily under physiological conditions. From the energetic point of view, the reaction involves utilization of the "acetyl-group potential" of one equivalent of acetyl CoA to effect the formation of a carbon-carbon bond in the synthesis of a β-ketoacid. It is evident that the thiolester energy thus consumed is maintained in a biologically available form since cleavage of acetoacetyl CoA by the reverse of Eq. (4) readily gives rise to two equivalents of acetyl CoA.

As shall be pointed out later, the utilization of one equivalent of acetyl CoA for the synthesis of acetoacetyl CoA is of critical importance in the over-all energy metabolism of *C. kluyveri*, since under growth conditions, this precludes the generation of ATP from acetyl CoA.

The Thiolalkyl Transfer Function of Acetyl CoA

The high *thiolalkyl-group potential* of acetyl CoA was clearly established by the discovery in cell free extracts of *C. kluyveri* of an enzyme that catalyzes the reversible transfer of the CoAS moiety from acetyl-SCoA to butyrate to form butyryl-SCoA (Stadtman 1953). The reverse of this reaction [Eq. (8)] is the terminal step in the synthesis of butyrate by *C. kluyveri*. It is of considerable importance in the energy metabolism of the organism since it provides a means of utilizing the thiolester-group potential of butyryl CoA (an otherwise useless end product) for the synthesis of acetyl CoA which is needed for the continued synthesis of acetoacetyl CoA [Eq. (4)].

Following the discovery of the CoA transferase system in *C. kluyveri*, analogous reactions have been observed in a number of other organisms. It is therefore evident that such thiolalkyl group transfer reactions constitute a fundamental mechanism for the quantitative utilization of acetyl CoA-group potential in the activation of various carboxylic acids required for specific biosynthetic purposes. The discovery that formate will serve as a CoA acceptor in the CoA transferase system of *C. kluyveri* (Sly and Stadtman, 1963) deserves special attention as a mechanism for the synthesis of formyl CoA. This fact and the further observation that formyl CoA may be converted to formyl-P by a reaction analogous to Eq. (11) (Sly and Stadtman, 1963a) are further illustrations of energy transfer at the high-energy level and emphasize the potential role of formyl CoA as an activated one-carbon compound in intermediary metabolism.

The Nonavailability of Acetyl CoA as a Source of Energy for the Growth of *C. kluyveri*

In the preceding sections the enzymatic mechanism for the conversion of ethanol and acetate to butyrate by *C. kluyveri* has been outlined and several reactions have been cited to illustrate how the energy conserved in the oxidation of ethanol to acetyl CoA may be utilized for the synthesis of other compounds with "high-group potentials." These reactions thus provide mechanisms for the conservation and transfer of metabolic energy in accord with Lipmann's basic concepts of energy metabolism.

With regard to the over-all energy metabolism of *C. kluyveri*, however, one must not lose sight of the fact that the conversion of ethanol to butyrate (or caproate) is the almost exclusive fermentative process carried out by *C. kluyveri* and its primary function is therefore to provide energy for growth.

On the basis of thermodynamic data Bornstein and Barker (1948) calculated that the standard free energy change ($\Delta F'$) for Eq. (1) is —11.7 kcal. It is therefore apparent that sufficient energy is available from butyrate synthesis to allow the formation of at least one equivalent of ATP.

As already pointed out, an examination of Eqs. (2)–(8) shows that only one step in butyrate synthesis, namely the oxidation of acetaldehyde to acetyl CoA, leads to the formation of an "energy-rich" intermediate. Utilization of this acetyl CoA for the synthesis of ATP [Eq. (13)] can be readily achieved by the coupling of Eqs. (11) and (12). However, Barker (1956) has called attention to the fact that this potential source of energy is not actually available for synthesis of cell material, since the acetyl CoA formed in the oxidation of acetaldehyde must be consumed in the highly endergonic Eq. (4) in order to provide the electron acceptors, acetoacetyl CoA and crotonyl CoA, without which the anaerobic oxidations of ethanol and acetaldehyde cannot occur. In other words, all the potential energy of acetaldehyde oxidation conserved in the formation of acetyl CoA is needed to provide the electron acceptors; little or none is available for the synthesis of ATP. Our original hypothesis that anaerobic organisms generate their ATP exclusively from substrate level energy-rich intermediates is not supported by these findings. If there is no net formation of energy-rich intermediates as a result of the butyrate fermentation, we are left with the inescapable conclusion that some other source of energy must be available to support the growth of *C. kluyveri*. In the absence of other obvious possibilities Barker (1956) has suggested the ATP may be formed by the coupling of phosphorylation with electron transport. Since molecular oxygen is excluded as a terminal electron acceptor in anaerobic fermentations, if electron transport phosphorylation does occur it must involve one or more of the steps involved in the fermentation itself. Barker (1956) has pointed out that the free energy change associated with the coupling of Eq. (2) with the reduction of crotonyl CoA to butyryl CoA [Eq. (7)], is approximately —18.0 kcal, which is more than enough to provide energy for the synthesis of one or even two equivalents of ATP from ADP and P_i.

To date, however, coupling of phosphorylation with Eq. (7) has not been established unequivocally. Shuster and Gunsalus (1958) reported that the reduction of the crotonyl CoA analog, S-crotonyl-N-acetylthio-ethanolamine, by molecular hydrogen, catalyzed by cell-free extracts of *C. kluyveri*, is accompanied by phosphorylation of ADP to form ATP. However, the possibility that the observed phosphorylation is derived indirectly, by Eqs. (11) and (12), from acetyl thiolesters formed in the dismutation of the crotonyl thiolester [Eq. (23)] does not appear to

$$2\text{Crotonyl-SR} + \text{RSH} \rightarrow \text{butyryl-SR} + 2\text{acetyl-SR} \qquad (23)$$

have been rigorously excluded. Experiments in this laboratory by Brown and Stadtman (1958) confirmed the observation that ATP is formed during the reduction of S-crotonyl-N-acetylthioethanolamine by cell-free extracts of *C. kluyveri*, but the amount of ATP produced never exceeded the amount of acetate formed. Moreover, efforts to demonstrate ATP formation during the anaerobic conversion of ethanol and acetate to butyrate by cell-free extracts were unsuccessful.

In spite of these negative results it seems highly probable that the reduction of crotonyl CoA is coupled with phosphorylation since this appears to be the only step in the butyrate fermentation that is sufficiently exergonic to support the synthesis of ATP. Nevertheless final judgment must be withheld until more definitive experimental data are available.

AMINO ACID FERMENTATIONS

Glycine Reduction

Many anaerobic organisms, especially those belonging to the genus *Clostridium*, derive energy for growth from the fermentation of amino acids. In some of these fermentations, one mole of amino acid undergoes oxidative deamination [Eq. (24)], whereas another undergoes reductive deamination [Eq. (25)]. Further oxidation of the α-ketoacid produced

$$\overset{+}{\text{RCHNH}_3}\text{COO}^- + \text{H}_2\text{O} + \overset{+}{\text{DPN}} \rightarrow \text{RCOCOO}^- + \overset{+}{\text{NH}_4} + \text{DPNH} + \text{H}^+ \qquad (24)$$

$$\overset{+}{\text{RCHNH}_3}\text{COO}^- + \text{DPNH} + \text{H}^+ \rightarrow \text{RCH}_2\text{COO}^- + \overset{+}{\text{NH}_4} + \overset{+}{\text{DPN}} \qquad (25)$$

in Eq. (24) is coupled with CoASH esterification [Eq. (26)] (Nisman, 1954) and provides a potential source of energy for growth.

$$\text{RCOCOO}^- + \overset{+}{\text{DPN}} + \text{CoASH} \rightarrow \text{RCOSCoA} + \text{CO}_2 + \text{DPNH} \qquad (26)$$

However, in addition, T. C. Stadtman and associates (T. C. Stadtman and Elliott, 1956; T. C. Stadtman *et al.*, 1958) have shown that reductive deamination may also be coupled with ATP formation. Though not anticipated, the latter discovery is readily understandable from thermodynamic considerations since reductive deamination is a strongly exergonic process. For example, the pyridine nucleotide-linked reduction of glycine to acetate and $\overset{+}{N}H_4$ [Eq. (29)] can be regarded as the sum of the two partial oxidation-reduction reactions described by Eq. (27) and (28). The $\Delta F'$ for the DPNH/DPN couple [Eq. (27)] has been established to

$$DPNH + H^+ \rightleftharpoons DPN^+ \qquad\qquad \Delta F' = +4.33 \text{ kcal} \tag{27}$$

$$^+NH_3CH_2COO^- \rightleftharpoons CH_3COO^- + {}^+NH_4 \qquad \Delta F' = -18.73 \text{ kcal} \tag{28}$$

$$\begin{aligned} Sum:\ DPNH + H^+ + {}^+NH_3CH_2COO^- & \\ \rightleftharpoons CH_3COO^- + {}^+NH_4 + DPN^+ \quad & \Delta F' = -14.4 \text{ kcal} \end{aligned} \tag{29}$$

be $+ 4.33$ kcal (Burton and Wilson, 1953), whereas the $\Delta F'$ for Eq. (28) as calculated from thermodynamic data is -18.73 kcal.* The calculated $\Delta F'$ for the coupled reaction, Eq. (29), is therefore -14.4 kcal. We see then that the DPNH-linked reductive deamination of glycine is theoretically capable of supporting the formation of nearly two equivalents of ATP.

In detailed studies with cell-free extracts of *Clostridium sticklandii* and *Clostridium lentoputrescens*, T. C. Stadtman and associates established that one mole of ATP is formed per mole of glycine reduced according to the following over-all equation [Eq. (30)] (T. C. Stadtman,

$$DPNH + H^+ + glycine + HPO_4^{-2} + ADP^{-3} \rightarrow DPN^+ + NH_3 + ATP^{-4} + acetate^- \tag{30}$$

1962; T. C. Stadtman and Elliott, 1956; T. C. Stadtman *et al.*, 1958). This reaction is of particular interest from the standpoint of anaerobic energy metabolism because it represents the first direct evidence that ATP can be generated anaerobically by a mechanism that probably does not involve the formation of substrate-level energy-rich compounds. The formation of substrate-level energy-rich compounds appears unlikely since plausible energy-rich compounds such as phosphoramidate and acetyl-P or acetyl CoA were excluded as intermediates. It is, therefore, tentatively concluded that ATP formation is associated with anaerobic electron transport. Evidence that the electron transport system may be highly complex is derived from the observations that the over-all reaction involves the

---

* The $-\Delta F'f's$ for glycine, acetate−, and $NH_4{}^+$ in aqueous solution are 89.26, 88.99, and 19.00 kcal, respectively (from critical tables prepared by Burton, 1957). The $\Delta F'$ for Eq. (28) is therefore $89.26 - (88.99) - (19.0) = -18.73$ kcal.

participation of several protein fractions one of which is identified as the electron-transport protein, ferredoxin, and another as an acidic low molecular weight protein (T. C. Stadtman, 1966). Furthermore, the participation of a quinone or related derivative is indicated by high sensitivity to inhibition by antimycin A and menadione and also by the fact that the activity of some enzyme preparations is stimulated by the addition of α-tocopherol (T. C. Stadtman, 1958). Finally, the participation of vicinal sulfhydryl groups in electron transport is suggested by the observations that arsenite at 10^{-4} to 10^{-5} M inhibits the over-all reaction and also by the fact that dithiol compounds such as 1,3-dimercaptopropanol can replace DPNH as an electron donor (T. C. Stadtman, 1962; T. C. Stadtman et al., 1958). Whereas the mechanism of this interesting reaction is still obscure, the unique properties of the enzyme system involved make it an attractive one in which to explore anaerobic oxidative phosphorylation in a completely soluble cell-free preparation.

Fermentation of γ-Aminobutyrate

In an effort to obtain an organism that might be better suited for investigation of the mechanism of reductive deamination, a new species of clostridium, *Clostridium aminobutyricum*, that can utilize γ-aminobutyrate as a major source of energy and carbon and nitrogen for growth, was isolated from soil enrichment cultures (Hardman and T. C. Stadtman, 1960). The fermentation of γ-aminobutyrate by this organism can be described by a minimum of eleven reactions (Hardman and T. C. Stadtman, 1963). However, if it is assumed that the only energy available for growth is derived from substrate-level "energy-rich" intermediates, then so far as the energy metabolism is concerned, the fermentation can be considered to involve the following four over-all reactions [Eqs. (31)–(34)] (Hardman and T. C. Stadtman, 1963a). The sums of Eqs. (31)–

$$2\gamma\text{-aminobutyrate} + 2\text{acetyl CoA} \rightarrow 2NH_3 + 2\text{crotonyl CoA} + 2\text{acetate} \tag{31}$$

$$\text{Crotonyl CoA} + \overset{+}{\text{DPN}} + \text{CoA} + H_2O \rightarrow 2\text{acetyl CoA} + \text{DPNH} + H^+ \tag{32}$$

$$\text{Crotonyl CoA} + \text{DPNH} + H^+ \rightarrow \text{butyryl CoA} + \overset{+}{\text{DPN}} \tag{33}$$

$$\text{Butyryl CoA} + P_i + \text{ADP} \rightarrow \text{butyrate} + \text{ATP} + \text{CoA} \tag{34}$$

$$\textit{Sum: } 2\gamma\text{-Aminobutyrate} + P_i + \text{ADP} \rightarrow 2NH_3 + \text{butyrate} + 2\text{acetate} + \text{ATP} \tag{35}$$

(34) is described by Eq. (35) which shows that in the over-all fermenta-

tion only one mole of ATP can be expected for each two moles of γ-aminobutyrate fermented. The suspiciously low yield of ATP derivable from substrate-level phosphorylation invites speculation on the possibility that another, as yet unrecognized, source of energy may be available for growth.

In an effort to determine the actual energy yield in the γ-aminobutyrate fermentation, advantage was taken of the fact that the amount of growth (dry weight of bacteria) obtained through anaerobic metabolism is directly proportional to the amount of substrate fermented (Monod, 1942; DeMoss et al., 1951), and is absolutely related to the number of moles of ATP produced. (Bauchop and Elsden, 1960; Gunsalus and Shuster, 1961). Thus, in the fermentations of certain substrates by established metabolic pathways, it was established with a variety of microorganisms, that 10 mg of dry microbial cells are produced for each millimole of ATP produced in the fermentation. [For an extensive review of the subject see Gunsalus and Shuster (1961).] In view of the constancy of the empirical relationship between growth and energy yield for those situations in which the metabolism is well established, it appears justified to use the yield of growth as a measure of energy yield for those fermentations in which the energy-yielding steps are not established. Accordingly, the molar growth yield associated with the fermentation of γ-aminobutyrate was determined. It was found that 7.6 mg of dry cells are derived from the fermentation of 1 mmole of γ-aminobutyrate (Hardman and T. C. Stadtman, 1963a). This is considerably in excess of 5.0 mg predicted by Eq. (35) and suggests that existence of an unidentified energy-yielding step. The possibility that the extra energy is derived from the deamination reaction is excluded by the fact that a comparable molar growth yield (8.9 mg/mmole) is obtained when γ-hydroxybutyrate, an early intermediate in the fermentation, replaces γ-aminobutyrate as the fermentable substrate (Hardman and T. C. Stadtman, 1963a). Except for the production of ammonia, the stoichiometry of the γ-hydroxybutyrate fermentation is the same as that obtained with γ-aminobutyrate. It is therefore probable that cell yields in excess of that predicted by Eq. (35) reflect an energy-yielding step that is common to fermentation of both substrates. The possibility remains that ATP might be generated as a result of electron transport phosphorylation involved in the highly exergonic reduction of crotonyl CoA to butyryl CoA [Eq. (32)]. Such phosphorylation could provide one equivalent of ATP for each two moles of γ-aminobutyrate fermented, and together with the ATP available from substrate level phosphorylation [Eq. (34)], could account for the over-all yield of ATP anticipated by the growth data. Unfortunately, efforts to obtain experimental support for phosphorylation in the reduction of crotonyl CoA to butyryl CoA have been unsuccessful (Hardman and T. C. Stadtman, 1963a).

FERMENTATION OF SULFONIUM COMPOUNDS

It has been calculated (Cantoni and Durell, 1960) that hydrolysis of the sulfonium bond [Eq. (36)] is a highly exergonic process, $\Delta F' = -8.5$

$$(CH_3)_2\overset{+}{S}R + H_2O \rightleftharpoons CH_3SR + CH_3OH + H^+ \qquad (36)$$

kcal. Sulfonium compounds can therefore be regarded as "energy-rich" compounds in a class along with ATP and acyl CoA derivatives. The fact that the potential energy of hydrolysis of the sulfonium bond is a source of utilizable chemical energy is evident from the fact that S-adenosyl-methionine functions biologically as a donor of methyl, adenosyl, or amino butyryl groups in selected biosynthetic reactions. On the other hand no mechanism has been demonstrated by which the potential energy of hydrolysis of the sulfonium bond can be made more generally available for growth, as, for example, through the synthesis of ATP. If such a mechanism does exist it might be expected to be found in those organisms that can utilize sulfonium compounds as a major source of carbon and energy. Accordingly, in order to examine the possibility that cleavage of the sulfonium bond may be coupled with phosphorylation, Wagner and Stadtman (1962) isolated a clostridium from the soil that could grow on dimethylpropiothetin (DMPT) as a main source of carbon and energy. The selection of an anaerobe for such studies was prompted by the consideration that they are more restricted in their energy resources than aerobic organisms and might therefore be more likely to make use of the "sulfonium bond energy" for growth. Detailed studies of the un-identified clostridium showed that it catalyzes the over-all fermentation as described by Eq. (37).

$$3(CH_3)_2\overset{+}{S}-CH_2CH_2COO^- + 2H_2O \rightarrow 2CH_3CH_2COO^-$$
$$+ CH_3COO^- + 3(CH_3)_2S + CO_2 + 3H^+ \quad (37)$$

From studies with cell-free extracts (Wagner and Stadtman, 1962, 1962a; Wagner, 1965), it is tentatively concluded that the over-all fermentation involves the following series of reactions.

$$3(CH_3)_2\overset{+}{S}{-}CH_2CH_2COO^- + 3CH_3COSCoA$$
$$\rightleftharpoons 3(\overset{+}{CH_3})_2S^+{-}CH_2CH_2COSCoA + 3CH_3COO^- \tag{38}$$

$$3(CH_3)_2\overset{+}{S}{-}CH_2CH_2COSCoA$$
$$\rightleftharpoons 3(\overset{+}{CH_3})_2S + 3CH_2{=}CHCOSCoA + 3H^+ \tag{39}$$

$$CH_2{=}CHCOSCoA + CoASH + H_2O + CH_3COO^- + H^+$$
$$\rightarrow 2CH_3COSCoA + CO_2 + 4H \tag{40}$$

$$2CH_2{=}CHCOSCoA + 4H$$
$$\rightarrow 2CH_3CH_2COSCoA \tag{41}$$

$$2CH_3CH_2COSCoA + 2CH_3COO^-$$
$$\rightarrow 2CH_3CH_2COO^- + 2CH_3COSCoA \tag{42}$$

Sum 38–42: $3(CH_3)_2S^+{-}CH_2CH_2COO^- + CoASH + H_2O$
$$\rightarrow 3(CH_3)_2S + 2CH_3CH_2COO^- + CH_3COSCoA + CO_2 + 2H^+ \tag{43}$$

According to this mechanism, as is shown by the over-all equation [Eq. (43)], there is a net formation of only one equivalent of energy-rich bond (i.e., one acetyl CoA) for each three moles of DMPT fermented. Although precise thermodynamic data are not available for the free energies of formation of all of the reactants and products, reasonable estimates of the over-all free energy change for reaction (37) can be made assuming it to be achieved by the following coupled reactions [Eqs. (44) and (45)]:

$$3(CH_3)_2\overset{+}{S}{-}CH_2CH_2COO^- + 3H_2O$$
$$\rightleftharpoons 3(\overset{+}{CH_3})_2S + 3CH_2OHCH_2COO^- + 3H^+ \tag{44}$$

$$3CH_2OHCH_2COO^-$$
$$\rightleftharpoons 2\,CH_3CH_2COO^- + CH_3COO^- + CO_2 + H_2O \tag{45}$$

Sum: $3(\overset{+}{CH_3})_2SCH_2CH_2COO^- + 2H_2O$
$$\rightleftharpoons 3(CH_3)_2S + 2CH_3CH_2COO^- + 3H^+ + CO_2 + CH_3COO^- \tag{37}$$

If it is assumed that the free energy change for the hydrolysis of the sulfonium bond in DMPT is the same as that calculated for the comparable hydrolysis of the sulfonium bond in S-adenosyl methionine [Eq. (36)], then the $\Delta F'$ for Eq. (44) is 3×-8.5 kcal $= -25.5$ kcal. On the basis of available data for the free energy of formation of acetate, CO_2, and H_2O, and by making reasonable assumptions for the free energies of formation of β-hydroxypropionate and propionate it can be calculated that the $\Delta F'$ for Eq. (45) is -39.5 kcal.* The over-all $\Delta F'$ for

---

* The $-\Delta Ff$ for acetate$^-$, CO_2, and H_2O are 88.99, 92.31, and 56.69 kcal, respectively (free energy data tabulated by Burton, 1957). Although no free energy

Eq. (37) is accordingly $-39.5 + (-25.5) = -65$ kcal. It is therefore apparent that the net energy yield of only one equivalent of acetyl CoA for each three moles of DMPT fermented by the mechanism involving Eqs. (38)–(42) is only about 15% of that theoretically available from the fermentation. The existence of additional energy-yielding steps, that have not yet been identified, is contraindicated by results of several experiments showing that 3.3 mg of dry cell material are formed for each mole of DMPT fermented (Wagner and Stadtman, 1962a). It is therefore tentatively concluded that only one mole of ATP is derived from the fermentation of three moles of DMPT. We see then, that the formation of acetyl CoA by Eq. (43) can fully account for all of the growth supported by the DMPT fermentation, and we are left with the disappointing conclusion that, at least in the particular clostridium studied, the fermentation of DMPT is a highly inefficient process and that no mechanism is available for the utilization of the energy that is potentially available from hydrolysis of the sulfonium bond. Whereas this does not preclude the use of such energy for the synthesis of ATP in other organisms, this possibility seems unlikely in view of the consideration that the clostridium used for the present experiments depends upon the anaerobic decomposition of DMPT for its major energy supply and it might therefore be expected to possess a mechanism of converting sulfonium bond energy to pyrophosphate bond energy if such a mechanism does exist.

FERMENTATION OF ETHYLENE GLYCOL

Clostridium glycollicum catalyzes the anaerobic conversion of ethylene glycol to a mixture of ethanol and acetate according to Eq. (46) (Gaston and Stadtman, 1963). Studies with cell free extracts have shown that the

data are available for propionate⁻, the $-\Delta F'f$ for propionate⁻ can be assumed to be 86.60, which is intermediate between the $-\Delta F'f$ for acetate⁻ (88.99) and for butyrate⁻ (84.28). A comparison of the $-\Delta F'f$ for acetate⁻ with glycolate⁻ and of butyrate with β-hydroxybutyrate⁻ shows that the $-\Delta F'f$ of the hydroxy acids are 37.91 and 36.72, respectively, greater than that of the corresponding unsubstituted fatty acids. It is therefore obvious that, in the range of fatty acids with two to four carbon atoms, the conversion of a saturated fatty acid to its hydroxy derivative is associated with an increase in the $-\Delta F'f$ that is essentially independent of chain length (average = 37.32 kcal). Accordingly it can be assumed that the $-\Delta F'f$ for β-hydroxpropionate⁻ is equal to the estimated value for propionate⁻ + 37.32, i.e., $86.60 + 37.32 = 123.9$ kcal. The latter value is remarkably close to the value for lactate⁻ (123.76). Based on these data the over all $\Delta F'$ for Eq. (45) is given by the expression

$$3(123.9) - 2(86.6) - (88.99) - (92.31) - (56.69) = 371.7 - 411.19 = 39.49 \text{ kcal}$$

$$2 \begin{array}{c} CH_2OH \\ | \\ CH_2OH \end{array} \rightarrow CH_3COO^- + CH_3CH_2OH + H_2O + H^+ \tag{46}$$

fermentation involves the intermediary formation of acetaldehyde [Eq. (47)] which undergoes a dismutation to form ethanol and acetate. Although the mechanism of the dismutation reaction has not been definitely established in this organism, by analogy to the reactions catalyzed by *C. kluyveri* it is assumed that the dismutation involves coupling of the oxidation of one mole of acetaldehyde to acetyl CoA [Eq. (48)] with the reduction of another to ethanol [Eq. (49)].

$$2 \begin{array}{c} CH_2HO \\ | \\ CH_2HO \end{array} \rightarrow 2CH_3CHO + 2H_2O \tag{47}$$

$$CH_3CHO + CoASH + DP\overset{+}{N} \rightleftharpoons CH_3COSCoA + DPNH + H^+ \tag{48}$$

$$CH_3CHO + DPNH + H^+ \rightleftharpoons CH_3CH_2OH + DP\overset{+}{N} \tag{49}$$

$$Sum: 2 \begin{array}{c} CH_2OH \\ | \\ CH_2OH \end{array} + CoASH \rightarrow CH_3COSCoA + CH_3CH_2OH + 2H_2O \tag{50}$$

On the basis of these reactions the over-all fermentation should yield only one mole of energy-rich compound [acetyl CoA or ATP by Eqs. (11)–(13)] for each two moles of ethylene glycol fermented [Eq. (50)].

If Eq. (48) represents the only energy-yielding reaction available to the organism, then the fermentation of ethylene glycol is a very inefficient process from the thermodynamic point of view. This follows from the fact that the over-all standard free energy change for Eq. (46), as calculated from thermo-dynamic data, is —40.62 kcal, or one-half this amount, —20.32 kcal, for each mole of ethylene glycol fermented.* Thus, under standard conditions, there is sufficient energy available for the synthesis of two or possibly three moles of ATP per mole of ethylene glycol decomposed, yet according to Eq. (50) only 0.5 mole of acetyl CoA is produced per mole of ethylene glycol fermented. In other words the anticipated yield of useful energy is only 25% or less of theory.

The possibility that the actual energy yield is greater than 0.5 mole of

---

* The free energies of formation, $-\Delta F'f$, of ethylene glycol (liquid), acetate (aqueous), ethanol (aqueous), and water at pH 7.0 are 77.12, 88.99, 43.39, and 56.69 kcal, respectively. The $-\Delta F'f$ for H+ is 9.55 kcal. Therefore the $\Delta F'$ for Eq. (46) is given by the expression

$$2(79) - (88.99) - (43.39) - (56.69) - (9.55) = 158 - 198.62 = -40.62 \text{ kcal}$$

ATP per mole of ethylene glycol is indicated by growth studies (Gaston and Stadtman 1963) showing that between 6.7 and 8.7 mg of dry cells are produced for each millimole of ethylene glycol fermented. This is considerably greater than a value of 5 mg that would be expected if Eq. (48) is the only energy-yielding step available for growth. It is therefore tentatively concluded that an additional energy-yielding step is available.

The $\Delta F'$ for the oxidation of acetaldehyde to acetyl CoA by DPN$^+$ [Eq. (48)] is —4.2 kcal (Burton and Stadtman, 1953) and for the reduction of acetaldehyde to ethanol by DPNH [Eq. 49)] is —5.4 kcal (Racker, 1950). The over-all dismutation of acetaldehyde to acetyl CoA and ethanol is therefore strongly exergonic, $\Delta F' = -9.6$ kcal. It is therefore theoretically possible that phosphorylation could be coupled with the anaerobic electron transport concerned with some step in the dismutation reaction.

However, one must consider also the possibility that phosphorylation may be associated with the conversion of ethylene glycol to acetaldehyde. On the basis of thermodynamic data, it can be calculated that the standard free energy change for Eq. (47) is —22.14 kcal or —11.07 kcal per mole of ethylene glycol.* This is considerably in excess of that required for the formation of an equivalent of ATP and emphasizes the desirability of studying the mechanism of Eq. (47) in great detail. Preliminary studies (Gaston and Stadtman, 1963) indicate that the enzyme system catalyzing this reaction is stimulated by pyruvate, Fe^{+2}, and unidentified factors present in boiled cell extract of *C. glycollicum*. It does not appear to involve a vitamin B_{12} coenzyme and therefore differs from the *Aerobacter aerogenes enzyme* that catalyzes the same over-all reaction (Lee and Abeles, 1963).

SUMMARY AND CONCLUSIONS

As can be seen from the foregoing discussions a part of the energy released in the anaerobic dissimilation of a variety of fermentable substrates is conserved through the formation of acyl CoA intermediates, which, in the thermodynamic sense as defined by Lipmann, belong in the class of "energy-rich" compounds along with acyl phosphates and pyrophosphate derivatives. Furthermore, in accordance with Lipmann's basic concept

---

* With the assumption that the $-\Delta F'f$ for ethylene glycol (aqueous) is 79 kcal., and from the known $-\Delta F°f$ for acetaldehyde (aqueous) and for H_2O, 33.38 and 56.69, respectively, the $-\Delta F'$ for Eq. (47) is
$$2(79)-2(33.38) - 2(56.69) = 158 - 180.14 = - 22.14 \text{ kcal}$$

of energy transfer we have seen how the metabolic energy conserved in these substrate-derived thiolesters can be transferred without substantial losses and can be utilized for the synthesis of carbon-carbon bonds or for the synthesis of ATP. In some instances, as, for example, in the fermentation of dimethylpropiothetin by an unidentified strain of *Clostridium,* the synthesis of acetyl CoA probably represents the sole energy supply available for growth. On the other hand, the energy conserved in the form of thiolester intermediates, is, in all instances, a minor fraction of the free energy theoretically available from the over-all fermentations and in most instances is insufficient to account for the observed growth yields. Thus, in the fatty acid fermentation by *C. kluyveri,* there appears to be no net yield of acyl CoA intermediate over and above that required to provide electron acceptors in the synthesis of butyrate and caproate; moreover, in the fermentations of ethylene glycol by *Clostridium glycollicum* and the fermentation of γ-hydroxybutyrate or γ-aminobutyrate by *Clostridium aminobutyricum,* the yield of bacterial cells is considerably greater than can be accounted for on the basis of the acyl CoA intermediates formed in the established pathways of fermentation. These observations lead to the conclusion that, contrary to former assumptions, anaerobic organisms do not depend exclusively upon substrate-level energy-rich intermediates as their source of ATP for growth. This conclusion appears to find direct support from the studies of T. C. Stadtman and associates showing that the anaerobic reductive deamination of glycine to acetate and ammonia is coupled with the formation of ATP by a mechanism that appears to be independent of the formation of substrate-level high-energy intermediates.

In view of these considerations it would seem profitable to reexamine the metabolism of anaerobic microorganisms for the existence of energy-yielding processes that are not directly related to substrate-level transformations. The most obvious possibility is that the anaerobic transfer of electrons is coupled with phosphorylation in a manner similar to the so-called oxidative phosphorylation that is characteristic of aerobic organisms. Although electron transport phosphorylation has been generally assumed to be an exclusive property of aerobic respiration, the occurrence of anaerobic electron transport phosphorylation should not come as a surprise, since at least two of the three phosphorylation steps associated with terminal respiration (i.e., the phosphorylations coupled with the oxidation of DPNH by flavoproteins and the oxidation of reduced cytochrome b by cytochrome c) do not involve molecular oxygen as an immediate electron acceptor. Strictly speaking, therefore, these are anaerobic processes. It is certainly not unreasonable to assume that comparable electron transport steps occur in obligately anaerobic organisms provided the fermentative metabolism involves the participation of electron carriers of suitable redox potentials. In this connection it is of interest that the $\Delta F'$ associated with the reduction of crotonyl CoA to butyryl CoA by DPNH is about -18.0 kcal, which is more than enough to support the synthesis of one mole of ATP, and is considerably greater than the $\Delta F'$ for the two anaerobic phosphorylation steps of aerobic respiration, i.e., the oxidation of DPNH by flavoproteins ($\Delta F' = -12.4$ kcal) and the oxidation of reduced cytochrome b by cytochrome c ($\Delta F' = -10.1$ kcal).

Whereas these considerations emphasized the potential importance of anaerobic electron transport phosphorylation in the energy metabolism of obligately anaerobic organisms, the fact remains that the synthesis of ATP in the reductive deamination of glycine (T. C. Stadtman and Elliott, 1956, 1958) constitutes the only direct evidence for the occurrence of anaerobic phosphorylation that does not appear to involve substrate-level energy-rich intermediates. If further investigation substantiates the assumption that this phosphorylation is in fact associated with electron transport, then the reductive deamination of glycine should become one of the most attractive model systems for studies of oxidative phosphorylation; for, in contrast to all other systems thus far examined, this process occurs in a completely soluble, nonparticulate, enzyme preparation. It should therefore offer obvious advantages in studies on the detailed mechanism of oxidative phosphorylation.

REFERENCES

Alberts, A. W., Majerus, P. W., Talmo, B., and Vagelos, P. R. (1964). *Biochemistry* 3, 1563.

Barker, H. A. (1937). *Arch. Mikrobiol.* 8, 415.

Barker, H. A. (1951). *In* "Phosphorous Metabolism" (W. B. McElroy and B. Glass, eds.), Vol. 1, pp. 204-245. Johns Hopkins Press, Baltimore, Maryland.

Barker, H. A. (1956). "Bacterial Fermentations," 95 pp. Wiley, New York.

Bauchop, T., and Elsden, S. (1960). *J. Gen. Microbiol.* 23, 457.

Bornstein, B. T., and Barker, H. A. (1948). *J. Biol. Chem.* 172, 659.

Brady, R. O., and Stadtman, E. R. (1954). Unpublished data.

Brown, E. B., Jr., and Stadtman, E. R. (1958). Unpublished data.

Burton, K. (1957). *In* "Energy Transformations in Living Matter" (H. A. Krebs and H. L. Kornberg, eds.), pp. 275-285. Springer, Berlin.

Burton, K., and Wilson, T. H. (1953). *Biochem. J.* 54, 86.

Burton, R. M., and Stadtman, E. R. (1953). *J. Biol. Chem.* 202, 873.

Cantoni, G. L., and Durell, J. (1960). *In* "Comparative Biochemistry" (M. Florkin and H. S. Mason, eds.), Vol. 1, pp. 217-221. Academic Press, New York.

De Moss, R. D., Bard, R. S., and Gunsalus, I. C. (1951). *J. Bacteriol.* 62, 499.

Eggerer, H., Stadtman, E. R., and Poston, J. M. (1962). *Arch. Biochem. Biophys.* **98**, 432.

Gaston, L. W., and Stadtman, E. R. (1963). *J. Bacteriol.* **85**, 356.

Gunsalus, I. C., and Shuster, C. W. (1961). *In* "The Bacteria" (I. C. Gunsalus and R. Y. Stanier, eds.). Vol. II, pp. 1-58. Academic Press, New York.

Hardman, J. K., and Stadtman, T. C. (1960). *J. Bacteriol.* **79**, 544.

Hardman, J. K., and Stadtman, T. C. (1963). *J. Biol. Chem.* **238**, 2081.

Hardman, J. K., and Stadtman, T. C. (1963a). *J. Bacteriol.* **85**, 1326.

Heath, E. C., Hurwitz, J., Horecker, B. L., and Ginsburg, A. (1958). *J. Biol. Chem.* **231**, 1009.

Kaplan, N. O. (1951). *In* "The Enzymes" (J. B. Sumner and K. Myrback, eds.) Vol. 11, part I, pp. 55. Academic Press, New York.

Lee, H. A., Jr., and Abeles, R. H. (1963). *J. Biol. Chem.* **238**, 2367.

Lipmann, F. (1939). *Cold Spring Harbor Symp. Quant. Biol.* **7**, 248.

Lipmann, F. (1941). *Advan. Enzymol.* **1**, 99.

Lipmann, F. (1944). *J. Biol. Chem.* **155**, 55.

Lipmann, F. (1946). *Advan. Enzymol.* **6**, 231.

Lynen, F., and Decker, K. (1957). *Ergeb. Physiol. Biol. Chem. Exptl. Pharmakol.* **49**, 327.

Monod, J. (1942). "Recherches sur la Croissance des Cultures Bactérienne." Herman, Paris.

Nisman, B. (1954). *Bacterial. Rev.* **18**, 16.

Racker, E. (1950). *J. Biol. Chem.*, **184**, 313.

Rose, I. A. (1955). *In* "Methods in Enzymology" (S. P. Colowick and N. O. Kaplan, eds.) Vol. I, pp. 591-595. Academic Press, New York.

Shuster, C. W., and Gunsalus, I. C. (1958). *Federation Proc.* **17**, 310.

Sly, W. S., and Stadtman, E. R. (1963). *J. Biol. Chem.* **238**, 2632.

Sly, W. S., and Stadtman, E. R. (1963a). *J. Biol. Chem.* **238**, 2639.

Stadtman, E. R. (1952). *J. Biol. Chem.* **196**, 527.

Stadtman, E. R. (1953). *J. Biol. Chem.* **203**, 501.

Stadtman, E. R. (1954). *Record Chem. Progr.* (*Kresge-Hooker Sci. Lib.*) **15**, 1.

Stadtman, E. R. (1954a). *In* "The Mechanism of Enzyme Action" (W. D. McElroy and B. Glass, eds.), pp. 581-597. Johns Hopkins Press, Baltimore, Maryland.

Stadtman, E. R., and Barker, H. A. (1950). *J. Biol. Chem.* **184**, 769.

Stadtman, E. R., Novelli, G. D., and Lipmann, F. (1951). *J. Biol. Chem.* **191**, 365.

Stadtman, E. R., Doudoroff, M., and Lipmann, F. (1951a). *J. Biol. Chem.* **191**, 377.

Stadtman, E. R., Katz, J., and Barker, H. A. (1952). *J. Biol. Chem.* **195**, 779.

Stadtman, T. C. (1958). *Biochem. Z.* **331**, 46.

Stadtman, T. C. (1962). *Arch. Biochem. Biophys.* **99**, 36.

Stadtman, T. C. (1966). *Arch. Biochem. Biophys.* **113**, 9.

Stadtman, T. C., and Elliott, P. (1956). *J. Am. Chem. Soc.* **78**, 2020.

Stadtman, T. C., Elliott, P., and Tiemann, L. (1958). *J. Biol. Chem.* **231**, 961.

Stern, J. R., Shapiro, B., Stadtman, E. R., and Ochoa, S. (1951). *J. Biol. Chem.* **193**, 703.

Vagelos, P. R. (1964). *Ann. Rev. Biochem.* **33**, 139.

Wagner, C. (1965). *Biochemistry* **4**, 2485.

Wagner, C., and Stadtman, E. R. (1962). *Arch. Biochem. Biophys.* **98**, 331.

Wagner, C., and Stadtman, E. R. (1962a). Unpublished data.

In Search of Simplicity and Generalizations*
(50 Years Poaching in Science)

Albert Szent-Györgyi

We mostly like to describe our work as a preconceived logical unit, running like a straight line, but the fact is that, depending on one's personality, the line has many breaks and detours and may seem to make no sense at all. We, ourselves, often understand what we are searching and doing only in retrospect. I, myself, see only now, at an advanced age, that what I was searching all my life was simplicity, generalizations, for generalization means simplification. I have a semipermeable mind which can take in simple things only. The three generalizations I arrived at and will discuss are "organization" and its two variants, which I will call "horizontal" and "vertical."

When starting research in biology I was bewildered by the complexity and inexhaustible wealth of living nature in form, size, and color. I started my work with rabbits, but soon I found them much too complex for my simple mind and shifted to pharmacology where one of the two partners, the drug, at least, is simple. A drug is a substance which, if injected into an animal, produces a paper (O. Loewy). This sounded simple enough but did not help me because one of the two partners was still the same complex rabbit. So I turned to bacteriology, hoping to find those tiny bacteria simpler. Simpler they are, but soon I discovered that a bacterium is still a whole universe. So I became a biochemist, hoping that molecules would be simple enough. Eventually I wound up in the sub-

* The substance of this lecture was presented at the Chemical Society of Washington on February 10, 1966. Underlying work is being supported by a grant from the National Institutes of Health, GM-10383.

molecular dimension, muddling with electrons and quantum mechanics, which, at present, is the bottom of nature for us.

This wild-goose chase after the nature of life is not without humor or irony, for electrons have no life at all, and so now I am climbing back up, somewhat ashamed, on the ladder of complexity on which I took so many pains to descend. All the same, this wild-goose chase was perhaps not quite in vain for it kept me from getting married to any single branch of science. This made my relations to the various sciences very promiscuous and made me remain an amateur scientist but a professional poacher. The first generalization it led me to, which allowed me to create a certain order in my mind, was "organization."

ORGANIZATION

The underlying idea is simple: things can be put together in two different ways—at random, or meaningfully. If put together in a meaningful way something new is generated which can no more be described in terms of the qualities of its components. This happens, for instance, when protons and neutrons are put together to form an atomic nucleus, when nuclei are put together with electrons to form an atom—atoms to molecules, molecules to macromolecules, macromolecules to organelles, organelles to cells, cells to complex individuals, individuals to a race or society. This makes the whole into more than the sum of its parts. Organization has many levels. Every level offers fascinating vistas and at every step more complex and subtle qualities are created. This trend for meaningful combination stops in the inanimate nature at a fairly low level. Life pushes it much farther and this is why we find in the biosphere a subtlety and complexity which have no parallel in the inanimate world. At the level of macromolecules we already find a certain measure of "intelligence," macromolecules being able to arrange themselves spontaneously to higher structures, organelles, as fibers. On the next higher level, that of organelles, we even find a certain measure of "wisdom." One of the great physiologists of this country, Walter B. Cannon, wrote a great deal about the "wisdom of the body." (He never talked about the "wisdom of the mind.")

This idea of organization also has its inherent danger. The danger is in the fact that any level can better be understood by taking the mechanism to pieces, that is, by going to the next lower level. This may make us dive from level to level, as I have done, myself, to lose life altogether on the way.

BIOLOGICAL OXIDATION, HORIZONTAL ORGANIZATION

The living machine is driven by energy and so it can be approached from two different sides: that of the structure or that of the energy which drives it. Oxidation involved both—our body being driven by the chemical energy of our foodstuffs liberated by oxidation and then transduced in specific mechanisms. So I started my research with oxidation, the production of energy.

Color always had a childish fascination for me so I started my work with studying the brown or black color which developed when I dropped my apple or banana. This oxidation was known to be due to the oxidation of some polyphenol. There were complex chemical mechanisms proposed for this reaction involving peroxide formation. I could show in simple experiments that all that happened was that a polyphenol was oxidized by a ferment to the corresponding quinone [*Biochem. Z.* **162**, 399 (1925)]. This, then, tanned the damaged surface, forming pigments, closing the wound, and killing the invading bacteria. This system has a great survival value for the plant. It had a survival value, also, for myself, for, at that stage of my career, my personal difficulties seemed too great to allow me to continue research. To my good luck, my little paper fascinated the great British biochemist F. G. Hopkins, who, to my surprise, in his presidential address at the International Physiological Congress in Stockholm, mentioned my name several times and eventually invited me to come to Cambridge, England, and thus opened for me the way to science.

I continued my study of oxidation on plants, like cabbages or lemons, which do not turn brown on damage [*Biochem. J.* **22**, 138 (1928)]. The underlying oxidative system, too, had a survival value for me for it led me to the isolation of ascorbic acid, to which I owe, at least partly, a Nobel Prize. This isolation was a very simple matter. I performed the reaction, which is done every day a thousand times in elementary courses of biochemistry. If you add benzedine and peroxide to a peroxidase solution, a beautiful blue color appears immediately. I repeated this experiment with plant juices which contained peroxidase. There was a slight delay in the appearance of the color of the order of a half second, and I wondered what caused it. Once you have a good test, isolation of a simple substance is a relatively easy matter. The delay offered a simple test for the substance which caused it. So it took me but a couple of weeks to isolate it, and you know it today as "ascorbic acid" which turned out to be vitamin C. The existence of vitamin C was already known for one or two decades and many people tried to isolate it, but they used the scurvy of guinea pigs as test, which takes 2 months. In such an isolation one has to test, say, a thousand times, and a thousand times 2 months makes 160 years, not a very hopeful proposition. My test took 5 seconds, so the isolation was done in no time.

From here I turned to vertebrates. At that time Warburg and Wieland were at loggerheads about the question whether it is oxygen or hydrogen activation that underlay respiration. I could show, in a simple way [*Biochem*. Z. **150**, 195 (1924)], that both were correct and it is common knowledge today that it is the activated oxygen which oxidizes activated hydrogen. In these studies I introduced the pigeon breast muscle as material which, subsequently, became a widely used classic object. In this work I discovered that the C_4 dicarboxylic acids are not simple metabolites, but play a basic catalytic role in respiration, to which I owed the second half of my Nobel Prize.

This discovery was a simple matter, too. I was fascinated by the difference between the properties of succino- and citricodehydrogenase, and all the other dehydrogenases, which had been known for a long time. Bettelli and Stern wrote a whole book about this difference. These enzymes oxidased their substrate at a very high rate and were bound to structure, the machinery of life. My good friend J. H. Quastel, studying specificity, found earlier that the next lower dicarboxylic acid, malonic acid with three carbons, was not oxidized at all. Not only was it not oxidized, but prevented, also, the oxidation of succinic acid. So I added both together to the minced tissue and found that all respiration stopped, indicating that the succinic acid was a general catalyst and not just a substrate. As you know, this is the foundation of what is known today as "the Krebs cycle."

Looking back on all this work, today, I think that bananas, lemons, and men, all have basically the same system of respiration, however different they may appear. Like the plants, we, too, have in our own oxidation-system polyphenols and ascorbic acid, but nature is clever enough to kill several birds with the same stone and so emphasizes in the various species, for certain ends, the one or the other member of the system, as it emphasizes the polyphenols in bananas and ascorbic acid in lemons. This I would call the *horizontal organization,* by which I mean that in the various species we find the same row of substances or reactions from which one may be pushed to the fore. The most classic example is the electric fish, Torpedo, which organizes the action potential of muscle cells in such a way that they produce a strong electric shock.

MUSCLE

When I finished my studies on oxidation I did not understand life any better than before. This question of the nature of life was a queer one. Although we do not know what life is, we can still tell exactly the difference between life and death. I know exactly when my dog is dead: when it moves no more, has no reflexes, and leaves my carpet clean, that is, does not transduce oxidative energy into mechanic, electric, or osmotic work. This transduction occurs in specific mechanisms and may hold the key to the understanding of life. So I turned from oxidation, that is, the *production* of energy, to its *transduction*. From the various transducting mechanisms I chose muscle, because it is in muscle that the most violent physical and chemical changes occur. If science is the art of measuring, then it can expect to be the more successful the more there is to measure. Not only are changes violent, but their final product is motion, which is one of the oldest signs of life by which man always knew life from death, which can be observed even by the naked eye.

If one embarks in a new field, then the first question is what to do with oneself? There is always one thing one can do: repeat the work of old masters. These old masters, having little hardware, were greatly dependent on two instruments which, since then, have greatly gone out of fashion: eyes and brains. So I repeated what Willy Kühne did almost a century earlier, extracting minced muscle with strong KCl solution and then diluting the extracts with water which precipitates great quantities of a protein that Kühne called "myosin," which was, evidently, the main instrument of contraction. The trouble was that myosin refused to do anything outside the body. A contractile protein should contract wherever it is. I never cut out a muscle but gently peeled it off the rabbit. I did the same with myosin, that is, extracted it most carefully, but it refused to move. Keeping my eyes open I noticed that extracts, made slower than usual, were more sticky than those made fast, and this without containing considerably more protein. They contained small quantities of a new protein which was, then, isolated brilliantly by my pupil F. B. Straub. We called it "actin." It made a complex with myosin, which we called, with J. Banga, "actomyosin." H. H. Weber taught us earlier how to make little threads, "muscles," out of myosin. Actomyosin made even nicer threads, and to make them feel more at home I suspended them in the boiled juice of muscle which contained the smaller heat-stable molecules of muscle, and the threads contracted. To see this contraction the first time, reproduce this age-old sign of life in the bottle with "muscles" built of "known" substances, was the most exciting moment of my scientific life. It took only a little cookery to show that what made the threads contract in the boiled juice were adenosine triphosphate (ATP) and ions. All this was simple once one kept one's eyes open and looked at the biological material itself instead of only looking at pointers in one's laboratory hardware.

For further experimentation I needed long single muscle fibers of real muscle, which can be had only from muscle poor in connective tissue. It is easy to find the muscle poorest in connecting tissue because the quantity of connective material is inversely proportional to the commercial value of that muscle. So all one has to do is to go into a restaurant and go through the column of numbers on the right side of the menu. They usually move between $1.50–$3.00. On top, however, there is mostly a significant difference, a jump to $5.00–$6.00. Corresponding to this, on the left side one finds "filet mignon," and in one's books at home one finds that "filet mignon" is "the musculus psoas major." It has little connective material because it does not need it, being protected from the back by the vertebral column and from the front by the varying bulk of the belly. The psoas of the rabbit is 6–10 cm long and single fibers of this length can easily be secured from it. This made the rabbit psoas into a classic material for muscle research.

One day I put bundles of these fibers into 50% glycerol and kept them in my deep-freeze. I found that they conserved motility even after years of storage. This method of conserving motility or other vital functions has since become very important, even in animal husbandry, e.g., to conserve the motility of sperm.

Not long ago I was asked by a pupil of mine why I chose 50%, which is the optimal concentration. I had to confess that I did not even know why I chose glycerol at all. This I mention because it shows that in research one not always follows rigid logic and is more often led by obscure, subconscious feelings. With my wife we could also show that "rigor mortis," the stiffness of death, was due to the exhaustion of the ATP reserves.

When I saw actomyosin contract for the first time, I was convinced that in a fortnight I would understand muscle completely. Then I worked 20 years more without learning a thing. The more I knew the less I understood and was afraid to know everything in the end and understand nothing. Something seemed to be missing. Perhaps I did not go down deep enough on the scale of organization! So I began to muddle in quantum mechanics and electrons. This work brought one and another petty result as, for instance, the demonstration that electrons can jump from one molecule to another not only between flat surfaces (π-π interaction) but also at certain specific points, as, for instance, C_3 in indole ("local transfer") and that such a transfer was probably responsible for the action of halucinogens (both observations having been corroborated lately).

VERTICAL ORGANIZATION, CELL DIVISION

Having arrived at my third and last generalization, I must ask you to climb with me on the evolutionary ladder up to the cell, the most wonderful product of the biosphere, the cornerstone of life. I will even have to take you one rung higher, to the multicellular state.

The lowest rung of the evolutionary ladder, the simplest form of independent life known today is represented by the bacteria. Their existence must have been based originally on the discovery of nature that energy can be released from molecules by twisting or breaking them, preserving the energy thus liberated in the form of what are called "high-energy bonds," mostly high-energy bonds of phosphate. This process is called "fermentation."

The next important rung on the ladder of evolution was the construction of the porphyrin ring, which made oxidation and photosynthesis possible and also introduced beauty into life, for what is more beautiful than the green of the forest, the pink of the cheek of girls (as far as it is not due to aniline dyes)! In the next step of development order was made and the new functions with their mechanisms were enshrined in little boxes by putting membranes around them. So the genetic material was rounded off as a nucleus, the oxidative apparatus as mitochondria, the instruments of photosynthesis as chromophores or chloroplasts. After this nothing basically new was added, but once order was achieved the way was opened for cells to get together to form more complex organisms which could perform more complex functions.

The principle which emerges here is what I would like to call "vertical organization," by which I mean that if nature discovers a new principle it does not throw the old ones away: It simply builds the new one on top. So fermentation, the most primitive form of energy release, is still the basis of our metabolism. Not only does nature not throw old things away, but the older a process, the deeper it is ingrained, and the less the chance to lose it. The opposite may also hold true: the newer a mechanism, the more superficially anchored, and the more easily disturbed.

Although nothing basically new came into the picture by building multicellular organisms, the cells had to learn to live together, give up certain liberties, and have regard for their neighbors and the common interest, as individuals or nations have to do when wanting to form bigger viable units. While the cells lived alone, their surface had to protect them only. Now, in the multicellular state, it had to join them and mediate their interactions. The individual motility had to be given up, also, and so the unlimited proliferation. Life wants to grow and multiply with no limits. This is one of its most basic characteristics, but now, in the multicellular state, proliferation had to be subjected to strict regulation. All this had to be done in a reversible way, enabling the cell to revert to the monocellular way of living at short notice. In your skin most cells are quiescent, but should you cut yourself it is of vital interest that the wound should heal, for, if left open, the smallest wound might kill you. So if you make a cut in your skin, at the side of the cut cells revert to the monocellular state, make themselves free, resume motility, creep into the wound, and proliferate, but do so only as long as this is needed and the wound is filled, healed. Then the brake is put on, cell joins cell, and everything comes to rest again. In the healing process the whole life of the cells reverts to a more primitive evolutionary state, as shown by Warburg's discovery, that in multiplying cells even metabolism turns back toward the more primitive fermentation. Coman showed that cancer cells stick, also, less strongly to their neighbors than normal ones, and it was a century ago that Virchow showed that cancer cells, when getting free, are mobile. They have less tendency to build well-organized tissues (Abercrombie and Ambrose, P. Weiss). This is not empty speculation, but has an important bearing on one of medicine's most important problems, spontaneous human cancer. Cancer research, for a long time, was held up by two factors. The one was that researchers asked what makes the cells suddenly grow? This is a wrong question for unlimited growth is one of the most basic features of life. As Bullough puts it: "It is the nature of cells to prepare and undergo mitosis wherever they are not prevented. Opportunity, not stimulus is needed for cell division." The problem is: where has the break gone wrong? The cancer cell is a normal cell with the brake out of order. It is a disordered mechanism and it is plain that we can repair a mechanism only if we know how it works, and research was, for a long time, too hasty in finding a cure for cancer, before understanding it, by a random trial of the substances found on the chemist's shelf.

Although our understanding of synthetic processes has made great strides lately, the problem of cell division is still a fairly obscure one, especially in higher animals. Modern genetics, done mostly on bacteria, has brought out two facts clearly. The one can be summed up by saying: "one gene, one enzyme." The other fact is that even the production of a relatively simple substance, like histidine or tryptophan, involves half a score of enzymes or more. There would be no point in producing one of these enzymes if not producing all of them. Synthesis of a substance has to be an "all-or-none" process. This is achieved, as we know chiefly from the work of Jacob and Monod (honored by the last Nobel Prize), by having the group of enzymes involved in the production of one substance under command of an "operator gene," which gives the red or green light. The operator, in its turn, is subjected to a "regulator gene," which communicates its orders to the operator by chemical signals, repressors, or inducers. Monod and Jacob also showed that the genes, responsible for the production of the enzymes involved in the synthesis of one substance, are often (though not necessarily) clustered, in physical contact, which makes communication easier.

Now I have arrived at my present problem: cell division. If a cell divides, a new cell has to be produced with the many hundreds of substances which a cell has to contain. Here again, we can expect that the "all-or-none" principle holds, for there would be no sense in producing only part of these. The cell has to start its division when all the building material for the new cell is collected, for in later phases of cell division synthetic processes are arrested. But if the synthesis of a single simple substance, like an amino acid, involves half a score of enzymes and genes, then the syntheses of a great number of substances, some of which are very complex, have to involve thousands of enzymes, thus thousands of genes, which all have to work in concert, or do nothing. This can be achieved only by having all the operators, in one way or another, connected to one regulator gene. We can expect all the single operators to be sensitive to the same signals and have receptors for them in common. The chemical nature of the transmitting signals is a virgin field of research, a most fascinating one. It must also be a most difficult, subtle, and complex one for it must contain both a mechanism for production, transmission, and deletion of the substances in question.

The first question is how such a field can be approached experimentally. It cannot. It is too complex and subtle. It is also full of pitfalls.

If we cannot approach a problem the only thing we can do is to wait until the problem approaches us. I was approached by it more than a score of years ago when, working with J. McLaughlin. We found that the thymus gland contained something which promoted the growth of cancer and another thing which retarded it. Such actions by various extracts were observed previously and since by others. For convenience we gave a name and called the promoting substance "promine," the retarding one "retine." We thought, first, that we had the "thymus hormone" in hand, but later experience, with A. Hegyeli, showed that such actions could be found in all tissues, even in plants and urine, and thus could not be thymus hormones but had to be general cell constituents. M. Rosarii Schmeer made similar observations on molluscs, M. Parshley on tissue cultures. Biochemists are simple people, and so our first primitive idea was to isolate these substances and then see what they are, what they do, and what they are good for. Gallons of that classic mixture of inspiration and perspiration were produced in these efforts of isolation with no result.

It is easy to see now why these efforts were unsuccessful: the basic knowledge was missing. If retine and promine existed at all, they had to be involved in that complex mechanism of gene action connected with that mechanism of transmission of information from regulator to operator and had to have a mechanism for both their production and deletion, so if the first produced it, the latter destroyed it. Moreover, they could have been present only in minimal quantity and had to have a great affinity to cell constituents and could easily be lost.

All the same, our efforts were not quite useless because our most purified extracts contained a ketone, and, possibly, an aldehyde at the side of it, which could make these groups very reactive. "Ketoaldehydes," that is, are glyoxal derivatives, and "glyoxal" struck a familiar chord in our mind for practically all cells contain a very powerful enzymatic system, a "glyoxalase" which uses glutathione as coenzyme and decomposes glyoxal derivates into the corresponding oxy acids. So, for instance, it transforms methylglyoxal into lactic acid. If this glyoxal derivative were biologically active, this change would correspond to its inactivation, lactic acid being a relatively inert substance. The "glyoxalase" actually consists of two enzymes, called glyoxalase I and II, which use glutathione as coenzyme (see Fig. 1). The first step, in this reaction, probably is a spontaneous interaction of glutathione with the ketone aldehyde to form a hemiacetal-like complex, a hemimercaptal. Glyoxalase I then shifts the H-S to the next carbon atom and glyoxalase II splits the complex hydrolytically, recovering the glutathione and leaving the ketone aldehyde behind as lactic acid.

This enzymatic system has a noble history having occupied a number of leading biochemists like F. G. Hopkins, Lohman, Dakin, and Racker, who all finished their work disappointed, no glyoxal derivative being known to lie on the pathway of metabolism; and what's the use of an enzyme without a substrate! If a glyoxal derivative would participate in regulations this enzymatic system would find its sense. The other familiar chord which the word ketoaldehyde struck in our minds was the fact that ketoaldehydes react readily with SH, and the basic role of SH in cell division was known for a long time. There is no cell division once these groups are interfered with (Hammet, Rapkine) and it was known from

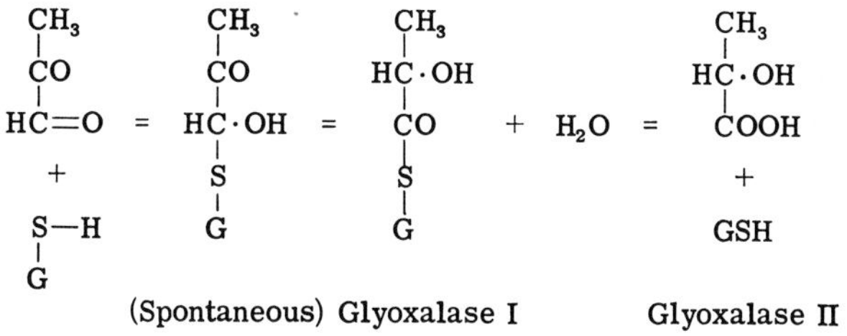

$$
\begin{array}{ccccccc}
CH_3 & CH_3 & CH_3 & & & CH_3 \\
| & | & | & & & | \\
CO & CO & HC\cdot OH & & & HC\cdot OH \\
| & | & | & & & | \\
HC{=}O & = & HC\cdot OH & = & CO & + H_2O = & COOH \\
+ & & | & & | & & + \\
& & S & & S & & \\
S{-}H & & | & & | & & GSH \\
| & & G & & G & & \\
G & & & & & &
\end{array}
$$

(Spontaneous)   Glyoxalase I   Glyoxalase II

FIG. 1.   Formation of lactic acid by glyoxalase. GSH represents glutathione.

Schubert's work, for 30 years, that the ketoaldehydes form well-defined complexes with sulfhydryl compounds. So SH-s could be the common receptors of repressors. All this made the idea unavoidable that retine may be the repressor of cell division and glyoxalase the system which deletes it. Promine may be glyoxalase or its activator, or any other substance competing for the glyoxal containing active S or NH_2 groups.

What made these ideas rather exciting is the nature of the S atom. It is a most versatile and reactive atom, with expandable orbitals, and within a bigger molecule its reactivity depends on the surrounding atomic groups, can thus become very specific. Equally, the reactivity and affinity of glyoxal derivatives depend on their substituents. All this may lead to very specific interactions and open up an exciting new field of chemistry. The relation of this field to cancer is suggested by the fact that carcinostatic action of glyoxal derivatives is discovered with increasing frequency and carcinogens have been discovered recently which owe their carcinogenic action to their reaction with SH.

Warned by the disappointments of the past we thought it wise to look for some circumstantial evidence before a broadside attack. There were a few simple things suggesting themselves. One could say, for instance, that if the repressors of cell division have as active groups a ketoaldehyde, are thus methylglyoxal derivatives, then the simplest derivative, methylglyoxal itself, should inhibit cell division in a reversible manner, even if higher concentrations may be needed of it than of an inhibitor, expressly built by nature for that specific purpose. So we tried to find out whether methylglyoxal is capable of inhibiting cell division reversibly.

We tested various materials, fertilized sea urchin eggs, plant seeds, flagellates, cells of tissue culture, and bacteria. The division of all of them was arrested by 0.001 M methylglyoxal in a reversible manner, a fairly low concentration. If 0.001 M methylglyoxal was added to a culture of *Escherichia coli*, all cell multiplication stopped immediately. But these bacteria contain glyoxalase, which can be expected to decompose the added methylglyoxal in time, allowing the bacteria to break through the inhibition. In our experiments the breakthrough occurred mostly after 5–6 hours, after which time the bacteria multiplied at the same rate as those of the control. In the logarithmic phase the glyoxalase and glutathione content of the bacteria is higher and the breakthrough occurs earlier. That methylglyoxal is actually capable of reacting quantitatively with SH groups in this dilution could be shown simply by adding an equimolar cysteine solution to the culture, completely inhibited by 0.001 M methylglyoxal, and growth is immediately resumed at the maximal rate. That methylglyoxal inhibits SH enzymes was shown by Kun and the specific nature of these reactions is indicated by the fact that contraction in glycerol-treated muscle is not inhibited by methylglyoxal in concentrations ten times higher than those needed to stop cell division, although muscle just does not work any more if its SH groups are blocked.

If an OH group was introduced into the methyl end of the methylglyoxal, making that end of the molecule more electropolar, then the biological activity of the molecule dropped to one-tenth of its earlier value, although the ketoaldehyde group was left untouched. One can hope that if one substituent can decrease activity, another may greatly increase it, lending very special affinities to the molecule.

The possible specificity of these reactions might make subtle interactions between the various genes and regulators possible. It also makes it evident that this complex problem cannot be approached in a simple, direct way. What is needed in the first place is a sensitive reaction for the estimation of ketoaldehydes, which will enable us to ask very exciting and new questions about regulations and cancer, and may also open the way to the final isolation of these substances. Dr. Együd, actually, has such a method in hand; while I hope to isolate the precursor of a biological glyoxal derivative in crystals. Együd's experiments with M. Baylor indicate that even the multiplication of viruses is arrested by methylglyoxal and so bacteria, at least temporarily, can be protected by this substance. So it seems that, after a score of years of hard labor, we begin to approach our problem and see what we are really after, and I can sum up by saying that I hope to have shown that the search for general principles in biochemistry has its place in research, giving a direction to the little experiments one is doing, or, at least, giving sense to them in retrospect, if any.

Present State of Knowledge Concerning the Biochemical Lesion in Thiamine Deficiency

Rudolph A. Peters

It is a great privilege to be invited to submit a contribution to this volume. Rather than discuss some of his other great achievements, I propose in this chapter to appraise the present position of some conclusions reached by Dr. Lipmann (*1*) about 30 years ago, in the context of some recent work (*2*). Lipmann's paper has always interested me very much, both at the time of publication and since, because of its close relation to our own work and also because I feel that it must have had an influence on some of his important researches afterwards.

THE PIGEON

Using brain slices from the pigeon, he studied respiration and glycolysis in bicarbonate solutions of normal and thiamine-deficient* animals. Using glucose he confirmed our discovery of a rise in pyruvate in thiamine deficiency, that diminished on adding the vitamin *in vitro*. Aerobic glycolysis increased in avitaminosis and lactic acid formation diminished on adding the vitamin. He added the further, very important point that when the vitamin was added to slices from avitaminous animals, the respiration was stabilized for 4 hours, instead of gradually falling. Our experiments were done with brain brei; with this, even the respiration from the normal animal continuously falls; but if the vitamin is added, the fall is much less pronounced, so that over a period more oxygen is taken up by the tissue to which vitamin has been added. We called this the catatorulin effect and were able to correlate this action *in vitro* directly with the development of the acute clinical condition

---

* Then called "vitamin B."

of opisthotonus in the rice-fed pigeon. It will clarify my further remarks, if I make it clear at this stage that in the brei the nerve cells as such have been destroyed, but that very stable mitochondria are present.

The next point to note in the paper is that by employing the Thunberg technique using dyes he studied the "Dehydrierung" of a thoroughly washed suspension of brain cells from the pigeon. He obtained decolorization in the presence of pyruvate; in general, there was no effect caused by adding vitamin to tissue from avitaminous brain. This failure might have been due to a failure in the capacity of the washed tissue to form thiamine pyrophosphate, unknown at that time. I am not certain of this, however, because later we (3) had great difficulty in getting a brain dispersion which differentiated between thiamine and thiamine pyrophosphate (TPP). Furthermore, Ochoa (4) obtained some synthesis of TPP even anaerobically. It should be realized also that there was much evidence at the time that the anaerobic reaction of tissues with dyes, essentially the pyruvate dehydrogenase step, never showed any difference owing to avitaminosis. The matter was thoroughly investigated by Rydin (5).

There seems to be some need to mention this because there have been papers even recently [e.g., (6)], in which little difference has been shown in brain tissue from normal or avitaminous rats using dyes as acceptors; this I do not find surprising.

Taking the work of Lipmann into account, it seems fair to conclude that in the pigeon the connection of the acute opisthotonus signs with a critical loss of thiamine in the pyruvate oxidase system in the lower parts of the brain (especially the optic lobes and the rest) is well established. This critical loss was estimated to be approximately 20% of the TPP normally present (7). Even in the critical stage 10% of the cocarboxylase was still stable. In anticipation of remarks below, it should be added that in the Oxford work, we always emphasized that the chronic avitaminous condition involved other secondary factors (8).

THE RAT

Continuing with the 1937 paper, some further experiments were recorded on the brain of the rat, that have turned out to be permanently significant. His conclusions contain the following statements. "Under anaerobic conditions in N_2, CO_2, the brain brei of the rat gives a dismutation of pyruvate according to the following equation (1)."

$$2CH_3 \cdot CO \cdot COOH + H_2O = CH_3 \cdot COOH + CO_2 + CH_3 \cdot CHOH \cdot COOH \quad (1)$$

When the brei is ground to a fine suspension and examined with pyruvate in the presence of methylene blue, pyruvate is metabolized according to Eq. (2).

$$CH_3 \cdot CO \cdot COOH + O = CH_3 \cdot COOH + CO_2 \qquad (2)$$

The rat differs from the pigeon in that homogenates made by grinding show quite different results. With the pigeon, one can make a ground homogenate (3), which for a short time has the total pyruvate oxidase system present, i.e., one that we now know includes the citric acid cycle and the compounds which lead to its entry. Although much more unstable than the pigeon brain brei, the metabolic reactions are essentially the same with suitable reinforcement with a C_4 acid. In our experience with the rat, grinding of the brei in KCl is fatal to any further oxidation of pyruvate beyond that of Eq. (2). This statement is based upon many failures in 1940–1944. Total pyruvate oxidase preparations can only be made from the rat brain by using sucrose in preparing the homogenate (8a). Failure to recognize this has led to discrepant reports in the literature. I have pointed out already the very different behavior of the two types of preparation to some arsenicals (9). It is likely that this is due to a difference in the stability of the mitochondria. It is, however, fundamental. Using washed pigeon brain brei, Long and Peters (10) were able to verify Eq. (2) for brain tissue. In this only the pyruvate dehydrogenase is present (EC 1.2.2.2.). The preparation reacted in this sense with α-ketobutyrate; the respiratory quotient (RQ) obeys the equation also. It shows a small catatorulin effect upon addition of vitamin and it is a preparation which clearly contains the cocarboxylase in a very stable form. We know well the fascinating developments by Lipmann in this field, carried out mainly with pyruvate systems from microorganisms, among which may be mentioned the delineation of acetyl phosphate and the various researches which led to coenzyme A (CoA) and its applications. I feel that these may be said to have originated with the 1937 work.

In the rat, with an unwashed brain brei, much of the total pyruvate oxidase system is still present, and we were able to demonstrate some catatorulin effects (11). I mention this as a background to the discussion of new and interesting developments in the thiamine field based upon the rat, in which those engaged are setting forth the conclusions that the biochemical lesion is not in the pyruvate system. In reviewing these the following points may be noticed.

Brin et al. (12) in 1958 made the most interesting observation that the activity of transketolase, an enzyme of the pentose-phosphate shunt requiring TPP in erythrocytes (rat) fell quickly when thiamine was withheld from the diet; thereby they demonstrated that the TPP component was very loosely bound. This provided for the first time something which we have needed badly—a sign to be used as a warning signal of an approaching deficiency. At the same time, no biochemical lesion was demonstrated, because there was no evidence that the deficiency induced a pathological state in the erythrocytes. The matter has been taken much further by Dreyfus and colleagues (2). With an elegant (micro)technique, they have studied in detail, the condition of the transketolase in different parts of the brain during a developing thiamine deficiency and in the terminal stages, finding both narrowly localized histological lesions in the pontine region and a very rapid fall of the transketolase in these sites. From their point of view, therefore, they feel that the fall in transketolase is very significant and that it may well be connected with Wernicke's encephalopathy. This significance is enhanced for them by parallel experiments on a pyruvate carboxylase* using a specially devised vessel, in which the evolution of CO_2 from labeled pyruvate could be studied. Their experiments showed a hardly significant difference between the control and avitaminous tissue in the cortex measured in moles of pyruvate decarboxylated per gm protein per hour; in the brain stem, however, there was a lowering from 0.59 $\pm$ 0.11 to 0.39 $\pm$ 0.04 (the P being 0.01).

In considering these impressive results, it must be noted that the tissue was homogenized without sucrose; in view of our experience it is difficult to evaluate their observation without knowledge as to the exact component of the pyruvate oxidase system which was studied. If this is almost entirely the dehydrogenase component (EC 1.2.2.2.), one could not expect a larger difference than they found [cf. (10)]. As they point out, no one has yet shown that the pentose phosphate pathway is critically important in the sense that the glycolytic-citric acid cycles are necessary for energy metabolism and adenosine triphosphate (ATP) synthesis.

Considering the stabilities *in vivo* and *in vitro* of various TPP-requiring enzymes, one can establish a kind of order for the stability of TPP with the complex, from least to most stable: transketolase < pyru-

* The enzyme estimated appears to have been EC 1.2.2.2. with possibly some of EC 1.2.4.1.; the aldehyde formed in EC 4.1.1.1. would surely be very toxic to brain tissue.

vate dehydrogenase, EC 1.2.4.1. < pyruvate dehydrogenase 1.2.2.2. < α-ketoglutarate dehydrogenase.*

Interesting as the results with transketolase undoubtedly are and important as a test, I find it difficult to accept the implied conclusion that in rat brain "the principal biochemical lesion consists of a failure in the transketolase system." This certainly could not be extended to the pigeon without much more evidence; and it must be remembered that much clinical observation supports the view that rises in pyruvate in the blood are significant. There is another point which requires mention, as it seems to be giving rise to confusion. Deficiencies in thiamine in parts of the body other than the nervous system may or may not be significant depending upon whether the deficiency progresses to the critical stage of the biochemical lesion, as evidently can sometimes occur initially in cases of beriberi in man.

Whichever way one looks at these problems, the most urgent need appears to be to find out more about the intact total pyruvate oxidase system, which contains the citric acid cycle and gives a complete oxidation of pyruvic acid. The greatest difficulty with this system lies in its insolubility. We want to understand why, in Lipmann's slice experiments, the addition of thiamine to the avitaminous brain tissue led to stabilization of the respiration for over 3 hours. Such an explanation would carry with it an explanation of the reason why in our experiments the respiration of tissue, even from the normal, fell, but fell less quickly than in the presence of added vitamin. His work on CoA and all that this implied has carried our knowledge much further, so that we have recently a wonderful study by L. J. Reed and colleagues on the pyruvate dehydrogenase complex of *Escherichia coli*; they can dissociate this complex with a molecular weight of over two million into three subunits which can then be recombined (15). Let us hope that before long, something similar can be done for the animal pyruvate oxidase system. It was perhaps as well that some of us did not realize the complications of this system, when we were "playing" with it years ago!

REFERENCES

1. Lipmann, F., *Skand. Archiv. Physiol.* **76**, 255-272 (1937); also *Enzymologia* **4**, 65-72 (1937).

---

* In an isolated system, Green and colleagues (13) found that TPP was more dissociable in the α-ketoglutarate dehydrogenase system than in the pyruvate, whereas we (14) could not find a deficiency in α-ketoglutarate metabolism in the avitaminous pigeon, a fact which has been confirmed by others and which is not yet understood.

2. Dreyfus, P. M., and Hauser, G., *Biochim. Biophys. Acta* **104**, 78-84 (1965); see for further references.
3. Banga, I., Ochoa, S., and Peters, R. A., *Biochem. J.* **33**, 1109-1121 (1939).
4. Ochoa, S., *Biochem. J.* **33**, 1262-1270 (1939).
5. Rydin, H., "Über Gewebsoxydation bei B-Avitaminose und Inanition." Ph.D. Dissertation, Uppsala, 1935; also *Biochem. J.* **29**, 860-865 (1935).
6. Gubler, C. J., *J. Biol. Chem.* **236**, 3112-3120 (1961).
7. Ochoa, S., and Peters, R. A., *Biochem. J.* **32**, 1501-1515 (1938).
8. For other references, see Peters, R. A. "Biochemical Lesions and Lethal Synthesis." Pergamon Press, Oxford, London, New York, and Paris, 1963; *Chem. Ind. (London)* **59**, 373-378 (1940).
8a. Aldridge, W. N., *Biochem. J.* **67**, 423-431 (1937).
9. Peters, R. A., *Bull. Johns Hopkins Hosp.* **97**, 13 (1955).
10. Long, C., and Peters, R. A., *Biochem. J.* **33**, 759-773 (1939).
11. O'Brien, J. R. P., and Peters, R. A., *J. Physiol.* **85**, 454-464 (1935).
12. Brin, M., Schohet, S. S., and Davidson, C. S. *J. Biol. Chem.* **230**, 319-326 (1958).
13. Green, D. E., Herbert, D., and Subrahmanyan, V., *J. Biol. Chem.* **138**, 327-339 (1941).
14. McGowan, G. K., and Peters, R. A., *Biochem. J.* **31**, 1637-1641 (1937).
15. Fernandez-Moran, H., Reed, L. J., Koike, M., and Willms, C. R., *Science* pp. 930-932 (1964).

Theoretical Concepts in Biological Sciences

H. A. Krebs

The concept of the energy-rich phosphate bond and its central role in the energy transformations in living cells which Fritz Lipmann clarified and consolidated by his 1941 review is one of the major theoretical contributions to modern biology. The twenty-fifth anniversary of this event seems an appropriate occasion for a general discussion of the importance of theoretical concepts in biology and biochemistry today.

EARLIER ATTITUDES TOWARD THEORETICAL CONCEPTS IN BIOLOGY

Many classical biologists and chemists have looked askance at theorizing. Ever since Francis Bacon's *Novum Organum* (1620) the discovery of new facts had been regarded as the primary business of the scientist. Darwin (1861) was one of those who protested against this view when he wrote: "There was much talk that geologists ought to observe and not theorise; and I well remember someone saying that at this rate a man might as well go into a gravel-pit and count the pebbles and describe the colours. How odd it is that anyone should not see that all observation must be for or against some view if it is to be of any service." Similarly Claude Bernard (1865) pointed out that experiments should always be undertaken in view of a preconceived idea: "People who condemn the use of preconceived ideas in the experimental method make the mistake of confusing invention of an experiment with noting its results." So it became generally accepted that working hypotheses had to be formulated and facts had to be explained in terms of coordinating and unifying concepts, but it was understood that hypotheses must never move far away from the facts. Krogh (1929) expressed this by the statement: "The problems of physiology are so complicated that, to put it tersely, one cannot expect to be able to reason correctly from the facts for more than five minutes at a stretch." In other words, hypotheses must be close enough to the experimental area to be tested forthwith.

These views are sound and they are still valid today. They apply in particular to the day-to-day specialized working hypotheses of the experimental scientist who tries to interpret an experimental observation and to plan the next experiment. But in recent years there has been a gradual and deliberate shift in favor of the cultivation of other kinds of hypotheses dealing with broader aspects of biology. Journals devoted to this field have been established. Greater latitude is given in journals to the theoretical discussion of experimental data. Reflective and speculative essays appear in book form and in journals. The change of attitude which has taken place is brought home by reading the comments which Kolbe (1877) meted out to van't Hoff after the appearance of the latter's epoch-making theoretical paper on the tetrahedral structure of the carbon atom and the nature of the optical activity of organic compounds (see Appendix 1), or the fierce criticisms which Armstrong (1927) offered to the Braggs' interpretation of the X-ray diffraction pattern of sodium chloride crystals (see Appendix 2). Today the attitudes behind these comments appear very short-sighted.

THEORETICAL PHYSICS AND CHEMISTRY

The importance of theoretical work has long been established in physics, and thanks to the triumphs of the work of Newton and his successors, like Boltzmann, Planck, and Einstein, theoretical physics became a universally recognized subject. What may have contributed to this was perhaps the circumstance that the dangers of idle speculation in physics are somewhat restricted because mathematics, an important tool in theoretical physics, provides safeguarding checks; they prevent the theoretician from straying too far into the realms of fantasy. Theoretical chemistry became respectable when it established close links with physics and mathematics. A milestone was Nernst's book *Theoretische Chemie* (1893) covering the application of thermodynamics, reaction kinetics, and electrophysics to chemistry. A more recent stage in the progress of theoretical chemistry was the development of quantum mechanics which abolished the borderline between chemistry and physics and made it possible, in principle, to deal with chemistry in terms of physics.

THE PRESENT STANDING OF THEORETICAL BIOLOGY

The situation is different in biology. It is an essential aspect of biology that many of its problems are not (yet) within the range of mathematics. Examples of primarily unmathematical biological theories are those of evolution and natural selection, unifying concepts of greatest value and far-reaching consequences, exemplifying theoretical biology at its best (see Appendix 3). Unifying concepts are needed more urgently now than ever before because new facts are brought to light at a breath-taking tempo. They are needed because they may tell us what the observed facts mean; they guide us in the search for new relevant facts and guard us against accumulating useless facts.

It is true there are many treatises on some sort of theoretical biology but only a very few address themselves to the kind of theory which is most needed. Thus, Netter's *Theoretische Biochemie* (1959) limits itself to the application of physical chemistry to biological systems. It is physical chemistry rather than biology. Other works, for example, Woodger's *The Axiomatic Method in Biology* (1937), are mainly concerned with the application of mathematics to living systems. Again others, like the works of Driesch (1908) and Popper (1963), are nearer to philosophy and logic than to experimental biology. They do not provide the experimentalist with working hypotheses or interpretations of data. They aim at a logical order rather than conceptional or organizational order.

An example of a type of theoretical concept needed is that of the energy-rich phosphate bond and its essential features are therefore worth examining. Although the term "rich" indicates a numerical content, the concept is primarily a nonmathematical one. Its main feature is the idea that the energy released in the degradation of foodstuffs, before it can do work, must be converted to one particular form of bond energy, that stored in certain phosphate esters. This concept has illuminated the whole organization of energy transformations in living matter.

It is indeed a mistake to equate "theoretical" with "mathematical" biology, just as it is a mistake to equate theoretical and mathematical physics. Mathematics is a language in which scientific ideas can be expressed, and owing to the inherently clear and rigid logic of this language, mathematics is of unique value in science. But it must not be forgotten that all scientific statements gain by clarity and rigidity of their logic and that the content of the ideas which a formula expresses may be primarily nonnumerical. Thus the application of mathematics to biological systems is not yet theoretical biology. What theoretical biology must look for are ideas on the nature of biological systems. Theoretical biology is thus in the first place concerned with concepts rather than quantitative treatment. If these concepts can be expressed mathematically, so much the better, but the mathematical part is not essential, anyhow at the beginning. And a mere translation of a biological situation in the language of mathematics is not necessarily useful as Eddington (1949) pointed out, quoting Rankine's (1874) verses:

> Let x denote beauty, y manners well-bred,
>   z fortune (this last is essential),
> Let L stand for love—our philosopher said—
> Then L is a function of x, y and z
>   Of the kind that is known as potential.
>
> Now integrate L with respect to dt
>   (t standing for time and persuasion)
> Then, between proper limits, 'tis easy to see
> The definite integral Marriage must be
>   (A very concise demonstration).

THE ORIGIN OF THEORETICAL CONCEPTS IN BIOLOGY

How do successful theoretical concepts arise in biology? An examination of some recent examples, taken from biochemistry, such as the Watson-Crick model of the structure and replication of DNA, the organization of genes with the subdivision of operator genes, structural genes, and regulator genes, and the theory of repression and induction (Monod and Jacob, 1961), the theory of the regulation of enzyme activity by "allostery" (Monod et al., 1965), shows that they all began with unexplained experimental facts calling for interpretation. The originators of these concepts were primarily experimentalists whose main concern was to devise experiments which would prove or disprove an idea formulated to explain facts. The concepts mentioned are "models," i.e., simplified systems which present some of the essential features of reality and provide explanations of experimental observations, insights, and starting points for a fuller exploration of the real thing (see Rashevsky, 1965). The status of models has long been recognized in the physical sciences. Models can be of different degrees of complexity. The energy-rich phosphate bond is relatively simple. The concepts of the structure and replication of DNA or of allosteric interactions are far more involved, but in principle models are not different from the pattern of working hypotheses. It is true, though, that from the start some of the modern models were daring enough to venture rather further afield from the experimental test than Krogh's time limit of 5 minutes.

There are other kinds of theoretical concepts which do not fit into the category of models. They do not immediately arise from a set of unexplained observations. They have their origins in the search for ideas which provide law and order in situations of bewildering complexity. Theoretical concepts belonging to this category are: (a) evolution, the greatest unifying theory of biology; (b) natural selection; (c) the wholeness of living organisms, i.e., the idea that the whole is more than the sum of its parts; that the parts are related to each other and cannot be isolated without altering them; (d) the purposiveness of living organisms, i.e., the phenomenon that the great majority of, if not all, biological processes are directed toward the aim of preserving the individual and the species; and (e) the stability of the internal environment.

These concepts, because they are all part of that one phenomenon, life, are closely interlinked. Natural selection is part of evolution; purposiveness part of the wholeness.

From these fundamental concepts many subsidiary ones are derived. Examples are: (a) the nonsurvival, in the course of evolution, of nonfunctional characters, a concept which implies that every character found in living organisms is likely to contribute toward the survival of the organism, although the occurrence of vestigial characters is possible; and (b) evolutionary branching, i.e., the multiple use to which basic characters can be put.

BIOLOGICAL AXIOMS

If it is evident that such concepts are not "models," what is their epistemological status? They may be looked upon as the biological equivalents of those basic concepts in the physical sciences which, although supported by a vast body of evidence, cannot be rigidly proved or disproved, but are nevertheless real and essential. At the foundation of all sciences, as Born (1949) has put it, there are "fundamental assumptions which cannot be further reduced but have to be accepted by an act of faith." Born's remark "even an exact science like physics is based on fundamental beliefs" echoes an earlier sentence of Planck (1922): "Auch in der Physik gilt der Satz, dass man nicht selig werden kann ohne den Glauben." The concepts listed above are the fundamental principles— the acceptance of which by biologists involves an act of faith (though faith firmly based on experience). This view is supported by a quotation of Niels Bohr (1933): "The existence of life must be taken as a basic fact for which no specific reason can be given and which must be accepted as the starting point of biology in the same way in which the quantum together with the existence of the elementary particles form the basis of physics."

It is not easy to settle on a suitable general term for these types of concept. Theory, theorem, and axiom come to one's mind. The differences between an axiom, in the sense of self-evident truth, and a theory or a theorem, in the sense of a supposition well supported by evidence, are not clear-cut because a self-evident truth can be supported by experimental evidence. I prefer "axiom" because the self-evident element (or belief) is a major feature of the concepts. Axioms on the nature of biological systems are of decisive importance in shaping the day-to-day working hypotheses of the experimenter. What follows is intended to illustrate this for biochemistry.

THE NONSURVIVAL OF NONFUNCTIONAL CHARACTERS

At the biochemical level the concept that nonfunctional characters do not survive raises for every cell constituent the question of what role it plays in the life of the organism. In this sense Pontecorvo (1963) speaks of histones as substances "in search of employment." For many substances the nature of the employment has long been obvious. For others it remained puzzling for a long time, but a good answer eventually emerged. Thus creatine was discovered as a muscle constituent (Chevreul, 1834) almost 100 years before the Eggletons established its physiological role as an energy store in the form of creatine phosphate (Eggleton and Eggleton, 1927). The role of nucleic acids as carriers of genetic information (Avery *et al.*, 1944) and as templates in protein synthesis (Caspersson, 1941; Brachet, 1942) became known some 70 years after their discovery (Miescher, 1871). A function of carnitine as carrier of long-chain fatty acids, in the form of acylcarnitine, was established only a few years ago (Fritz and Yue, 1963), although carnitine has been known as a cell constituent since 1905 (Gulewitsch and Krimberg, 1905; Kutscher, 1907). The time interval between the discovery of the main blood-group substances by Landsteiner (1900) and the recognition by Ford (1942) of the physiological advantages which this "polymorphism" confers upon the species was over 40 years. It was in 1942 that myoinositol was discovered to be a constituent of phosphatides (Folch-Pi and Woolley, 1942), although as early as 1850 the presence of a hexitol, the structure of which was established as myoinositol by Eastcott (1928), was first reported in animal tissues (Scherer, 1850). The occurrence of succinate in muscle and its conversion to fumarate, as well as the ready oxidation of citrate and malate were known (Thunberg, 1910; Batelli and Stern, 1910) more than 27 years before the physiological significance of the phenomena was clarified by the formulation of the tricarboxylic acid cycle (Krebs and Johnson, 1937).

There are biochemical equivalents of analogous histories at the physiological level. The elucidation of the function of many structures, such as the lung or the endocrine organs or mitochondria, depended on the progress of chemistry and biochemistry. Thus the discovery in the late eighteenth century of O_2 and CO_2 and of the nature of combustion had to precede the clarification of the gas exchanges in the lung. The function of the thymus gland as the primary source of lymphocytes, a line of cell responsible for the production of antibodies, was brought to light as late as 1961 (Miller, 1961, 1962; Burnet, 1962), some 2000 years after the first description of the gland.

There still remain many substances the biological significance of which cannot be satisfactorily explained though tentative suggestions have been made. Examples are: (a) spermine and spermidine in sperm and tissues, (b) carnosine and anserine in muscle (possibly buffers?), (c) alcohol dehydrogenase in species not ingesting alcohol nor obtaining it through gastrointestinal fermentations, (d) D-amino acid oxidase in liver and kidney, (e) xanthine oxidase in milk, (f) ergothioneine in sperm, (g) N-acetyl aspartate in brain, (h) γ-aminobutyrate in animal tissues (possibly parent substance of physiological regulators), (i) plasma choline esterase (unspecific), (j) light-producing enzyme systems (luciferase) in bacteria (Achromobacter), and (k) alkaloids and glucosides in plants.

The fact that it has proved worthwhile in numerous cases to pursue the search for a physiological role of given properties of living matter justifies efforts to find the still missing roles. Some have hesitated to accept the idea of the nonsurvival of nonfunctional characters as an axiom because no causal mechanism of operation could be visualized. This difficulty is now beginning to disappear. The shedding of useless characters may be related to the phenomenon of atrophy and hypertrophy following nonuse and extensive use of an organ, e.g., of striated muscles, and the adaptive disappearance and formation of liver enzymes in response to changes in the dietary regimen (see Schimke, 1964; Schimke et al., 1965). Atrophy and hypertrophy and changes in enzyme activities involve changes in the rates of protein synthesis and degradation. Synthesis can be stimulated by the presence of "inducers" or the absence of "repressors," and degradation, as Schimke has shown for tryptophan oxygenase and for arginase, depends on the availability of substrate. The latter stabilizes the enzyme molecule, an experience often met with in preparative enzymology. Thus a mechanism can be visualized for the absence of nonfunctional characters in the phenotype. Their deletion from the genome is another matter, the mechanism of which remains to be clarified.

That nonfunctional characters in fact disappear is known at the physiological level. The eyes of amphibia living in the perpetual darkness of caves (*Proteus*) or soil (*Icthyophis*) have vanished as effective functional units. Other examples are the involution of the thymus gland, when its work has been done or is ready to be taken over by other lymphatic tissues, and the involution of the sex organs. An interesting question is that of the bearing of the axiom of the disappearance of characters of no-survival value on the ethics of man. This was first mentioned by Darwin in his *Expression of the Emotions in Man and Animals* in 1872 and afterward discussed by Herbert Spencer and the "Social Darwinists" (see Hofstadter, 1945). It was later dismissed by Moore (1903) and his followers (see Warnock, 1960) as the "naturalistic fallacy." It is true that Spencer's treatment of the subject was naive and crude, but if he was wrong in detail this does not imply that evolutionary progress has no bearing on ethical theory. The view is gaining powerful support that it has, and that the argument of the naturalistic fallacy is irrelevant (Huxley, 1947; Waddington, 1941, 1942, 1960; Leake, 1945; Hebb, 1965). But an appraisal of this matter is beyond the scope of this essay.

EVOLUTIONARY BRANCHING

Biologists have long been aware of the variety of uses to which a basic structural or functional potential has been adapted in the course of evolution. The forelimb of vertebrates is modified for running, flying, grasping, or swimming. The nose becomes a trunk, i.e., a grasping organ, in the elephant. The salivary glands serving digestion become venom-producing glands serving defensive purposes in snakes (the main constituents of snake venoms, like those of saliva, being enzymes). Sebaceous glands are modified to the smell-producing glands of the skunk or goat and the preen gland of birds, whereas the salt glands of marine birds are probably modified lacrimal glands.

In plants the capacity to form leaves—primarily the organ of photosynthesis—can be adapted to form food-catching organs in insectivorous plants (*Drosera, Nepenthes*), or tendrils which attach plants to a support (*Lathyrus*), or protective organs like bud scales (*Fagus*), or brightly colored structures attracting pollinators (*Bougainvillaea*), or storage tissues (bulbs), or organs from which plants can be vegetatively reproduced (*Bryophyllum*). Stems, the primary function of which is to support and to conduct, can be modified to form rhizomes (*Iris*) or tubers (potato), or corns (*Crocus*), or runners for vegetative reproduction (strawberry), or tendrils (Virginia creeper), or protective organs like thorns and spines.

Analogous considerations hold at the biochemical level. A given substance or enzyme is often put to a variety of uses.

Thus purine synthesis, needed for the formation of nucleic acids, is also used for the disposal of excess ammonia in birds and reptiles (which excrete uric acid as an end product of nitrogen metabolism). Only a few steps are required to form uric acid from purine bases.

Adenine, apart from being a constituent of nucleic acids, is also a component of catalysts such as adenosine triphosphate (ATP) and the nicotinamide adenine nucleotides.

Ribose phosphate, in addition to being a constituent of ribonucleic acid (RNA), is an intermediate in the pentose phosphate cycle which generates reduced nicotinamide adenine dinucleotide phosphate ($NADPH_2$) for reductive syntheses.

Many amino acids play a role additional to that of protein constituents. Thus glycine takes part in the synthesis of purine bases, porphyrins, creatine, glutathione, bile acids, and hippuric acid. Serine is a precursor of ethanolamine and choline, both of which are constituents of phospholipids. Methionine plays a role in the synthesis of creatine and choline; aspartic acid is a precursor of pyrimidines, and tyrosine is a precursor of adrenaline, noradrenaline, and thyroxine.

These few examples illustrate at the biochemical level the widespread phenomenon of the multiple uses of basic units. The multiplicity of uses can refer to several species and may also occur within one organism. This implies that when a function of a cell constituent has been established, this is not necessarily the whole answer.

This discussion is an attempt to express, in the form of an axiom, one special aspect of evolution, with reference to biochemistry. Although there is extensive literature on biochemical evolution (see Florkin, 1949; Anfinsen, 1959), there is still a need for formulating laws embodying the detailed consequences of the general concept of evolution.

CONCLUDING COMMENT

The time is ripe for considering many other theoretical concepts of biology from the biochemical point of view. Just as the biochemical approach has deepened the experimental study of innumerable biological problems, so theoretical biological concepts are bound to benefit, by gaining greater clarity and depth, from a translation into the language of biochemistry and from an elaboration in the biochemical direction.

Theoretical pursuits of this kind are not a waste of time. They are valuable because, as already mentioned, models of, and axioms on, the nature of living systems shape the biologist's attitude to his problems. There are many occasions when he has to make value judgments, for example, when choosing a subject of research or when designing an experiment. In arriving at a judgment his thoughts are often more effectively guided by models and axioms than by mathematical biology, and he is not likely to gain much benefit from the philosophical analyses offered by logicians and epistemologists. Such analyses are all too often far removed from the practical realities of biological research. They supply general definitions such as that given for a living organism by Driesch (1921) (see Appendix 4). These may be satisfying to the logician, but offer little to the biologist. There is no need for the all-embracing generalizations which may be very true—and also very empty. What is needed are specific models and axioms which convey ideas of the nature of the components of living systems. These are not necessarily the full truth, but by providing a guide to experimentation they may lead to the truth. In other words they mold the working hypotheses of the research worker. Incidentally, they are no less important to the day-to-day decisions of those who practice applied biology, e.g., the physician. Thus, whether in any given situation, signs and symptoms such as pain, fever, or fatigue are to be looked upon as defensive and therefore essentially helpful reactions of the body, or whether they are harmful and require countermeasures, depends on concepts on the nature of the body's reactions toward disease-making agents.

So there is something to be said in favor of attempts to derive unifying ideas, in terms of models and axioms, from the vast factual biochemical knowledge which is now accumulating. This should be regarded as one of the major aims of theoretical biology.

Appendix 1

Comment by H. Kolbe (1877) on van't Hoff's theory of the tetrahedral structure of the carbon atom and of the asymmetrical configuration around the carbon atoms of optically active compounds.

"Not long ago I expressed the view that the lack of general education and of thorough training in chemistry of quite a few professors of chemistry was one of the causes of the deterioration of chemical research in Germany. A consequence of this lamentable state of affairs is the spread of the weed, the seemingly learned and profound but in fact trivial and superficial speculative philosophy. Fifty years ago this kind of philosophy was eradicated by the advance of precise science, but now pseudo-scientists fetch it back from the limbo of human errors. Like an old whore, it is given a new dress and a lot of make-up and smuggled into polite society, where it does not belong. Will anyone to whom my worries may seem exaggerated please read—if he can—a recent memoir by a Herr van't Hoff on 'The Arrangements of Atoms in Space,' a document crammed to the hilt with the outpourings of a childish fantasy. This Dr. J. H. van't Hoff, employed by the Veterinary College at Utrecht, has, so it seems, no taste for accurate chemical research. He finds it more convenient to mount his Pegasus (evidently taken from the stables of the Veterinary College) and to announce how, on his daring flight to Mount Parnassus, he saw the atoms arranged in space.

It is typical of the present times—uncritical and even anti-critical—that a virtually unknown chemist from a Veterinary College arrogates to himself making pronouncements on one of the ultimate problems of chemistry, that of the arrangement of the atoms in space, which may never be solved and to supply a solution to this problem with a sureness and audacity, nay impudence, which can but amaze the genuine scientist."

[This translation (H.A.K.) is a somewhat pale reflection of the far more colorful and vitriolic German text.]

APPENDIX 2

Comment by H. E. Armstrong (1927) on the Braggs' claim based on the interpretation of X-ray diffraction patterns that NaCl is present in crystals in the form of Na and Cl ions and not as molecules.

"Professor W. L. Bragg asserts that 'In sodium chloride there appear to be no molecules represented by NaCl. The equality in number of sodium and chlorine atoms is arrived at by a chess-board pattern of these atoms; it is a result of geometry and not of a pairing-off of the atoms.'

This statement is more than 'repugnant to common sense.' It is absurd to the n...th degree, not chemical cricket. Chemistry is neither chess nor geometry, whatever X-ray physics may be. Such unjustified aspersion of the molecular character of our most necessary condiment must not be allowed any longer to pass unchallenged. A little study of the Apostle Paul may be recommended to Professor Bragg, as a necessary preliminary even to X-ray work, especially as the doctrine has been insistently advocated at the recent Flat Races at Leeds, that science is the pursuit of truth. It were time that chemists took charge of chemistry once more and protected neophytes against the worship of false gods: at least taught them to ask for something more than chess-board evidence."

APPENDIX 3

At a later stage a good deal of mathematics has been injected into these theories, especially by Hardy (1908), Weinberg (1908), Fisher (1922, 1930), Haldane (1932), and Wright (1931).

APPENDIX 4

Definition given by Driesch (1921) for the "living individual organism":

"Der individuelle Organismus als Gegenstand der Naturlehre ist ein aus organisch-chemischen Stoffen weniger Gruppen bestehendes, im Stoffwechsel stehendes, sich entwickelndes materielles System von anfangs niedrigstufiger, im Endstadium hochstufiger Mannigfaltigkeit, welches der adaptiven und restitutiven Regulation fähig ist und in seinem gesamten Werden, sei dieses evolutiv, funktionell oder regulativ, einer Gesetzlichkeit vom Typus der Ganzheitskausalität untersteht."

REFERENCES

Anfinsen, C. B. (1959). "The Molecular Basis of Evolution." Wiley, New York.

Armstrong, H. E. (1927). *Nature* 120, 478.

Avery, O. T., MacLeod, C. M., and McCarty, M. (1944). *J. Exptl. Med.* 79, 137.

Batelli, F., and Stern, L. (1910). *Biochem. Z.* 31, 478.

Bernard, C. (1865). "An Introduction to the Study of Experimental Medicine" (Engl. trans., Dover, New York, 1957).

Bohr, N. (1933). *Naturwissenschaften* 13, 245.

Born, M. (1949). "Natural Philosophy of Cause and Chance." Oxford Univ. Press, London and New York.

Brachet, J. (1942). *Arch. Biol.* (*Liege*) 53, 207.

Burnet, F. M. (1962). *Sci. Am.* November, 207, 50.

Caspersson, T. (1941). *Naturwissenschaften* 28, 33.

Chevreul, M. E. (1834). *Ann. Chem.* 4, 293.

Darwin, C. (1861). In a letter to Henry Fawcett, September 18th, 1861. Reprinted in "More Letters of Charles Darwin" (F. Darwin and A. C. Seward, eds.), Vol. I, p. 194. John Murray, London, 1903.

Darwin, C. (1872). "The Expression of the Emotions in Man and Animals," Murray, London.

Driesch, H. (1908). "The Science and Philosophy of the Organism. The Gifford Lectures 1907-8." Black, London.

Driesch, H. (1921). "Philosophie des Organischen," p. 556. Engelmann, Leipzig.

Eastcott, E. V. (1928). *J. Phys. Chem.* 32, 1094.

Eddington, A. (1949). "The Philosophy of Physical Science," p. 138. Cambridge Univ. Press, London and New York.

Eggleton, P., and Eggleton, G. P. (1927). *Biochem. J.* 21, 190.

Fisher, R. A. (1922). *Proc. Roy. Soc. Edinburgh* 42, 321.

Fisher, R. A. (1930). "The Genetical Theory of Natural Selection." Oxford Univ. Press (Clarendon), London and New York.

Florkin, M. (1949). "Biochemical Evolution" (edited and translated by S. Morgulis). Academic Press, New York.

Folch-Pi, J., and Woolley, D. W. (1942). *J. Biol. Chem.* 142, 963.

Ford, E. B. (1942). "Genetics for Medical Students." Methuen, London.

Fritz, I. B., and Yue, K. T. N. (1963). *J. Lipid Res.* 4, 279.

Gulewitsch, W., and Krimberg, R. (1905). *Z. Physiol. Chem.* 45, 326.

Haldane, J. B. S. (1932). "The Causes of Evolution." Harper, London.

Hardy, G. H. (1908). *Science* 28, 49.

Hebb, D. O. (1965). *Proc. Roy. Soc.* (*London*) B161, 377.

Hofstadter, R. (1945). "Social Darwinism in American Thought, 1860-1915." Oxford Univ. Press, London and New York.

Huxley, J. S. (1947). "Evolution and Ethics." Pilot Press, London.

Kolbe, N. (1877). J. Prakt. Chem. 15, 473.

Krebs, H. A., and Johnson, W. A. (1937). Enzymologia 4, 148.

Krogh, A. (1929). "The Anatomy and Physiology of Capillaries," p. 307. Yale Univ. Press, New Haven, Connecticut.

Kutscher, F. (1907). Z. Physiol. Chem. 56, 220.

Landsteiner, K. (1900). Zentr. Bakteriol Parasitenk. (Abt. I, Orig.) 27, 357.

Leake, C. D. (1945). Sci. Monthly 60, 245.

Lipmann, F. (1941). Advan. Enzymol. 1, 99.

Miescher, F. (1871). In "Medizinische-chemische Untersuchungen" (F. Hoppe-Seyler, ed.), Heft 4, p. 441 (submitted 1869).

Miller, J. F. A. P. (1961). Lancet ii, 748.

Miller, J. F. A. P. (1962). Proc. Roy. Soc. (London) B156, 415.

Monod, J., and Jacob, F. (1961). J. Mol. Biol. 3, 318.

Monod, J., Wyman, J., and Changeux, J. P. (1965). J. Mol. Biol. 12, 88.

Moore, G. E. (1903). "Principia Ethica." Cambridge Univ. Press, London and New York.

Nernst, W. (1893). "Theoretische Chemie." Enke, Stuttgart.

Netter, H. (1959). "Theoretische Biochemie," 816 pp. Springer, Berlin.

Planck, M. (1922). "Gesammelte Reden und Aufsätze." Hirzel, Leipzig.

Pontecorvo, G. (1963). Proc. Roy. Soc. (London) B158, 1.

Popper, K. R. (1963). Federation Proc. 22, 961.

Rankine, W. J. M. (1874). "Songs and Fables." Macmillan, London.

Rashevsky, N. (1965). Models and mathematical principles in biology. In "Theoretical and Mathematical Biology" (T. H. Waterman and H. J. Morowitz, eds.), pp. 36-53. Blaisdell, New York.

Scherer, (1850). Ann. Chem. 73, 322.

Schimke, R. T. (1964). J. Biol. Chem. 239, 3808.

Schimke, R. T., Sweeney, E. W., and Berlin, C. M. (1965). J. Biol. Chem. 240, 322, 4609.

Thunberg, T. (1910). Skand. Arch. Physiol. 24, 23.

Waddington, C. H. (1941). Nature 148, 220.

Waddington, C. H. (1942). "Science and Ethics." Allen and Unwin, London.

Waddington, C. H. (1960). "The Ethical Animal." Allen and Unwin, London.

Warnock, M. (1960). "Ethics Since 1900." Oxford Univ. Press, London and New York.

Weinberg, W. (1908). Jahreshefte Verein f. vaterl. Naturk. in Württemberg 64, 368 (partly translated by C. Stern (1943). Science 97, 137).

Woodger, J. H. (1937). "The Axiomatic Method in Biology." Cambridge Univ. Press, London and New York.

Wright, S. (1931). "Statistical Theory of Evolution." Am. Stat. J. (March Suppl.) p. 201.

Glutamate and Citrate Synthesis in *Clostridium kluyveri*

G. Gottschalk and H. A. Barker

The biosynthesis of amino acids and other organic compounds by *Clostridium kluyveri* has some special interest because of the simple nutritional requirements of the organism (Bornstein and Barker, 1948). The only carbon compounds required in substrate amounts for anaerobic growth are carbon dioxide and two C_2 compounds, ethanol and acetate. Both carbon dioxide and the C_2 compounds are incorporated in substantial amounts into cellular materials. Experiments with ^{14}C-labeled carbon dioxide or acetate have demonstrated that about 25% of the total cellular carbon is derived from carbon dioxide and about 75% from acetate and ethanol (Tomlinson and Barker, 1954). Therefore it became of interest to determine how the carbon skeletons of some typical cellular constituents are derived from these precursors.

Tomlinson (1954) determined the distribution of the carbon atoms of carbon dioxide and acetate in some amino acids isolated from acid hydrolyzates of cellular proteins and found a generally simple and unambiguous pattern. In alanine, for example, the carboxyl carbon was derived from carbon dioxide and the α and β carbons from the carboxyl and methyl carbons of acetate, respectively. In aspartate, the origin of the α-carboxyl and the α- and β-carbon atoms was the same as for alanine; in addition, the β-carboxyl carbon was derived from carbon dioxide. In glutamate, the α-carboxyl and β-carbon atoms originate mainly from the carboxyl carbon of acetate, and α-carbon and γ-carbon atoms from the methyl carbon of acetate and the γ-carboxyl carbon from carbon dioxide. A small part ($\sim 8\%$) of the α-carboxyl carbon of glutamate is also derived from carbon dioxide.

The biosynthesis of alanine was postulated by Tomlinson (1954) to involve the reductive carboxylation of an acetyl derivative, presumably Lipmann's acetyl-CoA, to give pyruvate.* This reaction was later demonstrated in *Clostridium butylicum* by Mortlock and Wolfe (1959), in *C. kluyveri* by Stern (1963), and in *C. pasteurianum* by Bachofen *et al.* (1964). The reductive carboxylation of acetyl-CoA is similar to the synthesis of pyruvate from acetyl phosphate and formate originally proposed by Utter *et al.* (1945). The formation of alanine from acetyl-CoA, carbon dioxide, and hydrogen by cell-free extracts of *C. kluyveri* was recently reported by Andrew and Morris (1965). The final step in alanine synthesis is a transamination between pyruvate and amino acids present in the crude extracts.

The formation of aspartic acid from acetate and carbon dioxide is readily explained by the carboxylation of pyruvate to give oxalacetate which is converted to the amino acid by transamination. Stern (1965) has reported that *C. kluyveri* contains an avidin-sensitive pyruvic carboxylase, catalyzing the reaction:

$$\text{pyruvate} + CO_2 + ATP \rightleftharpoons \text{oxalacetate} + ADP + P_i$$

Unlike the chicken liver enzyme first described by Utter and Keech (1963), this carboxylase appears not to be activated by acetyl-CoA.

Although the reactions involved in the biosynthesis of alanine and aspartate in *C. kluyveri* are now rather well established, the path of glutamate synthesis has remained uncertain. Glutamate cannot be formed by the usual reactions of the TCA cycle, because they would lead, in the absence of recycling, to the incorporation of the carboxyl carbon of acetate into the γ-carboxyl group of glutamate rather than into the α-carboxyl, as observed. Also the TCA cycle reactions would incorporate carbon dioxide, following the carboxylation of pyruvate, into the α-carboxyl group of glutamate, rather than into the γ-carboxyl, as observed. Tomlinson (1954), however, pointed out that the TCA cycle reactions could account for the unusual origin of glutamate carbon atoms in *C. kluyveri*, if an aconitase were present which acted on citrate so as to form the double bond in *cis*-aconitate between the central carbon atom and the methylene carbon atom originating from the methyl group of acetate, rather than between the central carbon atom and the methylene carbon derived from oxalacetate. This change in the position of the double bond would result in a reversal of the positions of the

---

* The following abbreviations have been used in this chapter: CoA, coenzyme A; ATP, adenosine 5'-triphosphate; ADP, adenosine 5'-diphosphate; TCA, tricarboxylic acid.

glutamate carbon atoms derived from carbon dioxide and acetate, as compared with glutamate formed by the usual tricarboxylic acid cycle.

Another variation of a tricarboxylic acid cycle reaction can account for the synthesis of glutamate in *C. kluyveri*. The condensation of 1-^{14}C-acetyl-CoA with oxalacetate in the citrate synthase reaction can theoretically occur in two ways (see Fig. 1) with respect to the arrangement of groups about the central carbon atoms of citrate. Product (A) contains ^{14}C in carbon 1 of citrate, whereas product (B) is labeled in carbon 5 of citrate. The two products are the isotopic antipodes of citrate, first prepared synthetically by Wilcox *et al.* (1950). The citrate

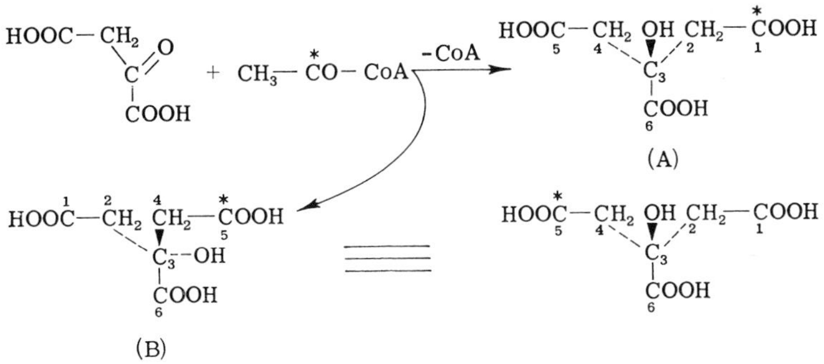

FIG. 1. The condensation of 1-^{14}C-acetyl-CoA with oxalacetate in the citrate synthase reaction.

synthase of aerobic organisms apparently always forms a product which has the configuration of citrate (A) (Hanson and Rose, 1963). Aconitase forms a double bond between carbon atoms 3 and 4. This finally results in the formation of glutamate labeled in the γ-COOH group. The same sequence of reactions acting on citrate (B) would give glutamate labeled in the α-carboxyl group.

Investigation of the reactions involved in glutamate synthesis by cell-free extracts of *C. kluyveri* has shown that citrate is formed from oxalacetate and acetyl phosphate in the presence of catalytic amounts of coenzyme A, and suitable enzymes are present to convert citrate to isocitrate, α-ketoglutarate, and glutamate. The level of citrate synthase in these extracts is very low (0.38 units per gram protein) as compared with yeast (100 units per gram) and other aerobic organisms (Ochoa *et al.*, 1951). This is to be expected in view of the fact that *C. kluyveri* does not have a complete tricarboxylic acid cycle and probably uses the citrate synthase reaction mainly for glutamate synthesis. The levels of aconitase (5 units per gram), isocitric dehydrogenase (12 units per gram), and glutamic dehydrogenase (7 units per gram) are higher, but still low in comparison with the levels in most aerobic organisms.

Tomlinson's theory that the unusual origin of the glutamate carbon atoms in *C. kluyveri* is the result of the action of an atypical aconitase has been tested by converting ^{14}C-citrate, prepared with extracts of *C. kluyveri*, to ^{14}C-isocitrate by means of either *C. kluyveri* or yeast aconitase, then converting the latter to ^{14}C-glutamate with purified isocitric dehydrogenase and glutamic dehydrogenase, and finally determining the distribution of ^{14}C in the glutamate. The ^{14}C-citrate was prepared from acetyl phosphate and ^{14}C-bicarbonate in the presence of coenzyme A, ATP, and hydrogen gas; the citrate was isolated before being converted to glutamate. The isotope was found mainly (85%) in the γ-carboxyl group of glutamate, and the distribution of ^{14}C between the two carboxyl groups was independent of the source of the aconitase. This demonstrated that the aconitases of yeast and *C. kluyveri* have the same stereospecificity. The results also indicated that the citrate synthase of *C. kluyveri* differs from that of yeast and other aerobic organisms in its stereospecificity.

In order to verify the latter conclusion, ^{14}C-citrate was prepared, by means of a *C. kluyveri* extract, from 4-^{14}C-oxalacetate and acetyl phosphate in the presence of a catalytic amount of coenzyme A. The ^{14}C-citrate was isolated and converted as before to ^{14}C-glutamate. In a control experiment, ^{14}C-citrate was also prepared from the same substrates by means of the synthase present in an extract of bakers' yeast and was then converted to ^{14}C-glutamate. Degradation of the glutamate samples showed that the distribution of isotope in the glutamate derived from *C. kluyveri* citrate was entirely different from that derived from yeast citrate. The former contained 96% of the ^{14}C in the γ-carboxyl group and 4% in the α-carboxyl group, whereas the latter contained 3% in the γ-carboxyl group and 97% in the α-carboxyl group.

In a second experiment of the same type, an extract of *C. kluyveri* or yeast was used to synthesize ^{14}C-citrate from oxalacetate and 1-^{14}C-acetyl phosphate, and the isolated citrate was converted to glutamate. Degradation of these samples showed that the ^{14}C-glutamate derived from *C. kluyveri* ^{14}C-citrate contained 94% of the isotope in the α-carboxyl group and 6% in the γ-carboxyl group, whereas the ^{14}C-glutamate derived from yeast ^{14}C-citrate contained 1% of the isotope in the α-carboxyl group and 99% in the γ-carboxyl group.

These results again confirm the conclusion that the citrate formed by extracts of *C. kluyveri* from oxalacetate and acetyl phosphate, when one of the substrates is labeled with ^{14}C, is the isotopic antipode of the citrate formed from the same substrates by the citrate synthase of yeast. When 1-^{14}C-acetyl phosphate is the labeled substrate, the ^{14}C-citrate formed by *C. kluyveri* has configuration (B) of Fig. 1. The atypical stereospecificity of the *C. kluyveri* synthase accounts for the unusual origin of the glutamate carbon atoms in this organism.

So far as we are aware *C. kluyveri* is the only organism that has been shown to contain a citrate synthase of this type. However, since the citrate synthases of other clostridia have not yet been studied, it is possible that the *C. kluyveri* type of synthase may occur in other members of this genus as well as in other groups of anaerobic bacteria. Further information concerning the occurrence of this atypical synthase will be of interest from an evolutionary point of view.

REFERENCES

Andrew, I. G., and Morris, J. G. (1965). *Biochim. Biophys. Acta* **97**, 176.

Bachofen, R., Buchanan, B. B., and Arnon, D. I. (1964). *Proc. Natl. Acad. Sci. U.S.* **51**, 690.

Bornstein, B. T., and Barker, H. A. (1948). *J. Bacteriol* **55**, 223.

Hanson, K. R., and Rose, I. A. (1963). *Proc. Natl. Acad. Sci. U.S.* **50**, 981.

Mortlock, R. R., and Wolfe, R. S. (1959). *J. Biol. Chem.* **234**, 1657.

Ochoa, S., Stern, J. R., and Schneider, M. C. (1951). *J. Biol. Chem.* **193**, 691.

Stern, J. R. (1963). *Federation Proc.* **22**, 355.

Stern, J. R. (1965). *In* "Non-Heme Iron Proteins: Role in Energy Conversion" (A. San Pietro, ed.), pp. 199. Antioch Press, Yellow Springs, Ohio.

Tomlinson, N. (1954). *J. Biol. Chem.* **209**, 597.

Tomlinson, N., and Barker, H. A. (1954). *J. Biol. Chem.* **209**, 585.

Utter, M. F., and Keech, D. B. (1933). *J. Biol. Chem.* **238**, 2603.

Utter, M. F., Lipmann, F., and Werkman, C. H. (1945). *J. Biol. Chem.* **158**, 521.

Wilcox, P. E., Heidelberger, C., and Potter, V. R. (1950). *J. Am. Chem. Soc.* **72**, 5019.

Oxygen, the Creator of Differentiation

Otto Warburg

During his famous experiments on anaerobiosis Pasteur (*1*) observed that anaerobically growing yeast degenerates in structure, if periods of aerobiosis are not interspersed. This was the first hint that oxygen may be involved in the formation of structure or, in other words, that oxygen may be involved in the creation of differentiation. Pasteur laid much stress on this observation. Indeed he suggested that here one of the great mysteries of life might be hidden, but concluded: "I do not dare to insist upon it today." It was the year 1876.

During the following 90 years many facts were observed that strengthened Pasteur's prophecy. Geochemistry (*2*) came to the conclusion that life without oxygen was the primary state of life, that this state was a very low state, and that this state changed abruptly (*3*) when 800 million years before our time oxygen appeared in the atmosphere, thus making possible oxygen respiration. Only from this time onward higher forms of differentiation developed, leading from the lowest organisms to the plant and animal kingdoms.

Geochemistry came to these conclusions by the measurement of sulfur isotopes in rocks of different ages. If free oxygen is in the atmosphere, sulfur bacteria can oxidize sulfur to sulfates. This reaction is best carried out with the heavy isotopes of sulfur that accumulate sulfur in the sulfates. Thus it was concluded that at the very time when heavy sulfur began to accumulate in the sulfate rock deposits, oxygen must have appeared in the atmosphere. The fact to be noted is that sulfur bacteria discriminate between the isotopes of sulfur.

By a second and even more convincing experiment the hypothesis presented by Pasteur was confirmed in recent years. When Pasteur observed the influence of oxygen on the structure of yeast, it was still unknown that cancer cells behave as facultative anaerobics like yeast, that they ferment like yeast and are dedifferentiated body cells. Indeed, cancer cells that come from liver, kidney, or muscles lose all their specific functions and only the now useless synthesis of nucleic acids and proteins is left. Thus geochemistry showed that oxygen *creates* differentiation, cancer cells showed that lack of oxygen *destroys* differentiation. Both proofs are complementary; but the second proof is the more convincing, because it is not founded on a nebulous past. On the contrary, the dedifferentiation of the human body cells to cancer cells occurs daily before our eyes to an enormous extent (4).

How were these facts discovered? Several years ago the lactic acid fermentation of cancer cells was discovered, but only recently has it been shown that cancer cells in the body use the energy of this fermentation to maintain life and growth. Experiments from 1962 to 1965 are so important (4a) that some of them should be described here in detail.

(1) Cancer cells, for example, Ehrlich ascites cancer cells of mice, can today be grown *in vitro* in manometric vessels when the necessary amino acids and coenzymes are supplied. They grow in the vessels even if the oxygen pressure is so low that 95% of the necessary energy must be supplied by fermentation (5).

(2) The same can be demonstrated for ascites cells growing in the abdomen of living animals. If a Beckman oxygen microelectrode is inserted into ascites tumors of living mice, oxygen pressures are found to be so low that 95% of the necessary energy must be supplied by fermentation (6).

(3) If tetanus spores, spores which germinate only at very low oxygen pressures, are injected (7) into the blood of a tumor-bearing mouse, the mouse dies of tetanus, because the tetanus spores can germinate in the tumors. If, on the other hand, these spores are injected into the blood of normal mice, the mice do *not* die of tetanus, because nowhere in the normal body is the oxygen pressure so low that tetanus spores can germinate. This is true also for the embryo growing in living animals, as experiments with pregnant mice have shown. Pregnant mice are *not* affected by tetanus spores. To summarize: the experiments with tetanus spores prove not only that tumors live in the body anaerobically, but, equally important, that no normal tissue that lives anaerobically exists in the living body. It is anaerobiosis which makes the difference between cancer cells and normal cells. It is true that previously when scientists still worked with dead tissues removed from the body, controversies were possible. Today, when

studies of growth in the living body are the only experiments that count, the results are clear-cut and controversies are no longer possible.

(4) When a tumor is growing in the body, the oxygen pressure in the tumor becomes lower and lower, as the tumor becomes larger. If the oxygen pressure approaches zero, it becomes too low even for the faculta-

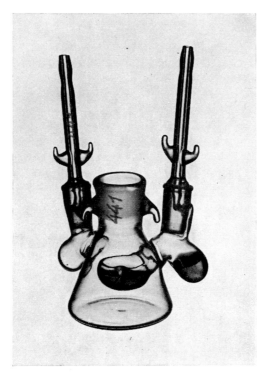

FIG. 1. Vessel with central trough connected to a sidearm (11). If the trough contains dry $CrCl_2$ and the sidearm contains water, oxygen is rapidly absorbed when the water is added to the $CrCl_2$ to establish anaerobic conditions. If the trough contains $Hg(CN)_2$ and the sidearm acid, HCN is rapidly developed when the acid is added to the $Hg(CN)_2$. The trough may contain H_2O_2 and the sidearm catalase to develop low oxygen pressures, or the trough may contain Na_2CO_3 and the sidearm H_2SO_4 to develop low CO_2 pressures.

tive anaerobic cancer cells, which in turn are damaged. They partly die, partly separate from the tumor, and spread over the whole body. Then they grow as "metastases"—first aerobically, later anaerobically, when they reach a larger size. By this cycle the necessary alternation between anaerobiosis and aerobiosis is secured—the necessity of which was dis-

covered by Pasteur in yeast. This cycle is commonly practised in all
breweries. In man, of course, this cycle is a vicious cycle that kills
the man.

(5) In Figs. 1 to 3 new manometric vessels (8) are shown which are
used today in manometry of growth (9). With the vessels pictured in

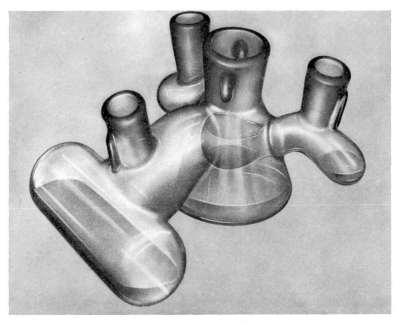

Fig. 2. Vessel with a large sidearm (*12, 13*). If the large sidearm contains
3 ml of 3 M carbonate mixture, a desired CO_2 pressure can be produced and kept
constant in the vessel, and oxygen can be determined directly. If a second such
vessel contains water in the large sidearm, the sum $CO_2 + O_2$ can be measured
and from both vessels x_{O_2} and x_{CO_2} can be calculated—a new and for many purposes
better two-vessel method.

Fig. 3 the metabolism of embryonic cells during growth has been measured. The main compartment contains the cell suspension. The sidearm
contains carbonate mixtures, if the CO_2 pressure has to be kept constant.
The sidearm contains water, if the CO_2 and O_2 pressures have to be measured. Because the embryonic cells grow only in contact with the glass
at the bottom of the vessels, the vessels must not be shaken during the
growth period. They have to be kept motionless in the thermostate and
shaken only for a short time before the manometric readings are taken.

Therefore the oxygen reaches the cells during growth not by convection, but only by diffusion, with the consequence that when the oxygen pressure in the chamber is 20% of an atmosphere, the oxygen pressure at the bottom of the vessels is only 1.5% of an atmosphere; and when the oxygen pressure in the gas chamber is 50% of an atmosphere, it is only 10% of an atmosphere at the bottom of the vessels.

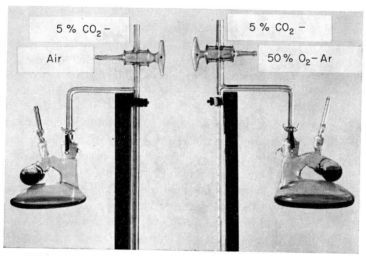

Fig. 3. Vessels to measure the metabolism during growth. The main compartment contains the cell suspensions, the sidearm of one vessel contains carbonate mixture that keeps the CO_2 pressure constant. In the other vessel the sidearm contains water. From the first vessel the value for x_{O_2} is obtained; from both vessels the values for x_{O_2} and x_{CO_2} are obtained. The vessels are kept motionless for 24 or 48 hours in the thermostate in which the temperature is kept constant not by stirring, but by streaming the water through. The vessels are only shaken shortly before the readings are taken.

With these vessels it was discovered that embryonic cells, which grow at low oxygen pressures during 48 hours, change quantitatively to a cancer metabolism (10), namely from $Q_{O_2} = -11$, $Q_\mu^{\text{Air}} = 0$, $Q_\mu^{\text{Argon}} = +13$ to $Q_{O_2} = -4$, $Q_\mu^{1.5\%O_2} = +29$, $Q_\mu^{\text{Argon}} = +45$. With this cancer metabolism the embryonic cells seem to grow infinitely at low oxygen pressures as facultative anaerobics. Higher oxygen pressure does not alter this metabolism, if growth is inhibited by shaking; but if higher oxygen pressures are applied during growth, then the cancer metabolism disappears and the strictly aerobic metabolism of the embryonic cells returns.* Thus low oxygen pressure during growth produces cells which have less respiratory enzymes and more fermentation enzymes; and high oxygen pressures during growth yield the reverse. If one calculates the sum of the energy produced by respiration and fermentation from the Q values before and after growth at low oxygen pressures, the sums are nearly equal.† This means that here we have a clear-cut case of the influence of oxygen on protein and enzyme synthesis—an influence *that is steered by the energy requirement of the cells.*

This result is also interesting from a medical point of view, because the low oxygen pressures that act in our *in vitro* experiments occur in the living body near the venous end of the capillaries. In the living body cancer metabolism may arise at some point and if such an event is repeated again and again, cancer metabolism may become irreversible, that is, cancer develops. Indeed what we observe at the bottom of our vessels (Fig. 3) during growth at low oxygen pressures—the instantaneous decrease in respiration and the increase in fermentation—may be the beginning of the genesis of cancer in the living body.

It is no guess that energy in general is needed to create and maintain differentiation, because thermodynamically differentiation is an improbable process, the equilibrium state being complete dedifferentiation. This becomes the more obvious the more highly differentiated the cells are— the simplest explanation of the frequency of human cancer and of the infinite variety of the so-called "causes" of cancer.

Let us hope that such thoughts may stimulate the interest of Fritz Lipmann, one of the few who may be able to solve the great problem of differentiation in life.

REFERENCES

1. Louis Pasteur, "Etudes sur La Biere." Paris, 1876.
2. H. Thode, J. MacNamara, and W. H. Fleming, *Geochim. Acta.* 3, 235 (1953).
3. R. Nursall, *Nature* 183, 1170 (1959).
4. Warburg, K. Gawehn, A. W. Geissler, D. Kayser, and S. Lorenz, *Klin. Wochschr.* 43, 289 (1965).
4a. O. Warburg, "Weiterentwicklung der zellphysiologischen Methoden." Thieme, Stuttgart and Wiley (Interscience), New York, 1962.
5. O. Warburg, A. W. Geissler, and S. Lorenz, *Z. Naturforsch.* 17b, 758 (1962).

* Since this paper was written we have discovered that the transformation of embryonic mice cells is irreversible.

† Before: $11 \times 5 \times 10^{-3} + 13 \times 1.2 \times 10^{-3} = 70.5 \times 10^{-3}$ cal. After: $4 \times 5 \times 10^{-3} + 45 \times 1.2 = 74 \times 10^{-3}$ cal. per milligram per hour.

6. O. Warburg, unpublished experiments.
7. R. M. Malmgreen and C. C. Flanigan, *Cancer Res.* **15**, 472 (1955).
8. O. Warburg, *Z. Klin. Chem.* **1**, 33 (1963).
9. O. Warburg, A. W. Geissler, and S. Lorenz, *Z. Naturforsch.*, in press.
10. O. Warburg, K. Gawehn, A. W. Geissler, and S. Loresz, *Z. Physiol. Chem.* **321**, 246 (1960).
11. O. Warburg, G. Krippahl, A. W. Geissler, and S. Lorenz, *Z. Naturforsch.* **17b**, 281 (1962).
12. O. Warburg, A. W. Geissler, and S. Lorenz, *Z. Naturforsch.* **16b**, 283 (1961).
13. O. Warburg, G. Krippahl, *Z. Naturforsch.* **17b**, 631 (1962).

The Metabolism of the Small Intestine[*]

K. Lohmann, Helene Graetz, and P. Langen

During investigations concerning the action of metabolites on Ehrlich ascites carcinoma cells of mice, it proved valuable to investigate the influence of these metabolites on normal, rapidly growing cells. In studying the intact small intestines of mice in glucose-containing Ringer's bicarbonate solution at 37.5°C, we found that the samples tested gave a high rate of respiration and aerobic glycolysis; however the rate of anaerobic glycolysis was found to be smaller than that for aerobic glycolysis. For example, in a 60-minute experiment, the values obtained were: Q_{O_2}, −12.5; $Q_S^{O_2}$, 16.6; and $Q_S^{N_2}$, 7.0. The enzymatic determination of L-lactate by the method of Schön[†] (15) gave satisfactory agreement with the manometric method. A review of the literature revealed that this finding had been reported by Dickens and Weil-Malherbe (6) as early as 1941 in a careful study on the mucous membranes' small intestines of the mice and rats. In the colon, anaerobic glycolysis was higher than aerobic glycolysis, as described even earlier in the literature. Also, because of the surprising results, Dickens and Weil-Malherbe compared their manometrically obtained observations with chemical determinations of L-lactate and thus established that in the small intestines of these animals less lactate is formed anaerobically than aerobically. In contrast to all other tissues and cells which have been investigated, the Pasteur effect is completely absent in the small intestine. Dickens and Weil-Malherbe concluded from their experiments that a high aerobic glycolysis is not necessarily specific for malignant tumors and that the absence of the Pasteur effect in the small intestine is unique.

Our own experiments have indicated the following results. (1) In the

[*] Given as a lecture before the Berlin Physiological Society on October 5, 1965.
[†] We thank Dr. Schön for the gift of the enzyme preparation.

small intestine of very young animals anaerobic glycolysis is greater than aerobic glycolysis and thus is "normal." The change to the "inverse" behavior of glycolysis is completed about 2–4 weeks after birth in rats and mice. (2) At lower temperatures (from 20°–30°C), anaerobic glycolysis is also higher than aerobic glycolysis in adult animals and thus is "normal." (3) By pretreatment with oxygen a "normal" anaerobic glycolysis can be obtained for 10–20 minutes. After the decrease in anaerobic glycolysis, another increased anaerobic glycolysis can be obtained by a short switchover to aerobiosis and anaerobiosis, although in a smaller degree. (4) Anaerobic glycolysis is strongly increased by the presence of pyruvate. The effect of pyruvate and the switch-over from aerobiosis to anaerobiosis appears to be additive. (5) The inverse glycolysis phenomenon has also been found in chickens and sparrows, as well as in mice, rats, and gold hamsters, but not in guinea pigs, frogs, or fish.

This chapter describes these experiments; preliminary studies are reported which may be of importance in the clarification of this peculiar behavior, namely, the absence of the Pasteur effect in the small intestine.

METHODS

The experiments, except when otherwise stated, were performed with white mice of an undefined strain which were inbred in the Institute for Medicine and Biology of the DAW, Berlin-Buch.† It is recommended that strong and well-fed animals be used. With underweight animals, the inverse effect is frequently less pronounced, especially when the animals also have a rough skin; anaerobic glycolysis in some of these obviously sick animals was equal to or even higher than aerobic glycolysis.

The animals were decapitated, and after removal of blood the jejuna was rapidly obtained by dissection. Short pieces of this tissue were rinsed with Ringer's bicarbonate solution at 4°C, or, after cutting into small pieces, freed from all food residues with the solution. This cleaning process is easier if one used animals which have been fasted overnight, and such animals were generally used in most experiments. Fresh opened pieces of intestines 9–10 mm long were dried with blotting paper and weighed on a fast balance. The dry weight was determined on a separate piece of the same tissue and the Q value was calculated in milligrams per

† In two experiments, the metabolism of the jejuna from mice of the strains BLA, SG, and C3H were investigated and all showed inverse behavior with respect to anaerobic glycolysis. We thank Dr. F. Schmidt of the Research Institute for Experimental Oncology of the DAW, Potsdam-Rehbrucke, for the gift of the animals.

hour in the usual manner. Intestine pieces of 40–60 mg wet weight in 2.0 ml of Ringer's bicarbonate solution were generally used. The volume for measuring glycolysis was 15–17 ml, and that for measuring oxygen uptake was 25 ml. The following mixtures were tested in the studies.

Ringer's bicarbonate solution. This solution was made up of 75.52 ml 0.155 M NaCl; 1:67 ml 0.155 M KCl; 1.67 ml 0.11 M CaCl$_2$; 0.87 ml 0.117 M phosphate buffer, pH 7.4; 16.70 ml 0.155 M NaHCO$_3$; and 3.57 ml 0.31 M glucose.[*]

Gas mixture. The gas mixture contained 5% CO$_2$ as well as O$_2$ and N. Respiration and aerobic glycolysis of the intact intestines were measured in 95% O$_2$ with 5% CO$_2$; those of the scraped-off mucosa were measured in O$_2$ or air with 5% CO$_2$. The thickness of the sections at the cut was always observed.

Respiration. Measurements were made in the Ringer bicarbonate solution, using the method of Warburg (cf. *16, 17*) as modified by Negelein and Noll (*9*). For calculation of aerobic glycolysis, a respiratory quotient (RQ) of 1 was assumed. (With the assumption of smaller RQ values, the value for the aerobic glycolysis is increased so that the difference between the aerobic and anaerobic glycolysis becomes still greater.)

At 37.5°C the absorption solution for 10 ml consisted of 7.7 ml 3.0 M KHCO$_3$, 1.8 ml 3.83 M K$_2$CO$_3$, and 0.5 ml carbonic anhydrase prepared from erythrocytes of cow's blood. For 20.0°C the composition was 8.07 ml 3.0 M KHCO$_3$, 1.43 ml 3.83 M K$_2$CO$_3$, and 0.5 ml carbonic anhydrase. These solutions were checked experimentally at particular temperatures, since the CO$_2$ mixtures, which had been prepared in steel cylinders, can vary by 0.1–0.2%.

RESULTS

In order to examine the methods used for measurement, an experiment (Table I) was performed in which different amounts of jejunum tissue from a mouse were investigated. Table I shows the variations normally to be expected in intestine pieces from the same animal.

Generally the respiration rate remains quite constant during the time of the experiment (60 minutes), whereas aerobic and anaerobic glycolysis may drop sharply in many experiments. An experiment with a constant metabolism is shown in Table II; an experiment with decreasing values is shown in Table XI.

---

[*] The salt solution is subsequently referred to as Ringer's bicarbonate solution. The addition of phosphate had no detectable influence on respiration and glycolysis.

The experiment shown in Table III establishes that an inverse glycolysis effect is present in all sections of the small intestine, but not in the colon, the cecum, as well as in parts of the stomach. The inverse metabolism is most pronounced in the jejunum, which has, as is well known, the greatest percentage of villi. Villi have also been found in the duodenum and quite regularly in the ileum. Occasional deviating values in the ileum are

TABLE I

METABOLISM QUOTIENTS OF DIFFERENT AMOUNTS OF MOUSE JEJUNUM TISSUE[a]

Dry weight (mg)	Q_{O_2}	$Q_S^{O_2}$	$Q_S^{N_2}$	$Q_S^{O_2}/Q_S^{N_2}$
4.0, 4.1, 4.0	−13.9	14.5	8.3	1.8
6.4, 6.2, 7.9	−13.2	17.7	9.4	1.8
12.1, 13.4, 14.2	−15.9	17.1	10.3	1.7

[a] Experimental conditions: 37.5°C, Ringer's bicarbonate solution, 0.2% glucose, measuring time 60 minutes.

TABLE II

CONSTANT METABOLISM QUOTIENTS OF MOUSE JEJUNUM TISSUE[a]

Measuring time (minutes)	Q_{O_2}	$Q_S^{O_2}$	$Q_S^{N_2}$	$Q_S^{O_2}/Q_S^{N_2}$
0–20	−20.4	17.5	8.1	2.2
21–30	−21.0	18.3	7.7	2.4
31–40	−19.8	16.4	7.7	2.1
41–50	−19.7	15.7	6.2	2.5
51–60	−18.6	16.9	7.7	2.2
61–70	−21.0	16.5	7.7	2.1
0–70	−20.1	17.0	7.6	2.2

[a] Experimental conditions: 37.5°C, Ringer's bicarbonate solution; 0.2% glucose.

associated with a stronger development of solitary fascicula or even Peyer's patches which have a smaller development of villi. Each experiment was performed with tissues from the same animal. Experiment number 1 in Table III shows the effect of inactivated calf serum in a 1:1 ratio. In this (unphysiological) medium, the ratio of aerobic to anaerobic glycolysis is very high. Upon dilution of the serum, we obtained values comparable to those obtained in Ringer's bicarbonate solution. In addition, experiments with 10, 20, and 50% inactivated serum are also given.

The small intestines of mice and rats are comparatively strongly populated with intestinal flora, which cannot be completely removed by rinsing the intestines. It appears possible that in multiple-hour experiments this flora might contribute to the glycolytic effect. In Table IV, the influence of 7, 20, and 60 µg of terramycin on metabolism was investigated. In this particular experiment, the respiration increased with increasing amounts

TABLE III

METABOLISM QUOTIENTS OF DIFFERENT PIECES OF MOUSE DIGESTIVE TRACT[a]

Experiment no. and organ	Q_{O_2}	$Q_S^{O_2}$	$Q_S^{N_2}$	$Q_S^{O_2}/Q_S^{N_2}$
1. Duodenum, middle part	− 7.7	10.7	3.8	2.8
Jejunum, proximal part	− 9.6	17.1	5.4	3.2
Ileum, distal part	−12.5	11.2	6.0	1.9
Colon, middle part	− 7.2	5.4	11.5	0.5
2. Jejunum	− 8.3	20.5	11.0	1.9
Cecum	−10.2	1.1	13.9	0.1
Colon	− 7.2	1.1	8.2	0.1
3. Jejunum	−18.3	23.1	16.2	1.4
Omasum	−6.4	3.7	11.3	0.3
Glandular part of stomach	− 6.4	2.5	6.2	0.4

[a] Experimental conditions: 37.5°C; (1) in calf serum, 1:1; (2) and (3) in Ringer's bicarbonate solution; 0.2% glucose.

TABLE IV

METABOLISM QUOTIENTS OF MOUSE JEJUNUM IN THE PRESENCE OF TERRAMYCIN[a]

Terramycin (µg)	Q_{O_2}	$Q_S^{O_2}$	$Q_S^{N_2}$	$Q_S^{O_2}/Q_S^{N_2}$
0	−11.3	17.1	11.6	1.5
7	−13.2	20.7	11.3	1.8
20	−14.7	21.1	13.8	1.5
60	−15.1	20.7	10.7	1.9

[a] Experimental conditions: 37.5°C, 2.0 ml Ringer's bicarbonate solution with 0.2% glucose.

of terramycin; however, the results are not statistically significant. With similar levels of aureomycin, the respiration was about the same, with only a small increase in aerobic glycolysis and a small decrease in anaerobic glycolysis. The ratio of aerobic to anaerobic glycolysis was thus increased still further. These results strongly indicate that the intestinal flora play no role in the "inverse" glycolysis phenomenon.

Of the monosaccharides tested, glucose is glycolyzed in the intact jejunum of mice at a rapid rate; fructose, mannose, and galactose are glycolyzed at a slower rate (Table V). With fructose, aerobic glycolysis is higher than anaerobic; with mannose, both rates are equal; and with galactose, the reverse is observed. The respiration rate is about equal with all sugars; this is also the case in experiments in which no substrate is added. (At this point attention should be given to experiments concerning the Crabtree effect. With strongly aerobic metabolizing tissues— especially malignant tumors—the respiration rate without glucose addition is higher than with glucose; with the equally strong aerobically oriented intestine, the respiration without glucose addition is generally less than in the presence of glucose.)

TABLE V

METABOLISM OF MONOSACCHARIDES IN MOUSE JEJUNUM[a]

Sugar	Q_{O_2}	$Q_S^{O_2}$	$Q_S^{N_2}$
Glucose	−14.0	23.7	12.1
Fructose	−13.3	4.1	2.6
Mannose	−12.7	5.5	5.4
Galactose	−14.1	2.9	5.0

[a] Experimental conditions: 37.5°C, Ringer's bicarbonate solution; concentration of the sugar, 0.011 M.

Of the disaccharides, maltose and sucrose have been both aerobically and anaerobically utilized with the inverse effect. However, the jejunum of an adult mouse showed no aerobic glycolysis with lactose, in contrast to that of an 18-day-old, still unweaned mouse.

The inverse metabolism was found with certainty only in adult mice and rats, but not in newborn animals. Table VI shows an experiment with animals from the same litter at different ages.

It is noteworthy that the jejunum of newborn animals has a higher respiration rate and considerable anaerobic glycolysis but practically no aerobic glycolysis. The formation of the villi in these very young animals is already very well pronounced, as determined histologically.* Aerobic glycolysis increases with age, whereas anaerobic glycolysis decreases. In the experiment shown in Table VI, aerobic and anaerobic glycolyses are equal in 16-day-old rats; the jejunum of 4-week-old rats shows the

* We thank Professor Kettler and Dr. Jurgens, Pathology Institute of Humboldt University in Berlin for making these preparations available. Comparative histochemical and electromicroscopic studies of the intestines of infant and adult animals have been started.

completely defined inverse metabolism. The changes in the ileum are definitely slower; after 4 weeks anaerobic glycolysis is still a little higher than aerobic glycolysis in this organ. A more precise time for the inversion cannot be given since this is completely dependent on species; certain

TABLE VI

METABOLISM OF RATS OF DIFFERENT AGES[a]

Age after birth (days)	Intestine part	Q_{O_2}	$Q_S^{O_2}$	$Q_S^{N_2}$	Meyerhof quotient	$Q_S^{O_2}/Q_S^{N_2}$
30[b]	Jejunum	−12.3	0.2	15.9	1.3	—
2	Jejunum	−13.2	4.2	15.6	0.9	0.3
2	Ileum	−15.6	1.2	15.8	1.0	0.1
11	Jejunum	−17.9	9.0	17.3	0.5	0.5
11	Ileum	−10.6	5.2	14.6	0.9	0.4
16	Jejunum	−15.2	13.1	13.9	—	1.0
16	Ileum	−10.0	4.1	16.0	1.2	0.3
28	Jejunum	−11.7	18.3	10.5	—	1.7
28	Ileum	−10.4	6.5	8.1	0.15	0.8
28	Colon	− 9.2	3.7	9.3	0.6	0.4

[a] Experimental conditions: 37.5°C, Ringer's bicarbonate solution, 0.2% glucose. The animals were delivered from their mothers about 3 hours before the experiment (the 30-minute-old infant had not yet drunk).

[b] Age given in minutes.

differences also exist among individual animals (Table VII). In rats and mice, 1-week differences may occur. The development of the intestines of the mouse seems to be slightly slower than that of the rat. In any case, from the great number of experiments, it could not be concluded that the inversion in nursing animals is slower than in animals that were fed early on solid food.

The dependence of inversion on development of a species is especially clear with the autophagous chicken, in which inversion is complete within 6 days; in contrast the heterophagous pigeon still shows higher anaerobic than aerobic glycolysis in 8-day-old animals. The inverse metabolism has also been found in adult sparrows, which have long intestines, thus making experiments with the intact organ possible. Measurements were taken at 37.5° and 40.0°C.

The finding that the conversion to an inverse metabolism in the small intestines is dependent on development brings upon the general question of how the metabolism of the intestines is influenced by nutritional factors. To date we have examined avitaminoses A and B_1 of rats (Table

TABLE VII
DEPENDENCE OF INVERSE METABOLISM ON SPECIES[a]

Animal	Age	Temperature ($°C$)	$\%O_2$	Q_{O_2}	$Q_S{}^{O_2}$	$Q_S{}^{N_2}$	$Q_S{}^{O_2}/Q_S{}^{N_2}$
Chicken	1 day	37.5	95	− 8.9	8.5	13.8	0.6
(leghorn)	6 days		95	− 8.7	18.4	7.6	2.5
Sparrow	Adult	37.5	95	− 8.0	15.6	11.8	1.3
Guinea pig							
Duodenum	Adult	37.5	95	− 6.4	0.4	8.1	—
Jejunum	Adult	37.5	95	− 9.7	0.3	4.1	—
Jejunum	Adult	37.5	20[b]	− 5.8	3.1	4.1	—
Jejunum							
(mucosa)	Adult	37.5	20	−11.7	0	3.7	—
Ileum	Adult	37.5	95	− 9.3	0.2	6.0	—
Rana							
temporaria	Adult	20.0	95	− 3.2	0.3	1.6	—
Fish[c]	Adult	20.0	95	− 1.6	0	1.6	—

[a] Small intestines of animals.

[b] The thickness of the carefully removed intestine wall (matrix included) of this guinea pig (weight 600 gm) was 0.44 mm. This thickness is just below the allowable thickness for 95% O_2/5% CO_2, but not below that for the partial pressure of oxygen in the air, where the respiration decreases to 60% and aerobic glycolysis increases considerably.

[c] Leuciscus (roach).

TABLE VIII
METABOLISM QUOTIENTS OF RAT JEJUNUM AFTER VITAMIN A-
AND VITAMIN B_1-FREE FEEDING[a]

Vitamin	Vitamin-free diet (days)	Age (weeks)	Weight (gm)	Q_{O_2}	$Q_S{}^{O_2}$	$Q_S{}^{N_2}$	$Q_S{}^{O_2}/Q_S{}^{N_2}$
A	0	5	58	−10.8	11.0	7.6	1.5
A	14	5	63	−10.8	12.8	6.1	2.1
A	0	7	105	−10.7	15.3	6.7	2.3
A	—	7	96	−10.4	13.5	7.6	1.8
B_1	0	5	46	−10.1	11.5	9.9	1.2
B_1	14	5	40	− 9.9	12.0	8.3	1.45
B_1	0	7	85	−11.5	13.9	8.4	1.7
B_1	28	7	48	−10.1	11.5	4.7	2.4

[a] Experimental conditions: 37.5°C, Ringer's bicarbonate solution, 0.2% glucose. Rats from the same litter were put on a vitamin A- or vitamin B_1-free diet at 3 weeks of age. Members of the same litter were used as controls by feeding them the same food, to which vitamins had been added.

VIII) and the fatty degeneration of mice upon injection with aureothio-glucose as described to Brecher and Waxler (4) (Table IX).[*] In rats with avitaminosis as well as in mice having fatty degeneration an inverse glycolysis is still present.

TABLE IX

METABOLISM QUOTIENTS OF THE JEJUNUM FROM MICE WITH FATTY DEGENERATION[a]

Weight (gm)	Q_{O_2}	$Q_S^{O_2}$	$Q_S^{N_2}$	$Q_S^{O_2}/Q_S^{N_2}$
32	− 9.6	14.7	7.5	2.0
53	−12.5	18.7	7.2	2.6
68	−12.8	22.5	9.0	2.5

[a] Experimental conditions: 37.5°C, Ringer's bicarbonate solution, 0.2% glucose. The mice (AB line) received 1 mg of aureothioglucose per gram of body weight at the age of 7 weeks and a body weight of 19–21 gm. The experiment was performed after 9 weeks. Two animals with higher body weight have an especially high aerobic glycolysis.

TABLE X

METABOLISM QUOTIENTS OF MOUSE JEJUNUM AT DIFFERENT TEMPERATURES[a]

Experiment no.	Temperature (°C)	Q_{O_2}	$Q_S^{O_2}$	$Q_S^{N_2}$	$Q_S^{O_2}/Q_S^{N_2}$
1a	37.5	−14.8	18.3	8.5	2.2
1b	20.0	− 3.8	1.9	9.2	0.2
2a	37.5	−10.7	14.6	8.2	1.8
2b	28.0	−10.8	3.3	7.2	0.5
3a	37.5	−12.4	14.2	7.6	1.9
3b	31.0	−11.7	5.4	7.5	0.7
4a	37.5	−12.2	16.9	9.4	1.8
4b	34.0	−14.0	9.5	8.6	1.1
5a	37.5	−10.8	15.1	8.7	1.7
5b	43.5	− 7.8	9.7	4.7	2.1

[a] Experimental conditions: Ringer's bicarbonate solution, 0.2% glucose. Every experiment was also performed at 37.5°C with the jejunum of the same mouse as a comparison.

The metabolism of the intact small intestines is very dependent on temperature. Table X includes experiments on the jejunum of the mouse at different temperatures, namely from 20.0° to 43.5°C in comparison with 37.5°C. Although aerobic glycolysis generally has the same tempera-ture quotient as for enzyme reactions, the temperature quotient for anaerobic glycolysis is practically unchanged between 20.0° and 37.5°C.

[*] We thank Mr. Proll and Dr. Pose of the Institute for Nutrition of the DAW in Potsdam-Rehbrücke for making these animals available.

This accounts for the increase in the ratio of aerobic to anaerobic glycolysis of about 10-fold. The respiration rate increases sharply only between $20.0°$ and $28.0°C$. In this respect, the small intestine also shows an abnormal behavior, not common to other types of cells (to date we have tested testes and kidneys of rats, Ehrlich ascites carcinoma cells of mice, and Walter tumor cells).

$Q_S^{N_2}$ Values of 2–4 for rat liver slices *in vitro* have been reported using glucose as substrate. Rosenthal (*14*) and Negelein and Noll (*9, 12*), who refer again to this phenomenon, found that these low values for anaerobic glycolysis can be increased considerably by pretreatment of the liver slices with oxygen. The anaerobic values decrease rapidly and the

TABLE XI

EFFECT OF OXYGEN PRETREATMENT ON MOUSE JEJUNUM

Time (minutes)	Q_{O_2}	$Q_{CO_2}^{O_2}$	$Q_{CO_2}^{N_2}$	$Q_{CO_2}^{N_2}$ after O_2 treatment[a]
0– 20	−15.4	25.0	13.8	34.0 (10–20)
20– 40	−15.0	20.4	9.0	15.0 (20–30)
				8.4 (30–40)
40– 70	−14.7	18.5	8.1	25-min O_2 pretreatment
70– 80	−13.6	18.0	4.9	15.5 (70–80)
80–110	−13.9	15.0	4.9	7.2 (80–110)
0–110	−14.6	19.0	8.1	25-min O_2 pretreatment

[a] Values in parentheses are given in minutes.

process is no longer reversible. Anaerobic glycolysis in the intact intestines of the mouse likewise has been increased by an aerobic pretreatment, and in general the values have doubled. This increase remains for about 10–20 minutes and is somewhat reversible. Table XI describes a typical experiment. The intestines behave like the liver, but whether the same mechanism is involved in both cases has not yet been established (see the discussion section).

Besides oxygen, pyruvate also can increase anaerobic glycolysis after anaerobiosis. Mendel and co-workers (*7*) in 1931 pointed out this effect when taking measurements of anaerobic metabolisms. Malate, fumarate, glutamate, and other substitutes are without effect. Glutamate and fumarate inhibit the increase found in anaerobic glycolysis that has been induced by pyruvate. These results are summarized in Table XII.*

* The increasing effect of pyruvate on the anaerobic glycolysis of glucose does not occur when fructose is glycolyzed.

TABLE XII
Influence of Pyruvate, Fumarate, and Glutamate on
Metabolism Quotients of Mouse Jejunum[a]

Addition (μM)		Q_{O_2}	$Q_S^{O_2}$	$Q_S^{N_2}$
Experiment 1				
None		−13.4	14.5	9.7
3.3	Pyruvate	—	—	23.4
10	Pyruvate	—	—	22.4
10	Fumarate	—	—	10.3
10	Glutamate	—	—	8.7
3.3	Pyruvate + 10 fumarate	—	—	16.8
10	Pyruvate + 10 fumarate	—	—	17.5
3.3	Pyruvate + 10 glutamate	—	—	15.9
10	Pyruvate + 10 glutamate	—	—	16.5
Experiment 2				
None		−16.1	16.5	6.0
1	Pyruvate	—	—	17.1
3	Pyruvate	—	—	17.3
10	Fumarate	—	—	6.3
10	Glutamate	—	—	5.5
1	Pyruvate + 10 fumarate	—	—	9.7
3	Pyruvate + 10 fumarate	—	—	12.2
1	Pyruvate + 10 glutamate	—	—	8.8
3	Pyruvate + 10 glutamate	—	—	11.3

[a] Experimental conditions: 37.5°C, Ringer's bicarbonate solution, 0.2% glucose. In contrast to pyruvate, fumarate and glutamate do not increase the anaerobic glycolysis, but even decrease the pyruvate glycolysis.

2,4-Dinitrophenol

Although the small intestines of infant mice and rats show a well-marked Pasteur effect, this is completely absent in the small intestines of adult animals at physiological body temperatures. It is, however, very well pronounced at lower temperatures. The increase in aerobic glycolysis to anaerobic values caused by the well-known action of 2,4-dinitrophenol as an uncoupler of the oxidative phosphorylation leads to a loss of the Pasteur effect. Hence it proved of interest to investigate the behavior of dinitrophenol on the small intestine. The results, obtained with $2.0 \times 10^{-4} M$ dinitrophenol, are shown in Table XIII. (The action of dinitrophenol is strongly dependent on its concentration.) At 20.0°C the Meyerhof quotient was 1.3 without dinitrophenol; with dinitrophenol and the same values for respiration and anaerobic glycolysis aerobic glycolysis was strongly increased. The Meyerhof quotient decreased to 0.2 at 37.5°C,

TABLE XIII

EFFECT OF 2,4-DINITROPHENOL ON METABOLISM QUOTIENTS OF MOUSE JEJUNA[a]

Temperature (°C)	Concentration of 2,4-DNP (M)	Q_{O_2}	$Q_S^{O_2}$	$Q_S^{N_2}$	Meyerhof quotient	$Q_S^{O_2}/Q_S^{N_2}$
37.5	0	−13	12.8	3.1	—	4.1
37.5	2×10^{-4}	− 7.5	7.3	9.2	0.25	0.8
20.0	0	− 5.3	1.3	8.3	1.32	0.2
20.0	2×10^{-4}	− 5.4	7.4	8.6	0.2	0.9

[a] Experimental conditions: Ringer's bicarbonate solution, 0.2% glucose.

respiration and aerobic glycolysis were decreased; anaerobic glycolysis was strongly enhanced, even slightly more than the value for aerobic glycolysis. The ratio of aerobic to anaerobic glycolysis at 37.5°C decreased from 4.1 (which in this case was exceptionally high) to 0.8 and at 20.0°C the ratio increased from 0.2 to 0.9.

ATP AND ADP CONCENTRATION

The determination of adenosine triphosphate (ATP) and adenosine diphosphate (ADP) showed that anaerobically at 37.5°C (in contrast to 20.0°C) an extensive decrease of ATP occurred. This was less pronounced

TABLE XIV

CONCENTRATION OF ATP AND ADP IN MOUSE JEJUNUM[a]

Time (minutes)	Temperature (°C)	ATP		ADP	
		Aerobic	Anaerobic	Aerobic	Anaerobic
0	37.5	35.6		24.0	
5	37.5	37.0	9.6	16.7	15.6
25[b]	37.5	33.0	10.8	31.3	20.3
30	37.5	28.4	4.4	32.0	12.7
5	20.0	76.3	39.3	22.5	65.3
15	20.0	90.0	31.2	18.2	39.8
60	20.0	76.7	27.0	28.9	43.7

[a] Experimental conditions: 1-cm pieces of intestine (250–300 mg) from three animals with empty stomachs placed in 6.0 ml of Ringer's bicarbonate solution and frozen in liquid air, deproteinated with trichloroacetic acid (including the experimental solution), extracted with ether, fractionated on a Dowex column, and determined analytically for ATP and ADP (as phosphate) after fractional hydrolysis. Data given in µg ATP and ADP per 100 mg of fresh weight. For the zero-time values pieces of the intestines from all three animals were taken immediately after the abdominal cavities were opened and they were then frozen in liquid air.
[b] Pyruvate added.

at 37.5°C in the presence of pyruvate. Total ATP and ADP decreased sharply anaerobically; however, NH_3 determinations in Conway vessels showed no significant deamination. (AMP has not yet been determined.)

Investigations with the common enzyme poisons yielded some peculiarities, though not of a fundamental nature, which were especially noticeable during the comparison of the small intestines with other tissues and cells at lowered or raised temperatures. The experiments at the elevated temperature of 43.5°C were mainly performed in view of the work of Ardenne (1, 2). This will be reported elsewhere.

DISCUSSION

Although the small intestines amount to more than 1% of the total body weight, very little research has been carried out on this organ. Dickens and Weil-Malherbe, in their standard work on the metabolism quotients of the small intestines in rats and mice in 1941, were surprised that the remarkable finding of a complete lack of a Pasteur effect had not been previously reported. This was 15 years after Warburg inaugurated the possibility of measuring metabolism. Now 25 years later we are even more surprised to find that this observation by Dickens and Weil-Malherbe was hardly noticed in the literature. Among other reasons, this lack of further study is doubtlessly due to the fact that the small intestines, as such, are morphologically very heterogeneous organs, and also the mucosa, composed of villi, is normally not homogeneous cell material, in contrast to most other tissues. According to measurements of the villi from humans (3) as well as our own measurements on the small intestines of mice, the one-layer upper epithelial cells (including goblet cells) amounts to 75–85% of the total volume. Only the use of ultramicro-techniques will prove whether the peculiarity of the metabolism of the small intestines is due to the specific upper epithelial cells. To support this view, we have found that the inverse effect in the ileum, where the amount of villi strongly decreases, is usually less than in the jejunum. Since this effect is also found in the duodenum which has a high content of Brunner's glands, to attribute essentially this phenomenon to the epithelial cells which are specifically responsible for the resorption seems to us to be quite definitely established. It is not yet known to which part of the cells this property can be attributed. Appropriate experiments with homogenates produced no results. The epithelial brush border membrane [Miller and Crane (8), Noack and Schenk (11)] may contribute to a small part of this effect, but it would be slight because of the small amount of this membrane available. The effect cannot be contributed to the intestinal wall, as such, which has various muscle layers.

The inverse effect has been shown in the mucosa as well as in the intact intestines of mice, rats, gold hamsters, birds, chickens, and sparrows. However, it has not been found in the guinea pig (mucosa and intact intestines), frog (*Rana esculenta* and *Rana temporaria*), and fish (*Leuciscus*) in studies at temperatures of 20° and 37.5°C. In larger animals, and of course in humans, only the mucosa can be investigated in order to guarantee an adequate oxygen supply.

The absence of a Pasteur effect and even the considerable predominance of aerobic glycolysis over anaerobic glycolysis is unique. As long as the enzyme pattern has not been accurately established qualitatively and quantitatively, our findings that very young animals do not show this effect and that the effect also does not appear at lower temperatures at this time contribute only little to the interpretation. The finding, however, that anaerobic glycolysis after pretreatment with oxygen and especially with pyruvate is, at least for a limited time, enhanced over the value for aerobic glycolysis offers the first possibility to interpret the inverse effect. Negelein and also one of us (H. G.) observed that anaerobic glycolysis of Ehrlich ascites carcinoma cells from mice is strongly inhibited by a liver extract. Noll (13) explained this inhibition by saying that the glutamate-pyruvate transaminase of liver causes a lowering of anaerobic glycolysis of the ascites cells up to 70% in the presence of glutamate in the medium. The pyruvate formed as an intermediate is converted to alanine and thus does not take part in the oxidation of reduced nicotinamide adenine dinucleotide (NADH). Owing to a lack of NAD this will finally result in an inhibition of the glycolysis.

According to our recent investigations (unpublished) a transaminase reaction does not seem to play a role in the inverse metabolism. The decrease in ATP can be interpreted as a result and not as a cause of the inverse glycolysis. At present appropriate experiments with quantitative determinations of enzymes are being conducted including the comparison of the behavior and action of NAD and its reduced form on adult and infant animals and especially at different temperatures. To date the experiments concerning the influence of the two forms of the coenzyme on anaerobic glycolysis of adult and infant animals and at different temperatures have not yielded a clear picture.

The latter experiments may also be able to yield information about the peculiar behavior at different temperatures. This behavior can also be described as unique since we have not found this to be true to the same extent in any other tissues or cells (rat testes and kidneys, Ehrlich mice ascites carcinoma cells, and Walker tumor cells between 20.0° and 37.5°C).

During this renewed investigation of the Pasteur effect, we again studied with great satisfaction the lecture given by D. Burk—"A colloquial consideration of the Pasteur and neo-Pasteur effects" (5)—which is still worth reading because of its comprehensive description as well as its ideal historical review. The discussion is opened by F. Lipmann. The list of classic and neoclassic interpretations, introduced by Burk in 1939, contains a collection of about fifty effects, from "Pasteur-Burk" to "Pasteur-du Vigneaud-Irish." During the past 25 years, this number has been considerably extended because of our increased knowledge and methodology with respect to the accurate control of a mechanism in the cell. We think that especially our findings concerning the inversion of the metabolism of the small intestine during development and its dependence on temperature may indicate an improved method of approach to the problem of the Pasteur effect. In this chapter we have avoided further discussion of this effect and also the "Pasteur-Lohmann-Graetz-Langen" explanation.

SUMMARY

The finding of Dickens and Weil-Malherbe has been confirmed that aerobic glycolysis of the mucosa and the entire small intestines of mice and rats, especially the jejunum with its great density of villi, is higher than anaerobic glycolysis. The small intestines also do not have a Pasteur effect. We have observed this inverse metabolism only in the small intestines and not in the other parts of the digestive tract. The ratio of aerobic to anaerobic glycolysis in this "inversed" metabolism is between 1.5 and 2.5 in Ringer's bicarbonate solution, as well as in dilute serum, but can reach values up to 3 and 4. Aerobic glycolysis gives Q_{O_2} values from −10 to −20, $Q_S^{O_2}$ values from 10 to 20 (to 25); anaerobic glycolysis gives values from 5 to 10 (to 15) at measurement times of 60 minutes.

Very young animals, especially nursing animals, have "normal" metabolisms with aerobic glycolysis being lower than anaerobic glycolysis. In mice, the inversion occurs at the latest when the animals have a body weight of 6 to 10 gm, but in rats the body weight must be 20–40 gm.

In adult animals anaerobic glycolysis of the small intestines can be increased by pretreatment with oxygen. The increase is partly reversible. Pyruvate also increases anaerobic glycolysis and both effects are additive. Glutamate and fumarate have no effect on anaerobic glycolysis; they inhibit the pyruvate effect.

Of the monosaccharides, glucose, fructose, mannose, and galactose, only glucose is utilized to a great extent.

The inverse metabolism is not caused by a contamination of the intestine with flora since in the presence of terramycin and aureomycin aerobic glycolysis is higher than anaerobic glycolysis. The inverse metabolism is also found in vitamin A and B_1 hypovitaminotic or avitaminotic animals and also in mice with fatty degeneration after injection with aureothioglucose.

Anaerobic glycolysis does not change between 20.0° and 37.5°C, whereas aerobic glycolysis increases with a temperature quotient normally found in enzyme chemistry. Between 20° and 30°C, anaerobic glycolysis is higher than aerobic glycolysis; a Pasteur effect is also found at these temperatures. With $2 \times 10^{-4} M$ 2,4-dinitrophenol at 20°C the Meyerhof quotient is lowered, at 37.5°C it is increased.

At 37.5°C a very strong decrease in ATP level ensues, in contrast to that at 20°C. The sum of ADP and ATP is decreased more anaerobically than aerobically.

Of the animals investigated to date, the small intestines of mouse, rat, gold hamster, chicken, and sparrow show the inverse metabolism at physiological temperature. The effect has not been found in the small intestines of guinea pig, frog, and fish.

REFERENCES

1. Ardenne, M. V. *Naturwissenschaften* **52**, 419 (1965).
2. Ardenne, M. V., and Kirsch, R. *Deut. Gesundheitsw.* **20**, 1935, 1980 (1965).
3. Bargmann, W. "Histologie und mikroskopische Anatomie des Menschen." Thieme, Stuttgart, 1962.
4. Brecher, G., and Waxler, S. *Proc. Soc. Exptl. Biol. Med.* **70**, 498 (1949).
5. Burk, D. *Cold Spring Harbor Symp. Quant. Biol.* **7**, 420 (1939).
6. Dickens, F., and Weil-Malherbe, H. *Biochem. J.* **35**, 7 (1941).
7. Mendel, B., Bauch, M., and Strelitz, F. *Klin. Wochschr.* **10**, 118 (1931).
8. Miller, D., and Crane, R. K. *Biochim. Biophys. Acta* **52**, 281 (1961).
9. Negelein, E., and Noll, F. *Biochem. Z.* **338**, 728 (1963).
10. Negelein, E., and Noll, F. *Naturwissenschaften* **52**, 138 (1965).
11. Noack, R., and Schenk, G. *Biochem. Z.* **343**, 139 (1965).
12. Noll, F. *Biochem. Z.* **338**, 735 (1963).
13. Noll, F. *Z. Naturforsch.* **20b**, 245 (1965).
14. Rosenthal, O. *Biochem. Z.* **207**, 263 (1929); **211**, 295 (1929); **227**, 354 (1930); **233**, 62 (1931); **244**, 133 (1932).
15. Schön, R. *Anal. Biochem.* **12**, 413 (1965).
16. Warburg, O., and Krippahl, G. *Z. Naturforsch.* **15b**, 364 (1960).
17. Warburg, O., Geissler, A. W., and Lorenz, S. *Z. Naturforsch.* **16b**, 283 (1961).

Regulation of Glycolysis in Muscle

IV. Effects of Anaerobiosis, Insulin, and Electrical Stimulation on the Penetration and Phosphorylation of 2-Deoxyglucose in Isolated Frog Sartorius Muscle*

Simon Karpatkin,† Ernst Helmreich, and Carl F. Cori

INTRODUCTION

Anaerobiosis (2), treatment with insulin (3), and electrical stimulation (4, 5) cause increased permeability of frog muscle to sugars. Utilization of sugar is enhanced also under these conditions, but it is not clear whether this is the result of more ample supply of substrate for the hexokinase reaction or whether there is also a change in the total concentration of active enzyme. In this study an attempt was made to distinguish between these possibilities. For this purpose rates of penetration and phosphorylation of 2-deoxyglucose (2-DG) were compared and related to the free sugar content of the intracellular water space of frog muscle. This glucose analog is readily phosphorylated by hexokinase and since the product, 2-deoxyglucose-6-P (P, phosphate), is not utilized appreciably by muscle enzymes, its formation can serve as a measure of hexokinase activity *in vivo*. The results reported here show that anaerobiosis and electrical stimulation increased the rate of phosphorylation in frog sartorius muscle twice as much as the rate of penetration. With insulin, phosphorylation and penetration were increased to the same

* A preliminary report of this work has appeared (1). This work was supported in part by research grants AM-6830 and AM-9242 from the National Institutes of Health, United States Public Health Service.

† Postdoctoral Fellow of the American Cancer Society.

127

extent. It thus appears that the activation of hexokinase in frog muscle made anaerobic or stimulated electrically is similar to that recently described for phosphorylase and phosphofructokinase in stimulated frog muscle (6, 7). It is suggested that the increase in enzyme activity results from an increase in V_{max} rather than from substrate saturation.

The effect of insulin on the penetration and phosphorylation of 2-deoxyglucose in diaphragm of normal and diabetic rats has been studied by Kipnis and Cori (8, 9). In normal diaphragm significant amounts of free deoxyglucose did not accumulate intracellularly, in contrast to what is observed with frog muscle. This is due to the much greater phosphorylating capacity of the mammalian muscle as compared to frog muscle. Measurements of hexokinase activity in homogenates of rat diaphragm and frog sartorius showed that the former contained about six times more enzyme than the latter (2, 10). Helmreich and Eisen investigated the phosphorylation of 2-deoxyglucose in isolated lymph node cells (11). In both diaphragm and lymph node cells the intracellular accumulation of 2-deoxyglucose-6-P exerted an inhibitory effect on the penetration of 2-deoxyglucose. The inhibition was noncompetitive and was half maximal at an internal concentration of about 15 µmoles per ml in the presence of insulin (8). In the present experiments the accumulation of 2-deoxyglucose-6-P was considerably below this value in most cases and hence less inhibition of transport would be expected.

EXPERIMENTAL PROCEDURE

Winter and summer frogs were kept at 4°C as described previously (6)

INCUBATION

Following dissection, the sartorii were allowed to rest for at least 2 hours at 4°C in frog Ringer's solution gassed with 95% O_2–5% CO_2. Incubations were carried out, except as noted, in 4 ml of frog Ringer's solution, pH 7, containing ^{14}C-mannitol for measurements of extracellular space and ^{3}H-2-deoxyglucose for measurements of intracellular distribution and phosphorylation. The temperature of incubation was 20°C, and the gas phase was 95% O_2–5% CO_2 or 95% argon–5% CO_2.

STIMULATION

Frog sartorii were mounted on electrode holders and stimulated electrically with single shocks of 2-msec duration while immersed in 10 ml of frog Ringer's solution. Stimulation was supramaximal at a rate of 48 shocks per minute for 30 to 120 minutes. A Dubnoff shaker modified as described previously (6) was used for these experiments.

PRIOR INCUBATION

It is known that a relatively long lag period precedes the onset of the effect of insulin and anaerobiosis on the permeability of the frog muscle membrane to sugars (2, 3). In order to minimize these transition effects the muscles were incubated for 1 hour with 0.4 units of insulin per milliliter at 20°C either aerobically or anaerobically and then transferred to medium containing radioactive sugars and insulin for the actual experiment. Further details are given in the legends to the tables and figures.

PREPARATION OF MUSCLE EXTRACTS FOR ANALYSIS

At the termination of the experiments, the muscles were immediately plunged into liquid nitrogen. Each frozen muscle was weighed and ground to a fine powder with sand in a precooled mortar. Extracts were prepared by addition of 1.8 ml of 0.5 N perchloric acid to the muscle powder. The extract was neutralized with 0.20 ml of a mixture containing 5 N KOH and 0.25 M Tris-acetate. Potassium perchlorate, debris, and sand were removed by centrifugation at 2000 $\times g$ in the cold. Aliquots of the supernatant solution were treated with $Ba(OH)_2$ and $ZnSO_4$ followed by centrifugation.

MEASUREMENTS OF RADIOACTIVITY

The perchlorate extracts and those treated additionally with Ba-Zn were analyzed for radioactivity. The radioactivity in the former extract represents ^{14}C-mannitol and the sum of free and phosphorylated ^3H-2-deoxyglucose, whereas the radioactivity in the latter extract represents ^{14}C-mannitol and free ^3H-2-deoxyglucose. Discrimination of ^{14}C from ^3H radioactivity was achieved by a procedure described by Narahara and Özand (12). Aliquots of 0.1 ml of the above extracts were added to 20-ml glass counting vials containing 2 ml of ethanol and 10 ml of a scintillator solution. The samples were counted on two channels of a Packard Liquid Scintillation Spectrometer with discriminator settings and voltage gain adjusted so that approximately 94% of the ^3H counts were obtained in one channel and about 75% of the ^{14}C counts in the other channel. The amount of each isotope present could then be calculated from two simultaneous equations. The background was 37 to

40 cpm in the ^{3}H channel and 25 to 30 cpm in the ^{14}C channel. In each instance the radioactivity of the experimental sample was at least ten times greater than background. All samples were counted in duplicate. Control experiments showed that there was no serious interference with counting efficiency by addition of supernatant solutions from potassium perchlorate or from Ba-Zn precipitates.

CALCULATIONS

The total water content of sartorii was found to be 84 ml per 100 gm of muscle. Extracellular space was determined in each experiment, based on the distribution of ^{14}C-mannitol between medium and muscle water. From this value and the value for the total water content of tissue one obtains the intracellular water content. Previously an average value of 58 ml per 100 gm of muscle has been reported (3).

From the value for extracellular space and from the ^{3}H radioactivity of the medium one obtains the radioactivity of free 2-deoxyglucose in the extracellular space. Subtracting these counts from the ^{3}H counts in the muscle extract after treatment with Ba^{++} and Zn^{++} gives the radioactivity of free 2-deoxyglucose inside the muscle cell. The ^{3}H counts representing phosphorylated 2-deoxyglucose are calculated by subtracting ^{3}H counts in the Ba-Zn filtrate from ^{3}H counts in the perchlorate extract of the muscle sample. Based on the specific activity of the 2-deoxyglucose added to the medium the data are calculated in terms of μmoles per milliliter of intracellular water.

SUBCELLULAR DISTRIBUTION OF HEXOKINASE ACTIVITY

All operations were carried out in a cold room. For fractionation of hexokinase activity by differential centrifugation, 3–10 gm of muscle from the hind legs were used. The fresh muscle was weighed, minced with scissors, and ground in a mortar with a few grains of sand in a solution containing 50 mM Tris-acetate, 0.8 mM EDTA-Na$_2$, and 100 mM NaF, pH 8.5. The ground muscle was homogenized with three strokes in a Potter-Elvejhem glass homogenizer. The homogenate containing about 1 gm of muscle in 2.5 to 3 ml of buffer solution was centrifuged at 1500 $\times g$ for 30 minutes. The precipitate was discarded. The remaining supernatant solution was centrifuged at 33,000 $\times g$ for 35 minutes. The pellet obtained at this speed was taken up in 2 ml of the above Tris buffer solution and the remaining supernatant solution was subjected to centrifugation at 105,000 $\times g$ for 3 hours. The pellet was resuspended in 2 ml of buffer solution and homogenized with the aid of a Teflon piston.

MEASUREMENT OF HEXOKINASE ACTIVITY

Aliquots (0.1–0.5 ml) of the supernatant fractions and the resuspended pellet fractions containing from 2 to 10 mg of protein were added to 0.5 ml of a reaction mixture containing 0.05 to 0.1 µmole of U*-^{14}C-glucose, 3 µmoles adenosine triphosphate (ATP); 3 µmoles magnesium acetate; 2.7 µmoles Na-Mg-EDTA (ethylenediaminetetra-acetic acid); 10 µg glucose-6-P dehydrogenase, 0.6 µmole nicotinamide adenine dinucleotide phosphate (NADP), and 17.5 µmoles Tris-acetate, pH 8.5. The reaction mixture was made up to 1 ml by addition of the Tris buffer containing 100 mM NaF. Glucose-6-P dehydrogenase and NADP were added to remove glucose-6-P which acts as a noncompetitive inhibitor of hexokinase (13). An aliquot of the reaction mixture was inactivated immediately following mixing and the remaining solution was incubated at 20°C for 10 to 20 minutes. Inactivation of the initial and final samples was effected by addition of $ZnSO_4$ and $Ba(OH)_2$ solution. The Ba-Zn precipitates were removed by centrifugation and 0.1 ml of the supernatant solution containing ^{14}C-glucose was added to glass vials and dried. After addition of 10 ml of toluene and the scintillator solution, radioactivity was measured in a scintillation spectrometer. On the basis of the specific activity of the glucose added, hexokinase activity was expressed in terms of mµmoles of glucose used per minute per milligram of protein under the above assay conditions. It was shown by paper chromatography and radioactivity scanning of the chromatogram that no radioactivity other than that of glucose was present in the solutions analyzed. In particular, the presence of radioactive lactate and sugar phosphates was excluded by recovering all the activity after passage of the solution through an Amberlite resin (MB-3).

ANALYTICAL PROCEDURES

Inorganic P, glucose-6-P, ATP, and lactate were determined as described previously (6, 14). Protein concentration was determined with the biuret method of Weichselbaum as modified by Dittebrandt [see (15)] and by the method of Lowry et al. (16), using bovine serum albumin as standard. Paper chromatography of sugars was carried out ac-

---

* U stands for uniformly labeled.

cording to procedures described in (17). Radioactivity on paper was measured with a Vanguard 880 automatic paper chromatogram scanner.

MATERIALS

D-Mannitol-1,6-^{14}C was obtained from Volk Radiochemical Co., Skokie, Illinois. The specific activity of the compound was 3 mcuries per mmole; it was used without further purification. The 2-deoxyglucose, a product of the Aldrich Chemical Co., Milwaukee, was labeled with ^{3}H by the New England Nuclear Corporation, Boston, according to the Wilzbach procedure (18). The readily exchangeable tritium was removed by repeatedly dissolving the compound in water and drying it *in vacuo*. It was further purified by recrystallization from methanol and by chromatographic separation on paper. The product had a specific activity of about 2 mcuries per mmole. U-^{14}C-D-Glucose was a product of Volk Radiochemical Company, Skokie, Illinois. It had a specific activity of 1 mcurie per mmole.

All reagents were analytical grade. Hexokinase and 2-deoxyglucose-6-P were purchased from the Sigma Chemical Co., St. Louis. Glucose-6-P dehydrogenase, free of hexose isomerase, was a product of Boehringer and Sons. The enzyme was diluted and dialyzed as previously described (6). Insulin was a product of Eli Lilly and Co.

RESULTS

UPTAKE AND PHOSPHORYLATION OF 2-DEOXYGLUCOSE

Uptake (or penetration) refers to the sum of free and phosphorylated 2-deoxyglucose found in the intracellular compartment of muscle. The rate of this process under various experimental conditions at a constant external concentration of 10 μmoles of 2-deoxyglucose per milliliter is shown in Fig. 1.

The rate of uptake under aerobic or anaerobic conditions without insulin (curves 1 and 2) remained fairly linear with time, presumably because even after 3 hours of incubation the intracellular concentrations of free and phosphorylated 2-deoxyglucose were too low to exert an appreciable inhibitory effect on penetration. Insulin exerted its characteristic effect on the rate of penetration both aerobically and anaerobically (curves 3 and 4). The initial rates during the first hour were increased five to four times over the respective rates without insulin. Transition effects were avoided by exposing the muscle for 1 hour to insulin prior to the measurement of sugar uptake. Without this prior incubation, one observes a pronounced lag period in the penetration of 2-deoxyglucose, as illustrated by the dotted line which joins curve 3 in Fig. 1. Narahara *et al.* (*3, 12*) have shown that this lag phase is due to the relatively slow action of insulin on the permeability of the cell membrane of frog muscle to sugars.

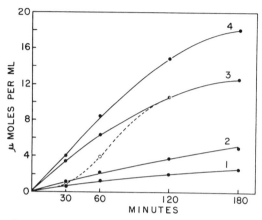

Fɪɢ. 1.   Rate of penetration of 2-deoxyglucose at 20°C in μmoles per milliliter of intracellular water from a medium containing 10 μmoles of 2-deoxyglucose per milliliter. Curve 1, aerobic; curve 2, anaerobic; curve 3, aerobic plus insulin; curve 4, anaerobic plus insulin. The muscles were given a prior incubation for 1 hour at 20°C, aerobically or anaerobically and without or with insulin, before being transferred to media containing 2-deoxyglucose and mannitol. The dotted curve shows the result of omitting the preliminary incubation with insulin.

The rate of accumulation of free and phosphorylated 2-deoxyglucose with insulin under aerobic and anaerobic conditions is shown in Figs. 2 and 3. It can be seen that more phosphorylated product and less free sugar accumulate anaerobically than aerobically. Since the rate of penetration is also faster anaerobically, the two experiments should be compared at points at which the total amount of 2-deoxyglucose which has penetrated is equal. Choosing a penetration of 5 μmoles per milliliter for comparison, one finds that this point is reached in 45 minutes in the aerobic experiment at which time 1.9 μmoles of 2-deoxyglucose have been phosphorylated. Anaerobically, a penetration of 5 μmoles of 2-deoxyglucose is reached in 35 minutes and results in a phosphorylation of 3.8 μmoles. Thus, phosphorylation is twice as fast anaerobically than aerobically, in spite of the fact that the internal concentration of free 2-deoxyglucose is lower in the former than in the latter case (1.2 as compared to 3.1 µmoles per milliliter). If enzyme saturation were the only determining factor, one calculates from the K_m for 2-deoxyglucose that the rate of phosphorylation anaerobically should have been 60% of that aerobically.[*] The data in Table I show quite generally that when

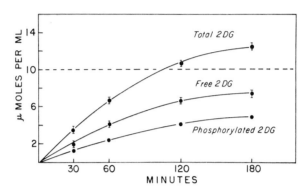

FIG. 2. Accumulation of free and phosphorylated 2-deoxyglucose (2 DG) during aerobic incubation with insulin. The dotted line corresponds to the external concentration of 2-deoxyglucose. An average of three to six experiments is shown, with the standard error of the mean.

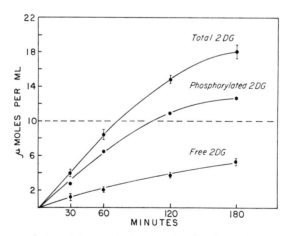

FIG. 3. Accumulation of free and phosphorylated 2-deoxyglucose (2 DG) during anaerobic incubation with insulin. The dotted line corresponds to the external concentration of 2-deoxyglucose. An average of three to six experiments is shown, with the standard error of the mean.

[*] A K_m determination for 2-deoxyglucose with frog muscle hexokinase gave a value of 2.3×10^{-3} M, as compared to 9×10^{-5} M for glucose (2). The enzyme was

TABLE I

ACCUMULATION OF FREE AND PHOSPHORYLATED 2-DEOXYGLUCOSE AS PERCENTAGE OF UPTAKE[a]

Concentration of 2-deoxy-glucose (mM)	Period of incubation (hours)	Conditions of incubation[a]							
		Aerobic		Anaerobic		Aerobic + insulin		Anaerobic + insulin	
		I	II	I	II	I	II	I	II
10	1	59	41	36	64	64	36	24	76
10	2	55	45	21	79	61	39	25	75
10	3	54	46	28	72	60	40	30	70
1	1	—	—	—	—	56	44	36	64

[a] In each case values given in column I are for free 2-deoxyglucose; in column II, for phosphorylated 2-deoxyglucose.

conditions are aerobic, irrespective of whether or not insulin is present, a larger percentage of the sugar which has entered the cell appears as free sugar than as phosphorylated sugar. Under anaerobic conditions the opposite is true, again irrespective of whether or not insulin has been added. The most likely explanation for these observations is that anaerobiosis leads to an increase in the amount of active enzyme. The fact that a considerable part of the hexokinase activity in frog muscle is present in a particulate fraction may be significant in this respect (see below).

AVAILABILITY OF ATP

Since the rates of phosphorylation in the experiments in Figs. 2 and 3 appear to fall off, especially during the last hour, the question was raised whether this might be caused by limitation in the supply of ATP, owing to inhibition of glycolytic reactions by 2-deoxyglucose-6-P. This compound is known to be a competitive inhibitor (competitive with respect to glucose phosphates) of phosphoglucomutase (8) and phosphogluco-

TABLE II
CONCENTRATIONS OF ATP AND INORGANIC P IN FROG MUSCLE INCUBATED
WITH 10 mM 2-DEOXYGLUCOSE AND INSULIN

Substance measured	Conditions of incubation[a]			
	Aerobic		Anaerobic	
	I	II	I	II
ATP	7.8 ± 0.8	7.7 ± 0.3	6.9 ± 0.2^b	4.2 ± 0.5^b
ATP	—	—	6.0 ± 0.4^c	6.0 ± 0.5^c
Inorganic P	1.6 ± 0.2	1.5 ± 0.2	3.3 ± 0.4	3.6 ± 0.3

[a] Values (μmoles per milliliter) given in column I are after a 30-minute incubation period; in column II, after a 180-minute incubation period.

[b] The hourly rate of lactate formation between 30 and 180 minutes was 9.2 μmoles per milliliter.

[c] No 2-deoxyglucose was added; the hourly rate of lactate formation between 30 and 180 minutes was 7.2 μmoles per milliliter.

not inhibited by 2-deoxyglucose-6-P. In the presence of 0.07 M NaF there was good correspondence between the disappearance of ATP and the formation of 2-deoxyglucose-6-P. The latter compound was measured with glucose-6-P dehydrogenase and NADP in a reaction mixture containing 1 to 2 mM magnesium acetate, 0.6 mM NADP, 33 mM Tris-acetate, 1.3 mM disodium EDTA, 0.66 mM 2-mercaptoethanol, and 4 μg of glucose-6-P dehydrogenase at pH 7.8. Since the reaction with 2-deoxyglucose-6-P is slow, 90 to 120 minutes of incubation at 37°C were required until an endpoint was reached. After incubation, the mixture was centrifuged for 10 minutes at 2000 $\times g$ and the absorbance at 340 mμ was measured using a Beckman DU spectrophotometer. Added 2-deoxyglucose-6-P reacted quantitatively.

seisomerase (8, 19). Data bearing on this question are shown in Table II. Under aerobic conditions during 3 hours of incubation with 2-deoxyglucose and insulin there was no significant change in the level of ATP and inorganic phosphate.* Anaerobically there was a decrease in the level of ATP at the end of the 3-hour incubation period. When 2-deoxyglucose was omitted, a decrease in ATP did not occur. This seemed to indicate inhibition of glycolysis by 2-deoxyglucose-6-P, but actual determinations did not bear this out. Thus, the hourly rate of lactate formation in the anaerobic experiments in Table II was 9.2 μmoles per milliliter with the addition and 7.2 μmoles per milliliter without the addition of 2-deoxyglucose. No explanation is at present available why 2-deoxyglucose-6-P fails to inhibit glycolysis in intact muscle. In any case, the data do not support the idea that the concentration of ATP becomes rate-limiting for the phosphorylation of 2-deoxyglucose in frog muscle.

EFFECT OF STIMULATION

An increased rate of uptake of various sugars in stimulated muscle has been demonstrated in experiments with intact animals (4). Recently, Holloszy and Narahara (5) investigated this phenomenon in isolated frog sartorius. During stimulation at various frequencies up to 20 shocks per minute the rate of uptake of 3-O-methylglucose increased in proportion to the rate of stimulation. There was a definite time lag until the change in permeability produced by stimulation reached its maximum. The effect on permeability persisted for some time after the stimulation. The results with 2-deoxyglucose were similar. In the experiment in Fig. 4, it took 30 minutes at a rate of stimulation of 48 shocks per minute until a constant rate of uptake of 2-deoxyglucose was reached. This rate of 5.6 μmoles per milliliter per hour by stimulated muscle in the absence of insulin may be compared with a rate of uptake of 6.6 μmoles per hour in a muscle treated with insulin and incubated aerobically (cf. Fig. 2, first hour of penetration). Although the amount of 2-deoxyglucose which had penetrated into the muscle in a period of 2 hours was similar in the two experiments, the rate of phosphorylation was much faster in the stimulated muscle as compared with the muscle treated with insulin; expressed as percentage of uptake it was 81% in the former and 39% in the latter case. The results suggest that stimulation like anaerobiosis increases hexokinase activity of muscle.

---

* If 2-deoxyglucose-6-P were dephosphorylated to an appreciable extent in frog muscle, one would have expected a rise in the concentration of inorganic P during incubation.

In the following analysis use is made of the fact that a steady state is attained in the stimulated muscle, where the rate of penetration is balanced by the rate of phosphorylation, so that there is no further change in the intracellular concentration of 2-deoxyglucose. In the steady state, $K'(a—x) = V_h$, where K' is the rate constant for penetration, $(a—x)$ is the concentration difference of 2-deoxyglucose across the cell membrane, and V_h is the rate of phosphorylation of 2-deoxyglucose per hour.

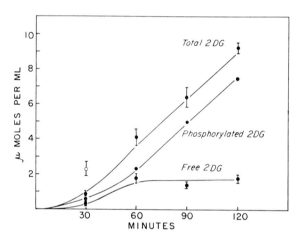

FIG. 4. Effect of stimulation on penetration and phosphorylation of 2-deoxyglucose (2 DG). The muscles were stimulated at 48 shocks per minute for the time indicated while immersed in an oxygenated solution containing 10 mM 2-deoxyglucose. No insulin was added. The value for total 2 DG indicated by an open circle was obtained by first stimulating the muscle for 30 minutes in the absence of 2-deoxyglucose and then incubating it at rest for 30 minutes in the presence of 2-deoxyglucose. An average of four to eight experiments is shown, with the standard error of the mean.

In Fig. 4, V_h was 5 µmoles per milliliter and x was 1.7 µmoles per milliliter, giving a value for K' of 0.6 hour^{-1}. In experiments with resting frog sartorius incubated at 19°C in 11 mM glucose plus insulin, V_h was 1.1 µmoles per ml and K' was 0.85 hour^{-1}. At 29°C the respective values were 5.3 and 1.4 (3). The relative effects of an experimental procedure on phosphorylation and penetration can be expressed by the ratio, V_h/K', in the above equation. This ratio was 8.3, 1.3, and 3.8 for the three examples given, from which it follows that stimulation has relatively a much greater effect on phosphorylation than on penetration.

The question of how long the effects of stimulation on permeability and phosphorylation persist after stimulation has been investigated as follows. The muscles were first stimulated in oxygenated Ringer's solution at 48 shocks per minute for 30 minutes and were then incubated at rest for 30 minutes in fresh medium containing 2-deoxyglucose. The total amount of 2-deoxyglucose taken up has been marked by an open circle in Fig. 4. It can be seen that the lag period of penetration has been largely abolished by this preliminary period of stimulation. Fur-

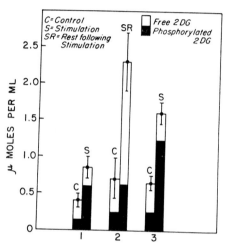

FIG. 5. Penetration and phosphorylation of 2-deoxyglucose (2 DG) during stimulation and during rest following stimulation. The experiment was performed on paired muscles, one of which served as control (C) while the other was stimulated (S) at 48 shocks per minute for 30 minutes either aerobically (groups 1 and 2) or anaerobically (group 3). In group 2, the column marked SR refers to muscles first stimulated for 30 minutes in the absence of 2-deoxyglucose and then incubated at rest for 30 minutes in the presence of 10 mM 2-deoxyglucose. An average of six to eight experiments is shown, with the standard error of the mean.

thermore, judging from the rate of uptake, the effect of stimulation on penetration must have persisted in the resting muscle. The effect of prior stimulation on phosphorylation is shown in Fig. 5. On comparing groups 1 and 2 one finds that prior stimulation causes a large increase in free 2-deoxyglucose without a corresponding increase in the rate of phosphorylation. This indicates that the effect of stimulation on the rate of phosphorylation does not persist. The predicted rate, had the effect persisted, would be that shown during the steady-state period in Fig. 4, about 2.5 μmoles of 2-deoxyglucose-6-P formed in 30 minutes. Actually only 0.7 μmole of 2-deoxyglucose-6-P was formed in the 30-

minute period following stimulation (group 2, Fig. 5). By contrast, the increased uptake of 2-deoxyglucose in muscle stimulated under anaerobic conditions (group 3, Fig. 5) is accompanied by a large increase in the rate of phosphorylation. This experiment also seems to rule out the possibility that insufficient oxygenation is responsible for the results obtained in group 1 during aerobic stimulation.

The effects of insulin and stimulation on permeability and phosphorylation do not appear to be additive under conditions where each agent alone presumably causes a nearly maximal change (Table III).

TABLE III

COMPARISON OF EFFECT OF INSULIN AND STIMULATION ALONE AND COMBINED[a]

Conditions	Free 2-DG (μmoles per milliliter)	2-DG-6-P (μmoles per milliliter)	Total uptake (μmoles per milliliter)
Insulin	1.92 ± 0.38	1.24	3.16 ± 0.55
Stimulation	1.78 ± 0.33	2.31	4.09 ± 0.46
Stimulation + insulin	1.77 ± 0.23	2.65	4.42 ± 0.59

[a] The period of aerobic incubation with 2-deoxyglucose was 1 hour. Muscles were given 48 shocks per minute. An average of four to six experiments is shown, with the standard error of the mean. These experiments were carried out with muscles from summer frogs.

SUBCELLULAR DISTRIBUTION OF HEXOKINASE

Crane and Sols (20) reported that significant proportions of the hexokinase activity of homogenates of rat heart, liver, and kidney were bound to particles. Homogenates of frog muscle in 0.3 M sucrose and 0.005 M EDTA at pH 7.7, when subjected to differential centrifugation, yielded a mitochondrial (27,600 $\times g$) and a microsomal (105,000 $\times g$) fraction which contained 28 and 9% of the total hexokinase activity, respectively (2). Similar results were obtained when frog muscle was homogenized in 0.88 M sucrose, 0.05 M Tris, 0.005 M EDTA, pH 8.0. The pellet obtained at 75,000 $\times g$ contained about 26% and that obtained at 105,000 $\times g$ about 9% of the total hexokinase activity.[*]

[*] The pellet obtained at 105,000 $\times g$, when examined under the electron microscope, was found to contain typical vesicles which are recognized as part of the structure of the sarcotubular system of frog muscle (21). We are indebted to Dr. S. Clark, Jr., from the Department of Anatomy, Washington University School of Medicine for the electron microscopic examination of this fraction. As a further check for the absence of mitochondria, tests for cytochrome oxidase were carried out with this fraction with negative results. A K_m determination for 2-deoxyglucose

When sucrose was omitted from the fluid used for homogenization, most of the hexokinase activity was recovered from the microsomal fractions (Table IV). The specific activity in this fraction was increased about 9-fold over that found in the crude extract. Several other experiments gave similar results. However, similar experiments with muscle frozen in isopentane at —170°C yielded about 30% of the total hexokinase activity in the mitochondrial pellet and about 9% in the micro-

TABLE IV
SUBCELLULAR DISTRIBUTION OF HEXOKINASE IN FROG MUSCLE[a]

Fraction	Relative activity (%)	Protein (%)	Specific activity
Supernatant solution (1500 ×g)	100	100	0.65
Supernatant solution (33,000 ×g)	86.8	81.4	0.70
Pellet (33,000 ×g)	10.6	24.3	0.29
Supernatant solution (105,000 ×g)	7.7	79.2	0.064
Pellet (105,000 ×g)	72.0	8.1	5.8

[a] Specific activity of hexokinase is expressed in terms of mμmoles of glucose used per minute per milligram of protein under assay conditions. Experimental details are given under experimental procedure.

somal fraction. A more detailed study will be required before the effects of muscular activity on the subcellular distribution of hexokinase can be evaluated.

DISCUSSION AND SUMMARY

The summary of results presented in Table V shows that when insulin is the only variable aerobically or anaerobically as in conditions 1 and 2, phosphorylation and penetration are accelerated to about the same extent. On the other hand, when anaerobiosis is the only variable as in conditions 3 and 4 or stimulation as in conditions 5 and 6, phosphorylation is accelerated more than penetration. Under all these conditions, there is little correlation between the internal concentration of free 2-deoxyglucose and the rate of phosphorylation (cf. Figs. 2–5 and Tables I and III). These results indicate that anaerobiosis as well as stimulation

with the hexokinase present in this high-speed fraction gave a value of 1.2 × 10^{-3} M.

increase phosphorylation directly rather than as a result of substrate saturation associated with increased penetration.

The effect of stimulation on penetration persists for some time after stimulation, but that on phosphorylation quickly returns to the resting condition (cf. Fig. 5). A similar type of activation and deactivation of other glycolytic enzymes has been observed in the absence of sugar when the reaction glycogen → lactate was investigated during and fol-

TABLE V

COMPARISON OF INCREASE IN RATES OF PHOSPHORYLATION AND PENETRATION OF 2-DEOXYGLUCOSE[a]

Experimental conditions	Increase in phosphorylation	Increase in penetration
1. Aerobic vs. aerobic + insulin	5.0-fold	5.3-fold
2. Anaerobic vs. anaerobic + insulin	4.0-fold	3.7-fold
3. Aerobic vs. anaerobic	4.1-fold	1.8-fold
4. Aerobic + insulin vs. anaerobic + insulin	3.2-fold	1.3-fold
5. Aerobic vs. aerobic + stimulation	10.6-fold	4.2-fold
6. Anaerobic vs. anaerobic + stimulation	4.8-fold	2.5-fold

[a] These estimates are based on maximal rates which were obtained in each case by drawing tangents to the rate curves in Figs. 1–4. The values of experiment 6 were calculated from Fig. 5.

lowing electrical stimulation of anaerobic muscle, except that the rates of these enzymes have been much faster (6, 14). Thus, at the same rate of stimulation (48 shocks per minute for 30 minutes) lactate formation from glycogen was increased 85-fold, whereas phosphorylation of 2-deoxyglucose was increased only 10-fold. It appears that glycogen is a more readily available source of energy for the working muscle than is sugar.

The well-known effect of anaerobiosis on the rate of glycolysis has recently been studied by Helmreich and Eisen (11) with isolated lymph node cells. These cells have the advantage that they contain practically no glycogen. Glucose uptake and lactate formation increase fourfold anaerobically without any change in the intracellular concentration of free glucose or glucose-6-P. Although muscle contains glycogen, it responds to anaerobiosis in the same way, namely, by increasing the phosphorylation of sugar.

The mechanism of activation of hexokinase could involve conversion of an inactive form of enzyme to an active one as exemplified by the phosphorylase-phosphorylase *b* kinase system (22). Another possibility is relocation (23), suggested by the fact that a considerable part of hexokinase in muscle is particle-bound. These problems are being investigated at the present time. In the case of insulin it is not possible to determine whether only one or both processes are influenced by the hormone, since both penetration and phosphorylation are speeded up to the same extent.

REFERENCES

1. Karpatkin, S., Helmreich, E., and Cori, C. F., *Federation Proc.* **24**, 423 (1965).
2. Özand, P., Narahara, H. T., and Cori, C. F., *J. Biol. Chem.* **237**, 3037 (1962).
3. Narahara, H. T., Özand, P., and Cori, C. F., *J. Biol. Chem.* **235**, 3370 (1960).
4. Helmreich, E., and Cori, C. F., *J. Biol. Chem.* **224**, 663 (1957).
5. Holloszy, J. O., and Narahara, H. T., *J. Biol. Chem.* **240**, 3493 (1965).
6. Karpatkin, S., Helmreich, E., and Cori, C. F., *J. Biol. Chem.* **239**, 3139 (1964).
7. Özand, P., and Narahara, H. T., *J. Biol. Chem.* **239**, 3146 (1964).
8. Kipnis, D. M., and Cori, C. F., *J. Biol. Chem.* **234**, 171 (1959).
9. Kipnis, D. M., and Cori, C. F., *J. Biol. Chem.* **235**, 3070 (1960).
10. Cori, C. F., *in* "Molecular Structure and Biochemical Reactions," Vol. V. p. 247 *Proc. Robert A. Welch Found. Conf. Chem. Res. Houston, Texas, 1961.* Robert A. Welch Foundation, 1962.
11. Helmreich, E., and Eisen, H. N., *J. Biol. Chem.* **234**, 1958 (1959).
12. Narahara, H. T., and Özand, P., *J. Biol. Chem.* **238**, 40 (1963).
13. Crane, R. K., and Sols, A., *J. Biol. Chem.* **210**, 597 (1954).
14. Helmreich, E., and Cori, C. F., *Advan. Enzyme Regulation* **3**, 91 (1965).
15. Kabat, E., and Mayer, M. M., "Experimental Immunochemistry," p. 559. Charles C Thomas, Springfield, Illinois, 1961.
16. Lowry, O. H., Rosebrough, N. J., Farr, L., and Randall, R. J., *J. Biol. Chem.* **193**, 265 (1951).
17. R. L. Whistler and M. L. Wolfrom (eds.), "Methods in Carbohydrate Chemistry," Vol. 1, p. 21. Academic Press, New York, 1962.
18. Wilzbach, K. E., *J. Am. Chem. Soc.* **79**, 1013 (1957).
19. Wick, A. N., Drury, D. R., Nakada, H. I., and Wolfe, J. R., *J. Biol. Chem.* **224**, 963 (1957).
20. Crane, R. K., and Sols, A., *J. Biol. Chem.* **203**, 273 (1953).
21. Muscatello, U., Andersson-Cedergren, E., Azzone, G. F., and von der Decken, A., *J. Biophys. Biochem. Cytol.* **10** (Suppl.), 201 (1961).
22. Danforth, W. H., and Helmreich, E., *J. Biol. Chem.* **239**, 3133 (1964).
23. Rose, I. A., and Warms, J. V. B., *Federation Proc.* **24**, 297 (1965).

Properties of the Acetylcholine Receptor Protein Analyzed on the Excitable Membrane of the Monocellular Electroplax Preparation*

David Nachmansohn

ROLE OF ACh IN EXCITABLE MEMBRANES

The existence of cell membranes and their active role in the selective transport of compounds into and out of the cell have long been suspected. However, only in the last two decades, owing to electron microscopy in combination with biochemical studies, factual information has begun to accumulate as to structure and organization and functional and chemical properties of cell membranes. Robertson (1960*a,b*) proposed the concept of a "unit membrane" about 80 Å thick, formed by a bimolecular leaflet of phospholipids and surrounded on the inside and outside by a protein layer. This view has been challenged by Sjöstrand (1963). He proposes at least three different types of cellular membranes and has raised questions as to the structural organization proposed. One of the problems arising from recent discussions is the question of how far the structural patterns observed by means of electron microscopy represent the actual situation in the living tissue and whether artifacts as to details of substructure are introduced during fixation and preparation for the examination under the electron microscope. Although the control of exchanges across the membrane and selective permeability are common features of all cell membranes, it seems certain that important

* The work reported in this paper was supported by grants from the National Science Foundation (NSF-GB-1913), the Division of Research Grants and Fellowships, U. S. Public Health Service (NB-03304) and by a gift from the Muscular Dystrophy Associations of America, Inc.

details vary and that there are distinct characteristics for different types of membranes according to their different types of functions. If we accept the commonly held view that membranes are a mosaic of functional units, the heterogeneity may be compounded by thickness, stratifications, and, in particular, by marked differences of chemical composition and enzyme activities.

Excitable membranes covering nerve and muscle fibers are endowed with the special ability to change, in a precise way, rapidly and reversibly, the permeability to ions. This permeability cycle controls the movements of the ions which are the carriers of electrical currents propagating nerve impulses. The idea of a simple diffusion process (Hodgkin, 1951) became untenable when A. V. Hill and his associates, using rapid recording instruments, observed large heat productions coinciding with electrical activity (Abbott et al., 1958). The data have been recently confirmed and greatly extended by Abbott et al. (1965). There is no alternative to the assumption that chemical reactions must control these ion movements.

The well-known theory of neurohumoral transmission assumed that acetylcholine (ACh) is a transmitter of nerve impulses being secreted from the nerve terminal and acting as a mediator between two cells. This idea was never accepted by many leading neurobiologists who questioned the interpretation, although not the observations, which had led to the hypothesis. The theory was based on classic methods of physiology and pharmacology. Although the value of these methods for many fields and aspects of biology is not questioned, they are inadequate for the analysis of the molecular basis of the permeability changes in excitable membranes during activity, processes taking place in a few millionths of a second in a structure 100 Å thick.

However, in the three decades which have passed since the proposal of neurohumoral transmission, life sciences have undergone a spectacular growth owing to the rise of dynamic biochemistry, in particular, of enzyme, protein, and macromolecular chemistry, and the development of a variety of new methods and instrumentation, such as isotope techniques, electron microscopy, X-ray diffraction and many optical methods. They have provided powerful tools for analyzing cellular mechanisms on cellular, subcellular, and molecular levels.

Biochemical investigations on the role of ACh and the basis of the permeability cycle of excitable membrane during electrical activity have been, moreover, helped in a decisive way by the availability of a special tissue, the electric organs of electric fish, which are not only the most powerful generators of electricity created by nature, but in addition are highly specialized in their function. They have been used since 1937 for the study of the biochemical basis of bioelectrogenesis and especially for the isolation and analysis of the proteins and enzymes closely associated with the permeability cycle.

During the last 20 years a huge amount of evidence has accumulated supporting the view that the action of ACh is not that of a mediator between two cells, but is an intracellular process. Its action is essential for the permeability cycle during electrical activity in all excitable membranes, those in nerve and muscle fibers, in the membranes of the nerve terminal, and the postsynaptic membranes (Nachmansohn, 1959, 1964a, b). No serious attempt has ever been made to provide an alternative explanation for the great variety of biochemical data obtained. Occasionally, an isolated observation, completely taken out of context, has been presented as being in contradiction to the role of ACh proposed. It has been easy to explain these apparent contradictions as arising from misconceptions of basic biochemical facts (see, for instance, Nachmansohn, 1965, 1966). ACh is the "specific operative substance" in the permeability cycle in the sense applied by Otto Meyerhof to adenosine triphosphate (ATP) in muscular contraction.

Although the essential role of ACh in excitable membranes during electrical activity is well established, many details of the elementary process are far from having been elucidated, as is also true for the chemical processes of muscular contraction. The picture which has emerged from the many data accumulated and best fits the available information may be briefly described. In resting condition ACh is present in bound form. Any stimulus producing a response of the excitable membrane releases ACh from the complex. The free ACh reacts with a specific receptor protein. During this reaction there seems to be, as will be discussed later, a conformational change which may lead to a shift of charge. This triggers off a chain of reactions leading to an increased permeability. The free ACh is in a dynamic equilibrium with free receptor and the ACh-receptor complex. In free form ACh is attacked and hydrolyzed by ACh-esterase, a process which according to the turnover time, takes place in a few millionths of a second (Rothenberg and Nachmansohn, 1947; Lawler, 1961). The receptor is now able to return to its original form, the processes initiated by the conformational change are reversed, and the barrier for ions is reestablished. Like the respiratory enzyme and the electron transfer systems (Fernandez-Moran et al., 1964) or the fatty acid synthesis (Lynen, 1964), the ACh system seems to be structurally organized within, or adjacent to, the excitable membrane, as supported by biochemical data, by the results of differential ultracentrifugation, in which ACh-esterase was found to be tightly bound to the fraction rich in membranes (Karlin, 1965), and by many recent electron microscope studies combined with histochemical staining techniques (see, e.g., Barrnett, 1962). Such an organization would account for the extraordinary speed, precision, and efficiency of the process.

The crucial evidence for the role of ACh has been provided by the use of potent, specific, and competitive inhibitors. It has been shown that it is impossible to separate electrical activity from the activity of the two proteins involved according to theory in the elementary process: ACh-esterase and ACh-receptor. Blocking of either of the two components leads to loss of excitability. A great variety of different types of excitable membranes were tested in support of this view.

ACh-esterase was obtained in solution in highly active form in 1938 from electric tissue (Nachmansohn and Lederer, 1939). The molecular forces of its active site have been extensively analyzed with appropriate substrates and inhibitors and the results have been frequently reviewed (see, e.g., Nachmansohn and Wilson, 1951; Nachmansohn, 1959). Much pertinent information has been obtained with organophosphates, which are irreversible inhibitors of ACh-esterase and other ester-splitting enzymes. The organophosphates phosphorylate the nucleophilic oxygen of the serine in the active site. The phosphorylated enzyme is inactive. A dephosphorylation is, however, possible by nucleophilic attack on the P atom, whereby the phosphoryl group is removed, in a displacement reaction, from the enzyme. A potent and rather specific reactivator of ACh-esterase is pyridine-2-aldoxime methiodide (PAM), which proved to be an efficient antidote in the whole animal (Kewitz et al., 1956) and has been widely and successfully applied to humans in insecticide poisoning. Although exposure of nerve axons to organophosphates leads to irreversible loss of excitability due to irreversible blocking of the enzyme, it was recently possible to demonstrate that PAM, under appropriate experimental conditions, may restore electrical and enzyme activity of axons (Dettbarn et al., 1964). Thus, formation of a specific P—O bond in the active site of ACh-esterase blocks excitability, breaking this particular bond restores it.

The ACh-receptor has not been isolated as yet. The report of Ehrenpreis (1960) has not been confirmed by Beychok (1965). However, during the last few years much information has accumulated about the receptor and its reaction with ACh and related compounds with the aid of a monocellular preparation obtained from electric tissue of *Electrophorus electricus*. This chapter will discuss some recent progress concerning this particular aspect.

THE ACh-RECEPTOR

THE MONOCELLULAR ELECTROPLAX PREPARATION

Although a receptor of ACh has been postulated for a long time on a purely theoretical basis (see, e.g., Clark, 1937), experimental evidence for the existence of a component distinguishable from ACh-esterase was obtained only about 10 years ago in experiments with electroplax, when it was shown that ACh and some related compounds may block electrical activity, while ACh-esterase activity remains virtually unaffected even when applying concentrations of these compounds one hundred times or more in excess of those required for blocking excitability (Altamirano *et al.*, 1955). Although it cannot be claimed that two different proteins are involved, it is evident that the two active sites must differ. In the specific reaction with the receptor two types of compounds were distinguished: one group blocks and simultaneously depolarizes the membrane, thus producing the biological action postulated for ACh, i.e., it induces the conformational change leading to increased permeability; another group blocks by competition with ACh for the active site, but does not depolarize, i.e., it is apparently unable to induce the conformational changes. In analogy with enzyme chemistry, the first group has been referred to as receptor activators, the second as receptor inhibitors. To the first group of compounds belong, for instance, in addition to ACh, carbamylcholine, neostigmine, nicotine, succinoyl choline, decamethonium, etc.; to the second group curare, procaine and related anesthetics, atropine, and many others.

A much more quantitative evaluation of the interaction between ACh-receptor and ACh and related compounds became possible when Schoffeniels, in 1956, introduced the monocellular electroplax preparation (Schoffeniels, 1957, 1959; Schoffeniels and Nachmansohn, 1957). One single cell from the posterior part of the electric organ of *Electrophorus electricus,* generally referred to as the Bundle of Sachs, is dissected and mounted between two chambers, so that the cell separates the two pools of fluid. The cell is kept between two nylon sheets, one with a window adjusted to the dimensions of the cell, and another with a grid consisting of nylon threads and used for pressing the cell against the window. The usefulness of this preparation is based on several special features of the cell. (1) It is a cell of extraordinarily large dimensions: 6 to 10 mm long, 1 to 2 mm high, and 0.2 mm thick. Owing to this size it is a favorable experimental material. (2) Only one face is innervated and has a conducting membrane, whereas the other face is not innervated and is nonconducting. Therefore, the fluid of one chamber is bathing one type of membrane, that of the second chamber the other type. (3) The innervated membrane has a rectangular shape and is, therefore, uniquely suitable for many types of studies, such as ion movements across the membrane. The window faces the innervated membrane. All compounds moving from one pool to the other must cross the cell; there is no leakage, as has been established repeatedly with radioactively labeled sulfate. (4) the innervated membrane is formed by many thousands of synaptic junctions, which cover about 5 to 10% of the surface. However, 90% or more is conducting membrane surrounded by a structural barrier, as is the case with all excitable membranes in conducting fibers. Electrical parameters readily permit one to distinguish between the action on the junction (the response to neural stimulation) and that on the conducting membrane (the response to direct stimulation). At the level of the junction the reaction of the ACh-receptor with the micromolecule applied externally is measured more or less directly with a minimum of interference, if any, by structural barriers. The effect on the conducting excitable membrane offers the possibility of studying separately those features of molecular structure which permit a penetration through structural barriers and thereby an action on the ACh-receptor in the conducting excitable membrane.

The value of this preparation, unique in many respects, has been greatly increased by several refinements and improvements of technique by Higman, Bartels, and Podleski (Higman and Bartels, 1961, 1962; Higman et al., 1963, 1964). The use of intracellular electrodes combined with a special switching device permits the precise recording of various electrical parameters, such as, simultaneous measurements of the potential difference across the conducting and nonconducting membranes and across the whole cell.

A quantitative method for analyzing the reactions of ACh and related compounds with the receptor has been worked out during the last 2 years, which is extremely sensitive and reproducible not only with cells of the same organ, but with cells from different specimens. The method is based on recording steady-state potentials with increasing concentrations of the compound used. An experiment with ACh is reproduced in Fig. 1 (Bartels and Nachmansohn, 1965). Smallest modifications of structure may have extremely potent effects. Owing to the many features described, the preparation has become a material which permits quantitative measurements and evaluations of structure-activity relationships of compounds acting on the receptor and on the permeability of ions across the excitable membrane.

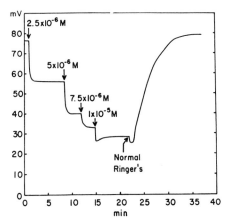

Fig. 1.   Depolarizing potency of acetylcholine (ACh) determined by the steady-state potentials reached with increasing concentrations. On return to Ringer's solution the effect is reversed and the resting potential is restored. Physostigmine ($5 \times 10^{-5} M$) was present in all test solutions (Bartels and Nachmansohn, 1965).

Some 20 years ago, many biochemists and especially protein and enzyme chemists would have been skeptical as to the value of measuring the reactions of a protein in an organized structure such as the excitable membrane. Certainly it is still desirable and essential to isolate the receptor protein for studying its properties in solution and to get information about its primary, secondary, and tertiary structure, the groups in the active site, etc. During the last two decades, however, it has become increasingly apparent that the reactions of enzymes and proteins are greatly influenced and modified by the environment. Structure and organization of the cell and subcellular formations, reactions of other enzymes, ion composition, and many other factors greatly affect and modify enzyme and protein activities. They may accelerate or slow down activity, but the changes may be much more drastic. It is known that some reaction sequences would not take place at all in solution because they require structural organization, such as electron transfer and respiratory enzyme systems or fatty acid synthesis. An excellent illustration is the substructural formations required for the vital function of nucleic acids.

Even intermediary metabolism, which had been studied for a long time largely with isolated enzyme systems, depends to a large extent on factors which only in recent years have become the subject of intensive investigations, such as metabolic feedback control mechanisms (Yates and Pardee, 1956; Umbarger, 1964; Atkinson, 1965), allosteric effects (Monod and Jacob, 1961), and spatial relationships. The development shows that all the information obtained in solution, although essential and important, leaves us still ignorant of many of the events affecting and modulating the reactions when they take place in a cellular or sub-cellular structure. A novel type of study of the effects of environment are the observations of Ephraim Katchalski and his associates (Levin *et al.*, 1964; Goldstein *et al.*, 1964) on the activities of an enzyme to which long-chain synthetic charged polymers are attached. When the enzyme is surrounded by this kind of a "Faraday cage," striking modifications of reactivity were observed, although these systems are still simplified when compared to the conditions of the living cell or even to those in a sub-cellular structure, such as a membrane.

These developments have brought about a great change in our thinking and attitude toward studying proteins and enzymes. Information about their properties must be obtained not only in solution, but within their natural environment and structure. The importance of such studies has become of a significance equal to that of studies of pure proteins in solution. Both aspects are essential for the understanding of the proper-ties and function of a macromolecule. The value of studies on reactions within a cellular or subcellular structure depends, however, to a large extent on the conditions under which the analysis takes place. In view of the complexity of living cells, there is frequently an interference by too many factors, whereby the interpretation and quantitative evaluation become difficult sometimes to a degree which may make them meaning-less for the protein chemist. However, sometimes structural preparations and conditions may be obtained, especially of subcellular structures, such as membranes of mitochondria, where interference by other factors is limited and does permit testing of reactions of proteins or enzymes in their natural environment.

The complications by structure are limited to a remarkable degree in the monocellular electroplax preparation, especially at the level of the junctions, where the excitable membrane is poorly, if at all, protected. Thus, the electrical parameters offer a remarkably sensitive indicator of the interaction with the receptor protein and its relation to the primary function. ACh and related compounds may react with the receptor in

10^{-6} to 10^{-8} M concentration, an affinity of the order of magnitude of tightly bound coenzymes, or competitive and potent inhibitors reacting with an enzyme in solution. The assumption of a direct interaction is further supported by the fact that some very minor and specific modifications of molecular structure parallel the interaction with the receptor in a way similar to that observed with ACh-esterase in solution, although other modifications have a different effect, as would be expected from a protein reacting with the same molecular structure, but having a different type of function. It appears probable, therefore, that the reaction with ACh and related compounds tested with this preparation represents essentially that with the specific protein and that the interference by other factors is essentially due to the fact that the biological action takes place within a structure and not in solution. Many differences in the properties may be attributed to this particular condition intrinsically related to the biological function. The reactions of the protein within the intact membrane are, therefore, of real interest to the protein chemist concerned with the properties and function of this protein.

Determination of Dissociation Constants with the Receptor

Applying the method of recording steady-state potentials, the reactions of compounds have been analyzed with a satisfactory degree of precision as a function of concentration and used for determining dissociation constants according to the usual Michaelis-Menten type of analysis (Higman et al., 1963). Thus, the dissociation constant K for a compound A (activator), reacting with a receptor, R, is:

$$K_A = \frac{[R][A]}{[R \cdot A]}$$

and of a competitive inhibitor measured by its potency to diminish the response of an activator is:

$$K_I = \frac{[I][A]}{[A'] - [A]}$$

where $[A']$ and $[A]$ represent concentrations of the activator which elicits the same response in the presence and absence, respectively, of a concentration $[I]$ of the inhibitor.

Equal responses probably correspond to the occupancy of the equal number of receptor sites, although it is possible that the strength of the response may not be proportional to the fraction of sites occupied by the activator or inhibitor. This is even likely, except for a very narrow range of concentrations. If the relationship is linear, the maximum response, r_{max}, would be expressed by

$$K_A = \left(\frac{r_{max}}{r} - 1 \right) [A]$$

and

$$r = \frac{r_{max} [A]}{K_A + [A]}$$

where [A] is free concentration of A at equilibrium, and r is response produced by [A]. It appears unlikely that the maximum response requires that all the receptor sites are occupied by A; however, this question can not be answered at present.

Theoretically, the response would be hyperbolically related to the activator concentration. However, in biological systems a response is usually obtained only after the activator concentration has reached a certain threshold value. Thus,

$$r + a = \frac{r_{max} [A]}{K_A + [A]}$$

where a is a constant and may be determined graphically from a simple plot of r versus [A]. Once a is determined, r_{max} and K_A may be readily calculated. It may be stressed that similar equations have been frequently applied to pharmacological effects used for evaluating dissociation constants (see, e.g., Ariens et al., 1960; Ariens, 1964; Gaddum, 1943). However, these pharmacological effects were usually evaluated on rather complex biological materials, such as nerve muscle preparations, rat diaphragm, frogs rectus abdominis, and guinea pig ileum. In such preparations a secondary event, muscular contraction, is recorded, whereas on the electroplax preparation the primary event is measured. Moreover, the usual preparations are quite sensitive to pH changes; therefore, the pH must be kept within a narrow range. The electroplax preparation permits one to work over a wide pH range, thereby making it possible to evaluate many features of molecular structure that are pH dependent.

Most of the excitable membrane of the innervated surface of the electroplax is protected by structural barriers against quaternary nitrogen derivatives which are capable of reacting with the receptor at the junction only. Dissociation constants can therefore only be determined with compounds reacting exclusively at the junction, since for all others the penetration through the protecting barrier introduces an unknown and unmeasurable component. Although the determination of K for receptor inhibitors is relatively simple and unequivocal, that for activators may be more complicated in those cases where the gradual increase of concentration, after having reached the maximum depolarization, leads to repolarization. The phenomenon is not yet explained; it is possible to think of a bell-shaped curve in respect to the interaction between activator and protein. This effect offers some difficulty for determining the V_{max} of activators on the basis of the degree of depolarization. For all practical purposes the potency of activators can be accurately and adequately evaluated as compared to the potency of other activators by determining the concentration required for a steady-state potential equal to 50% of the initial.

DIFFERENCES AND SIMILARITIES BETWEEN DISSOCIATION CONSTANTS WITH ACETYLCHOLINESTERASE AND ACh-RECEPTOR

Since the ACh-receptor has not yet been isolated, it cannot be claimed with certainty that it is a protein. Such an assumption, however, is strongly supported by indirect evidence. Two members of the ACh system, i.e., the two enzymes ACh-esterase and choline acetylase, which form and hydrolyze the ester, have been isolated and extensively studied *in vitro*. Many compounds reacting specifically with the active site of ACh-esterase show similarities of behavior in their reaction with the ACh-receptor, which are sometimes striking. Sometimes, however, there are also marked differences. The difference of function of the two proteins would lead to the assumption that some groups in the active site of the protein may react with ACh by similar chemical forces, but some others must be different. This difference in function is indeed marked; one reaction triggers off a series of others leading to a permeability change in the membrane, apparently without forming a covalent bond; in the other a covalent bond is formed and the small molecule is hydrolyzed in this process. When the structure of a compound related to ACh is modified, the affinity to the two proteins varies sometimes in the same, sometimes in different, directions. A striking similarity, for instance, is the much stronger reaction of both proteins with quaternary nitrogen derivatives as compared to that with the tertiary analog. This supports the assumption of the presence of an anionic site in both proteins. The role of the extra methyl group on the nitrogen of the small molecule will be discussed later.

Some recent data of Webb (1965) are an illustration of the difference in affinities to receptor and enzyme. He determined the dissociation constants of a series of N,N'-bis(diethylaminopropyl)quinone (benzoquinonium) and N,N'-bis(diethylaminoethyl)oxamide-bisbenzylhalide salts (ambenonium) derivatives with the ACh-receptor on the electroplax preparation with the method outlined above and compared them with those obtained with an active ACh-esterase preparation purified from electric tissue.

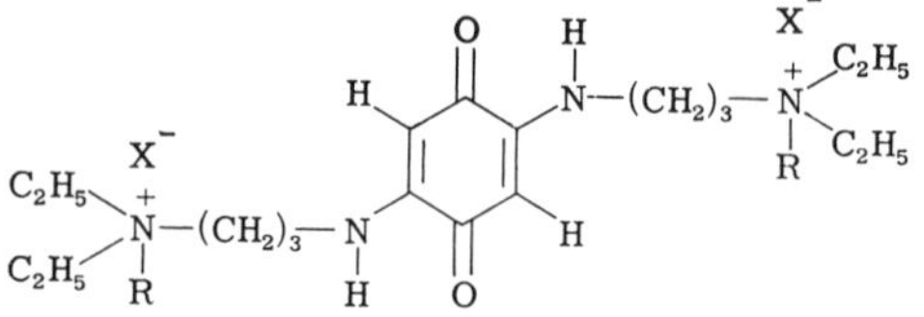

N,N'-bis(diethylaminopropyl)quinones

(I)

In benzoquinonium, R = ⟨benzene⟩—CH₂—

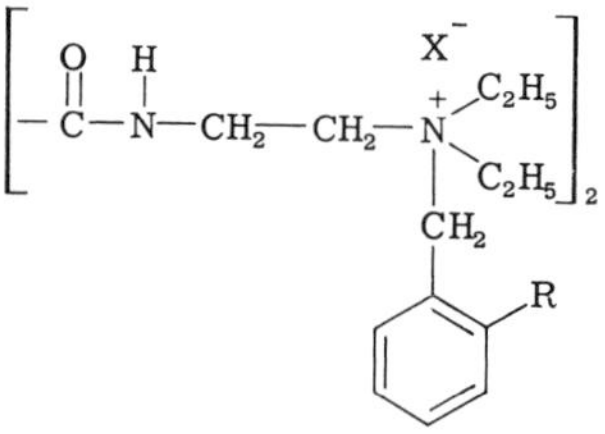

N,N'-bis(diethylaminoethyl)oxamide-bisbenzyl halide

(II)

In ambenonium, R = Cl

As seen in Table I, when R in the benzoquinonium is an ethyl group, the dissociation constants of both receptor and esterase are about equal. Substituting the ethyl by a methyl group hardly affects the affinity to the esterase, but decreases significantly that to the receptor. Substitution of the ethyl by a phenyl group increases affinity to both, but stronger to the receptor than to the esterase. Most pronounced is the effect of the addition of a Cl atom to the phenyl group; in the *ortho* position the affinity to the receptor is hardly affected, that to the enzyme is 6-fold increased, whereas in the *para* position the affinity to both is decreased, but that to the esterase much stronger than that to the receptor.

Still more striking are the differences observed with the ambenonium derivatives. With either Br or Cl on the benzene ring, the affinity to the enzyme is three orders of magnitude greater than to the receptor. Substitution by a proton brings the two affinities very close to each other. It is difficult to attribute these similarities and differences of dissociation constants, observed on the basis of very minor modifications of structure of relatively large molecules, to an entirely different type of molecule. Although one would be inclined to assume a priori that the macromolecule critically involved in the primary cell mechanism, such as perme-

TABLE I

DISSOCIATION CONSTANTS OF BENZOQUINONIUM AND AMBENONIUM DERIVATIVES[a]

R	$K_{\text{ACh-R}}$	$K_{\text{ACh-E}}$	$\dfrac{K_{\text{ACh-R}}}{K_{\text{ACh-E}}}$
Benzoquinonium derivatives			
C_2H_5	3.8×10^{-7}	2.9×10^{-7}	1
CH_3	1.2×10^{-6}	2.6×10^{-7}	5
⟨O⟩—CH_2	1.4×10^{-8}	8.1×10^{-8}	0.2
Cl-⟨O⟩—CH_2—	1.6×10^{-8}	5×10^{-9}	3
Cl—⟨O⟩—CH_2	3.1×10^{-8}	3.2×10^{-7}	0.1
Ambenonium derivatives			
Br	1.2×10^{-6}	2.1×10^{-10}	6000
Cl	1.6×10^{-6}	5.1×10^{-10}	3000
H	3.4×10^{-6}	2.1×10^{-7}	16

[a] Constants with ACh-receptor (ACh-R), tested on the monocellular electroplax preparation, and with ACh-esterase (ACh-E), tested in purified enzyme solution prepared from electric tissue of *Electrophorus*. The last column indicates the strong differences in affinity to the two proteins expressed by the ratio of $K_{\text{ACh-R}}/K_{\text{ACh-E}}$.

ability change of a membrane, would be a protein, as is known to be the case in other primary cellular functions, the experimental evidence just described lends experimental support to this assumption. There are other observations in favor of the view that both components are proteins, but with different active sites. Recent observations of Karlin and Bartels (1966) on the monocellular electroplax preparation have demonstrated a critical involvement of SH and S-S groups in the permeability changes of the excitable membrane induced by ACh and related compounds. Several reactants specific for these groups, such as p-chloromercuribenzoate (PMB) and 1,4-dithiothreitol (DTT), markedly reduce the response.

The effects of PMB may be reversed by subsequent treatment with thiol compounds and those of DTT by oxidizing agents and by cysteine. Washing alone has no effect on the inhibition due to either agent. Since SH and S-S groups are generally associated with proteins, these results lend strong new support to the assumption of a critical role of proteins in the permeability change underlying the depolarization effected by ACh. Further additional support are the studies on the action of sulfur and selenium isologs of ACh, choline and related compounds which will be discussed later.

Conformational Changes of the Receptor Protein

It has been assumed for more than 20 years, although mostly on theoretical basis, that proteins may change their conformation during their interaction with micromolecules. In the last two decades much information has accumulated about primary, secondary, and tertiary structures of protein. Especially X-ray diffraction and the method introduced by Pauling and Corey for the prediction of possible polypeptide conformation led not only to the discovery of the α-helix, but has provided insight into the many forces which play a fundamental role in determining protein structure, such as hydrophobic side chains, hydrogen bonds, and requirements of free energy minimum. The method of X-ray diffraction has been supplemented by a variety of techniques, in particular, optical methods. The complete structure of myoglobin and lysozyme and the partial structure of hemoglobin were elucidated by X-ray analysis (Kendrew 1963, 1964; Perutz 1962; Blake et al., 1965). Experimental evidence was offered for conformational changes taking place during the reaction with oxygen. Conformational changes of proteins during their activity is today a widely accepted notion and a very active area of protein research. It is to be expected that in some reactions such changes may be limited to a small fraction of the protein and not readily detectable. However, with the continuous improvement of instrumentation, even small changes may eventually become measurable. Recently, e.g., it was possible to demonstrate with ORD* and circular dichroism, that by the removal of the heme from myoglobin about 10% of the 154 amino acids of this molecule changed from a helical to a nonhelical form; the process was reversed by the addition of the heme to the apomyoglobin and the amino acids returned to their α-helix form (Breslow et al., 1965).

Conformational changes of a protein as a factor in the permeability

---

* ORD, optical rotary dispersion.

change of excitable membranes were first envisaged by Meyer (1937), although only on a purely hypothetical basis. Such a conformational change may lead to a shift of charge which for a long time has been considered to be an essential factor in the permeability changes (see, e.g., Teorell, 1953). Later it was proposed more specifically that ACh may produce a conformational change of the ACh-receptor protein and that the resulting shift of charge may trigger off the sequence of reactions responsible for the permeability cycle (Nachmansohn, 1955, 1959).

During the last decade a considerable amount of indirect evidence has been obtained supporting the view that conformational changes take place in all three protein members of the system specifically associated with the function of ACh, when they are in an active state, i.e., the receptor and the two enzymes. Kinetic and thermodynamic studies have revealed a striking difference in the reaction of quaternary nitrogen compounds with ACh-esterase as compared to that of their tertiary analogs. For instance, the binding of NH_4 ions to the enzyme increases with each substitution of a protein by a methyl group, owing to van der Waals' forces until three protons are replaced. However, between tri- and tetramethyl ammonium ions there is no difference in binding power (Wilson, 1952). This may be readily explained by the tetrahedral structure of the quaternary compound, since the fourth methyl group is oriented toward the solution and would, therefore, have no close contact with the protein surface, thus being unable to contribute to the binding by van der Waals' forces. In contrast, when the hydrolysis of ACh by ACh-esterase is compared with that of its tertiary analog, the K_3 of the latter is only one-tenth of the former. Such a remarkable increase in hydrolytic efficiency by the presence of one extra methyl group might be explained by a change of conformation of the protein. The rearrangement may enable the protein to carry out the hydrolytic process in a much more effective way. This assumption is supported by the remarkable difference of the entropy of activation of the hydrolytic process catalyzed by ACh-esterase; when the $\Delta S^{\ddagger}$ with ACh is compared to that with its tertiary analog, a very strong difference is observed. Whereas the entropy of activation is negative with the tertiary, it is very favorable and positive with the quaternary group. The difference amounts to about 30 to 40 entropy units (Wilson and Cabib, 1956). This seems to be true even for some other related quaternary esters (Allen M. Gold, unpublished data). This large favorable entropy of activation and the higher rate of hydrolysis of quaternary esters, when catalyzed by the enzyme, appear all the more significant in view of the recent observations of Chu and Mautner (1966), that the nonenzymatic hydrolysis of the tertiary ester is much faster than that of the quaternary analog. Thus, the actual difference of efficiency between the enzyme-catalyzed hydrolysis of tertiary and quaternary compounds seems to be much greater than is apparent simply on the basis of the comparison of the two enzymatic reactions.

A similar difference of catalytic efficiency between quaternary and tertiary analogs has been observed with choline acetylase, the enzyme

TABLE II

COMPARISON OF THE POTENCY OF SOME ACh ANALOGS[a]

Compound	Concentration (M)
$CH_3-\overset{\overset{\displaystyle CH_3}{\oplus\mid}}{\underset{\underset{\displaystyle CH_3}{\mid}}{N}}-CH_2-CH_2-O-\overset{(+)}{\underset{\underset{\displaystyle CH_3}{\mid}}{C}}-O^{(-)}$	5×10^{-6}
$CH_3-\overset{\overset{\displaystyle CH_3}{\oplus\mid}}{\underset{\underset{\displaystyle H}{\mid}}{N}}-CH_2-CH_2-O-\overset{(+)}{\underset{\underset{\displaystyle CH_3}{\mid}}{C}}-O^{(-)}$	1×10^{-3}
$CH_3-\overset{\overset{\displaystyle H}{\oplus\mid}}{\underset{\underset{\displaystyle H}{\mid}}{N}}-CH_2-CH_2-O-\overset{(+)}{\underset{\underset{\displaystyle CH_3}{\mid}}{C}}-O^{(-)}$	2.5×10^{-2}
$CH_3-\overset{\overset{\displaystyle CH_3}{\oplus\mid}}{\underset{\underset{\displaystyle CH_3}{\mid}}{As}}-CH_2-CH_2-O-\overset{(+)}{\underset{\underset{\displaystyle CH_3}{\mid}}{C}}-O^{(-)}$	1×10^{-4}

[a] The potency is compared on the basis of molar concentrations required for blocking the direct and indirect response within comparable periods of exposure time, usually 3 to 5 minutes. For details, see Bartels (1962).

which transfers the acetyl group from acetyl-CoA to choline. The rate of acetylation of choline is about twelve times as high as that of dimethylethanolamine.

If one assumes that the conformational change of the receptor protein is an essential factor in increasing permeability, then the depolarizing potency would reflect the ability of a compound of inducing the conformation. Comparing the potency of the depolarizing action of ACh with that of its tertiary analog on the monocellular electroplax preparation, Bartels (1962) found a 250-fold decrease owing to the removal of the extra methyl group (Table II). It would be difficult to attribute such a striking difference only to van der Waals' forces due to the presence of one extra methyl group or to Coulombic forces, since at the pH used in the experiments, most of the molecules of the tertiary analog are in cationic form. In view of the observations on the enzyme activities in the presence and absence of the extra methyl group on the nitrogen, the assumption of conformational changes seems to be the most likely explanation. If a second methyl group is removed, the difference between two and three methyl groups is less than 20-fold. For such a difference, van der Waals' forces may be partly responsible. The sensitivity of the preparation to a modification of chemical structure is so high that a 20-fold decrease of potency is observed if the quaternary ammonium is substituted by a quaternary arsonium, although charge, dimension, and shape of the two molecules are quite similar.

Local Anesthetics

An interesting illustration of the usefulness and versatility of the monocellular electroplax preparation is the analysis of the molecular features by which ACh is transformed into a so-called local anesthetic (Bartels, 1965; Bartels and Nachmansohn, 1965). Procaine, tetracaine, and similar local anesthetics are analogous in structure to ACh and have been shown to be competitive inhibitors of the ACh-receptor; they are typical antimetabolites. This is of general interest in respect to the problem of the role of ACh in excitable membranes. It is well known that these compounds block electrical activity in all types of excitable membranes; if the effect is due to competition with ACh for the active site of the ACh-receptor, it follows that electrical activity cannot be dissociated from the reaction between ACh and the receptor. Thus, the protein is just as essential for the permeability cycle as was previously shown for ACh-esterase with the use of potent, specific, and competitive inhibitors.

Procaine and tetracaine differ from ACh in their action on the excitable membrane in two respects. (1) They are receptor inhibitors, i.e., unlike ACh or other activators, they react with the active site, but are unable to induce the conformational change postulated by theory. (2) They are capable of penetrating the structural permeability barriers surrounding the conducting membrane, which permits them to react with the receptor. By blocking the active site of the receptor to the ACh released intracellularly, they prevent excitation and propagation—hence, their action as local anesthetics. The electroplax preparation permits the separate analysis of the two properties by which local anesthetics are distinguished from ACh for reasons discussed before.

The analysis of the action of great number of compounds in which

TABLE III
SOME MODIFICATIONS OF CHEMICAL STRUCTURE ILLUSTRATING THE TRANSFORMATION OF ACh[a]

Compound	Synaptic junctions		Conducting membrane
	Activator	Inhibitor	

Acetylcholine — Activator: 2.5×10^{-6}, Inhibitor: 0, Conducting membrane: 0

Hexahydrobenzoylcholine — Activator: 5×10^{-4}, Inhibitor: 0, Conducting membrane: 0

Benzoylcholine — Activator: 5×10^{-4}, Inhibitor: 5×10^{-4}, Conducting membrane: 1×10^{-3}

p-Aminobenzoylcholine — Activator: 0, Inhibitor: 1×10^{-3}, Conducting membrane: 2.5×10^{-3}

Procaine — Activator: 0, Inhibitor: 2.5×10^{-4}, Conducting membrane: 5×10^{-4}

Tetracainemethiodide — Activator: 0, Inhibitor: 2×10^{-5}, Conducting membrane: 1×10^{-5}

either the quaternary ammonium or the ester-containing group of ACh was systematically modified, has provided a large amount of information about the molecular features responsible for the two different properties. When, for instance, the methyl group on the carbonyl group is substituted by a saturated benzyl ring, the potency of the compound as an activator is decreased about 200-fold compared to that of ACh. But it is still an activator and acts at the synaptic junction only, i.e., the compound is unable to reach the receptor in the conducting membrane even if applied in high concentrations (Table III). However, the same compound, but with the small modification that an unsaturated ring is substituted for the saturated one, benzoylcholine, may be already partly activator, partly inhibitor according to experimental conditions. When applied, for instance, to the electroplax together with carbamylcholine, the effect of hexahydrobenzoylcholine is additive, that of benzoylcholine, on the other hand, is antagonistic. Morover, in relatively high concentrations, 10^{-3} M, benzoylcholine acts on the conducting membrane. Thus, benzoylcholine is a typical transitory form in structure as well as in action between acetylcholine and the local anesthetics. Addition of an NH_2 group to the phenyl group in *para* position transforms the analog into a receptor inhibitor and increases the penetrating ability; thus, the molecule has acquired the two features characteristic of a local anesthetic. Both inhibitory potency and ability of penetration are greatly increased when the three methyl groups of the quaternary nitrogen are replaced by two ethyl groups (procaine). A still greater enhancement of both properties is achieved by substituting one proton of the NH_2 group by a butyl (tetracaine). Substitution of the methyl groups on the nitrogen also changes both depolarizing potency and ability of penetration; substitution

---

[a] The transformation of ACh involves changing a receptor activator acting on synaptic junctions only, into a receptor inhibitor acting on junctions as well as on the receptor in the conducting membrane (so-called "local anesthetic"). Substitution of the methyl group of the acyl by a saturated ring decreases the activating (depolarizing) potency by a factor of 200. But the compound is still an activator and acts on the junction only. With an unsaturated ring (benzoylcholine) the compound becomes a transitory form; it may act, according to experimental conditions, either as a weak activator or as a weak inhibitor, and its acts on the conducting membrane, although only in high concentrations. By the addition of an NH_2 group to the phenyl ring the compound is transformed into a "local anesthetic," acting only as an inhibitor at the junctions, but acting also on the conducting membrane. Both effects may be greatly enhanced by small additional modifications: substitution of the three methyl groups on the quaternary N by two ethyl groups (procaine) or substitution of one proton of the NH_2 group by a butyl (tetracaine methiodide). The latter is a very potent "local anesthetic." The molar concentrations indicate the comparable potency.

of one methyl by one ethyl group decreases the depolarizing effect four to five times; substitution of two methyl by two ethyl groups 100 to 200 times. Both compounds act on the junction only. The triethyl analog of ACh, however, is already a transitory form like benzoylcholine. Its depolarizing action is insignificant. It antagonizes the depolarizing action of the carbamylcholine at the junction. In high concentrations it blocks the direct response, i.e., it penetrates the structural barriers, although poorly. Both effects, at the junction and at the conducting membrane, are weaker than those obtained with benzoylcholine.

SULFUR AND SELENIUM ISOLOGS OF ACh, CHOLINE, AND RELATED COMPOUNDS

A novel way of studying the reaction of the ACh-receptor and the characteristic of its active site has become possible by the availability of sulfur and selenium isologs of ACh, choline, benzoylcholine, and related compounds synthesized by Mautner and his associates. Molecular size and shape of these isologs are similar and therefore their ability to fit the active receptor site should not differ markedly. However, kinetic, spectroscopic, and dipole moment measurements of isologous esters indicate that electron distribution may be quite different (Mautner and Guenther, 1961; Mautner et al., 1963). Scott and Mautner (1964) observed that the pharmacological effects on guinea pig ileus and frog rectus abdominus preparations were affected when the O, S, and Se stereoisomers were compared. In view of the complexity of the preparation used, these results were, however, more of a qualitative than of a quantitative nature.

The monocellular electroplax preparation, thanks to the special features discussed previously, offers an unusually favorable possibility to test the effect of these isologs on the receptor and to evaluate quantitatively the difference between these isologs especially as to their ability to induce conformational changes. Such studies may help to find out how differences of electron distribution of stereoisomers may affect the reaction with the protein. Investigations of this type have been initiated by (Mautner et al., 1966; Rosenberg et al., 1966). Some of the results obtained may be mentioned.

One of the most striking observations is the remarkable difference between choline and its S isolog, cholinethiol. Choline, even in 10^{-1} M concentration, is virtually unable to produce a depolarization, i.e., in about 40,000-fold concentration of that at which ACh has a strong depolarizing action. In contrast, the S isolog has only a slightly less depolarizing effect than ACh itself; at 5×10^{-5} M the effect is about equal to that of ACh at 3×10^{-6} M. It is biologically, of course, desirable, for an extremely rapid and reversible trigger action, that the hydrolytic product should be as inactive as possible. But it is surprising and at present difficult to explain, what the basis of the extraordinary lack of activity of choline is, although it is apparent that the oxygen atom is responsible. Although the S atom has a higher electron density, it is not the better binding of the anionic form to which the potency can be attributed, since replacement of a proton by a methyl group increases the effect; methylcholinethiol is more than twice as potent as cholinethiol. Moreover, since the preparation is not affected by changes of pH over a wide range, the depolarizing activity of cholinethiol, which has a pK_a of 7.7 (Heilbronn, 1958), was tested at 6.2, where only 3% is ionized, and at 9, where 95% is ionized. The compound was found to be more active at the lower pH, i.e., in its mercaptan, rather than in its mercaptide form. The methyl group apparently contributes to the binding by hydrophobic bonds, since both methyloxycholine and methylselenocholine are more potent than the corresponding protonated forms. Methoxycholine is still the weakest of the methylated compounds, whereas the selenol isolog is the strongest. The remarkable decrease of potency owing to the presence of the O atom in the position which it has in choline also becomes apparent from other modifications. When, for instance, the three-carbon analog is used, $(CH_3)_3N(CH_2)_3OH$, it is much more potent than choline itself, although even in this case the S isolog is more potent than the S isolog of choline; in fact, its depolarizing power becomes nearly as strong as that of ACh itself (Mautner and Webb, 1966).

In looking for an explanation for this peculiar lack of activity of the oxygen, it is of interest that substitution of the O (or S and Se) atom by a methyl group greatly increases the reactivity. Tetramethyl ammonium ion depolarizes, although it is 100 times weaker than ACh, but it is several hundred times stronger than choline. However, trimethylethyl-, propyl-, and butylammonium ions are, in this order, increasingly stronger depolarizing agents, the trimethylbutyl ammonium is as strong as ACh (T. Podleski, 1966). The bisquaternary ammonium with ten methane groups between the two nitrogens, the decamethonium, is also as active as ACh itself. These data make it apparent that the active site of the protein must be different from that of ACh-esterase. There is quite obviously a similar "anionic" site reacting with the cationic quaternary nitrogen group, but the "esteratic" site is different. There is some equivalent of the esteratic site in the receptor, since the potency of the tetramethyl ammonium ion is markedly smaller than that of cholinethiol or of the compounds where the methyl is replaced by ethyl or butyl. Since the latter equals that of ACh, but does not have the ester group capable of forming a covalent bond, Mautner has proposed to refer to this site tentatively as to a hydrophobic bonding site. While hydrophobic bonding appears to be an important factor in the interaction between activator and receptor, additional forces seem to be involved. Trimethylpentylammonium ion is markedly weaker than the trimethylbutyl ion. The complexity of the forces in the reaction with the receptor protein inducing the postulated conformational change is also apparent from the observations of Podleski (1966) with a series of aryl ammonium and isomeric quinolinium derivatives, in which he compared the reactions with the receptor on the electroplax to those with ACh-esterase in solution. Although the anionic group in the active site of both proteins appears to be similar, the nature of the molecular forces acting in the neighborhood of the anionic group in the receptor remains unclear.

Although the choline isologs increase in potency by the substitution of the oxygen atom by S and Se, the opposite is true for the esters. Ach is a markedly more effective receptor activator than acetylthiocholine or acetylselenocholine. These widely different potencies of the three stereoisomeric esters is another support for the difference between the active site of the enzyme and that of the receptor, because the hydrolysis rates of the esters catalyzed by the enzyme are similar. Moreover, the interesting feature emerges from these studies that the biological ester is by far the most active of the three isologs, its hydrolytic product the most inactive.

It may be mentioned that cholinethiol and cholineselenol are readily oxidized and form disulfied and diselenol compounds. The rapid rate of formation of the latter compound makes the quantitative evaluation of the activity of cholineselenol difficult. The oxidation products have a slight blocking effect, but only in concentrations higher than those used in these tests.

The study of the O, S, and Se isologs is still in an early phase. More data are required for permitting the evaluation of the effects of electronic distribution compared to molecular size and shape. But it is apparent that the analysis of stereoisomers may provide not only useful information for the interaction of these molecules with proteins, but may also open an entirely new field and provide a tool for changing the biological activity of compounds used in pharmacodynamics.

PERSPECTIVES

The isolation and analysis of a protein is essential for the understanding of many of its properties, but for reasons discussed before, such studies must be supplemented by studying the properties and the function of this protein within the organized cellular or subcellular structure. Among these subcellular structures, membranes, especially those of mitochondria, have attracted, in recent years, the considerable interest of many biochemists. In contrast, the excitable membranes have so far been comparatively neglected by biochemists, in spite of the interest of many physicochemists in artificial membranes with selective ion permeability. One factor may have been the lack of interest of many electrophysiologists in biochemical aspects; some of them still vigorously maintain that electrical activity of excitable membranes may be fully explained by ion movements and that the permeability changes during activity are a purely physical event, a simple diffusion process (see, for instance, Baker *et al.*, 1962; Keynes and Aubert, 1964; Eccles, 1957). This attitude certainly did not encourage biochemists, who otherwise might have been tempted, to investigate the biochemical basis of the activity of these membranes. The elaborate techniques and the complicated electronic equipment required for such studies are not easily available to biochemists without active cooperation of electrophysiologists.

There are, however, also intrinsic difficulties of which many biologists were, and still are, unaware. Excitable membranes are usually surrounded by large, protective structural barriers. Even in the so-called unmyelinated squid giant axon, one of the most widely used preparations by electrophysiologists, the excitable membrane (100 Å) is surrounded by a layer of Schwann cell several thousand Ångstroms thick. This is not surprising from a teleological point of view; nature protects excitable membranes by structures which form a strong barrier for most compounds which may otherwise trigger off too easily the excitatory process and thereby readily interfere with thousands of precise signals carried over a long distance. But these barriers create serious difficulties for the chemical study of the reactions taking place in the excitable membrane proper. Only at the junction between two cells the excitable membranes are poorly or not at all protected. This again is teleologically not surprising, since at these points strong barriers would make difficult the propagation of the impulse across the junction. The adjustment of the process to the needs of the cell at these junctions, such as one-way direction, is apparently effected by modifications of shape, structure, and organization, although other additional factors may be involved, e.g., chemical modulators (Nachmansohn, 1966). It is not an accident that since the middle of the last century the use of classic methods of pharmacology has revealed the powerful actions of curare, ACh, and a great variety of other compounds acting on the excitable membranes at the level of the junctions only. Since these powerful actions were observed only there, the limitation was for a long time interpreted as indicating that the junctions are the only site of action and that the properties of the excitable membranes there are different. This was the basis for the view of the role of ACh as a mediator between two cells. For the biochemist, however, the junctions are not a suitable material, since they are usually not readily accessible and the events taking place there are, for a variety of reasons, of a very complex nature.

The monocellular electroplax preparation offers a unique material for the biochemist for studying specific reactions with the ACh-receptor, primarily linked with the permeability change, since this cell is specialized for bioelectrogenesis, i.e., the result of the activity of the excitable membrane. The electrical parameters in this preparation are recorded directly and not, as in many other preparations, by a secondary event elicited by the electrical activity. The highly sensitive techniques developed permit accumulation of valuable information about direct reaction with the receptor and their relationships with function. Specific reactions with special cellular components in the intact cell were frequently used by biochemists in the past for characterizing specific properties of these components. A classic example are the observations of Otto Warburg applying optical methods for the study of the heme of the "Atmungsferment" in the intact cell long before the electron-transfer system was discovered and understood. His studies laid the foundation and provided important clues for many later developments.

The preparation described offers, in addition, the best promise to find reactions which may lead to the isolation and purification of the receptor protein and thus eventually provide the necessary complementary information. Studies are in progress with the aim to find specific groups in the receptor which may form covalent bonds with micromolecules applied to the electroplax. Such compounds may then be used as markers for isolation. Some selenium-containing analogs of ACh appear, for instance, to react with the receptor irreversibly. Use of radioactive isotopes of such type of compounds or of chromophores of high affinity combined with a variety of other methods may be helpful in achieving the isolation.

Work is at present in progress to obtain adequate amounts of pure and possibly crystalline ACh-esterase for analyzing its structure, including optical and X-ray analyses, especially in reference to possible conformational changes. Assuming that the receptor too will be eventually isolated and subjected to a similar analysis, the information obtained as to the function of the receptor would still remain incomplete. How do these conformational changes of a protein and the resulting shift of charge effect the permeability change of the membrane? The altered arrangement of charges in the organized protein network may itself be primarily responsible for the altered permeability. However, the shift of charges may induce some additional reactions; it may lead, for instance, to the binding (or release) of Ca ions by carboxyl groups. There seems to be some reason to believe that Ca ions may play a role in the chain of events. They may interact with phospholipids, lipoproteins, or other polyelectrolytes. These interactions may be involved in the accelerated flows of Na or K ions. Studies on the sequence of events resulting from the ACh-protein interaction require an intact membrane preparation, such as the electroplax.

Progress of science depends on a combination of a great variety of factors: new concepts, imagination, development of new methods and instrumentation, and many others. One of the elements that has frequently contributed to the progress in the past is a profound analysis of basic principles which begins to emerge from the accumulation of a wide variety of information. Such an analysis may serve as a guideline and stimulation for future endeavors. As an illustration may be mentioned Otto Meyerhof's well-known lecture "Zur Energetik der Zellvorgaenge," which he gave in 1913 as Privatdozent in Kiel and which greatly influenced contemporary thinking. It is perhaps not quite accidental that a quarter of a century later an article of great impact was written by Fritz Lipmann, who had once been associated with Otto Meyerhof, in which he integrated the newly acquired knowledge of energy-rich phosphorylated compounds in terms of their basic role in biochemical reactions and the fundamental principles underlying energy transformations. It is a pleasure for the author, a colleague and friend since the years spent together in Meyerhof's laboratory, to contribute this chapter to the dedicatory volume.

REFERENCES

Abbott, B. C., Hill, A. V., and Howarth, J. V. (1958). *Proc. Roy. Soc. (London)* **B148**, 149.

Abbott, B. C., Howarth, J. V., and Ritchie, J. M. (1965). *J. Physiol. (London)* **178**, 368.

Altamirano, M., Schleyer, W. L., Coates, C. W., and Nachmansohn, D. (1955). *Biochim. Biophys. Acta* **16**, 268.

Ariens, E. J. (1964). "Molecular Pharmacology." Academic Press, New York.

Ariens, E. J., van Rossum, J. M., and Koopman, P. C. (1960). *Arch. Intern. Pharmacodyn.* **120**, 459.

Atkinson, D. E. (1965). *Science* **150**, 851.

Baker, P. F., Hodgkin, A. L., and Shaw, T. I. (1962). *J. Physiol. (London)* **164**, 355.

Barrnett, R. J. (1962). *J. Cell Biol.* **12**, 247.

Bartels, E. (1962). *Biochim. Biophys. Acta* **63**, 365.

Bartels, E. (1965). *Biochim. Biophys. Acta* **109**, 194.

Bartels, E., and Nachmansohn, D. (1965). *Biochem. Z.* **342**, 359.

Beychok, S. (1965). *Biochem. Pharmacol.* **14**, 1249.

Blake, C. C. F., Koenig, D. F., Mair, G. A., North, A. C. T., Phillips, D. C., and Sarma, V. R. (1965). *Nature (London)* **206**, 757.

Breslow, E., Beychok, S., Hardman, K. D., and Gurd, F.R.N. (1965). *J. Biol. Chem.* **240**, 304.

Chu, S. H., and Mautner, H. C. (1966). *J. Org. Chem.* **31**, 308.

Clark, A. J. (1937). In "Handbuch der Experimentellen Pharmakologie" (W. Heubner and J. Schueller, eds.), Vol. IV, 228 pp. Springer, Berlin.

Dettbarn, W.-D., Rosenberg, P., and Nachmansohn, D. (1964). *Life Sciences* **3**, 55.

Eccles, J. C. (1957). "The Physiology of Nerve Cells," 270 pp. Johns Hopkins Press, Baltimore, Maryland.

Ehrenpreis, S. (1960). *Biochim. Biophys. Acta* **44**, 561.

Fernandez-Moran, H., Oda, T., Blair, P. V., and Green, D. E. (1964). *J. Cell Biol.* **22**, 63.

Gaddum, J. H. (1943). *Trans. Faraday Soc.* **39**, 323.

Goldstein, L., Levin, Y., and Katchalski, E. (1964). *Biochemistry* **3**, 1913.

Heilbronn, E. (1958). *Acta Chem. Scand.* **12**, 1492.

Higman, H. B., and Bartels, E. (1961). *Biochim. Biophys. Acta* **54**, 543.

Higman, H. B., and Bartels, E. (1962). *Biochim. Biophys. Acta* **57**, 77.

Higman, H. B., Podleski, T. R., and Bartels, E. (1963). *Biochim. Biophys. Acta* **75**, 187.

Higman, H. B., Podleski, T. R., and Bartels, E. (1964). *Biochim. Biophys. Acta* **79**, 138.

Hodgkin, A. L. (1951). *Biol. Rev. Cambridge Phil. Soc.* **26**, 338.

Karlin, A. (1965). *J. Cell Biol.* **25**, 159.

Karlin, A., and Bartels, E. (1966). *Biochim. Biophys. Acta* (in press).

Kendrew, J. C. (1963). *Brookhaven Symp. Biol.* **15**, 216.

Kendrew, J. C. (1964). In "New Perspectives in Biology" (M. Sela, ed.), pp. 18-27.

Kewitz, H., Wilson, I. B., and Nachmansohn, E. (1956). *Arch. Biochem. Biophys.* **64**, 456.

Keynes, R. D., and Aubert, X. (1964). *Nature* **203**, 261.

Lawler, H. C. (1961). *J. Biol. Chem.* **236**, 2296.

Levin, Y., Pecht, M., Goldstein, L., and Katchalski, E. (1964). *Biochemistry* **3**, 1905.

Lynen, F. (1964). *In* "New Perspectives in Biology" (M. Sela, ed.), pp. 132-146, Elsevier, Amsterdam.

Mautner, H. G., and Guenther, W. H. H. (1961). *J. Am. Chem. Soc.* **83**, 3342.

Mautner, H. G., and Webb, G. D. (1966). *Biochem. Pharmacol.* (in press).

Mautner, H. G., Chu, S. H., and Guenther, W. H. H. (1963). *J. Am. Chem. Soc.* **85**, 3458.

Mautner, H. G., Bartels, E., and Webb, G. D. (1966). *Biochem. Pharmacol.* **15**, 187.

Meyer, K. H. (1937). *Helvet. Chim. Acta* **20**, 634.

Monod, J., and Jacob, F. (1961). *Cold Spring Harbor Symp. Quant. Biol.* **26**, 389.

Nachmansohn, D. (1955). *Harvey Lectures* (1953–1954), 57-99.

Nachmansohn, D. (1959). "Chemical and Molecular Basis of Nerve Activity," 235 pp. Academic Press, New York.

Nachmansohn, D. (1964*a*). In "New Perspectives in Biology" (M. Sela, ed.), pp. 176-204. Elsevier, Amsterdam.

Nachmansohn, D. (1964*b*). *J. M. Sinai Hosp. N.Y.* **31**, 549.

Nachmansohn, D. (1965). *Israel J. Med. Sci.* **1**, 1201.

Nachmansohn, D. (1966). *Ann. N.Y. Acad. Sci.* (W. Loewenstein, ed.) **137**, 877.

Nachmansohn, D., and Lederer, E. (1939). *Bull. Soc. Chim. Biol.* **21**, 797.

Nachmansohn, D., and Wilson, I. B. (1951). *Advan. Enzymol.* **12**, 259-339.

Perutz, M. F. (1962). "Proteins and Nucleic Acids: Structure and Function," 211 pp. Elsevier, Amsterdam.

Podleski, T. R. (1966). Doctor Dissertation, Columbia University, N.Y.

Robertson, J. D. (1960*a*). *Progr. Biophys. Biophys. Chem.* **10**, 343.

Robertson, J. D. (1960*b*). *In* "Molecular Biology" (D. Nachmansohn, ed.), pp. 87-151. Academic Press, New York.

Rosenberg, P., Mautner, H. C., and Nachmansohn, D. (1966). *Proc. Nat. Acad. Sciences* **55**, 835.

Rothenberg, M. A., and Nachmansohn, D. (1947). *J. Biol. Chem.* **168**, 223.

Schoffeniels, E. (1957). *Biochim. Biophys. Acta* **26**, 585.

Schoffeniels, E. (1959). Thèse d'agrégation, Université de Liège, Liège.

Schoffeniels, E., and Nachmansohn, D. (1957). *Biochim. Biophys. Acta* **26**, 1.

Scott, K. A., and Mautner, H. G. (1964). *Biochem. Pharmacol.* **13**, 907.

Sjöstrand, F. S. (1963). *J. Ultrastruct. Res.* **9**, 561.

Teorell, T. (1953). *Progr. Biophys. and Biophys. Chem.* **3**, 305.

Umbarger, H. E. (1964). *Science* **145**, 674.

Webb, G. D. (1965). *Biochim. Biophys. Acta* **102**, 172.

Wilson, I. B. (1952). *J. Biol. Chem.* **197**, 215.

Wilson, I. B., and Cabib, E. (1956). *J. Am. Chem. Soc.* **78**, 202.

Yates, R. A., and Pardee, A. B. (1956). *J. Biol. Chem.* **221**, 757.

Some Biochemical Aspects of Epigenesis*

W. F. Loomis

INTRODUCTION

I am more than glad to write a chapter for a volume commemorating Fritz Lipmann's great article of 1941 on the high-energy phosphate bond. Working in his laboratory shortly after World War II was a scientific turning point in my life. Before that, I had worked with David Green on the respiration, but not the phosphorylation, of mitochondria (Green *et al.*, 1948). Since adenosine triphosphate (ATP) did not accumulate in these early preparation of "cyclophorase," it was not known whether this oxidative power could be turned into ATP. I can still remember the day when Fritz Lipmann suggested that I try adding some yeast hexokinase that he had in his deepfreeze to see whether the hexokinase reaction could not trap the newly made $\sim$P before adenosinetriphosphatase (ATPase) could degrade it back to adenosine monophosphate (AMP). Needless to say, this reaction worked (Loomis and Lipmann, 1948) and a phosphate to oxygen ratio of 2:2 was demonstrated. When Lipmann then suggested that this first mitochondrial system able to phosphorylate might be used to show that dinitrophenol uncoupled oxidation from phosphorylation, an experiment was run that afternoon that was later published exactly as it came off the manometers (Loomis and Lipmann, 1948). These examples of the fertile imagination of Fritz Lipmann are all the more remarkable since he was not engaged in this problem at that time but instead was focusing singlemindedly on the structure and function of coenzyme A.

About this time I was asked to teach a course at Massachusetts Institute of Technology on experimental embryology and it was this piece of

---

* Publication No. 444 from the Graduate Department of Biochemistry, Brandeis University, Waltham, Massachusetts.

serendipity that focused my interest on trying to apply biochemistry to the miraculous process of embryological development in general and cellular differentiation in particular. In a later section I will briefly describe why the primitive coelenterate *Hydra* was chosen as an experimental animal with which to pursue this work. Before doing so however, I would like to present the problem posed by the epigenetic process of cellular differentiation in some of its broader aspects.

THE PROBLEM OF EPIGENESIS

Understanding the phenomenon of cellular differentiation has become one of the major objectives of modern biochemical research. Translated into biochemical terms, this involves an understanding of the chemical nature of the various inducers and repressors that mask and unmask different sections of the constant deoxyribonucleic acid (DNA) genome within a developing organism so that different phenotypes appear from one genotype.

Cellular differentiation, in other words, involves not only all the complexities of quantitative growth as seen, for example, in a growing bacterial clone, but also those processes that result in qualitative change within the cellular population. To use a crude analogy, it is as if a penny were to reproduce itself until a raft of a thousand pennies was produced when, suddenly, a nickel were to appear within the center of the raft, grow into a cluster of nickels, in the center of which a dime appears once a critical mass of nickels and/or pennies have been produced by undifferentiated growth.

An explanation of this seemingly miraculous process was proposed by August Weismann in 1892. He suggested that different chromosomes and chromosome pieces were broken off the original full complement of the fertilized ovum and handed, one at a time, to the daughter cells who then had fates wholly determined by which chromosomal piece they happened to receive. This theory was soon shown false by experimental tests that, in essence, showed that any penny could differentiate into a nickel if it were placed within the center of a penny-raft as described above.

The fact that all pennies had within them the unexpressed genomes sufficient to make nickels and dimes gradually become clear to experimental embryologists, as well as the fact that the nucleus of cells even in advanced tissues such as the endoderm of swimming tadpoles was as totipotent as a sperm cell in that it could induce a normal tadpole when it alone was artificially injected into a *Xenopus* egg whose own nucleus had been previously removed (Gurdon, 1962).

This dramatic experiment confirmed the earlier experiments of Driesch, Spemann, and Briggs and King in showing that embryological development was *not* a genetic process in the Mendel-T. H. Morgan sense but was something beyond normal genetics; an epiphenomenon added on to the already complex process of heredity and labeled "epigenetics" by Driesch before the turn of the century. Unfortunately this name for ignorance has often only added to the confusion, for until genetics was understood, something "beyond it" was not very meaningful.

The difference between genetic and epigenetic variation lies chiefly in two areas. *De novo* genetic change by and large consists of random mutational changes in the genome, whereas epigenetic events are non-random, highly repeatable phenotypic developments within a population of tissue cells rather than of sexually breeding organisms. X-Rays, UV, and other mutagenic agents, for example, increase the randomly directed genetic mutations studied in *Drosophila, Escherichia coli*, etc.; these same agents do not speed up embryogenesis but instead interfere with its orderly progression by producing monsters similar to those produced by the drug thalidomide.

"Epigenetic" today means therefore the orderly expression of different parts of the genotype during embryological development so that one cellular phenotype is produced in one place and a second cellular phenotype in another even though both are expressions of one-and-the-same genome. How the multipotent DNA of the zygote is "masked" (as if with masking tape) so that only a small part of its DNA is uncovered and able to make messenger ribonucleic acid (RNA) in any given cell, is thus one of the central problems of cellular differentiation and embryogenesis. The nature of the masking material (histones?), the control of when and where it will form, the enzymes that strip it off, etc., are thus some of the chemical problems behind the ordered production of a beating heart, an eye primordium, etc., that occur within 48 hours in a developing chicken egg.

SOME MODERN INSIGHTS

Jacob, Monod, and their associates have recently studied the problem of "masking" in a model system in bacteria where differentiation is limited to the biochemical level and never expressed morphologically. Taking the adaptive enzyme region of the single circular chromosome of these organisms—the region that synthesizes β-galactosidase when, and only when, the *E. coli* are grown on lactose—they have shown: (1) that a *z* region synthesizes the enzyme (2) when an operator or *o* gene is turned on (3) by the inactivation of a cytoplasmic repressor (*rep*) (4) released by an *i* or inhibitor gene (5) by externally supplied inducer (lactose or thiomethylgalactoside-TMG) (6) and that the *o* gene not only turns on the *z* gene when derepressed, but also a *y* or permease gene that does not make an enzyme as such but instead somehow induces a permease pump that can concentrate the extracellular inducer inside of the bacterial cell.

This familiar work demonstrates that within as simple a system as this —in bacteria, not metazoan cells—there are at least four kinds of genes at work: enzyme-synthesizing genes, assisting genes such as *y*, operator genes that turn on both *z* and *y*, and inhibitor or repressor-making genes such as *i*. If now further feedback loops are introduced into this system, it is possible to envision cellular differentiation taking place by some such system in which the final product of a *z*-like gene is itself an inducer in a second system, so that a whole chain reaction becomes possible in theory, only the original inducer being extracellular in its origin. "Masking" in such a system therefore would be largely self-controlling in that an external inducer would somehow inactivate a cytoplasmic repressor whose function is to "mask" an operator gene that in turn keeps a whole string of DNA cistrons from becoming unmasked and hence going into action (see Jacob and Monod, 1963).

This tantalizing glimpse into epigenetic mechanisms in bacteria stands nearly alone at the present time. Its relation to true cellular differentiation is weakened by its inducer being an unusual food—lactose—while no such external inducer is needed for a developing egg to differentiate according to its preprogrammed time schedule. What the self-generated inducers are that cause gastrulation or the infolding of the future neural crest are completely unknown today although this may not be the case in 10 years time. The value of this work to epigenesis lies largely in that it provides a model of how differentiation might work in higher animals, and Novick and Weiner (1957) have used this knowledge to produce two stable populations of *E. coli* from one population within a chemostat; only one of the daughter populations containing the enzyme β-galactosidase.

The delicacy of the mechanisms that control which segments of the chromosomal DNA helices will be masked and inoperative is seen in such cases as the *Drosophila* phenocopies described by Goldschmidt

(1955). He showed that a large number of standard mutant types could be copied from one wild-type genome by simply imposing different schedules of temperature treatment on the wild-type larvae at different specific stages of development. Proof that the DNA genome was unaffected by these treatments was provided by the fact that these temperature-induced characteristics were not transmitted sexually to succeeding generations, thus indicating that only the epigenetic programming had been affected and not the basic DNA behind it all.

The picture that emerges from these and similar results (hair pigmentation in the Himalayan rabbit, Sonneborn's mating and serotypes in *Paramecia*, etc.) is one of such incredible complexity that it would seem almost visionary to ever hope for its description in any biochemical detail. Yet, only a decade or so ago the problem of coding for protein synthesis by the living cell seemed equally distant. Since the biochemical problem posed by epigenetic events consists essentially of understanding the *programming* of the unmasking schedule of the totipotent DNA genome during the development of the fertilized egg, it would seem that future advances depend largely on finding experimentally advantageous and simplified systems with which to attack the problem. Slime molds, for example, present the phenomenon of cellular differentiation clear and apart from that of simple growth (Sussman, 1958), whereas the sexual differentiation of the coelenterate *Hydra* likewise offers a simplified system amenable to intensive biochemical investigation (Loomis, 1964).

Two routes of attack would seem to be open to the experimentalist today. One lies in the newer *in vitro* techniques of functional cell culture as exemplified in the work of Konigsberg (1963) on the differentiation of single muscle cells and of Sato on steroid-producing adrenal tumor cells (Sato and Buonassisi, 1964). The other would lie in intensive study of *in vivo* systems on the microbiological level or in simple plant or animal forms. All of these routes should be investigated in the search for a clear-cut system with which to investigate epigenesis.

Even if it were possible to describe the above events biochemically, it would be but a beginning to an understanding of embryogenesis. Over and above the problems of helix unwinding and RNA polymerase action at definitely programmed sites appear such further problems as how a partly masked DNA helix can reproduce itself and still keep its pattern of active and inactive sites intact. Chondrocytes, for example, are able to fix inorganic sulfate and elaborate an extracellular matrix *and* transmit these capacities to their daughter cells! The *replication of the masking pattern* during the mitosis of differentiated cells is thus involved over and apart from the replication of the total genomal DNA helix.

One further complexity needs to be mentioned even in the briefest survey of the biochemical problems posed by epigenesis. This lies in the conditions needed to maintain the integrity of the genome itself, for it now appears that the euploid condition of normal cells is not necessarily self-sustaining. Cells in tissue culture, for example, often are karyologically unstable, with tetraploid and subtetraploid states appearing frequently. Parker and others have shown that "feeder layers" of nondividing X-irradiated cells are capable of maintaining normal morphology, continuing function and euploidy in cells grown below a population density of 3×10^3 cells per Petri dish, while Rothfels and associates (1963) found that the cells within a feeder layer had to be actively metabolizing living cells, capable of generating CO_2. Together with oxalacetic acid (OAA), CO_2 can duplicate in part this euploid-maintaining capacity of a "feeder layer," a finding that is of interest since these two feedback metabolites are also part of the picture in the sexual differentiation of *Hydra* as discussed below.

THE DIFFERENTIATING EFFECTS
OF HIGH CELL DENSITY

One of the vital findings of tissue culture research has been the importance of cell density. In case after case, normal diploid integrity and continuing function and morphology have been shown in compact tissues, whereas uncrowded monolayers often lose their cellular identity, both morphologically and chemically. Thus Holtzer et al. (1960) have shown that freshly isolated cartilage cells can be aggregated by centrifugation and then give rise to a typical mass of cartilage, whereas monolayers of these same cells increase logarithmically in number but do not give rise to cartilage. In similar fashion, Moscona (1960) has shown the controlling importance of high levels of population density on such phenomena as the reconstitution of embryonic cells, rosette formation by neuroretinal cells, and hair formation by skin cells. Hilfer (1962) has shown that chick thyroid cells form follicles and produce thyroxin when reaggregated from single cell suspensions, whereas these same cells do not do so when grown in monolayers, or even when reaggregated after a few days of monolayer culture, thus suggesting that irreversible damage has been done to such cells by culture at low levels of population density.

Another insight into the conditions responsible for the differentiation of embryonic cells *in situ* has appeared from the many attempts to grow cells outside of the body *in vitro*. The over-all generalization in such work has been that the larger the mass of tissue maintained *in vitro*, the more normal are the reactions of the cells involved. Fell, for example, has obtained amazingly normal differentiation in chick limb buds maintained in "organ culture." Even though such tissues are fed peripherally with nutrient medium, rather than centrally by the bloodstream, normal muscle and cartilaginous tissues appear (Fell and Robinson, 1929).

Primary cells taken freshly from a living animal promptly change under the usual conditions of tissue culture; a loss of function and a change in morphology being universally documented in many studies. The eventual failure of primary cells to proliferate *in vitro* has been generally established (Harris, 1964) even under conditions that mutant strains of "established lines" find quite adequate for indefinite growth. Looking through the mass of the evidence. it appears that all tissue cells are "leaky," i.e., unable to retain within their cell walls many of the metabolites they need for growth and differentiation. This conclusion is well documented in Eagle's careful studies (Eagle and Piez, 1962) on the nutritional needs of established cell lines. He found that such lines need not only all the essential amino acids needed by the intact animal, but an extended list of others including alanine, asparagine, aspartate, glutamate, glycine, proline, and serine that are made by the cells themselves and so are not included in W. C. Rose's original list of amino acids needed by the intact (and hence "unleaky") rat. It is clear from such work that cells grown in monolayers are unable to maintain their growth or differentiation by themselves, but need a microenvironment such as is usually found only within a tissue. The importance of a feeder layer for clonal culture reinforces this conclusion, as does the finding that methylcellulose aids in the cloning of cells by helping each cell form a tiny world within which its own leakage products can produce an enriched microenvironment similar to that within an intact tissue.

STUDIES WITH *HYDRA*

Soon after leaving Fritz Lipmann's laboratory I decided to try a new approach to cellular differentiation. The idea was to work on as simple a metazoan animal as possible so that the biochemical problems would be relatively easy when compared to those involved in the differentiation of a frog or higher animal. Since sponges did not seem promising as experimental material, hydra were selected as representative coelenterates, and methods worked out for culturing hydra in the laboratory for the first time (Loomis and Lenhoff, 1956).

A hydra is composed of only seven types of cells in the adult organism, compared to about one hundred in a mouse or other mammal. The basic idea was to dissociate hydra into their seven types of cells, separate them by differential centrifugation, grow them individually in tissue culture, and study their differentiation and reassociation under accurately controlled conditions. As luck would have it, it was found that the differentiation of one of these seven cells could be controlled even in intact hydra so that the chemical identity of the inducers involved could be studied on the whole animal level rather than in tissue culture with all the complications inherent to that technique.

The cell involved was the interstitial cell of the ectoderm, a cell that can either differentiate (1) into the nematocysts (or stinging cells) that characterize the *Cnidaria* as a group, or (2) into functional gonads. It was found that increased population density generally tended to induce sexual differentiation of *Hydra littoralis*, and an intensive search was made for the chemical mechanism behind this observation.

Since reduced oxygen tension did not produce sexual differentiation, experiments were run with increased levels of carbon dioxide tension or pCO_2. It was found that under certain defined conditions this gaseous variable was capable of controlling the differentiation of the interstitial cells along the gonadal pathway. Further experiments showed that α-ketoglutaric acid and indeed any metabolic source of oxalacetic acid (OAA) could also influence the reaction, a result reminiscent of Rothfels' finding (Rothfels *et al.*, 1963) that CO_2 and OAA were able to partly substitute for "feeder layers" in tissue culture referred to above.

At the present time it appears that hydra enrich their intimate microenvironment with both of these factors as well as with further metabolites that "leak" out of their tissues (Loomis, 1964). This process of microenvironmental enrichment explains the original observation that high levels of population density often resulted in sexual differentiation. Thus, a single isolated hydra can enrich its own microenvironment if it is left stagnant in 1 ml of culture water, whereas a similar hydra maintained in a flowing stream of water remains asexual because all these enrichment factors are swept away (Table I). The advantage of the hydra system lies in the fact that liters of solution containing these enrichment metabolites may be collected, concentrated by boiling, and after chemical analysis used to artificially induce the differentiation of this single cell type. Since the chief problem in identifying the inducers responsible

TABLE I

SEXUAL DIFFERENTIATION IN HYDRA[a]

Vessel	1	2	3	4	5	6	7	8	9	10
Twice/day additions Solution (ml)	—	Enriched-BVC[b]				α-Ketoglutaric acid[c]			pCO$_2$[d]	
		0.01	0.03	0.1	0.3	0.05	0.1	0.17	5	10
Day		Sexual Hydra (%)								
0	0	0	0	0	0	0	0	0	0	0
1	0	0	0	0	0	0	0	0	0	0
2	0	0	0	0	0	0	0	0	0	0
3	0	0	0	0	0	0	0	0	0	0
4	0	0	0	0	0	0	0	0	0	0
5	0	0	0	0	10	0	0	0	0	0
6	0	0	0	0	20	0	0	0	0	0
7	0	0	0	0	30	0	0	0	0	0
8	0	0	0	0	40	0	0	0	0	0
9	0	0	0	0	70	0	30	0	40	70
10	0	0	0	0	100	0	60	50	100	100
11	0	0	0	10	100	0	70	70	100	100

[a] Summarizing experiment showing: (1) asexual maintenance by rinsings twice per day with fresh BVC (100 mg/l NaHCO$_3$; 50 mg/l Versene; 25 mg/l CaCl$_2$ (Loomis, 1964); (2) induction of sexual differentiation by boiled concentrated enriched-BVC; (3) partial induction with α-ketoglutaric acid; or (4) elevated levels of pCO$_2$. All cultures consisted of 10 hydra grown in 15-ml beakers in BVC changed twice per day, i.e., after feeding with *Artemia* and about 5 hours later. Beakers filled to top with 17 ml BVC. All newly dropped buds removed daily. Temperature, 80°F.

[b] Enriched-BVC: 1000 ml deionized water poured over two crowded trays of hydra (*ca.* 5000 hydra) right after they had been fed with *Artemia* and rinsed with deionized water. Five hours later, this water was filtered and boiled down to a final volume of 10 ml and stored in an ice box for the 11 days of the experiment.

[c] α-Ketoglutaric acid: 36.5 mg dissolved in 50 ml BVC and stored in ice box.

[d] pCO$_2$: 500 ml BVC bubbled for 20 minutes in a 1-liter graduate cylinder with 10% CO$_2$-in-air. This solution then pulled up into four 100-ml syringes and stoppered. Five and 10 ml of this CO$_2$-enriched BVC solution were then injected into the appropriate vessels at every rinsing.

for cellular differentiation has been the difficulty of sampling the minute volumes of intercellular water that exist between the cells of an embryo or tissue culture, it would seem likely that further work using the hydra system (where one hydra contains *ca.* 100,000 cells) should be able to unravel the chemical nature of the inducers active within this particular differentiating system.

REFERENCES

Eagle, H., and Piez, K. (1962). *J. Exptl. Med.* **116**, 29.

Fell, H. B., and Robinson, R. (1929). *Biochem. J.* **23**, 767.

Goldschmidt, R. B. (1955). "Theoretical Genetics," 563 pp. Univ. of California Press, Berkeley, California.

Green, D. E., Loomis, W. F., and Auerbach, V. H. (1948). *J. Biol. Chem.* **172**, 389.

Gurdon, J. B. (1962). *J. Embryol. Exptl. Morphol.* **10**, 622.

Harris, M. (1964). "Cell Culture and Somatic Variation," p. 163. Holt, New York.

Hilfer, S. R. (1962). *Develop. Biol.* **4**, 1.

Holtzer, H., Abbott, J., Lash, J., and Holtzer, S. (1960). *Proc. Natl. Acad. Sci. U.S.* **46**, 1533.

Jacob, F., and Monod, J. (1963). *In* "Cytodifferentiation and Macromolecular Synthesis" (M. Locke, ed.), pp. 30-64. Academic Press, New York.

Konigsberg, I. R. (1963). *Science* **140**, 1.

Loomis, W. F. (1964). *J. Exptl. Zool.* **156**, 289.

Loomis, W. F., and Lenhoff, H. M. (1956). *J. Exptl. Zool.* **132**, 555.

Loomis, W. F., and Lipmann, F. (1948). *J. Biol. Chem.* **173**, 807.

Moscona, A. (1960). *In* "Developing Cell Systems and Their Control" (D. Rudnik, ed.), p. 45. Ronald Press, New York.

Novick, A., and Weiner, M. (1957). *Proc. Natl. Acad. Sci. U.S.* **43**, 553.

Rothfels, K. H., Kupelwieser, E. B., and Parker, R. C. (1963). *Can. Cancer Conf.* **5**, 191.

Sato, G., and Buonassisi, V. (1964). *Natl. Cancer Inst. Monograph* **13**, 81.

Sussman, M. (1958). *In* "A Symposium on the Chemical Basis of Development" (W. D. McElroy and B. Glass, eds.), p. 264. Johns Hopkins Press, Baltimore, Maryland.

From ~ P to CoA to Protein Biosynthesis[*]

G. David Novelli

INTRODUCTION

The contributors to this volume are all indebted in varying degrees to Fritz Lipmann and the ideas he presented in that classic article on "energy-rich phosphate bond," which we are now commemorating on the 25th anniversary of its publication (Lipmann, 1941). For me the indebtedness is large, direct, and very personal. My work in biochemistry has been, for the most part, molded by the ideas expressed in the article and originated by its author.

I would like to take this opportunity to present a personal account of the impact on my career of the ideas in this article and those generated during my long association with Fritz Lipmann.

It was in the fall of 1942, as a beginning graduate student in marine microbiology at Scripps Institute of Oceanography, that I first delved into the then new article in Volume 1 of *Advances in Enzymology*. At this stage in World War II graduate students were scarce and there were but two of us at Scripps—hardly enough to warrant formal courses. Instead we were given free rein to read the literature and to write term papers on various subjects. I elected to write on oxidation-reduction potentials and anaerobic fermentations. The article on the generation of phosphate bond energy fascinated me, but I had to struggle with the new ideas and new language—"group potential, anhydrization, energy-rich bonds, the metabolic wheel," etc. I was particularly pleased with the timeliness of the presentation of glycolysis, with its pre-O/R transformation period or preparatory stage, the O/R reaction itself, and the post-O/R transformation

[*] Research sponsored by the U.S. Atomic Energy Commission under contract with the Union Carbide Corporation.

period. In the United States at that time, microbial metabolism was largely influenced by the work of the Werkman School and the Van Niel School where the emphasis was placed on studies of the intermediary metabolic reactions in various anaerobic fermentations, especially the propionic acid fermentation and the intermediates in degradative pathways (Werkman and Wood, 1942; Van Niel, 1941). Little effort was being expended in studies of biosynthetic reactions. Therefore Lipmann's ideas concerning group transfer of small molecules in biosynthetic pathways were exciting to me. As a neophyte whose information was derived exclusively from the literature, Lipmann's article, as best I could understand it, seemed to contain a message that was important in understanding these fermentations. But at the time, though I struggled hard, the complete importance of these ideas escaped me. At that time there was no one with whom to discuss these ideas around Scripps and I was left with the feeling of having had a door opened but I was looking into a black room. Later, in 1944, while stationed at the 4th Service Command Medical Laboratory at Fort McPherson in Atlanta, Georgia, I met a young officer, John Spizizen, who also had been very impressed with the article on "high-energy phosphate." It chanced that a small group of microbiologists and biochemists were stationed at this laboratory who felt that they were losing touch with the world of science because of their military duties. Several of us, including Spizizen, Al Borg, Jerry Harris (who was Commanding Officer), and Henry Kamin (of this group I was the only non-Ph.D.), decided to utilize our lunch periods to refresh ourselves with the mainstream of biochemistry. We started with the article by Lipmann and by dint of much effort and discussion came to appreciate fully the wealth of ideas expressed in this paper. With access to the library of Emory Medical School and the current journals we were able to visualize the impact of the concept of "energy-rich phosphate" on the developing biochemical research. As the war was coming to an end, our thoughts turned to civilian life and a resumption of interrupted careers. Since I was no longer interested in marine microbiology, I was faced with the problem of resuming graduate studies—but where? Because of the great respect for Lipmann that the group had developed through the intensive study of his paper, I was urged to seek his advice in selecting a school to complete my education. Spizizen was the main force in urging me to write to Lipmann, an idea reinforced by Herb Jaffe who had recently entered the service. He had come from Massachusetts Institute of Technology and knew that Lipmann had a vague association with Harvard. Lipmann replied to my inquiry that it was possible to do a Ph.D. thesis with him—"for which to apply you should better hurry"—and I did. This was in March 1946.

COENZYME A PERIOD

When I joined Lipmann in August 1946, Nate Kaplan was working in the laboratory on postdoctoral research. I learned biochemistry through countless discussions with Lipmann and Kaplan sitting at the circular lunch table in the cafeteria at "Mass. General." It was here—from the master himself—that I learned to connect the ideas in this early article with the then current findings in biochemistry. This was a period when much activity was centered around the Krebs cycle and oxidative phosphorylation (Krebs, 1947). It was also the period when, through the use of heavy isotopes in whole-animal studies (especially at Columbia) evidence was accumulating indicating that large molecules like fatty acids and cholesterol are synthesized through repeated condensations of two-carbon fragments (Rittenberg and Shemin, 1946; Bloch, 1946). I can remember many lively discussions about acetyl phosphate, "the two-headed monster," as a donor of high-energy acetyl or phosphoryl groups. When Lipmann had discovered acetyl phosphate as a product of pyruvate oxidation in bacteria and showed that it could transfer its phosphoryl group to adenosine diphosphate (ADP) he believed that he had found the elusive "active acetate." In 1946 in another article in *Advances in Enzymology* he reviewed all of the work on acetyl phosphate. However, a note of disappointment that his acetyl phosphate might not be the universal active two-carbon fragment is seen in his statement: "Tests with added acetyl phosphate have not been encouraging, but for reasons discussed above such tests do not eliminate it as a possible intermediary, all the more since phosphate and adenyl pyrophosphate have been found necessary for fatty acid oxidation" (Lipmann, 1946). Lipmann never gave up on the ideas expressed in his early article that carboxyl activation through phosphorylation may be a major phase in biosynthetic reactions, especially for fatty acid and protein synthesis. Swallowing his disappointment in the lack of activity of acetyl phosphate in mammalian systems, he continued to search for an *in vitro* system in which he could study the formation and utilization of "active acetate." At the same time he continued to study the behavior of acetyl phosphate in microbial extracts where the possibility of it being a true intermediate seemed promising.

Lipmann was attracted to the study of the acetylation of sulfanilamide because of the report by Klein and Harris (1938) that the acetylation by rabbit liver slices was coupled to respiration (this is the same Jerry Harris who was my Commanding Officer in the Service). Rabbit liver homogenates proved to have little ability to carry out the acetylation reaction, but by examining liver extracts from different species, he found that extracts of pigeon liver catalyzed a vigorous acetylation reaction (Lipmann, 1945). This was a fortunate choice indeed, for it subsequently turned out that although there was good acetylation by livers and liver slices of a number of mammals and birds, we were unable to prepare active cell-free extracts from livers of rats, rabbits, beef, hog, chicken, and turkey. Here was one of the most important lessons I learned as a student. It has been characteristic of Fritz Lipmann not to become "married" to one or two experimental techniques or to a specific tissue. He taught the principle that the successful investigator should be prepared to utilize whatever experimental approach and whichever tissue or species is most likely to yield a solution to the problem under investigation. At the present time the statement of such a principle might appear trite, but 20 years ago it was not a general rule. The average investigator was trained in a limited number of techniques with one specific tissue, usually during his thesis research, and more often than not continued to apply these techniques to this same material even long after productive results had ceased to appear.

The work on the acetylation of sulfanilamide led to the discovery, in 1945, of coenzyme A (CoA). By the time I joined the laboratory, Lipmann and Kaplan had succeeded in preparing some partially purified samples of CoA that were sent out to various laboratories for vitamin analysis. None of the known vitamins was found to be present in more than trace amounts, except that Beverley Guirard in the laboratory of Roger Williams found an unusually high concentration of β-alanine after acid hydrolysis of the sample, suggesting the possible presence of pantothenic acid (Lipmann et al., 1947). My first assignment was an attempt to determine whether the β-alanine was present as a part of pantothenic acid or in some other linkage. This launched me on a series of investigations into the enzymatic degradation and resynthesis of coenzyme A that was to occupy a fair proportion of my time for the next 6 years. We eventually succeeded in working out the structure of the coenzyme by an almost strictly enzymatic approach and I came to appreciate the great value of the use of highly specific enzymes in the determination of structure, an art that was in its infancy at that time (Novelli, 1953).

Lipmann has always been concerned with large and fundamental problems and much of our discussions in those early days centered around the question of what kind of interaction was taking place between CoA, adenosine triphosphate (ATP), and acetate to make the latter such a good acylating agent for aromatic amines. At the national meetings we were frequently plagued by our colleagues with the query: "Why are you wasting your time studying the acetylation of sulfanilamide by pigeon liver when it is unlikely that a pigeon will ever encounter such a compound in its lifetime?" Lipmann had always taken the position that this reaction was a model system for studying the mechanism of group transfer reactions. As soon as CoA was shown to be involved in the synthesis of acetylcholine (Lipmann and Kaplan, 1946), this concept gained support that was further emphasized by the discovery of a variety of acceptor systems, such as histamine, glucosamine, amino acids, and oxalacetate, that utilized CoA (Lipmann, 1948).

One interesting and instructional aspect of the acetylation of sulfanilamide came about in an unexpected fashion. In 1949, Chou succeeded in separating the pigeon liver acetylating system into two parts by acetone fractionation (Chou et al., 1950). Neither fraction by itself was able to catalyze the reaction, but would do so when combined. This proved to be a big break in attempting to understand the mechanism involved in the reaction, since it suggested at least a two-step reaction with the possibility of observing the accumulation of an intermediate. However, at that time, there was no way of determining which fraction was catalyzing which partial reaction. Meanwhile we had been fractionating extracts of *Escherichia coli* in the study of citrate synthesis and had obtained a fraction that would catalyze a CoA-dependent synthesis of citrate from either acetate plus ATP or from acetyl phosphate (Novelli and Lipmann, 1950). When this fraction from *E. coli* was tested with each of the fractions from pigeon liver, it was observed that the *E. coli* fraction plus the fraction from pigeon liver, precipitating at 60% acetone, brought about the acetylation of sulfanilamide (Chou et al., 1950).

This experiment was a turning point in studies of the functions of CoA. It revealed that the *E. coli* fraction was generating acetyl CoA, while the liver fraction catalyzed the transfer to sulfanilamide. Moreover in the combined experiment acetyl phosphate could substitute for acetate and ATP. I remember that Lipmann was pleased to see that under the appropriate circumstances his acetyl phosphate could function with a mammalian enzyme system. Our colleagues were at first horrified at these experiments, making remarks that it was bad enough to study the acetylation of a compound that a pigeon would be unlikely to see in its lifetime, but now to mix an extract from a bacterium with one from a pigeon—"What possible biological sense could this have?" Since that time it has become almost routine to mix preparations from plants, animals, insects, etc., in order to obtain a deeper insight into the mechanism of certain reactions. Thus another lesson was learned. When Stadtman arrived in Lipmann's laboratory we performed similar experiments on the arsenolysis of acetyl phosphate, a reaction discovered by Stadtman and Barker (1950), and demonstrated a CoA dependence which led to the purification of phosphotransacetylase (Stadtman et al., 1951).

Thus the door was opened to an explosive development of CoA reactions with many other investigators entering the field, and by 1953 most of the major metabolic pathways in which CoA and acyl group transfer were involved had been revealed (Lipmann, 1953).

PROTEIN BIOSYNTHESIS

From the very beginning Lipmann considered the possibility that carboxyl activation of amino acids might be involved in the synthesis of proteins. This possibility was further reinforced with the discovery that the acetylation of aromatic amines involved carboxyl activation. He often pointed out the similarity between the peptide bond connecting two amino acids and the bond between the acetyl and aromatic amine; this he called a "peptidic link" (Lipmann, 1949). During the period when we were largely occupied with CoA isolation, structure, and metabolic function, Lipmann kept a close eye on developments in the field of protein synthesis. The group working with Paul Zamecnik at Massachusetts General was one of the pioneering groups studying the incorporation of amino acids into protein. We frequently had lunch with Zamecnik, Franz, Hoagland, Siekevitz, Keller, and others in the group and we regularly discussed the latest developments in the two fields.

When Loomis and Lipmann (1948) showed that dinitrophenol uncoupled oxidative phosphorylation, Franz et al. (1948) in Zamecnik's laboratory showed that similar concentrations of dinitrophenol inhibit the incorporation of alanine by rat liver slices. This was the first result suggesting that an energy-rich phosphate bond transfer might be involved in protein synthesis.

Subsequently the elegant work from Zamecnik's laboratory resulted in a much more simplified system for amino acid incorporation. The system consisted of carefully prepared microsomes, cell sap, ATP, and an ATP-generating system (see review by Zamecnik et al., 1956). We all followed these developments with keen interest. The years 1952–1953 represent the time when a number of observations were made in the work on CoA that proved to have a profound bearing on the course of the development of research in the field of protein synthesis. Jones and Black (Jones *et al.*, 1953) observed that during the formation of acetyl-CoA from acetate and ATP with a partially purified enzyme from yeast, inorganic pyrophosphate (PP) was eliminated from ATP. Maas and I showed that during the condensation of pantoic acid with β-alanine to form the "peptidic" bond in pantothenate inorganic pyrophosphate was likewise eliminated from ATP (Maas and Novelli, 1953). Hoagland and I observed the reversible pyrophosphorolysis of dephosphoCoA during studies on the biosynthesis of CoA (Hoagland and Novelli, 1954). The sudden appearance in the laboratory of three different biosynthetic reactions, each involving this unusual elimination of inorganic pyrophosphate from ATP, caused all of us to wonder what this might imply. Under appropriate conditions all three of these systems can catalyze the reversible exchange of inorganic pyrophosphate with ATP. Lipmann was intrigued by these "pyrophosphoryl splits" and in particular the pantoate-dependent exchange of pyrophosphate with ATP as the first step in the synthesis of pantothenate. This suggested the carboxyl activation of pantoate prior to its reaction to form the "peptidic" link in pantothenate.

In the summer of 1953 at a symposium at Johns Hopkins, Lipmann pulled together his thoughts on activations and group transfer reactions and proposed a working model for polypeptide synthesis (Lipmann, 1954). He proposed that certain amino acid-specific sites on a template were activated by transfer of pyrophosphoryl groups from ATP. The second stage would be the exchange of the pyrophosphoryl groups for the carboxyl group of the amino acid specified by the template. When the amino acids were all in place a reaction between the activated carboxyl of one amino acid and the amino group of the neighboring amino acid would occur in a wave to form the polypeptide (at this time, a "zipper" mechanism for polypeptide synthesis was quite popular). Although this scheme is incorrect in detail, it predicted that if the postulated pyrophosphate split of ATP was similar to the three described above, one should observe an amino acid-dependent exchange of inorganic pyrophosphate with the pyrophosphoryl moiety of ATP. Shortly, this was found to be correct.

At the end of the summer of 1953, I left Lipmann's laboratory for Western Reserve University and Hoagland rejoined Zamecnik's group on the floor below Lipmann's laboratory and began to work on the rat liver amino acid-incorporating system that had been developed so well by Zamecnik's group. Hoagland set out to determine whether ATP reacted first with the amino acid or with the microsomal template, as was postulated by Lipmann. He discovered that the soluble fraction of a rat liver homogenate catalyzed an amino acid-dependent exchange of inorganic pyrophosphate with ATP. The exchange reaction was additive with increasing numbers of amino acids, and with the use of hydroxylamine he showed that the reaction involved carboxyl activation (Hoagland, 1955).

Meanwhile Berg started to reinvestigate the ATP-PP exchange in the formation of acetyl-CoA that had been reported to occur in the absence of acetate or CoA and for which Lipmann had, therefore, postulated some intriguing intermediates. By purifying the system further than had been done previously, Berg lost the exchange reaction, but found that he could restore activity with a boiled extract. He isolated two compounds from the boiled extract (acetate and methionine) that could restore the exchange reaction. In an elegant series of experiments Berg (1955) showed that the intermediate in the formation of acetyl-CoA is acetyl adenylate. The latter compound was synthesized and shown to react with PP to form ATP or with CoA to form acetyl-CoA. He mentioned that he had inadvertently purified a methionine-activating enzyme and suggested that methionine might react with ATP in a similar manner to form the adenylate of methionine.

DeMoss and I found the amino acid-dependent PP-ATP exchange in soluble extracts from microorganisms of more than a dozen genera (DeMoss and Novelli, 1955). This suggested that the reaction was of general occurrence and might be involved in protein synthesis, although there was at that time no evidence for this. Working with Genuth we synthesized leucyl adenylate and demonstrated that it could be converted to ATP in the presence of inorganic pyrophosphate. This confirmed the suggestion that the amino acids are activated in a manner similar to acetate in the formation of acetyl-CoA (DeMoss et al., 1956).

I have deliberately detailed the previous section because I wanted to show how the thread of ideas originating in the article on "energy-rich phosphate" came to fruition in the work on CoA and finally influenced so strongly the course of studies in protein biosynthesis. Like phosphotransacetylase, whose discovery permitted the analysis of partial reactions in metabolic pathways involving CoA and thereby gave a great impetus to future developments in this field, so too the discovery of the activating enzymes [now called aminoacyl transfer ribonucleic acid (tRNA) synthetases or aminoacyl ligases] permitted the investigation of partial reactions in protein biosynthesis that led directly to the discovery of transfer RNA and greatly accelerated the acquisition of knowledge of the pathway of protein synthesis.

REFLECTIONS ON PROTEIN SYNTHESIS

After working on amino acid activation for a few years without being able to show that the activation reaction was an obligatory step on the pathway to protein synthesis, I decided to attempt a classic biochemical approach to the study of the biosynthesis of a specific protein (Novelli, 1958). The idea was to obtain a cell-free system that synthesized a measurable amount of a recognizable product and proceed to 'dissect it into its component parts. We first started to develop a system that would carry out the derepressed synthesis of ornithine transcarbamylase. Initially, Rogers, in our laboratory, had some success with a cell-free system from disrupted protoplasts of *E. coli* that exhibited small increases in enzyme activity that was energy dependent (Rogers and Novelli, 1960). Although the increase in activity was small, it appeared to be real and we hoped that with refinements in technique we could enlarge the increase. We were unsuccessful in this attempt and eventually, through the use of isotopes and immunological analysis, the conclusion was reached that the observed increase was largely due to chain completion (Rogers, 1965). Kameyama and later Eisenstadt had more success with the induced synthesis of β-galactosidase, particularly when we found that prior exposure of the cells to X-irradiation yielded inactive extracts that could be activated by the addition of DNA containing the structural gene for β-galactosidase (Kameyama and Novelli, 1962; Eisenstadt *et al.,* 1962; Novelli and Eisenstadt, 1963). This system looked especially promising because we had the potential possibility of studying all the reactions between the transcription of the gene and the completed protein. The system had other interesting properties, in that the extracts had to be prepared from preinduced cells and yet required the continual presence of the inducer. With this system also, although the increases in enzyme activity were also small, we hoped by improvements in the system to magnify the effects.

From the very beginning our efforts with this system were fraught with frustrations. Our ability to obtain active preparations from day to day was entirely unpredictable and, although great effort was expended on it, we never succeeded in finding the factors responsible for the inconsistency. Nisman *et al.* (1961) had developed a similar system using a more gentle procedure for making the cell-free preparation; this we confirmed. However, their preparation suffers from similar difficulties in that the increase in enzyme activity is small, and furthermore the preparations are unstable and could not be stored. In retrospect it is clear that the decision in 1957 to launch a bold, frontal assault on the biosynthesis of a specific protein was more bold than prudent. The attempt was premature, as subsequent findings revealed that there were then and still are too many unknown elements involved in protein synthesis. Such things as the mechanisms in chain initiation and chain termination, for example, were unknown and still remain to be firmly established.

During the past 6 years we have had occasion to prepare and study amino acid-incorporating systems from a variety of tissues, including microbial, plant, and mammalian systems. From the experience gained in the study of these various systems certain generalities emerge. The first of these is that without exception the *in vitro* amino acid-incorporating systems are indeed feeble compared with the incorporation by cells from which they are derived. This becomes particularly striking when one considers that even with the availability of essentially pure messenger RNA in the form of RNA from bacterial RNA viruses, *in vitro* systems supplemented with relatively large amounts of these RNA's are nevertheless incapable of making significant quantities of specific proteins. This surely indicates that some essential unknown component(s) of the *in vivo* protein-synthesizing machinery is damaged or destroyed during the preparation of the cell-free system. During studies with regenerating rat liver, we observed, as have others, that microsomal systems prepared from rats at various times after partial hepatectomy show an increased rate of amino acid-incorporating ability. Microsomes from regenerating liver are more responsive to poly U than those from normal liver. The difference between the preparations from normal and regenerating livers disappears if microsomes are converted to ribosomes by treatment with deoxycholate. We also observed that ribosome populations from regenerating liver differ from those of normal liver insofar as they contain an increased complement of heavy polysomes and a strikingly decreased pool of monomeric ribosomes. The combined evidence indicates that the response of microsomal cell-free systems to added messenger RNA (poly U) depends on factors other than the relative concentrations of ribosomes and mRNA and suggests the involvement of membrane components in regulating the ribosome-mRNA interaction (Cammarano *et al.*, 1965).

In looking back at our preparation of the *in vitro* β-galactosidase-synthesizing system, which was in the days before our concepts of ribosomes and polyribosomes were formulated, it seems likely that our active preparations contained membrane-bound structures. The system prepared by Nisman contains a highly structured complex containing at least DNA, RNA polymerase, polyribosomes, transfer RNA, and activating enzymes in one complex, membrane-bound particle. It should be recalled that in early studies by Spiegelman (1959) in which microbial cells were pulsed-labeled with nucleic acid precursors or amino acids, the highest specific activities of both RNA and protein appeared first in a subcellular fraction sedimenting at 15,000 $\times g$, a fraction that has been called the membrane fraction, but quite possibly containing structured elements. In our efforts to purify the cell-free systems to work out intermediate reactions in protein synthesis and to study the Code, I am concerned that we may have purified ourselves out of business with respect to obtaining net protein synthesis. With either microsomal or ribosomal systems from plant, microbial, or mammalian sources as amino acid-incorporating systems, it is consistently observed that the bulk of the newly synthesized protein remains bound to the ribosomes or microsomes with a relatively small amount released as soluble protein. The systems are not catalytic in a true sense, in that they do not recycle and after exhaustion of what I have called "binding sites" they cease to incorporate amino acids. This raises the possibility that factors required for peptide-chain termination have been damaged during the preparation of the cell-free systems. It has been suggested that there may be special nucleotide sequences that do not recognize a specific aminoacyl tRNA, but function to indicate the termination of a polypeptide chain (Gilbert, 1963; Sarabhai *et al.*, 1964; Nirenberg *et al.*, 1965). Brenner *et al.* (1965) have suggested that such terminating codons might be UAG and UAA and that these codons are recognized by specific soluble RNA's (sRNA), just like other codons; these special sRNA's do not carry amino acids but a special compound that results in termination of the growing polypeptide chain. It is possible that the mechanisms for the formation of such a special compound on these special RNA's are complicated processes (like the formation of N-formylmethionyl-tRNA as a possible chain initiator) that may be destroyed during the preparation of the extracts.

When all of the foregoing considerations are taken together, one is left with the feeling that current methods of preparation of cell-free protein-synthesizing systems are inadequate and do not permit the preservation of unknown but critical components (possibly structural elements) of the protein-synthesizing apparatus. A reevaluation of this aspect of the problem is under consideration in a number of laboratories. It seems clear that a major innovation in our preparative methods will be required before *in vitro* systems become available that are capable of synthesizing proteins at a rate and efficiency approximating that occurring in the cell of origin.

TRANSFER RNA AND AMINO ACID ACTIVATION

The adaptor hypothesis of Crick (1957) postulates that the positioning of an amino acid into a peptide sequence is not determined by the amino acid itself, but by hydrogen bonding between a nucleotide sequence in tRNA and a complementary sequence in messenger RNA. The elegant experiment of Chapeville *et al.* (1962), in which cysteine, while attached to its specific tRNA, was reduced to alanine (i.e., cysteinyl-tRNA^{cys} is converted to alanyl-tRNA^{cys}), and with the appropriate synthetic poly-nucleotides, the latter compound was shown to be incorporated into a position normally occupied by cysteine, proved the adaptor hypothesis. This finding then places much of the fidelity of peptide synthesis on the specificity of the interaction of an amino acid-activating enzyme with its specific tRNA. Once the incorrect amino acid is placed on a transfer RNA a mistake in peptide sequence is inevitable.

At about this time, we became concerned with the increase in the in-discriminate use of tRNA from *E. coli* or yeast in conjunction with amino acid-incorporating systems from a large variety of different tissues. In many cases it was not possible to obtain tRNA from the same tissue, thus general use of tRNA from *E. coli* or yeast (readily available sources) was made. Since only the incorporation of a radioactively labeled amino acid into protein was being measured, it was impossible to know whether the amino acid, in such heterologous systems, was being carried by the same tRNA as it would be in a homologous system. Since Jacobson and Nishimura (1963) had developed a simple paper chromatographic pro-cedure for the separation of aminoacylated tRNA's, we decided to test the possibility of "mistakes" in recognition between activating enzymes and tRNA when these were from heterologous sources. Using tRNA from *E. coli* as a standard and activating enzymes from mouse liver, maize, and *Neurospora* we found cases in which heterologous activating enzymes utilized a tRNA from *E. coli* for activation of an amino acid not utilized by *E. coli* for that amino acid (Jacobson *et al.*, 1964). These mistakes were most pronounced when *Neurospora* enzymes were used to charge *E. coli* tRNA. These observations were followed up by Barnett and Jacobson (1964) who presented evidence for interspecies degeneracy, ambiguity, and lack of universality in the recognition mechanism. In one clear-cut case the phenylalanine-activating enzyme from *Neurospora* reacted with the valine- and alanine-specific tRNA of *E. coli* to form phe-tRNA[val] and phe-tRNA[ala].

In a related study, utilizing partial digestion of tRNA by *Bacillus subtilis* ribonuclease, Nishimura and I (1965) obtained evidence for species differences in tRNA's and also showed that the enzyme recognition site on tRNA for amino acid activation was different from the coding site involved in mRNA binding during the transfer reaction. Using selective bromination of tRNA, Chu and Zamecnik (1964) have reached the same conclusion.

The results discussed in this section have served to stimulate us, as well as others, to reevaluate the importance of the primary amino acid activation step in protein synthesis. The possibility of errors being made during recognition of a tRNA by an activating enzyme emphasizes the importance of understanding the mechanisms involved. Zamecnik (1966) has stated the situation particularly aptly:

"Since it is at this recognition site that the language of the amino acid is really translated into that of the nucleotide (and not at the later step where sRNA base pairs with mRNA in what has come to be known as the coding step in protein synthesis), the stakes and interest in the solution of this problem of recognition may in the future well be high."

We have thus returned to a detailed investigation of amino acid activation, the point where I began to work in protein synthesis in 1953. In order to do careful, quantitative, chemical studies of the groups on tRNA involved in recognition by the activating enzymes, it is necessary to have available pure species of individual tRNA's and specific activating enzymes in sufficient quantity to do structural chemical analyses. To this end we have undertaken a joint effort with the Chemical Technology Division of the Oak Ridge National Laboratory that has as its ultimate goal the development of new and improved methods for the large-scale preparation of biologically active macromolecules in pure form. Initially we developed methods for the separation of individual tRNA's from *E. coli* (Kelmers *et al.*, 1965; Pearson and Kelmers, 1966). Using one of these methods we have prepared about 100 mg of functionally pure phenylalanine tRNA and the method is presently being scaled up to produce this tRNA in gram quantities for structural studies. Simultaneously, Stulberg (1966) has isolated a homogeneous preparation of the phenylalanine-activating enzyme. The availability of these pure materials will permit more precise chemical studies on the recognition mechanism involved between the enzyme and tRNA.

In addition to the determination of nucleotide sequences, the availability of a variety of pure transfer RNA's from different sources can help to answer such questions as the role of the methylation of the bases, the differences between "degenerate" tRNA's, the differences between individual tRNA's from different species, the changes introduced into tRNA by suppressor mutation, phage infection, and during cellular differentiation. We can look forward to a flurry of activity in this area in the next few years and the attraction into the field of many new and young investigators.

I have tried to show, from one individual point of view, how a group of ideas concerning energy generation and group transfer reactions that were somewhat nebulous 25 years ago was seized upon at appropriate stages in the development of a research field and used to open up new areas for further investigation until a full vista was revealed. Hopefully the continued application of this principle in the next 5–10 years will lead to a fuller understanding of that still mysterious process we call life.

REFERENCES

Barnett, W. E., and Jacobson, K. B. (1964). *Proc. Natl. Acad. Sci. U.S.* **51**, 642.

Berg, P. (1955). *J. Am. Chem. Soc.* **77**, 3163.

Bloch, K. (1946). *In* "Currents in Biochemical Research" (D. E. Green, ed.), p. 291. Wiley (Interscience), New York.

Brenner, S., Stretton, A. O. W., and Kaplan, S. (1965). *Nature* **206**, 994.

Cammarano, P., Melli, M., and Novelli, G. D. (1965). *Biochim. Biophys. Acta* **108**, 329.

Chapeville, F., Lipmann, F., Von Ehrenstein, G., Weisblum, B., Ray, W. J., Jr., and Benzer, S. (1962). *Proc. Natl. Acad. Sci. U.S.* **48**, 1086.

Chou, T. C., Novelli, G. D., Stadtman, E. R., and Lipmann, F. (1950). *Federation Proc.* **9**, 160.

Chu, C. T., and Zamecnik, P. C. (1964). *Science* **144**, 856.

Crick, F. H. C. (1957). *In* "Structure of Nucleic Acids and Their Role in Protein Synthesis," p. 25. Cambridge Univ. Press, London and New York.

DeMoss, J. A., and Novelli, G. D. (1955). *Biochim. Biophys. Acta* **18**, 592.

DeMoss, J. A., Genuth, S. M., and Novelli, G. D. (1956). *Proc. Natl. Acad. Sci. U.S.* **42**, 325.

Eisenstadt, J. M., Kameyama, T., and Novelli, G. D. (1962). *Proc. Natl. Acad. Sci. U.S.* **48**, 652.

Frantz, I. D., Jr., Zamecnik, P. C., Reese, J. W., and Stephenson, M. L. (1948). *J. Biol. Chem.* **174**, 773.

Gilbert, W. (1963). *J. Mol. Biol.* **6**, 389.

Hoagland, M. B. (1955). *Biochim. Biophys. Acta* **16**, 288.

Hoagland, M. B., and Novelli, G. D. (1954). *J. Biol. Chem.* **207**, 767.

Jacobson, K. B., and Nishimura, S. (1963). *Biochim. Biophys. Acta* **68**, 490.
Jacobson, K. B., Nishimura, S., Barnett, W. E., Mans, R. J., Cammarano, P., and Novelli, G. D. (1964). *Biochim. Biophys. Acta* **91**, 305.
Jones, M. E., Black, S., Flynn, R. M., and Lipmann, F. (1953). *Biochim. Biophys. Acta* **12**, 141.
Kameyama, T., and Novelli, G. D. (1962). *Proc. Natl. Acad. Sci. U.S.* **48**, 659.
Kelmers, A. D., Novelli, G. D., and Stulberg, M. P. (1965). *J. Biol. Chem.* **240**, 3979.
Klein, J. R., and Harris, J. S. (1938). *J. Biol. Chem.* **124**, 613.
Krebs, H. A. (1947). *Enzymologia* **12**, 88.
Lipmann, F. (1941). *Advan. Enzymol.* **1**, 99.
Lipmann, F. (1945). *J. Biol. Chem.* **160**, 173.
Lipmann, F. (1946). *Advan. Enzymol.* **6**, 231.
Lipmann, F. (1948). *Harvey Lectures Ser.* **44**, 99.
Lipmann, F. (1949). *Federation Proc.* **8**, 597.
Lipmann, F. (1953). *Bacteriol. Rev.* **17**, 1.
Lipmann, F. (1954). *In* "Mechanism of Enzyme Action" (W. D. McElroy and B. Glass, eds.), p. 599. Johns Hopkins Press, Baltimore, Maryland.
Lipmann, F., and Kaplan, N. O. (1946). *J. Biol. Chem.* **162**, 743.
Lipmann, F., Kaplan, N. O., Novelli, G. D., Tuttle, L. C., and Guirard, B. M. (1947). *J. Biol. Chem.* **167**, 869.
Loomis, W. F., and Lipmann, F. (1948). *J. Biol. Chem.* **173**, 807.
Maas, W. K., and Novelli, G. D. (1953). *Arch. Biochem. Biophys.* **43**, 236.
Nirenberg, M., Leder, M., Bernfield, M., Brimacombe, J., Turpin, J., Rottman, F., and O'Neal, C. (1965). *Proc. Natl. Acad. Sci. U.S.* **55**, 1161.
Nishimura, S., and Novelli, G. D. (1965). *Proc. Natl. Acad. Sci. U.S.* **53**, 178.
Nisman, B., Cohen, R., Kayser, A., Fukuhara, H., Demailly, J., Genin, C., and Giron, D. (1961). *Cold Spring Harbor Symp. Quant. Biol.* **26**, 145.
Novelli, G. D. (1953). *Federation Proc.* **12**, 675.
Novelli, G. D., and Lipmann, F. (1950). *J. Biol. Chem.* **182**, 213.
Novelli, G. D. (1958). *Proc. Natl. Acad. Sci. U.S.* **44**, 86.
Novelli, G. D., and Eisenstadt, J. M. (1963). *In* "Informational Macromolecules" (H. J. Vogel, V. Bryson, and J. O. Lamper, eds.), p. 301. Academic Press, New York.
Pearson, R. L., and Kelmers, A. D. (1966). *J. Biol. Chem.* **241**, 767.
Rittenberg, D., and Shemin, D. (1946). *In* "Currents in Biochemical Research" (D. E. Green, ed.), p. 261. Wiley (Interscience), New York.
Rogers, P. (1965). *Arch. Biochem. Biophys.* **111**, 39.
Rogers, P., and Novelli, G. D. (1960). *Biochim. Biophys. Acta* **44**, 298.
Sarabhai, A. S., Stretton, A. D. W., Brenner, S., and Bolle, A. (1964). *Nature* **201**, 13.
Spiegelman, S. (1959). *In* "Recent Progress in Microbiology" (G. Tunevall, ed.), p. 81. Almqvist & Wiksell, Uppsala.
Stadtman, E. R., and Barker, H. A. (1950). *J. Biol. Chem.* **184**, 769.
Stadtman, E. R., Novelli, G. D., and Lipmann, F. (1951). *J. Biol. Chem.* **191**, 365.
Stulberg, M. P. (1966). In preparation.
Van Niel, C. B. (1941). *Advan. Enzymol.* **1**, 263.
Werkman, C. H., and Wood, H. G. (1942). *Advan. Enzymol.* **2**, 135.
Zamecnik, P. C. (1966). *Cancer Res.* **26**, 1.
Zamecnik, P. C., Keller, E. B., Loftfield, J. W., Hoagland, M. B., and Loftfield, R. B. (1956). *J. Cell. Comp. Physiol.* **47** (Suppl. 1), 102.

Views on Integrated Protein Synthesis in Liver*

Mahlon B. Hoagland

The line of indebtedness to Fritz Lipmann for some contributors to this volume is clear and direct. I came to work in his laboratory at a time when phosphate exchange reactions were fruitfully being used to study mechanisms of carboxyl group activation, having first breathed the early morning atmosphere of protein synthesis in the laboratories of Paul Zamecnik at the Massachusetts General Hospital. This exposure to a key technique, together with a faith in the importance of coupled reactions in biosynthesis—inspired by the insights of Lipmann, Borsook, Linder-strøm-Lang, and Kalckar—molded my experimental approach to protein synthesis when I rejoined Paul Zamecnik in 1953. He and his colleagues had by then succeeded in identifying two essential components of the amino acid incorporation system of rat liver—a soluble enzyme fraction and microsomes (ribosomes)—and had shown that the latter were the initial sites of peptide bond formation. They had also demonstrated that adenosine triphosphate (ATP) was an essential participant in the reaction. Both soluble and particulate components of the system were thus ripe for a study of amino acid-dependent catalysis of phosphate exchange reactions. It soon became clear that the soluble enzyme fraction catalyzed an amino acid-dependent exchange of inorganic pyrophosphate with ATP as well as a formation of aminoacyl hydroxamates. These observations verified Lipmann's expectation voiced 14 years earlier that the energy of activation of amino acids might be derived from phosphoanhydride linkages.

In the intervening years our vision has been enriched with an increasingly detailed picture of protein biosynthetic mechanism: the participa-

* Supported by a grant from the National Institutes of Health, Division of General Medical Sciences.

tion of guanosine triphosphate (GTP), the role of transfer ribonucleic acid (RNA), the elaboration of a bacterial cell-free incorporation system, the demonstration of the key position of messenger RNA, and the elucidation of the genetic code through the use of synthetic messengers.

It is worth pausing to note, that in addition to the discovery of the role of microsomes and amino acid activation in protein synthesis, the first three of these further advances were products of Zamecnik's laboratory. Together they opened protein synthesis to the scrutiny of the chemist, the physicist, and the geneticist.

The exuberant exploitation of the bacterial system has produced a picture of ribosome, messenger RNA, transfer RNA, and enzymes socializing in a soluble milieu, and this has colored much of the experimental approach to studies of integrated protein synthesis in animal cells. The result has been that investigators too often tend to study those aspects of protein synthesis that resemble the bacterial system, setting aside obvious inconsistencies that might suggest unique properties. The similarities between animal and bacterial systems are indeed impressive, but the differences may well be the key to further insights. The work in my laboratory has been predicated upon the belief that in studying animal-cell integrated protein synthesis one must return to cruder systems, dissect out the components by the gentlest possible means and study their interrelationships anew.

Most of the experimental work I shall describe, and much of its conceptual framework, has been that of my associates Dr. Oscar A. Scornik of Argentina (the microsomal inhibitor of protein synthesis), Samuel H. Wilson (polyribosomes in liver), and Marc Henri Dresden (polyribosomes in bacteria). The able technical assistance of Lorraine Pfefferkorn and Elizabeth Bishop has also been invaluable.

DYNAMICS OF POLYSOME ASSEMBLY AND DISASSEMBLY IN THE CYTOPLASM

The most careful quantitation of RNA distribution among various RNA-containing components has been carried out in bacteria growing exponentially in relatively rich media where it is found that some 80% of RNA is in ribosomes. A careful balance sheet of RNA in normal adult rat liver reveals that only about 42% of the total RNA occurs in ribosomes, the bulk of the remainder being 4 S RNA (1). This distribution is not unlike that found in bacteria growing at relatively slow rates, i.e., 0.2 doublings per hour (2). Incidentally, the liver is by no means a sluggish protein fabricator: it synthesizes a quantity of protein equivalent to its own weight in less than 2 days, [based on calculations from the data of Peters (3), Gordon and Humphrey (4), and Richmond et al. (5)].

What about the form and location of the ribosomes? If we prepare the appropriate fractions from well-fed adult rats by gentle homogenization at temperatures close to 0°C, using deoxycholate (DOC) and standard zone-centrifugation techniques, and correct optical density for ferritin, essentially all (more than 90%) of the ribosomes found in the cytoplasm are bound in ribonuclease-sensitive polysome structures greater than 150 S (1). The main source of free monosomes [and, interestingly, ribonuclease (RNase)-resistant disomes] is the nuclear fraction (1). Thus the bulk of the protein synthesis of the cell is proceeding in the cytoplasm on polysome structures in the absence of a substantial pool of free ribosomes. This observation suggests that messenger molecules must have a highly efficient means of reutilizing monosomes.

We become more impressed with the self-sufficiency of the cytoplasmic polysome when we examine the length of its life. This can be studied in liver by making use of the effects of starvation of the animal, followed by refeeding. This technique has proved extremely valuable in revealing subtle aspects of polysome function. Fasting rats for only short periods (as little as 10 hours) produces a rapid accumulation of small ribosomal units—monomers, dimers, and trimers (83–155 S)—at the expense of polysomes, at least as judged by the particles one obtains upon DOC extraction. After 4 days of food deprival almost all cytoplasmic ribosomes are converted to these forms. (This phenomenon, incidentally, is an important source of error in studying liver polysomes; many workers starve animals for varying periods before performing their analyses and gain quite erroneous pictures of the state of ribosome aggregation.) Refeeding animals after such a period of fasting produces a dramatic reversal of this process. The light units rapidly disappear and a full complement of heavy polysomes is restored within 10 hours (6).

The possibility that the "old" ribosomes produced during starvation had become degraded and that the new polysomes appearing on refeeding were derived from newly synthesized ribosomes was ruled out in two further experiments. (1) Long before refeeding, indeed, before starvation was instituted, ribosomal RNA was briefly labeled by injecting the rats with ^{14}C-orotic acid. After starvation, most of the label could be shown to be in the monomer-dimer-trimer region as expected. Upon refeeding essentially all of the radioactivity ("old" ribosomes) was rapidly swept into polysomes. (2) Conversion of the light particles to polysomes was shown to occur in the presence of a concentration of actinomycin D (0.55 mg/kg body weight) that inhibited all ribosomal RNA synthesis but permitted continued messenger RNA synthesis (see below).

Now the importance of the starvation-refeeding cycle lies in this: we induce the synchronous synthesis of a new population of polysomes whose life we can readily follow. If we give a dose of actinomycin D sufficient to stop all RNA synthesis (1 mg/kg), *after the polysomes have reformed* a large fraction of them remain intact in the cytoplasm for at least 30 hours. (The same dose of actinomycin D given *before* refeeding completely inhibits the formation of polysomes, of course.) Thus we conclude that at least a substantial fraction of messenger RNA's (about 35%) can function in the cytoplasm of the liver cell for prolonged periods. This direct measurement of polysome life is in agreement with the estimate of Revel and Hiatt based on the life of RNA derived from microsomes having messengerlike *in vitro* stimulatory activity (7).

Using this technique and obtaining extensive data on rate of polysome breakdown as a function of time, it has become apparent that the polysome decay curve in the presence of actinomycin D is clearly biphasic; one class of polysomes behaves as described above (estimated half-life 80 hours) but another class decays much more rapidly with an average half-life of 3 hours (6). Our present task is to attempt identification of the protein products of each of these classes of polysomes. We can say, however, that the decay in polysome structure is paralleled by a decay in ability to incorporate amino acids *in vivo* (as judged by injection of short pulses of amino acids).

PROTEIN MADE BY LONG-LIVED POLYSOMES

The liver synthesizes two general classes of protein—a vast array of proteins for the maintainance of self, and a few proteins, in large quantity, for export. Albumin is, of course, prominent among the latter. Since actinomycin D allowed the short-lived polysomes to decay without replacement, we could compare the nature of the protein made by the long-lived polysomes with that made by the total polysome population.

Animals were starved for 5 days, refed for 10 hours, given actinomycin D and, 27 hours later, given a pulse of ^{14}C-amino acid shortly before killing. The labeled proteins of the microsomal vesicles were released by sonication and separated by polyacrylamide gel electrophoresis. The results were striking: the long-lived polysomes synthesized a much higher proportion of albumin relative to total protein (70%) than was synthesized by the polysomes of normal or control starved-refed rat livers (27%). Furthermore, reinitiation of messenger synthesis in the liver (by discontinuation of actinomycin D treatment) led to return to the normal pattern of synthesis within a few hours (8).

These results suggest that the liver, while retaining its labile messenger system, has stabilized its system for manufacture of export protein.

THE RELATIONSHIP OF CYTOPLASMIC RIBOSOMES TO ENDOPLASMIC MEMBRANE

The rather dramatic shift in the sedimentation properties of DOC-isolated polysomes in response to starvation and refeeding is one example of the kind of change in the physical parameters of the protein-synthesizing machinery that may be studied. DOC, of course, disrupts all membranes and permits one to study the properties of polysomes, at least grossly free of membrane. (These polysomes contain, however, about 10-15% by weight phospholipid which is not removed by further DOC treatment.) A simple quantitative method for assessing the degree of association of ribosomes (polysomes) with membrane would be most useful in further characterizing the system. The method we have used (9) is a modification and an extension of one originally described by Henshaw et al. (10).

We place on a sucrose gradient a portion of a whole 15,000 × g supernatant, untreated with DOC, and therefore containing intact endoplasmic reticular membranes with associated ribosomes, subjected to minimal manipulation. We then centrifuge for 7 hours to bring 83–123 S material well down the gradient. Microsomes and polysomes are plastered on the bottom of the tube. The method should, theoretically, allow us to determine the degree to which small units (monomers, dimers, trimers) occur naturally free of membrane. We had previously determined that even moderately vigorous homogenization of liver does not disrupt polysomes provided the temperature of all operations is kept at 0°–4°C. When 15,000 × g supernatants from livers of normal well-fed adult rats are so centrifuged, and correction is made for ferritin, there is little detectable material in the 83–123 S region, as expected from our observations on DOC-isolated polysomes. If we add to a tissue homogenate radioactive 83–123 S particles, they separate nicely and appear where expected on such gradients, showing that if free particles do occur in the tissue they can be detected and will not be artificially trapped in the membranes and large polysomes sedimenting to the bottom of the tube. The sensitivity of the method for the detection of *naturally occurring* monomers and small aggregates is limited by the relatively high 260 mμ absorption of such gradients (owing to a variety of membrane-associated proteins), but we estimate that if 5 to 10% of all ribosomes occurred as small units they could be detected by the method.

Farber and his associates (*11, 12*) have shown by electron micrographic and centrifugal analyses that exposure of rats to ethionine results in an apparent breakdown of polysomes and endoplasmic reticulum and the appearance of free monosomes, no longer attached to membrane. The appearance of such free ribosomes should be a good test for our method and indeed we found that they were easily demonstrable; ethionine-poisoned rats showed a sharp peak of 83–123 S material on the 15,000 × g supernatant gradients. Thus, the method clearly permits the detection of free polysome subunits, if they exist *in vivo*.

We are now in a position to ask about the monomers and small aggregates produced during fasting of the rat, alluded to earlier. The striking finding here is that these particles *do not appear* in the monomer to trimer region of the gradients! Indeed, after 20 hours of starvation, when 75–85% of the polysomes have been degraded, there is no appearance of 83–155 S material. Yet, as we have said earlier, we know them to be present in the cytoplasm for treatment of the 15,000 × g supernatants with DOC shows that the loss of polysomes is balanced by the accumulation of small units. Thus, the ribosomes are not held together by messenger, and yet they fail to appear free in the cytoplasm. The only reasonable conclusion to be drawn is that *the breakdown of polysomes to subunits during starvation is not accompanied by a release of the ribosomes from the membrane.* (An alternative explanation for this striking finding, which seems improbable to us but must be explored, is that polysomes are not degraded during starvation, but are simply more susceptible to degradation by DOC.) It seems clear from both electron micrographic and density-equilibrium gradient studies of normal rat liver microsomes that *polysomal* ribosomes are also normally attached to membrane (*13, 14*).

The significance of this simple finding may be quite profound. It suggests that cytoplasmic ribosomes are affixed to the endoplasmic membrane regardless of whether messenger is present to program them! A reasonable interpretation would be that messenger output is reduced during starvation and when it again becomes available upon refeeding it threads its way through ribosomes affixed to a membrane surface. In the normal balanced metabolic state the quantity of messenger available would be sufficient to bind the available ribosomes and all ribosomes would be found in polysome structures when extracted from membranes by DOC. The physical association of ribosomes with membrane could facilitate a channeling or guiding of the messenger from ribosome to ribosome. Such a mechanism would afford an efficient means for threading together polysomes that would not require random contact of messenger and monosome in a soluble milieu.

Rather significantly, starvation followed by feeding results in a burst of new polysome synthesis followed, some 60 hours later, by the appearance of 85–185 S units, as though the liver had overcompensated in polysome production and was ridding itself of an excess of ribosomes no longer needed, once steady state has been reached. That the relation of these units to the membrane is quite different from that of the same units appearing following starvation (presumably they are the identical particles) is shown by the fact that they *do appear as free particles* on the gradients of whole $15,000 \times g$ supernatants, i.e., they are no longer attached to membrane.

BACTERIAL COUNTERPART OF THE STARVATION-REFEEDING EXERIMENTS IN LIVER

The development of a simple, reproducible technique (*15*) for preparing polysomes from bacteria has permitted us to examine the effects of starvation and refeeding upon polysome structure in bacteria. The technique involves a rapid centrifugal passage of a bacterial cell suspension sequentially through a layer of ethylenediaminetetraacetic acid (EDTA) and a layer of lysozyme followed by treatment of the partially opened cells by detergent. The speed of the procedure (the whole operation takes only 2 minutes) is essential to avoid chelating intracellular Mg^{++} and thereby degrading polysomes. One can obtain from *Escherichia coli* cells in exponential growth about 40% of the ribosomes in large polysome aggregates. *Aerobacter aerogenes* and *Micrococcus lysodeikticus* yield similar proportions of polysomes with the procedure.

If *E. coli* cells are deprived of a carbon source they very rapidly lose their polysomes, and within a few minutes only monosomes are extractable from the cells. Resupplying a carbon source results in a rapid reappearance of polysomes. That these polysomes are derived from the "old" monosome population produced by starvation can be shown by an experiment analogous to that used to demonstrate the same phenomenon in liver. Cells are exposed to a pulse of RNA precursor several generations before deprival of carbon, so that their ribosomes are labeled. They are then starved to produce monosomes, which appear as a single labeled peak of 70 S. The polysomes which then reappear upon supplying substrate are found to have the same specific radioactivity as the "old" monosomes from which they are fabricated. Thus, the starvation-refeeding cycle in both liver and bacteria appears very similar.

We can conveniently ask the bacterial system another question. Do the breakdown and resynthesis of polysomes accompanying the starvation-refeeding cycle require protein synthesis? The answer seems to be that they do; polysome degradation and resynthesis are both inhibited by chloramphenicol. By appropriate messenger RNA pulse-labeling experiments it can be shown that chloramphenicol does not appreciably interfere with messenger binding to polysomes, and that the size of messenger bound is the same as in growing cells. We conclude that protein synthesis is required to maintain polysome integrity and to reinstitute polysome assembly after starvation. We may further surmise that chloramphenicol acts by preventing the movement of ribosomes along the messenger from a limited number of entry points (16) (17).

EVIDENCE FOR THE EXISTENCE OF MESSENGER RNA IN RAT LIVER CYTOPLASM

There have been a number of recent reports demonstrating the occurrence of a messenger-like RNA associated with protein as a discrete particle in animal cell cytoplasm (18-22). One difficulty is that of distinguishing between a messenger-carrying particle ("informosome") and a ribosome precursor particle. Use of the starvation-refeeding system to obtain a burst of new messenger synthesis, together with actinomycin D administration to prevent new ribosome synthesis, offer a quite different approach to this problem (6). The plan of the experiment is as follows: animals are fasted for 6 days, then given the required dose of actinomycin D, and approximately 4 hours later are given food and C^{14}-orotic acid. Eighteen hours later, the animals are killed and their ribosomal material examined.

The period of starvation produced a large peak of mono-, di-, and trisome material; and the refeeding period, in the absence of drug, results in complete conversion of these units to polysomes as we noted earlier. Isolation and examination of the RNA produced during refeeding in the absence of drug shows all label to be in three well-defined, symmetrical peaks—4, 18, and 29 S. Refeeding in the presence of 1 mg actinomycin D/kg of rat (a high dose) shows only a small amount of label to be incorporated into RNA—less than 5% of that in the untreated refed animals—and this label is all 4 S RNA (presumably its terminal cytidylates). There is, of course, no reformation of polysomes.

At one-half the above dose of actinomycin D (0.55 mg/kg of rat) there is seen to be complete reformation of polysomes upon refeeding (i.e. essentially all the available monosomes are reutilized). This dose was chosen to inhibit completely ribosomal RNA synthesis but to allow messenger synthesis to proceed (23, 24). These polysomes are of course labeled and extraction of their RNA reveals it to have a labeling pattern quite different from the untreated animals. There is label in 4 S RNA, a very small amount in ribosomal RNA (less than 1% that of the untreated controls), and there is a large peak of label between 4 and 18 S RNA. The base composition of this RNA is identical to that of liver DNA, and quite different from that of ribosomal RNA. This is a clear demonstration of messenger RNA in liver cytoplasm.

A MEMBRANE-ASSOCIATED INHIBITOR OF PROTEIN SYNTHESIS

In bacteria, the rate of protein synthesis is proportional to the ribosome content of the cell over a wide range of growth rates. On induction of more rapid growth, the synthesis of new ribosomes precedes the elevation of protein synthetic rate (2, 25). This apparently simple dependence of protein synthesis upon ribosome number does not seem to occur in the liver; when regeneration of the liver is induced by partial hepatectomy the rate of protein synthesis rises rapidly well before there is any detectable net increase in the ribosome population [cf. (26)]. The existence of factors regulating polysome activity in the normal adult tissue is strongly implied by such observations and led us some years ago to seek approaches to the problem using cell-free systems.

Earlier reports had suggested that fractions from normal and regenerating livers did show significant differences in protein synthetic activity (27–29). We were able to establish that very gently prepared regenerating liver polyribosomes, still attached to membranes (i.e., "heavy" microsomes), were substantially more active for amino acid incorporation than their normal liver counterparts (per unit of RNA). These large differences in activity (2- to 4-fold) were not found with DOC-purified polysomes. An equipart mixture of microsomes from the two sources was less active than one would predict were their activities simply additive. The difference in activity of microsomes was sharply reduced in the presence of GTP. This led to the isolation, by sonic disruption of microsomes, of a "soluble" lipoprotein fraction which strongly inhibited protein synthesis on liver polyribosomes, in a standard assay system containing, in addition, whole 100,000 $\times$ g supernatant, ATP, an ATP-generating system, and a ^{14}C-amino acid. GTP largely counteracted the effect of the inhibitor (30).

We have since found that a substantial part of the difference in activity of crude microsomes from regenerating and normal livers can be accounted for by lysosomes. The lysosomes of normal liver seem to release more readily their content of degradative enzymes during an *in vitro* incubation, thereby irreversibly shutting off protein synthesis after about 10 minutes. Regenerating microsomes continue functioning for 50-60 minutes.

The possibility that our GTP-reversible inhibitor had some role in the control of the rate of protein synthesis *in vivo* whetted our appetite for further knowledge of its nature, habitat, and mode of action. The ensuing account gives a general picture of more recent developments (31).

Since lysosomes contain certain factors inhibitory to the cell-free incorporation systems (distinguished from the inhibitor under discussion by *nonreversal* by GTP) we prepare inhibitor from "purified microsomes," i.e., microsomes from which lysosomes have been largely removed. This can be accomplished by a centrifugal flotation technique. Microsomes are suspended in sucrose of such density as to cause most lysosomes to rise, free ribosomes to pellet, and true microsomes ("rough vesicles") to move in neither direction during an 18-hour centrifugation at 30,000 $\times$ g. The microsome suspension, after removing the "skin" enriched in lysosomes, may then be diluted and centrifuged briefly to sediment the microsomes. This simple maneuver reduces the lysosome content 4- to 5-fold (as measured by acid phosphatase activity and by non-GTP-reversible inhibition of protein synthesis).

First consider the evidence that the inhibitor is truly membrane-associated. If purified microsomes are treated with 1.3% DOC and the particulate material removed by centrifugation, the resulting supernatant solution contains essentially all of the phospholipid, a little RNA, two-thirds of the total protein, and three-quarters of the inhibitory activity of the original microsomes. (Inhibitor assays are all based on a dose-response curve in the standard polysome assay system, using sonicated, uncentrifuged extracts of microsomes and fractions thereof. The difference between the 50% inhibition points with and without GTP are the basis of the inhibitory unit.)

Another method may be used for preparing purified membranes. Purified microsomes (RNA to protein ratio equals 0.2) are mixed with an excess of EDTA and placed on top of a solution of 0.5 M sucrose and centrifuged. The EDTA causes dissociation of membranes from ribosomes, and both components sediment through the sucrose to the bottom of the tube. The pellet is then suspended in sucrose of high density (1.5 M) and recentrifuged to remove the ribosomes, leaving the membranes in suspension. Dilution of this membrane suspension and recentrifugation gives a quite pure membrane pellet (RNA to protein ratio of 0.04). The inhibitory activity of this preparation, based on phospholipid or protein content, is essentially the same as the original purified microsomes.

Inhibitor is prepared for our usual studies by isolating purified microsomes, subjecting them to brief sonic disruption, centrifuging off the particulate material, and dialyzing the supernatant. Such preparations are strongly inhibitory to amino acid incorporation and are usually completely reversed by GTP.

All attempts we have made to separate inhibitory activity from the bulk of the membrane protein have been unsuccessful so far. Thus, use of Sephadex columns (G200, in which the activity appears at the front), extraction with various salts over a wide range of pH value, etc., have been to no avail. Inhibitor would thus appear to be a large protein, indistinguishable from the bulk membrane protein subunit.

Inhibitory activity is quite stable for prolonged periods in the cold and is labile to heating at 60°C for a few minutes.

The kinetics of the incorporation reaction in the presence of inhibitor showed that there was a definite lag in the establishment of inhibition (usually 10 minutes at 37°C). Furthermore, the addition of glutathione (GSH) or mercaptoethanol (ME) at any time *after inhibition had been established* produced complete reversal of inhibition, at least during the time period when the kinetics of the uninhibited reaction was linear (60–90 minutes). A similar response was elicited with GTP, but this, unlike the response to sulfhydryl reagents, gradually weakened with time. The lag in inhibition kinetics and the effect of sulfhydryl reagents suggested that some key component of the protein synthetic system was being oxidized. This was further supported by the observation that inhibition did not occur if molecular oxygen was strictly excluded from the system.

In the course of further purifying the components of the incorporation system we discovered that thorough dialysis of the $100,000 \times g$ supernatant fraction (or passage through Sephadex G25) completely abolished the capacity of the system to respond to inhibitor! Inhibitability could be restored by adding a bit of boiled supernatant. These findings implicated a small molecule as adjuvant in the inhibition and suspicion fell on GSH because it is abundant in liver and might be expected to participate in an oxidative process. GSH did indeed restore inhibitability to the system at low concentration (0.05 mM), but as mentioned earlier, it abolished inhibition at high concentration (0.5 mM or above). The kinetics of GSH-dependent inhibition showed the characteristic lag observed before in the undialyzed system and was strictly dependent on the presence of molecular oxygen. These two findings in turn suggested the likelihood that GSH was being converted to oxidized glutathione (GSSG) during the incubation and the latter was functioning as primary oxidant. When GSSG was added directly to the inhibitor-containing system inhibition was immediate (i.e., without the lag). GSSG was effective at concentrations of 0.01 mM and above, and it produced no inhibition in absence of the inhibitor. Furthermore, GSSG was equally effective under either anaerobic or aerobic conditions.

It seemed reasonable then to postulate that inhibitor was an enzyme catalyzing a GSSG-mediated oxidation of some SH-sensitive step in protein synthesis. It has been reported that one of the terminal transfer enzymes is sensitive to SH oxidation and there are indications that this enzyme is closely associated with microsomes in liver (32).

Using relatively crude supernatant fractions as a source of transfer enzymes together with amino acyl-sRNA and polyribosomes we have shown that the GTP-reversible inhibitor does indeed affect the transfer reaction (31). We are currently determining which of the enzymatic steps is involved.

In view of the fact that the transfer of amino acids from amino acyl-sRNA to protein is the inhibitor-sensitive step, we carried out experiments designed to assess the relative activity of the enzymatic transfer capacity of supernatant fractions from normal and regenerating liver. When initial rates of transfer reaction were measured at limiting enzyme concentration, we found the enzymes from regenerating liver 126% more active than the normal (12 animals, range 75–180%). These differences were abolished by any one of the following measures: (1) allowing the reaction to go to completion; (2) increasing the enzyme concentration; (3) adding GTP to the reaction mixture; or (4) allowing the crude supernatant fractions to age for several hours at 0°C. In the latter case the equalization of activity was due to an *increase* in the activity of the normal enzymes, while the regenerating enzymes remained unaffected by the aging process.

In spite of the intriguing circumstantial relationship of altered transfer capacity in regenerating liver fractions and the fact that our inhibitor acts upon the transfer reaction, we have no evidence that the two phenomena are related. We have not found total extractable inhibitory activity significantly altered during regeneration, nor can we find any but small differences in the activity of purified microsomes from normal and regenerating liver.

What about the role of GTP? It is possible that GTP directly antagonizes the action of inhibitor. It seems more likely that GTP participates in a terminal reaction in which the oxidation-sensitive component—the inhibitor target—is also involved. Oxidative limitation of a GTP-requiring enzyme would in effect increase the requirement of GTP. Such a view would be more in harmony with current concepts of the direct role of GTP in protein synthesis (32–34).

It is not implausible that the membrane-polysome complex might have built into it a system regulating the rate of over-all protein synthesis in the adult animal cell. Some general mechanism must exist that prohibits a population of adult cells from further net increase in cellular mass—a mechanism that can be temporarily or irreversibly set aside by signals sent forth upon induction of regeneration or malignant growth. On the other hand, endoplasmic membranes are rich in a variety of oxidative enzymes whose function may be physiologically entirely unrelated to protein synthesis. Their release upon disruption of the cell may result in oxidative inhibition of many sensitive processes, protein synthesis among them.

Perhaps this recital of some of our approaches to problems of protein synthesis in animal cells has value in restoring a healthy respect for the difficulties still to be faced in understanding intracellular synthetic mechanisms. At this juncture in the history of biology when the code is cracked and confidence is high, it is still abundantly clear that we have only "scratched the surface." This may be heartening to a new generation of biochemists who are willing to ask questions whose answers are not readily predictable.

REFERENCES

1. Wilson, S. H., and Hoagland, M. B., *Proc. Natl. Acad. Sci. U.S.* **54**, 600 (1965).
2. Kjeldgaard, N. O., and Kurland, C. G., *J. Mol. Biol.* **6**, 341 (1963).
3. Peters, T. *J. Biol. Chem.* **237**, 1186 (1962).
4. Gordon, A. H., and Humphrey, J. H., *Biochem. J.* **75**, 240 (1960).
5. Richmond, J. E., Shoemaker, W. C., and Elwin, D. H., *Am. J. Physiol.* **205**, 848 (1963).
6. Wilson, S. H., and Hoagland, M. B., *Biochem. J.* (submitted) (1966).
7. Revel, M., and Hiatt, H. H., *Proc. Natl. Acad. Sci. U.S.* **51**, 810 (1964).
8. Wilson, S. H., Hill, H. Z., and Hoagland, M. B. *Biochem. J.* (submitted) (1966).
9. Wilson, S. H., and Hoagland, M. B., In preparation.
10. Henshaw, E. C., Bojarski, T. B., and Hiatt, H. H., *J. Mol. Biol.* **7**, 122 (1963).
11. Ville-Trevino, S., Farber, E., Staehelin, T., Wettstein, F. O., and Noll, H., *J. Biol. Chem.* **239**, 3826 (1964).
12. Baglio, C. M., and Farber, E., *J. Mol. Biol.* **12**, 466 (1965).
13. Palade, G. E., and Siekevitz, P., *J. Biophys. Biochem. Cytol.* **2**, 171 (1956).
14. Rothschild, J., *Biochem. Soc. Symp. (Cambridge, Engl.)* **22**, 4 (1963).
15. Dresden, M. H., and Hoagland, M. B., *Science* **149**, 647 (1965).
16. Dresden, M. H., and Hoagland, M. B., *J. Biol. Chem.* (in press) (1967).
17. Dresden, M. H., and Hoagland, M. B., *J. Biol. Chem.* (in press) (1967).
18. Spirin, A. S., and Betitsina, N. V., Ajtkhozhin, M. A., *Zh. Obstch. Biol.* **25**, 321 (1964).
19. Joklik, W. K., and Becker, Y., *J. Mol. Biol.* **13**, 496 (1965).
20. Girard, M., Latham, H., Penman, S., and Darnell, J. E., *J. Mol. Biol.* **11**, 187 (1965).
21. Nemer, M., Infante, A. A., *Fed. Proc.* **24**, 283 (1965).
22. Henshaw, E. C., Revel, M., and Hiatt, H. H., *J. Mol. Biol.* **14**, 241 (1965).
22. Wilson, S. H., In preparation.
23. Georgiev, G. P., Samarina, O. P., Lerman, M. I., Smirnov, M. N., and Severtzov, A. N., *Nature* **200**, 1291 (1963).
24. Muramatso, M., Hodnett, J. L., and Busch, H., *Biochim. Biophys. Acta* **91**, 592 (1964).
25. Neidhardt, F. C., and Magasanik, B., *Biochim Biophys. Acta* **42**, 99 (1960).
26. Bucher, N. L. R., *Intern. Rev. Cytol.* **15**, 245 (1963).
27. von der Decken, A., and Hultin, T., *Exptl. Cell Res.* **19**, 591 (1960).
28. McCorquodale, D. J., Veach, E. G., Mueller, G. C., *Biochim. Biophys. Acta* **46**, 335 (1961).
29. Rendi, R., *Biochim. Biophys. Acta* **31**, 266 (1959).
30. Hoagland, M. B., Scornik, O. A., and Pfefferkorn, L. C., *Proc. Natl. Acad. Sci. U.S.* **51**, 1184 (1964).
31. Scornik, O. A., Hoagland, M. B., Pfefferkorn, L. C., and Bishop, E., *J. Biol. Chem.* (in press) (1966).
32. Gasior, E., and Moldave, K., *J. Biol. Chem.* **240**, 3346 (1965).
33. Arlinghouse, R., Schaeffer, J., and Schweet, R., *Proc. Natl. Acad. Sci. U.S.* **51**, 1291 (1964).
34. Conway, T. W., and Lipmann, F., *Proc. Natl. Acad. Sci. U.S.* **52**, 1462 (1964).

Recognition Problem: On the Specific Interaction between Coding Enzyme and Transfer RNA

V. A. Engelhardt and L. L. Kisselev

Our present knowledge of the multistage pathway of protein biosynthesis leading from amino acids to peptide bond formation has been profoundly influenced in two important ways by the deep insight and the brilliant experimental mastership of F. Lipmann. These two points concern, first, the very starting point of the long chain of events, namely, the initial activation of the amino acid, and, second, one of the final stages, the location of the aminoacyl group on the assembly line—on the messenger ribonucleic acid (mRNA) attached to the ribosome.

The activation step consisting in the formation of the carboxyl phosphate bond represents one particular case of the general principle of utilization of acyl phosphates for biosynthesis, as outlined by Lipmann (1941) in his classic article. In recent years the elegant experiments, in collaboration with Chapeville *et al.* (1962), have demonstrated unambiguously that the exact localization of the transfer RNA (tRNA), carrying an aminoacyl group on the template, mRNA, is determined exclusively by the particular tRNA and is completely independent of the nature of the acyl residue attached to the tRNA molecule.

The connecting link between the two stages just mentioned includes the transesterification of the aminoacyl group from adenosine monophosphate (AMP) into tRNA, catalyzed by the same enzyme as the activation step. The experiments reported here are concerned with certain properties of this enzyme, especially the interaction with its second substrate, the tRNA.

The tRNA is generally regarded now as part of the "translating system" in the process of protein biosynthesis. The molecules of tRNA have a double selective property, determined by the individual characteristics of the molecular structure. On the one hand, we have the specific inter-action of the anticodon with the corresponding coding triplet in the template, mRNA. The specificity of this interaction is sufficiently well explained in terms of complementary bonding between the nucleotides of the reacting molecules. On the other hand, tRNA is characterized by the specific affinity for the enzyme which attaches it to the particular amino acid. Thus tRNA fulfills the function of a molecular bilingual dictionary, which serves to establish the correct connection between the words of the "amino acid language" and the "nucleic acid language." In human practice a dictionary is operated by the translator, who finds the necessary word of the one or the other language. On the molecular level the function of operating the translating mechanism belongs to the enzyme, which actually carries out the coding.

The enzyme (E.C.6.1.1) has been given several names: pH 5 enzyme, activating enzyme, aminoacyl-tRNA synthetase or ligase. Fully aware that we might be reproached for proposing a new name for an enzyme already so rich in designations, we shall use, for the sake of convenience, a name, "codase," which combines brevity with an exact indication of its essential biological function.

The molecule of tRNA is composed of two parts: the coding triplet (anticodon) and the rest of the molecule (its "body" or corpuscular part). The question naturally arises—which part determines the specific inter-action with the enzyme, codase? We tried to examine this question by subjecting the tRNA to chemical or physical treatments that would produce selective modifications of definite nucleotides and comparing the effects with the known compositions of codons attributed to the dif-ferent amino acids (Table I). We obtained experimental evidence (Kisselev and Frolova, 1964) in favor of a dual role of the coding triplet, the latter appearing responsible for the interaction both with mRNA and with the enzyme. These experiments have been substantially extended and, as reported here, fully confirm the previous results and bring new evidence supporting the originally postulated conclusions.

A similar approach has been used by several authors, but the results have been inconclusive. The main reason for the uncertitude of the results of previous investigations undoubtedly must be attributed to the fact that the treatments employed were of very limited specificity. As a rule, not one particular kind of nucleotide was modified, but at least two or even three. This applies to reactions of methylation, bromination, de-amination, and treatment with formaldehyde (Weil *et al.*, 1964; Yu and Zamecnik, 1963; Carbon, 1964; Penniston and Doty, 1963; Kuchanova *et al.*, 1963). In our experiments we tried to avoid this difficulty as far as possible.

In addition to chemical modification, another approach was also used, namely examining the competitive inhibitory effect of suitably selected substances. Finally an attempt was made to modify not the nucleic acid, but the enzyme.

MATERIALS AND METHODS

In most experiments tRNA and codase preparations from yeast and rat liver prepared by routine methods were used. For special purposes heterologous systems (enzyme and tRNA from different sources) were employed. No characteristic differences attributable to the source of material were observed, but only moderate quantitative differences of the absolute values and not of the relative effects.

The experiments were, in general, carried out in such a way that the preparation of total tRNA was incubated with the corresponding reagent for different lengths of time and the reagent removed by repeated pre-cipitation of tRNA or by passing the solution through a suitable column. Various labeled amino acids were added to individual samples and upon addition of the complete enzymatic mixture the amount of ^{14}C-amino acid incorporated was measured. A sample of tRNA incubated without a modifying agent served as control. Details of experimental conditions are mentioned in the legends accompanying the figures and in the tables, as well as in previous publications (Kisselev and Frolova, 1964; Frolova *et al.*, 1965).

RESULTS

ELIMINATION OF URACYL: TREATMENT OF tRNA WITH NH₂OH

In accordance with known data (Schuster, 1961; Verwoerd *et al.*, 1961) analyses have shown that after 5-hour's treatment under the conditions of the experiments about one-quarter of the uracyl residues become modified (Kisselev *et al.*, 1965).

As can be seen from Figs. 1 and 2, after hydroxylamine treatment of the tRNA the incorporation of the different amino acids is affected in a very different degree. Acceptor activity of some of the tRNA's, namely those responsible for reacting with serine or with phenylalanine, remain almost completely unaffected by the treatment, which destroys the uracyl resi-

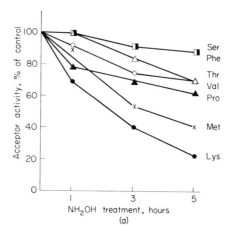

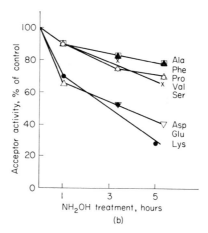

FIG. 1.   Acceptor activity of tRNA, treated with hydroxylamine (2.5 M NH$_2$OH, 0.1 M borate, pH 9.5, 30°C); tRNA from yeast, enzyme from rat liver (A) and yeast (B). Transfer RNA was isolated by phenol-water extraction, followed by purification with cethyltrimethylammonium bromide and gel-filtration (Kisselev and Frolova, 1964). After removal of tRNA the 105,000 ×g supernatant fraction served as the enzyme preparation. Each tube contained a total volume of 0.4 ml: 0.1 mg tRNA; 0.5–1 mg enzyme protein; Tris-HCl, pH 7.7, 25 µmoles; ATP (K salt), 3 µmoles; MgCl$_2$, 5 µmoles; KCl, 20 µmoles; and ^{14}C-amino acid, 0.05 µmoles (specific activity of amino acid was 5–15 mC/mmole). After reacting at 37°C for 15 minutes an equal volume of 10% trichloroacetic acid (TCA) was added; the precipitate formed was transferred to a Millipore filter disk, washed with cold 5% TCA and ethanol, dried, and counted in a gas-flow counter with ≈23% efficiency.

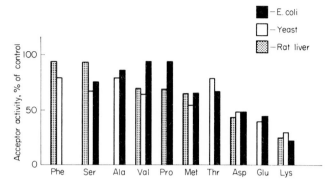

FIG. 2. A comparison of the degree of tRNA inactivation caused by NH_2OH treatment for 5 hours in different homologous systems. Assay was carried out as described in Fig. 1.

TABLE I

SUMMARY OF CODONS AND ANTICODONS

Amino acid	Codons[a]	Anticodons
Phe	UpUpU; UpUpC	ApApA; ApApG
Pro	CpCpU; CpCpC CpCpA; CpCpG	GpGpA; GpGpG GpGpU; GpGpC
Val	GpUpU; GpUpC GpUpA; GpUpG	CpApA; CpApG CpApU; CpApC
Ser	UpCpU; UpCpC UpCpA; UpCpG	ApGpA; ApGpG ApGpU; ApGpC
Ala	GpCpU; GpCpC GpCpA; GpCpG	CpGpA; CpGpG CpGpU; CpGpC
Thr	ApCpU; ApCpC ApCpA; ApCpG	UpGpA; UpGpG UpGpU; UpGpC
Met	ApUpG; ApUpA	UpApC; UpApU
Asp	GpApU; GpApC	CpUpA; GpUpC
Glu	GpApA; GpApG	CpUpU; CpUpC
Lys	ApApA; ApApG	UpUpU; UpUpC
Gly	GpGpU; GpGpC GpGpA; GpGpG	CpCpA; CpCpG CpCpU; CpCpC
His	CpApU; CpApC	GpUpA; GpUpG
Leu	UpUpG; CpUpU CpUpC; CpUpG	ApApC; GpApA GpApG; GpApC

[a] From Nirenberg et al. (1965).

dues. Alanyl-, prolyl-, and valyl-tRNA's show a decrease of activity of about 20–25% after 5 hours. In contrast to this, asparagyl-, glutamyl-, and especially lysyl-tRNA's lose as much as 70–80% of their reactivity. A look at Table I, in which the recent codon assignments (and the anti-codons of the corresponding tRNA's) are summarized, shows an obvious correlation between the presence (and number) of uracyl residues of the coding triplets of the different tRNA's and their susceptibility toward NH_2OH.

MODIFICATION OF CYTIDINE: TREATMENT WITH NH_2OCH_3

Table II shows that treatment with NH_2OCH_3 at pH 5, when according to Kochetkov et al. (1963) predominantly cytidyl residues are attacked,

TABLE II
ACCEPTOR ABILITY OF tRNA TREATED WITH NH_2OCH_3[a]

	Acceptor activity (cpm/mg)		Remaining activity (%)
[14]C-Amino acid	Control	Treated	
Lysine	12,000	9400	78
Phenylalanine	5000	3600	73
Serine	8000	5600	70
Proline	2000	1200	60
Methionine	8000	4100	51
Aspartic acid	15,000	7200	48

[a] $1.5\,M$ NH_2OCH_3 in $0.1\,M$ acetate buffer, pH 5.0 at 37°C. Enzyme and tRNA from rat liver, reaction time 6 hours.

results in a marked, but not widely different decrease in the accepting ability of tRNA toward the different amino acids. No such clear-cut differences are observed, as in the case of hydroxylamine treatment at pH 9.5. The decrease, more or less common to all kinds of tRNA, can easily be explained as the result of modification of the cytidyl residues of the common grouping, at the acceptor end of tRNA, with its two cytidine groups.

ELIMINATION OF GUANINE: PHOTOCHEMICAL DESTRUCTION

It is known (Simon et al., 1965) that photochemical oxidation, induced by methylene blue, attacks chiefly the guanine residues in nucleic acids. In our experiments this treatment produced an effect qualitatively similar to that of NH_2OCH_3, which shows poor selectivity; the incorporation of all amino acids was strongly reduced (Table III). The low degree of specificity is attributable to the modification of the common terminal

TABLE III

LOSS OF ACCEPTOR ACTIVITY AFTER PHOTOCHEMICAL REACTION OF tRNA
WITH METHYLENE BLUE IN THE PRESENCE OF O_2 AND LIGHT[a]

[14]C-Amino acid	Acceptor activity of tRNA (cpm)		Remaining activity (%)
	Control	Treated	
Valine	2550	630	25
Lysine	1900	440	23
Phenylalanine	1000	210	20
Histidine	3970	400	10
Arginine	5273	540	10
Proline	2800	140	5
Leucine	5618	123	2.5

[a] Enzyme from rat liver; tRNA from yeast. Samples were incubated (2 mg tRNA/ml in Tris-HCl, 0.05 M, pH 8.5 + 0.2 M NaCl at 20°C) and irradiated in the presence of O_2 for 5.5 hours with (treated) or without (control) methylene blue. The dye (0.2 mg/ml) was removed by passing the solution through an Amberlite IRC-120 column (Na form).

guanine residue at the nonacceptor end. These results can therefore be regarded as indicating that the ubiquituous presence of the terminal guanyl in all the tRNA's is connected with some specific role of this nucleotide in acceptor function.

COMPETITIVE INHIBITION

Evidence of an independent nature, based not on chemical modification of the tRNA, but on competitive effects, also supports the assumption of the role of the coding triplet of tRNA in the interaction with codase.

It has been reported (Hayashi and Miura, 1964) that tetranucleotides obtained from incomplete hydrolyzates of tRNA exhibit an inhibitory effect on the incorporation of amino acids in normal tRNA. In preliminary experiments we found (Kisselev and Frolova, in preparation) that alcohol-soluble fragments of polyadenylic acid produce an inhibitory effect of a competitive type on the incorporation of phenylalanine (anticodon rich in adenine); no effect is observed with lysine (anticodon rich in uracyl). This result obviously favors participation of the coding triplet in the interaction of tRNA and codase.

Competitive inhibition was also examined in another way, using tRNA chemically modified in two different manners. In one series of experiments a preparation of tRNA treated with NH_2OH or methylene blue was added to a complete system containing normal tRNA. As can be seen from Table IV no inhibitory effect was observed; on the contrary a slight increase in

TABLE IV

INFLUENCE OF MODIFIED tRNA ON THE INCORPORATION
OF ^{14}C-AMINO ACIDS INTO NORMAL tRNA

[14]C-Amino acid	Modifying factors	Amount of modified tRNA added (mg)	Acceptor activity (cpm)
Lysine	NH₂OH, pH 9.5, 6 hours	None	1510
		0.15	1600
		0.30	1650
		0.60	1665
Lysine	O₂, light, methylene blue, 6 hours	None	1150
		0.1	1230
		0.3	1330
Proline	O₂, light, methylene blue, 6 hours	None	1440
		0.1	1480
		0.3	1560

[a] Each sample contained 0.15 mg of yeast tRNA and 1.0 mg of enzyme protein. The slight increase in acceptor ability is due to residual activity of treated tRNA.

incorporation was noticeable, evidently owing to incomplete inactivation of the treated samples. In the other series tRNA was subjected to periodate oxidation, which deprives the tRNA of its acceptor properties without affecting the coding triplet. In this case a typical competitive inhibition is observed.

MODIFICATION OF THE CODASE PROTEIN: PHOTOCHEMICAL INACTIVATION

We first attempted to obtain information about the differences in the amino acid grouping, which is responsible for the binding of the coding nucleotide triplet of the corresponding tRNA (Kuchanova and Kisselev, 1966). We used a photochemical method, which is known to result not only in the oxidation of sulfhydryl groups, but also, what seemed more important, to attack selectively the histidine residues within the protein molecule.

The conventional codase preparation was subjected to irradiation in the presence of methylene blue as a photosensitizer. After incubation the dye was removed by passing the reaction mixture through a Sephadex G-25 column. Control samples were irradiated in the absence of dye or incubated with methylene blue in the dark; both controls gave results identical with the untreated sample. After the treatment the enzyme solution was divided into several samples to which different labeled amino acids were added together with all the factors needed to reconstitute the complete experimental system, and after incubation the incorporation of the label in tRNA was determined.

As can be seen from Fig. 3, the results of labeling with the various amino acids showed marked differences. In all cases a decrease of incorporation was noticeable, but the degree of inactivation toward the

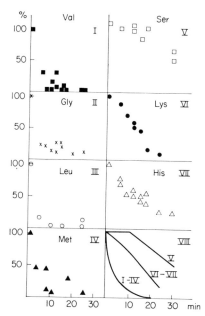

Fig. 3. The photooxidation of aminoacyl-RNA synthetase preparation caused by irradiation with light in the presence of O_2 and methylene blue. After removal of tRNA 50 mg of enzyme protein was incubated at 5°C with or without methylene blue (0.5 mg) in potassium phosphate buffer, 0.2 M, pH 7.0 (total volume, 5 ml). After irradiation samples were passed through a Sephadex G-25 column (20 × 1.5 cm) and incubated with tRNA immediately. Section VIII represents the summarized curves for different types of inactivation. The acceptor activity (% of control) is plotted against time of irradiation (in minutes); enzyme and tRNA from rat liver.

different amino acids varied considerably. The inactivation toward serine after 30-minutes' irradiation did not exceed 50%, with lysine and histidine the inactivation proceeded much further, but reached low levels only after prolonged irradiation. In samples with valine, glycine, leucine, and methionine almost complete inhibition of the enzymatic activity was often observed after just 5-minutes' irradiation. The curves in section VIII of Fig. 3 represent the average of the corresponding experiments.

DISCUSSION

Loftfield and Eigner (1963) expressed the opinion, based on experiments with heterologous systems, that there appears to be no stringent reason for admitting the existence of a special site in the tRNA for the interaction with the enzyme, besides the one which interacts with the mRNA. Yu and Zamecnik (1963) came to an opposite conclusion, but later Yu and Zamecnik (1964) considered the possibility of an overlapping of the two sites. Weil *et al.* (1964) and Carbon (1964) supported the view that two distinct reactive sites are present in the tRNA molecule.

From the results reported here the following conclusion appears justified—that the coding triplet of the tRNA molecule fulfills a dual role in the protein biosynthesis. On the one hand, we have the interaction with the template, mRNA, based on the complementarity of nucleotides. This could be called a homomolecular recognition between molecules of similar type, the two nucleic acids. On the other hand, we now see that the coding triplet plays an important, probably decisive role also in the interaction with the codase (heteromolecular recognition between protein and nucleic acid).

The specificity of the interaction of the coding triplet of tRNA with the codon in mRNA can be interpreted as the result of hydrogen bonding between the complementary nucleotides. It would be a fascinating task to find ways to obtain similar information concerning the interaction between the protein molecule of the codase and the nucleotide coding triplet of the tRNA. It is evident that to interact specifically with a given coding triplet the codase must possess a definite array of a certain number of amino acids, not necessarily adjacent to one another, but possibly also brought in close vicinity as the result of folding of the peptide chain within the tertiary structure of the protein molecule. For each coding triplet a strictly fixed combination of amino acids would appear necessary. It is tempting to suppose, by way of analogy, that just as there exists a nucleotide code, some kind of "amino acid code" might also exist, localized in the molecular structure of the various individual codases.

The nucleotides of the coding triplets in tRNA are generally regarded as being present in the free, unpaired state. It is not astonishing that these more reactive nucleotides play the predominant role in the interaction with the enzyme molecule and constitute the principal part of the recognition mechanism. As the number of unpaired nucleotides in tRNA amounts to approximately 25% of the total nucleotide content (Kisselev *et al.*, 1964), it is only reasonable to expect that other unpaired nucleotides may also play a certain role in the codase-tRNA interaction. But evidently this role would be of secondary importance; perhaps it manifests itself in the species specificity of the relationship between codase and tRNA.

A certain difficulty is introduced in the interpretations given here by the facts concerning the degeneracy of the genetic code. Would there necessarily be a strictly corresponding "degeneracy" or multitude of different codases for one and the same amino acid? The difficulty is increased still further by the bifunctionality of the codase. Assuming a degeneracy of codases it would be necessary to admit that one of the two functions of codases, namely that of activating a particular amino acid, remains constant, whereas the second function, that of recognizing a particular coding triplet, varies in several ways. One way to overcome this difficulty would be to consider the possible functioning of a mixed doublet-triplet code or, for some amino acids, a doublet code in interaction with codase. In this case only one type of codase molecules would be necessary for interaction with the "family" of coding triplets specific for one particular amino acid. It can hardly be doubted that the forces acting in the binding of protein and tRNA are not necessarily identical with those that act in the codon-anticodon pairing. Another possibility would be that the tRNA's corresponding to a particular amino acid and carrying different "degenerate" anticodons have a sufficiently similar chemical structure in certain regions of the noncoding, corpuscular part and in this case the "corpuscular" affinity could compensate for the lower coding triplet specificity. More definite answers can only be given when more is known about the recognizing site of the codase.

Decisive evidence pertaining to the questions raised here can be expected when a larger number of physical or chemical factors become available. They must possess a high degree of selectivity toward the separate nucleotides and amino acids. So long as this is not achieved, the method of competitive inhibition applied on a larger scale can be regarded as very promising. In this respect the results reported here are encouraging. The opposing effect of chemical changes, that affect in one case the specific coding triplet, and in the other the nonspecific, "common-accepting" terminal nucleotide is significant: in the first case the competitive property disappears, in the second it remains unchanged.

Perhaps the most challenging problem remains the examination of the "amino acid" code for the recognizing site of the codase. The difficulties here are considerable, but each step would bring us closer to an understanding of the crucial point involving the whole mechanism of biological coding—the functioning of the enzyme, codase, which brings about the translation from one molecular language to another.

ADDENDUM

More extensive examination of the tRNA preparations from *E. coli* and yeast treated with NH_2OH at pH 5.0 (Kisselev, Frolova, and Alexandrova, 1966) revealed a correlation between the deepness of the inactivation and the cytosine content of the anticodon.

A number of papers appeared recently which accept our general idea on the participation of the anticodon in the interaction with the codase (Ebel, Weil, Rether, and Heinrich, 1965; Hayashi and Miura, 1966; Burton, Varney, and Zamecnik, 1966).

The systematic study was undertaken (Kuchanova and Kisselev, 1966) on the inactivation of the various codases by means of photochemical oxidation. It was found that the enzymes so far examined could be separated roughly into two groups —those which are relatively resistant and those which are sensitive to the photochemical action. The enzymes from the first group activate polar amino acids whereas the enzymes from the second—the nonpolar ones. Therefore a correlation exists between the degree of the inactivation of the enzymatic activity and the polarity of the substrates. This fact may be considered as an indication that the "primary" recognition between the codase and amino acid involves some relatively nonspecific groupings common to the enzymes which react with similar amino acids. This primary recognition may be based on the hydrophilic or hydrophobic nature of the substrate and of the active site of the enzyme protein.

REFERENCES

Burton, K., Varney, N. F., and Zamecnik, P. C. (1966). *Biochem. J.* **99**, 29C.
Carbon, J. A. (1964). *Biochem. Biophys. Res. Commun.* **15**, 1.
Chapeville, F., Lipmann, F., Ehrenstein, von G., Weisblum, B., Ray, W. J., and Benzer, S. (1962). *Proc. Natl. Acad. Sci. U.S.* **4**, 1086.
Ebel, J. P., Weil, J. H., Rether, B., and Heinrich, J. (1965). *Bull. Soc. Chim. Biol.* No. 47, 1599.
Frolova, L. Yu., Kisselev, L. L., and Engelhardt, V. A. (1965). *Dokl. Akad. Nauk SSSR* **164**, 212.
Hayashi, H., and Miura, K. (1964). *J. Mol. Biol.* **10**, 345.
Hayashi, H., and Miura, K. J. (1966). *Nature* **209**, 376.
Kisselev, L. L., and Frolova, L. Yu. (1964). *Biokhimiya* **29**, 1177.
Kisselev, L. L., Frolova, L. Yu., Borisova, O. F., and Kuchanova, M. K. (1964). *Biokhimiya* **29**, 116.
Kisselev, L. L., Zaitseva, G. N., and Frolova, L. Yu. (1965). *Dokl. Akad. Nauk SSSR* **165**, 1188.

Kisselev, L. L., Frolova, L. Yu., and Alexandrova, N. A. (1966). *Biokhimiya*, **31**, in press.

Kochetkov, N. K., Budowsky, E. D., and Shibaeva, R. P. (1963). *Biochim. Biophys. Acta* **68**, 493.

Kuchanova, M. K., and Kisselev, L. L. (1966). *Dokl. Akad. Nauk SSSR* **169**, 1195.

Kuchanova, M. K., Kisselev, L. L., and Frolova, L. Yu. (1963). *Biokhimiya* **28**, 1053.

Lipmann, F. (1941). *Advan. Enzymol.* **1**, 99.

Loftfield, R. B., and Eigner, E. A. (1963). *Acta Chem. Scand.* **17**, 117.

Nirenberg, M., Leder, P., Bernfield, M., Brimacombe, R., Trupin, J., Rottman, F., and O'Neal, C. (1965). *Proc. Natl. Acad. Sci. U.S.* **53**, 1161.

Penniston, J. T., and Doty, P. (1963). *Biopolymers* **1**, 209.

Schuster, H. (1961). *J. Mol. Biol.* **3**, 447.

Simon, M. I., Grossman, L., and Vunakis, H. V. (1965). *J. Mol. Biol.* **12**, 50.

Verwoerd, J. R., Kolhage, H., and Zillig, W. (1961). *Nature* **292**, 1038.

Weil, J. H., Befort, N., Rather, B., and Ebel, J. P. (1964). *Biochem. Biophys. Res. Commun.* **15**, 447.

Yu, C.-T., and Zamecnik, P. C. (1963). *Biochim. Biophys. Acta* **76**, 209; *Biochem. Biophys. Res. Commun.* **12**, 457.

Yu, C.-T., and Zamecnik, P. C. (1964). *Science* **144**, 856.

Applications of RNA Polymerase in the Detection of Base Sequence Relationships between Ribonucleic Acids

Richard S. Hayward, Jean Legault-Demare, and Samuel B. Weiss

The ubiquitous distribution of enzymes which catalyze the DNA-directed synthesis of RNA is now widely recognized (Hurwitz and August, 1963; Smellie, 1963).* The senior author's search for such an enzyme, which led to its description in mammalian nuclei (Weiss and Gladstone, 1959), was largely stimulated by the experience he gained in the field of protein biosynthesis while working in the laboratory of Dr. Fritz Lipmann from 1956–1958. Today, our understanding of how ribopolynucleotides are synthesized *in vivo* has been considerably advanced by *in vitro* studies on the mechanism of ribonucleotide polymerization by highly purified preparations of RNA polymerase. Even so, the exact mechanism of polymer assembly, especially with respect to the biosynthesis of fully functional RNA molecules such as transfer RNA, remains unclear.

The experimental evidence to date suggests that most, if not all, cellular RNA's are assembled on DNA templates by the enzymatic action of RNA polymerase (Goodman and Rich, 1962; Robinson *et al.*, 1964; Yankofsky and Spiegelman, 1962). At the same time, it seems certain

---

* The following abbreviations are used in this chapter: DNA and RNA for deoxyribonucleic acid and ribonucleic acid; cRNA for RNA prepared synthetically with RNA polymerase and complementary in base sequence to its template; C, A, G, and U for cytidine, adenine, guanine, and uracil, respectively, and NTP for ribonucleoside triphosphate; RNase for a mixture of pancreatic and T_1 ribonuclease.

that many of the newly assembled ribopolymers are unfinished products and must undergo specific modifications before they are fully functional in the growing cell. Table I lists some of the various RNA species found in mammalian cell extracts. More than 90% of the cellular ribonucleic acid is composed of ribosomal (18 and 28 S) and soluble (4 S) RNA; the remainder includes components such as 45, 33, and 5 S RNA. Other "minor" RNA cell constituents are those utilized as templates for protein synthesis and commonly referred to as messenger RNA's. The stepwise conversion of 45 S RNA to 28 and 18 S ribosomal RNA by selective chain cleavage, as proposed by Scherrer *et al.* (1963), may be cited as one

TABLE I

RNA SPECIES FOUND IN MAMMALIAN TISSUES

Sedimentation characteristics (S)	Cell fraction	Function
RNA		
45	Nuclei	Ribosomal RNA precursor[a]
33	Nuclei	Ribosomal RNA precursor[a]
28	Ribosomes	Structural?
18	Ribosomes	Structural?
5	Ribosomes	Unknown
4	Supernatant	Adapter for protein synthesis
Others	Nuclei and ribosomes	Messengers for protein synthesis

[a] Ribosomal RNA may also serve as a template for ribosomal protein synthesis.

probable example of a modification occurring at the polynucleotide level. Chemical alterations of previously polymerized nucleotides, such as methylation (Borek, 1963), and possibly isomerization of uridine to pseudouridine (Weiss and Legault-Démare, 1965), belong to a different class of macromolecular modifications. Thus, it is highly probable that some of the "minor" RNA components represent molecules at intermediate stages of completion. The characterization of such intermediates becomes essential if the stepwise processes for the formation of biologically active ribopolymers are to be fully understood. Although characterizations of RNA species with respect to their molar base compositions, secondary structures, and molecular sizes are extremely helpful, a more distinctive property of any nucleic acid is its primary nucleotide sequence. With this in mind, we have attempted to devise a method for comparing the arrangement of nucleotide residues in two different RNA species. Figure 1 gives an outline of the proposed procedure for a hypothetical case in which it is desired to determine whether or not an unidentified RNA, prepared in a radioactive form, contains sequences of significant length in common with 28 S ribosomal RNA. In this case. purified 28 S RNA is used as a template for highly purified RNA polymerase, giving a product of complementary sequence (28 S cRNA).

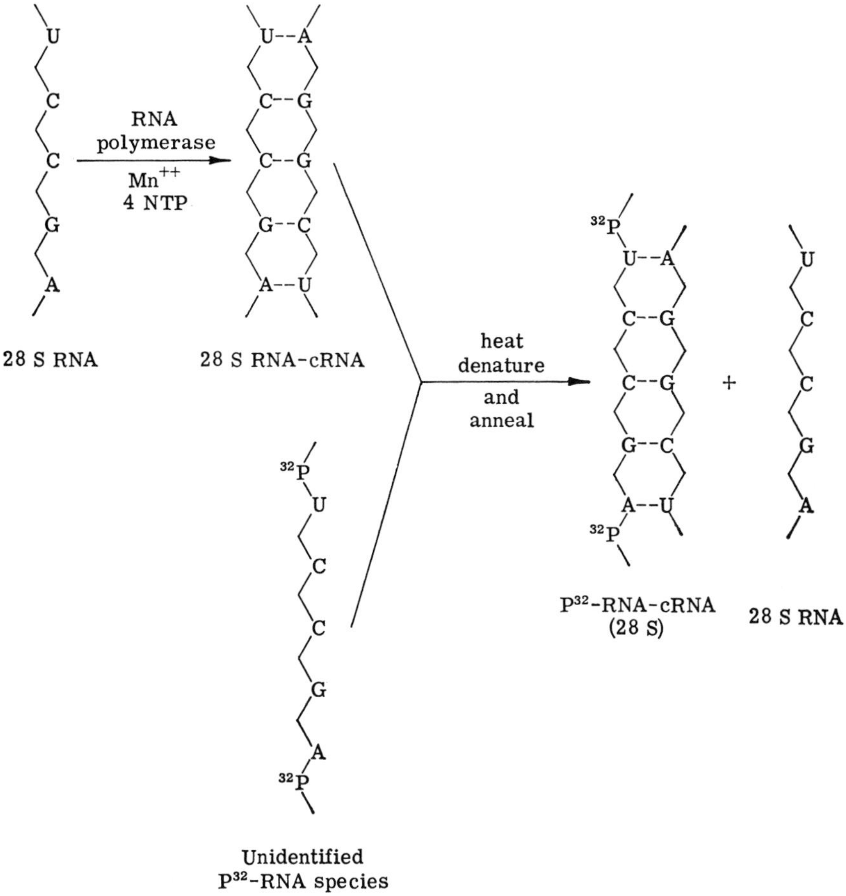

FIG. 1.   Hybridization scheme for comparing nucleotide sequences in RNA's.

The synthetic cRNA is shown hydrogen-bonded to its 28 S RNA template. It is not certain that the cRNA product is a complement of the complete sequence of the template; however, previous studies using different RNA templates have shown that the base composition of the product accurately reflects the base composition of the template in a complementary fashion (Fox *et al.*, 1963). Sequence complementarity of the "unidentified" ^{32}P-RNA and the 28 S cRNA may now be detected by hybridization. This procedure involves mixing of the synthetic and labeled RNA, heat denaturation to dissociate the cRNA from its template, and annealing of the mixture under conditions previously described (Robinson *et al.*, 1964). The annealed material is then subjected to ribonuclease treatment, and the surviving acid-precipitable radioactivity determined. Since only double-stranded RNA's are largely resistant to ribonuclease digestion, the amount of undigested ^{32}P-RNA may, given the proper controls, be used as an index of the quantity of labeled RNA-cRNA hybrid formed. In Fig. 1, hybrid formation is shown to occur between the 28 S cRNA and the ^{32}P-RNA, indicating that the latter shares a common nucleotide sequence with 28 S RNA. Labeled ribopolynucleotides which are not related to 28 S RNA in this manner should not be hybridizable.

The feasibility of detecting nucleotide sequence homologies by the above procedure was first tested with 45 S RNA and synthetic ribosomal cRNA. Tritiated 45 S RNA was prepared according to the procedure outlined by Scherrer and Darnell (1962). HeLa cells were exposed for 30 minutes to ^{3}H-uridine, collected by centrifugation, washed, and subjected to phenol extraction at 60°C. Labeled 45 S RNA was isolated and purified from the total RNA extract by successive sucrose-gradient centrifugations. Ribosomal RNA was prepared from nonradioactive HeLa ribosomes by phenol extraction, and the 28 and 18 S RNA species, isolated by sucrose-gradient centrifugation, were used separately as templates with *Micrococcus lysodeikticus* RNA polymerase to assemble the respective cRNA's. The results of annealing experiments carried out with the HeLa cell preparations are shown in Table II. Labeled 45 S RNA is not by itself, nor when annealed with 28 or 18 S RNA (not shown in Table II), resistant to nuclease digestion; however, when annealed with saturating amounts of the synthetic complements of either ribosomal RNA species, some 50% of the 45 S RNA resists enzymatic degradation. Since the 28 and 18 S RNA species have been shown to hybridize with different DNA cistrons (Yankofsky and Spiegelman, 1963), at least for bacteria, the presence of both 28 and 18 S cRNA in the annealing mixture would be expected to increase the percentage of 45 S ^{3}H-RNA hybridized. However, mixtures of this type afforded no better protection of the labeled RNA against RNase digestion than saturating amounts of each cRNA species alone. One plausible explanation for this result is that the 28 and 18 S RNA used as templates had been cross-contaminated. Previous experience in this laboratory has indicated that the clean separation of the two ribosomal RNA species by simple gradient centrifugation is quite difficult. In any case, the over-all results support the concept that 45 S RNA may be an intermediate in ribosomal RNA synthesis (Scherrer et al., 1963) and are in agreement with the conclusions of Perry et al. (1964), who showed that 28 and 18 S RNA could compete with 45 S RNA in hybridization to DNA. Annealing experiments with labeled 33 S RNA and ribosomal cRNA gave similar results.

TABLE II

HYBRIDIZATION ANALYSIS OF HeLa CELL 45 S ^{3}H-RNA

RNA components of annealing mixture[a]	Total counts in mixture (cpm)	RNase-resistant counts after annealing	
		cpm	%
Experiment 1			
45 S ^{3}H-RNA	615	18	2.9
45 S ^{3}H-RNA + 28 S-cRNA (0.25 μg)	615	109	17.7
45 S ^{3}H-RNA + 28 S-cRNA (0.75 μg)	615	283	46.1
Experiment 2			
45 S ^{3}H-RNA + 18 S-cRNA (0.6 μg)	702	216	30.8
45 S ^{3}H-RNA + 18 S-cRNA (3.0 μg)	702	324	46.1
45 S ^{3}H-RNA + 18 S-cRNA (6.0 μg)	702	352	50.2

[a] The amounts of cRNA shown are approximate estimates and in each case a 3- to 4-fold excess of either the 28 or 18 S template RNA was also present.

The studies described above suggested that the RNA-cRNA annealing technique could be used to identify the occurrence of common nucleotide sequences in different RNA preparations. Therefore, we next turned our attention to another RNA whose identity and relationship to the well-characterized species of cytoplasmic RNA's are far less certain than in the case of the 45 S material. Several investigators have described the presence of a 5-6 S RNA component in various organisms (Comb and Katz, 1964; Galibert et al., 1965; Rosset and Monier, 1963). We have used the procedure of Legault-Démare et al. (1964) to purify 5 S RNA from rat liver and mouse Ehrlich ascites tumor cells. This procedure involves the chromatography of microsomal RNA on a column of salmine-kieselguhr (Fig. 2). Under the chromatographic conditions employed, the 28 and 18 S ribosomal RNA's are not eluted; however, two discrete RNA fractions are obtained with approximate sedimentation rates of 4 and 5 S. Analyses of these two fractions indicate that, although they are very similar in their over-all base composition, they differ in their content of methylated bases and pseudouridine, the 5 S component being deficient (if not entirely lacking) in these nucleotide constituents. Furthermore, only the 4 S component serves as an acceptor for acyl-activated amino acids; the 5 S component is devoid of this activity. Similar properties for these two RNA components have been described by others (Comb *et al.*, 1965; Rosset *et al.*, 1964), who have further shown that 5 S has a higher molecular weight and different end-groups from those of 4 S. In spite of these differences, it has been suggested

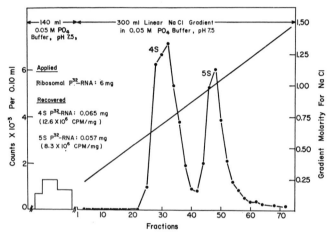

FIG. 2. Chromatography of Ehrlich ascites ribosomal ^{32}P-RNA on a column of salmine-kieselguhr.

on various grounds that 5 S RNA may be a precursor of 4 S transfer RNA, the conversion requiring appropriate alterations such as chain shortening, base modifications, and possibly CCA end-addition. If such a relationship exists between the two RNA species, they should also be related by common primary nucleotide sequences. This possibility has been examined by preparing both molecular species in a radioactive form and annealing them with synthetic 4 S cRNA.

Table III shows that neither 4 nor 5 S ^{32}P-RNA, alone or in the presence of excess nonradioactive 4 S RNA, develops resistance to ribonuclease digestion after annealing. The data also show that, whereas annealing of 4 S ^{32}P-RNA with synthetic 4 S cRNA does impart partial resistance to the labeled species, no such resistance is observed when 5 S ^{32}P-RNA is annealed with 4 S cRNA. The results suggest that the

4 and 5 S RNA's do not have a common pattern of nucleotide arrangement and hence make it seem unlikely that there is a precursor-product
relationship between these two ribopolynucleotides.

One objection which may be raised to our interpretation of the above
experiment is that the synthetic 4 S cRNA may not be a true complement of 4 S "precursor" RNA. In the assembly of 4 S cRNA by RNA
polymerase, which we presume to occur by base-pairing of the ribonucleotide substrates with the appropriate complementary nucleotides of
the template, it is possible that the presence of some of the "minor"

TABLE III
RIBONUCLEASE RESISTANCE OF ANNEALED 4 AND 5 S RNA's

RNA components of annealing mixture[a]	Total counts in mixture (cpm)	RNase-resistant counts after annealing	
		cpm	%
Experiment 1			
4 S ^{32}P-RNA (0.5 μg)	4760[b]	71	1.5
5 S ^{32}P-RNA (0.5 μg)	3537[b]	50	1.4
Experiment 2			
4 S ^{32}P-RNA (0.5 μg) + 4 S RNA (30 μg)	4650	37	0.8
5 S ^{32}P-RNA (0.5 μg) + 4 S RNA (30 μg)	3655	28	0.8
4 S ^{32}P-RNA (0.5 μg) + 4 S cRNA (1 μg)	4870	694	14.2
5 S ^{32}P-RNA (0.5 μg) + 4 S cRNA (1 μg)	3420	59	1.7

[a] The amounts of cRNA shown are approximate estimates and in each case a
25-fold excess of the 4 S template RNA was also present.

[b] These data were obtained in a later experiment and have been corrected for
isotope decay.

nucleotide components of 4 S RNA (methylated bases, inosine, pseudouridine, etc.) might affect the base-pairing relationship sufficiently
to give "false" synthetic 4 S cRNA (i.e., a product hybridizable to
"finished" 4 S RNA, but not correctly hybridizable to the original un-
modified 4 S precursor). This argument seems unlikely, since the number of "odd" bases in 4 S RNA is relatively small, and also because these
bases do not prevent hybridization of soluble RNA with DNA (Goodman and Rich, 1962), or with cRNA made on DNA templates (Robinson
et al., 1964). Moreover, in many cases the "minor" bases have been
found to hydrogen-bond in qualitatively the same way as their presumed
parent bases (Goldberg and Rabinowitz, 1963; Szer, 1965). However,
the above objection cannot yet be entirely rejected.

If a precursor-product relationship does not exist between the 5 and

4 S ribopolynucleotides, then one must look elsewhere to find a biological function for 5 S RNA or question its existence as a discrete molecular species. With respect to the latter point, other hybridization analyses indicate that there is no sequence homology between 5 S RNA and 18 S or 28 S RNA, suggesting that 5 S RNA is not a degradation product of these larger molecules. In our studies, as well as in others (Comb et al., 1965; Galibert et al., 1965; Rosset et al., 1964), the 5 S RNA species is found associated with ribosomes, and very little, if any, is present in the soluble fraction. The possibility arises that this RNA may be a structural component of ribosomes or that it plays a direct role in polypeptide formation. Preliminary assays for the stimulated binding of 5 S RNA to ribosomes by specific trinucleotides known to be protein chain termination or "nonsense" codons in Escherichia coli (Nirenberg et al., 1965) gave negative results.* However, these experiments were carried out with mammalian 5 S RNA and E. coli ribosomes and might merit further study in a homologous system.

In general, the comparison of RNA base sequences by the procedure outlined in Fig. 1 seems to be technically reasonable and sufficiently specific to serve as a valuable tool for determining relationships between different RNA species. Certain preparative difficulties have been encountered in the use of this procedure, but these have been largely overcome; at the same time there are certain advantages over other available procedures. One such advantage (especially in work with higher organisms) is that highly radioactive ribopolynucleotides are not required, as is usually the case in carrying out studies of competition between RNA's for annealing to DNA, where only a small fraction of the total DNA genome contains sequences complementary to those of a specific cytoplasmic RNA (Goodman and Rich, 1962; Yankofsky and Spiegelman, 1963). So far, our experience with the RNA-cRNA annealing assays suggests that, although they may be difficult to interpret quantitatively, they provide a satisfactory qualitative tool for RNA characterization in appropriate cases.

REFERENCES

Borek, E. (1963). Cold Spring Harbor Symp. Quant. Biol. **28**, 139.
Comb, D. G., and Katz, S. (1964). J. Mol. Biol. **8**, 790.
Comb, D. G., Sarkar, N., Devallet, J., and Pinzino, C. J. (1965). J. Mol. Biol. **12**, 509.

* Assays for binding of 5 S ^{32}P-RNA to Escherichia coli ribosomes were conducted by Dr. M. Nirenberg to whom we are deeply grateful.

Fox, C. F., Robinson, W. S., Haselkorn, R., and Weiss, S. B. (1963). *J. Biol. Chem.* **239**, 186.

Galibert, F., Larsen, C. J., Lelong, J. C., and Boiron, M. (1965). *Nature* **207**, 1039.

Goldberg, I. H., and Rabinowitz, M. (1963). *J. Biol. Chem.* **238**, 1793.

Goodman, H. M., and Rich, A. (1962). *Proc. Natl. Acad. Sci. U.S.* **48**, 2101.

Hurwitz, J., and August, J. T. (1963). *In* "Progress in Nucleic Acid Research" (J. N. Davidson and W. E. Cohn, eds.), Vol. 1, pp. 59-92. Academic Press, New York.

Legault-Démare, J., Rebeyrotte, N., Leprieur, A., and Roussaux, J. (1964). *Biochim. Biophys. Acta* **87**, 165.

Nirenberg, M., Leder, P., Bernfield, M., Brimacombe, R., Trupin, J., Rottman, F. and O'Neal, C. (1965). *Proc. Natl. Acad. Sci. U.S.* **53**, 1161.

Perry, R. P., Srinivasan, P. R., and Kelley, D. E. (1964). *Science* **145**, 504.

Robinson, W. S., Hsu, W.-T., Fox, C. F., and Weiss, S. B. (1964). *J. Biol. Chem.* **239**, 2944.

Rosset, R., and Monier, R. (1963). *Biochim. Biophys. Acta* **68**, 653.

Rosset, R., Monier, R., and Julien, J. (1964). *Bull. Soc. Chim. Biol.* **46**, 87.

Scherrer, K., and Darnell, J. E. (1962). *Biochem. Biophys. Res. Commun.* **7**, 486.

Scherrer, K., Latham, H., and Darnell, J. E. (1963). *Proc. Natl. Acad. Sci. U.S.* **49**, 240.

Smellie, R. M. S. (1963). *In* "Progress in Nucleic Acid Research" (J. N. Davidson and W. E. Cohn, eds.), Vol. 1, pp. 27-58. Academic Press, New York.

Szer, W. (1965). *Biochem. Biophys. Res. Commun.* **20**, 182.

Weiss, S. B., and Gladstone, L. (1959). *J. Am. Chem. Soc.* **81**, 4118.

Weiss, S. B., and Legault-Démare, J. (1965). *Science* **149**, 429.

Yankofsky, S. A., and Spiegelman, S. (1962). *Proc. Natl. Acad. Sci. U.S.* **48**, 1069, 1466.

Yankofsky, S. A., and Spiegelman, S. (1963). *Proc. Natl. Acad. Sci. U.S.* **49**, 538.

Microdifferentiation in Macromolecules

Rollin D. Hotchkiss

THE NATURE OF BIOCHEMICAL PATHWAYS

The chalk filigrees which cover the blackboards of modern biochemistry are woven with two kinds of reaction arrows, one expressing transfer of matter, the other of information. Although the two networks are often entangled, they are rather profoundly different.

Classic biochemical arrows link substances which are actually being converted, thus in

$$A + BX \xrightarrow{\text{enzyme}} AX + B \qquad (1)$$

the arrow means "is converted into." It is often useful to construct abbreviated reaction chains describing the path of an electron or a radioactive carbon atom, or the energy flow in the path of an active biochemist:

$$\text{Pyruvate} \rightarrow \text{acetyl-CoA} \rightarrow \text{acetyl-P} \rightarrow \text{ATP} \rightarrow \text{pantothenate} \qquad (2)$$

Here the expressions remain unbalanced but they still concentrate upon special conversions of matter, in which the arrow now conveys the idea, "leads to."[*]

But the expressions outlining information flow have a different purpose, for example, in

$$\text{DNA} \longrightarrow \text{RNA} \longrightarrow \text{protein} \qquad (3)$$

the arrows stand for "controls the synthesis of." With an inhibitor written over the arrow we get something different, too, such as "in a series of enzymatic steps of which one at least is inhibited by puromycin, controls the synthesis of." One must also be alert to another usage:

[*] Abbreviations used in this chapter: ATP, adenosine triphosphate; DNA, deoxyribonucleic acid; RNA, ribonucleic acid; acetyl-CoA, acetyl coenzyme A; acetyl-P, acetyl phosphate; DNase, deoxyribonuclease; RNase, ribonuclease.

$$\text{Adenine-thymine} \xrightarrow{\text{mutation}} \text{guanine-cytosine} \qquad (4)$$

where not a compound but a hydrogen-bonded pair of glycosylated bases "in opposed strands are replaced at the equivalent position in daughter cells by the pair." Many are the occasions on which these different languages are mixed on the same blackboard. It is particularly dangerous to do so when, in developing hypotheses, one needs clear thinking and would avoid schemes that while plausible are actually mixtures of stoichiometric, catalytic, and informational propositions.

But what are the significant differences after all? Does not DNA, for example, influence RNA simply by elegant pairwise monitoring of the nucleotide residues which go into its biosynthesis, that is, by a set of classic reactions?

WHAT IS AN INFORMATION TRANSFER?

The most important characteristic of information pathways, I believe, is that they utilize cooperative reactions and topological relations virtually to assure (i.e., "determine") the occurrence of a specific reaction. In information transfer, *opportunity* for interaction may reach otherwise unattainable probabilities, as notably it does in template-controlled biosyntheses. (Other macromolecular organizers seem to exist, too, such as mitochondria, chloroplasts, and membrane sites for replication and specific permeation.) For this reason, I have sometimes defined molecular biology as the biochemistry of improbable reactions.

When Improbability Becomes Probability

Biochemical conversions of small molecules ordinarily involve localized interaction of atom groups in which reacting nuclei must come together close enough so that their electrons can cross over. To accomplish reaction two probabilities must be satisfied, one involving *position* and the other the *state* of the atom groups. They may also be thought of as the opportunity and efficiency of collision. The opportunity or probability of close contact depends upon essentially random kinetic collisions and is strongly affected by mass concentration. The probability of having the collision be effective depends upon achieving thermodynamic activation sufficient to overcome energy barriers to reaction. An ionization or dissociation may contribute to activation, but the usual reaction between stable substances is improbable enough at low temperatures to require intervention of a catalyst. For these reasons, classic biochemical equations are actually only expressions of probabilities, no matter how definite the conversions look, or how well memorized in school. They are reported in terms of so many micromoles per second; often it is a very small fraction of the molecules available, and often too a reverse reaction sets in. Even simultaneous pairs, i.e., trimolecular reactions, are so improbable that they are usually supplanted by successive bimolecular reaction steps.

These limitations are lessened but not fully overcome by participation of enzymes, which are thought of as reducing energy barriers and permitting collisions to be effective. Probably, however, they cannot increase the number of total collisions of the small molecules, which move about much more rapidly than the proteins and, therefore, must do most of the "seeking." Even when a metabolic intermediate is produced upon, or remains attached to, an enzyme protein, it is still present only in low concentration and its opportunities for further reaction with another small molecule will not be increased so much as its efficiency per opportunity. So far as I can see, there is no sign that the enzymes involved in the template-controlled biosyntheses are in any way different in this respect. Monomers still must diffuse to the enzyme, which helps them one by one to form covalent bonds, but will discharge the same office without regard to specific side chains, for any monomer bearing the "class grouping," such as a 3'-hydroxyl or 5'-triphosphate, or the α-amino carboxyl residue.

If the enzymes help the collisions to be effective, it is the polynucleotides and ribosomes which increase the number, and especially the residue specificity, of the collisions. By forming loose associations (e.g., base pairs) with the otherwise rapidly moving monomers, these templates seem to detain them at the proper points and orientation for the next reaction step of biosynthesis. In effect, the small molecules are selected and brought to very high local concentration so that reaction becomes probable even when their over-all mass concentration is low. Most interesting is that the templates react selectively with the uniquely specific side chains (purines or pyrimidines in the nucleic acids or in the sRNA derivatives of amino acids) and leave the class groupings free for polymer formation. The enzymes of biosynthesis, on the other hand, ignore the side chains altogether and react with or activate the atoms around the class groupings, such as the hydroxyl, phosphate ester, and amino groups.

UNIQUENESS AND STOICHIOMETRY IN INFORMATION TRANSFER

Dealing with small molecules one is never in a position to predict exactly when any particular molecule will react or when it has reacted. On the other hand, an informational relationship may sometimes describe a supremely individual macromolecular event—a single specific occurrence. One can, for example, hope to observe a particular mutation [Eq. (4) occurring in a specific genetic region] within a context in which it has never occurred before in the history of the universe. In my own field, genetic transfer by DNA in microorganisms, one may contrive to introduce specific arrangements of DNA into cells which have never had them before. Similarly, one may arrange a rare recombination between two very unusual DNA's in some virus or cell.

After such a mutation, transformation or recombination, specific biosynthesis of complementary strands of DNA then appears to occur in recipient cells as it does *in vitro:*

$$\text{Strand X} \longrightarrow \text{strand X}' + \text{strand X} \longrightarrow \text{DNA}_{XX'} \qquad (5)$$

Examination of Eq. (5) will reveal that as written it combines the informational statement that strand X causes complementary strand X' to be synthesized and the biochemical statement that a strand X and a strand X' can unite in a transfer of matter to make $\text{DNA}_{XX'}$. In spite of the pitfalls mentioned before, it is almost unavoidable to write such partial processes in mixed language, for the template (here, strand X) takes part in the reaction and, unlike an enzyme, is not always regenerated.

Learning by Repetition

The involvement of the intermediate material transfer, however, becomes a mere detail in the informational statement that $\text{DNA}_{XX'}$ guides biosynthesis of molecules of its own kind:

$$1\text{DNA}_{XX'} \longrightarrow m\text{DNA}_{XX'} \qquad (6)$$

Now we are stressing instead the many repetitions which are possible in information transfer.

In fact, repetition is the main reason that, as noted above, a single occurrence of an informational event can sometimes be registered and detected. For amplification is possible at each step:

$$\text{DNA}_{XX'} \to m\text{DNA}_{XX'} \to mn\text{RNA}_X \to mno\text{polypeptide}_X \qquad (7)$$

The coefficients m, n, and o of the successive information transfers are biological *amplification factors* which are altogether different from *stoichiometric* constants (which in biochemical conversions also are often first empirical and then later rationalized). They are as yet only empirically measured, but they are not experimentally inaccessible. What is important to recognize is that their values are finite but neither equal to unity nor obvious by inspection; they are also surely *not intrinsic*, but vary from marker to marker, cell to cell, and condition to condition. It is a wonder to me that there is not even greater interest in and direct investigation on the challenging questions of how these fundamental amplification factors are quantitatively governed, increased, and decreased for the good of the cells.

The current study of control or regulation merely touches upon these questions. For the most part the enthusiasm is expended upon the discovery of qualitative relationships and the quantitative measurements are explored only as a device for making these discoveries. That is, investigators generally consider two cases, that in which the composite factor mno is zero and that in which it is finite but unknown.

BASIC MOLECULAR PARAMETERS OF GROWTH

Cumulative Values: Clonal and Population History, Evolution

Thoughtful use of Eq. (7) could do much to make biology a more quantitative science. Although the amplification factors m, n, and o seem usually to be small numbers (say 1 to 25) over a cell-division cycle or a messenger lifetime, they are expansible enough to take populations into account. Let us consider them first as cumulative numbers, summated over long periods of time, independent of temporary changes in time rates. The factor m (but not n and o) summated over time is an exponential function of the m value per replication (normally 2) in elapsed time t, for example, $m = (2)^{t/d}$ for division time d. The relations then describe biological history; we have only to define the limits of the system X. The system (X, X') can be taken to stand for a genome as well as a gene, whereupon Eq. (7) can represent the whole biological history of a vegetatively propagated cell clone (either haploid or diploid). The coefficient m of DNA replication furnishes a satisfactory record of the replication of biological units; multiplied by the inoculum or initial value (I), it gives the total census. In addition, the value of mn $(+m)$ (times I) gives the total mass of nucleic acid and $mnoI$ the total protein— consequently their sum $(m + mn + mno)I$ or, to within 2 or 3% $(mn + mno)I$ will fairly represent the total *mass* produced, the weight of all the individuals. It is also, therefore, a measure of their aggregate nutritional needs. Dividing their mass by mI, their number, of course, gives $n + no$ (roughly $= no$) as a measure of the average mass of an individual and, allowing for hydration (inverse density), also of its size.

All of these measures of the number, mass, size, etc., should be functions of composite m, n, and o values, averaged over all individual active units of DNA (or operons). In fact we commonly assume that m, the amplification factor for DNA, is the same for all units and parts of the DNA. To use these factors for organisms, most corrections, whether for inactivity or overactivity of certain gene regions, for numbers of cistrons per DNA unit, for constituents other than nucleic acids and protein (water, polysaccharides, cell walls, bones, etc.), as well as loss by death, could in general within a species be simply included in a single proportionality factor. This is because of the overall experience that the average chemical composition of individuals at different times and ages is relatively constant, within a species. Whenever this is not sufficiently true the differences can then be analyzed in just these same parameters, as will be discussed below.

When X represents a gene or a chromosome, Eqs. (7) and (6) describe (though perhaps could not predict) its success or fate in becoming established in the gene pool of an interbreeding population of a higher organism. Population geneticists would be interested in relative efficiencies m_x/m_y for different genes and gene groups. We can also expand the frame of the "inoculum" I to stand for an entire natural population, whereupon the relations given before speak about the entire history of the gene or chromosome—and if X is taken for the whole chromosome pool, they stand for the total progress, development, nutrition, and fate of the species.

In these last areas, particularly, one's first natural impression is that the quantitative meaning of these equations could only be general, fairly vague, and mainly descriptive or confirmatory of empirical observations. But I believe even here we can expect surprises. This is the way progress comes in area after area: first we doubt or despair of even having quantitative relations, then we sense them and describe them empirically, successively fitting them to principles that are more and more basic until we achieve some "predictability," and with that, what is called "theory."

BIOLOGICALLY RELATED TIME RATES: COMPOSITION, DIFFERENTIATION, PATHOLOGY

Each of these amplification factors can be considered not only cumulatively but as a function of time. Returning now to the more precise level of the cells and uniform tissues, we may let XX' and YY' stand for different genes or cistrons. It is desirable and potentially feasible to measure m, n, and o on the time rate of "copies per division cycle"; then they become parameters of enzyme activity levels, for they tell how much is partitioned out every time a new cell is made. On a comparative basis (n_x/n_y or no_x/no_y, etc.), they can outline the differential composition of cells in terms of separate components. Or if X and Y refer to cell and virus, similar ratios describe the competition between a virus and its host, and can reveal whether it is attributable to rapid replication(m) of the virus or superior expression in RNA(n) or protein synthesis(o).

Compared for the same gene and product between different cell lines, $no_x/n'o'_x$ they suggest the bases for differentiation within the organism or between species. These measures of "copies per gene per cell cycle" presumably would reveal exactly how and where repressors and suppressors alter the effective n's and o's and make cells different from each other. At this level, the factors describe cell composition and may be thought of ideally as quantitatively "determining" it, as the genes do in a qualitative sense.

More than that, our scheme is useful in suggesting gaps in our present knowledge and experiments we would not otherwise think about. It may be very important in distinguishing neoplasms from normal cells not only to know, as we now try to do, the enzyme levels of cancerous tissues, for example, but whether they attain these through changed values of n or o, or perhaps m, which should express any gene duplication or imbalance. The mode of action of hormonal, antibiotic, or other inhibitory or stimulatory substances affecting growth can be rather precisely sought among the average or specific m, n, and o factors of the affected cells, as well as in special enzyme inhibitions. Further, although we expect $m = 2$ per average division cycle, I do not think we know whether the newly replicated DNA as well as the old contributes already to its share of n copies of RNA within the division cycle in which it is synthesized. Perhaps the RNA only grows to $mn/2$ and polypeptide $mno/2$ molecules, or more precisely, we may underestimate by 2 the actual value of n and o. And looking at the newly investigated DNA's or RNA's of mitochondria, plastids or nucleoli, we may sharpen our questions about their functions by seeking to measure the time rates of their amplification factors.

ABSOLUTE TIME RATES: EFFICIENCY

But what if we estimate these parameters in absolute time units (copies per hour)? We are now dealing with efficiency. When not all of the units are reproducing, as is likely in higher organisms especially, the value of m per day or per hour is the measure of fertility or fecundity or reproduction potential. If, on the other hand, we are dealing with fully reproducing or mitotically propagating cells, it is the growth rate that is expressed by m (doublings per hour), or mno, which reflects it as the increases in mass, or nitrogen per hour. This last is, of course, more reliably true when we concern ourselves with whole genomes, but estimates can be made using single characteristic cell constituents. The n rates similarly tell how often a gene is used, and the absolute o rates in an equivalent way indicate the survival of different messenger RNA's.

These fundamental parameters are at the bottom, for example, of the differential synthesis of β-galactosidase after induction in *Escherichia coli*, classically measured in terms of enzyme units per unit of total bacterial mass over increasing time intervals (Monod *et al.*, 1952). Something related to this $mno_x/\Sigma mno$ was measured for amylomaltase in a population of pneumococci treated with transforming agents (Lacks and Hotchkiss, 1960). An approach to $m_x/\Sigma m$ is being estimated when increases in a specific marker DNA are measured against total DNA increase as a function of time after DNA transformation (Fox and Hotchkiss, 1960) or position in cell replication cycle (Yoshikawa and Sueoka, 1963). Furthermore, the individual parameters, no_x and no_y already mentioned, if measured on a per hour time basis, are the primary determinants of any tendency to change in composition with respect to constituents X or Y. It is, of course, clear that all such choice or change of parameter implies new proportionality constants which in general can be easily calculated, estimated, or experimentally measured. The principal weakness is that turnover and death would become large for certain of the broader long-term systems mentioned. They may not then be properly taken care of as mere "corrections" in the proportionality constants, but would have a more complex role.

Many of these relationships preferably depend upon *average m, n,* or *o* amplification factors, for example, one averaged for several genes or several cell types. This may be thought to require understanding that we shall never attain, but I think that as soon as we need them sufficiently we shall learn how to estimate the distribution or spread of these values in a more fundamental way than we can see how to do now. As indicated above, the differential values of n or o for different genes or cells should tell much about fundamental differences between them. They will have their own relations to each other and therefore become more and more predictable as we learn about their modifiers.

The potential meanings of these relationships are not exhausted with the above, but enough has perhaps been said to indicate that they will furnish a useful framework for discussing, comparing, and learning the basic properties which govern the output of biosynthetic mechanisms. Primarily, I believe that some part of the things now taught as empirical unexplained fact in biology of the species, organs, or cells—the things that are true "because they are that way"—will become more rational and more fundamentally understood, when related to this framework. Interested teachers and students are invited to try their hand at developing a more quantitative and more "theoretical" biology!

The processes of informational transfer, then, contain implications which go considerably beyond what we detect in ordinary biochemical conversion. Let us represent the first part of Eq. (3) in standard biochemical form (as we would if DNA were like an enzyme)

$$p\text{Ribonucleoside triphosphates} \xrightarrow[+\text{DNA}]{\text{polymerase}} \text{RNA} \qquad (7)$$

Considering the preceding discussion, it is clear that this leaves altogether out of account the most challenging aspects of the relation DNA $\rightarrow$ RNA. While both the polymerase and monomers are necessary for the reaction, they control only one aspect, the continuous and monotonously uniform part of the structure, the repeating $3',5'$-phosphate diester links. The modulations in RNA structure, the exquisitely specified base sequences, are chosen and controlled through the cooperative reactions made possible by the long-chain DNA templates. The RNA chains in part play a similar role in the choice of amino acid residues for the proteins.

THE ADVANTAGES OF LINEAR MACROMOLECULES

Let us try to define somewhat more precisely the nature of the information content of the polynucleotide templates and the polypeptides whose biosynthesis they govern. Part of the answer is to be found, I believe, in questions of structure and stability. Some of the principles perhaps to some degree apply also to networks of linear structures such as cell particles and membranes.

THE STABILITY OF LINEAR STRUCTURES

The polynucleotides and polypeptides may carry a large number of residues assembled by polymerases in a series of potentially reversible steps. Yet the enzymes to which they are mainly exposed and from which they are liable to degradation during the time of synthesis can only attack their end residues, one at a time. This is very important for stability, for it means that the whole long chain is as stable as its last-created linkage.

The "thermodynamic load" of maintaining the last residue on a giant polymer is not substantially greater than that slight overbalance in direction of synthesis which will make the first simple dimer stable. It is as though each new residue stabilizes or "locks into place" every residue which precedes it in the chain. This is a fact which I have never seen emphasized with the importance I think it deserves. It seems to me a broad principle governing biosynthesis and maintenance of the linear polymers, nucleotides, proteins, and polysaccharides whenever the crude degradative systems are not available. It seems to say that linear polymers are not very hard to maintain—and viewed simply as unspecified chains of random monomers, would not even be very improbable structures. One merely has to provide enough energy "pressure" at the end, and unit after unit should be ready to assume its place in the chain.

This feature of polymers is reminiscent of the spring-loaded dish-holding wells in modern restaurants: each new dish added to the top of the pile causes the whole to sink below the table an equivalent amount, so that the next can be added at the same energy level or height.

Of course, the precisely specified base sequences make the compositionally modulated nucleotide chains of actual nucleic acids highly improbable. Yet, as we have already pictured, in the presence of their templates, each specific monomer unit does actually become, by the monitoring effect of the complementary base residue, the most probable addition at each new site in the DNA. In these cases and in the assembly of aminoacyl-sRNA residues, weak interactions that are spontaneous guide each monomer into its proper place. The great importance of the weak interactions in providing orienting organization in biology has been very aptly pointed out by Watson (1965).

THE STABILITY OF CROSS-LINKED STRUCTURES

The principle of weak interactions is also used in holding together the already synthesized strands, especially in DNA. Here, a series of near-spontaneous pairings can with little effort bring whole complementary strands into paired configurations. By the same token since these are due to cooperation of *multiple weak forces*, the paired structures of DNA are at all times potentially capable of opening up locally. Such opening up is doubtless essential (as many have suggested) to enable them, e.g., in transcription, to express the singularities of their modulated base sequences, which are virtually covered up in the fully paired configuration.

Nevertheless, the binary structure lends to DNA further stability, both physical and chemical, as well as toward certain known enzymes. By contrast, in RNA, strands complementary to the active messengers are probably not often available. Correspondingly, RNA is physically less organized, more deformable, diffusible, and more available to metabolic pools than DNA, and more rapidly destroyed, even when organized in ribosomes. If RNA messengers have a tendency to combine with the complementary DNA strand along which they are presumably synthesized, they do so in competition with an equivalent DNA strand, and the nice regulation of this poised system may be a part of the control mechanism of the cells.

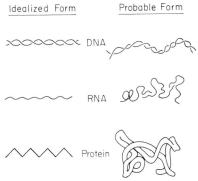

Fig. 1. Diagram suggesting the relative deviation of actual DNA, RNA, and protein structures in solution from their idealized informational forms. The DNA is nearly like its idealized form, whereas for proteins the idealized form is essentially a denatured molecule.

Polypeptide chains become rather highly organized in the natural proteins. The stereochemical configuration of the repeating amino carboxylmethyl units permits single-stranded helices to form, and the convenient basic, acidic, phenolic, sulfhydryl, and other groups allow numerous and various cross-links to hold the helices in specific three-dimensional roughly globular forms. Many of these cross-links are very strong, some at least like the disulfides being covalent bonds. These structural contrasts in the proteins and nucleic acids are indicated schematically in Fig. 1.

It was, in fact, the awesomeness of tertiary structure in the proteins that was brilliantly set aside by Crick when he proposed (Crick, 1958) that point-for-point linear correspondence between the nucleic acids and the polypeptide chains was at the basis of genetic control. Some of us, impressed that only denatured, inactive proteins were linear, doubted for a time that linear specification would sufficiently define each of the proteins. Luckily, Anfinsen *et al.* (1961) added to the list of spontaneously renaturable proteins (e.g., see Anson and Mirsky, 1931, 1934) the especially convincing example of specific disulfide bond formation during oxidation of reduced ribonuclease. If specific tertiary structures could sometimes be formed *in vitro,* we could expect even more favorable circumstances for folding up of proteins inside the cells.

Macromolecules as Reservoirs of Information

Linear structures are also *topologically* stable. No amount of bending, or tangling, of a chain molecule can alter one fundamental aspect, sequence, in the relation of each monomer residue in the chain to its neighbors. This would not be true for the information content of a nucleic acid or protein if, as once seemed reasonable enough, this were attributable to a two- or three-dimensional arrangement of its parts. Not only is a crumpled newspaper hard to read linearly—even the two-dimensional pictures it contains are distorted. A protein structurally coded in two or three dimensions by a specific DNA would have to go back to its DNA monitor for repair every time it was damaged. On the other hand, we can see that information in a linear coded chain could be to some extent immortal.

But only immortal if the metabolic and physical stability of the substances themselves permit. DNA, in solutions of moderate ionic strength a rather stiff rodlike molecule, is demonstrably highly stable in healthy cells, gaining, but only occasionally losing, labeled atoms, for example. It seems subject to enzymatic repair after structural damage by radiation and possibly shear. RNA is as already mentioned rather labile in all categories and especially as messenger. Proteins are subject to the infighting of active metabolism which involves some decay and also are thought to be in varying degrees liable to turnover or reutilization in response to the higher demands of the cell.

We can see then how the more stable DNA's seem dominant over RNA's where both are present and DNA comes to carry the "genes" although both can carry the same information. Perhaps in evolution too they came to stand in this relation to each other and in their turn toward the proteins, because *stability* of information had a high survival value. This point has been developed earlier (Hotchkiss, 1959). One may also speculate that even the relative irreversibility of the steps of Eq. (3) was developed afterward by successive evolutional selection of favorable and efficient mechanisms in the pathway.

THE CRYSTALLIZATION OF A MACROMOLECULAR MESSAGE

Finally, we can ask about the nature of the information involved in genetic determination of a protein. Of course, we often hear that there is translation from a four-letter into a twenty-letter alphabet—but that is only a statement about the code. What, after all, is the nature of the *messages* themselves? Here again it may be instructive to consider first for comparison and contrast a biochemical transfer.

ORGANIZATION OF STRUCTURE DURING BIOCHEMICAL CONVERSIONS

The well-known pathway of dissimilation and oxidation of glucose was central for the presentation of the concept of the concentration and transfer of energy in phosphate esters and anhydrides by Lipmann (1941). Both he and Kalckar (1941) at this time put needed emphasis on the role of the phosphate bonds, although well aware of the conversions of organic molecules which made the concentration of energy possible. The "metabolic wheels" often outlined by Lipmann and Krebs are a part of our modern systemization of biochemical knowledge and continue this trend of deemphasizing the purely material conversions which so much preoccupied earlier biochemists.

In reviewing this central pathway and one of its ramifications, I should like to propose a slightly different emphasis—the "meaning" to be found in each turn of a metabolic wheel, that is, the strategy of attack upon carbon atoms. The schematic outline given in Fig. 2 indicates one way of looking at parts of a glycolytic and oxidative dissimilation of glucose leading to fatty acid formation. The emphasis here is upon the "state of oxidation" of the individual carbon atoms, i.e., the extent to which their electrons have been drawn away by electron-hungry oxygen atoms. From this standpoint oxygen (or nitrogen) is the versatile electron collector, whereas the phosphate group appears more as lucky beneficiary than organizer.

Glucose represents an almost uniform dispersal of energy—each of its six carbon atoms has donated electrons to one oxygen atom and only the hemi-acetal carbon is associated with two. Progressively and irresistibly, however, the march of events leads to oxidation at one end of each carbon chain. Investment of phosphate esterification at the terminal positions achieves impermeability, which Davis (1958) has perceptively linked with the "importance of being ionized." Now, the glucose phosphate begins a most impressive series of conversions. An activating carbonyl group is moved to position 2 so that the chain will break at its middle.

The carbonyl group then returns to an end carbon, forming symmetrical triose phosphates having aldehyde groups which are readily oxidizable. With oxidation, a subtle insinuation of phosphate occurs and energy is drawn off as adenosine triphosphate, while a new set of rearrangements marches the original invested phosphate near to the new carboxyl group where it in turn receives an increment of energy concentrated from the

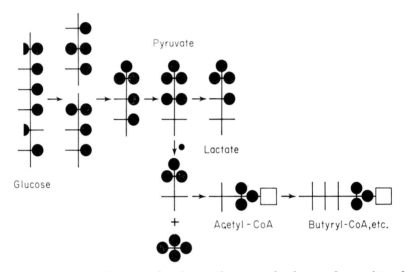

FIG. 2. Schematic diagram of carbon pathway in glycolysis and an arbitrarily chosen sequence of glucose oxidation and fatty acid biosynthesis. The filled circles may be thought of as oxygen atoms or more generally as electron-attracting centers indicating the degree to which the electrons of the carbon atoms have been drawn away ("degree of oxidation"). The hollow square designates coenzyme A. The evenly disseminated oxidation state of glucose is disproportioned in lactate, acetate, and the higher fatty acids into carbon chains nearly completely oxidized at one end and reduced at the other.

whole molecule, which is now a form of pyruvic acid. The elegant sequence can be looked upon as a device for marshalling and mobilizing the energy dispersed throughout the six carbons of glucose. The evenly oxidized glucose becomes the asymmetric pyruvic acid with now one reduced carbon atom and one nearly completely oxidized (carboxyl) carbon at the other end ready to be cast off as carbon dioxide. Even in the balanced exchange of anaerobic glycolysis (top line of Fig. 2) the lactate formed is highly asymmetric in regard to oxidation state.

As already mentioned, the activities of small molecules are described largely in statistical terms—energy content, lability, activation energies, probability of specific interaction, susceptibility to catalysis—properties which can only be defined for *populations* of molecules. Clearly it is just these statistical *tendencies* that are mobilized and organized by such biochemical conversions as those represented in Fig. 2. In fact, the activations occurring there can all be traced to proximity of the activated group to a carboxylate group (carboxyl phosphate, phosphoenol pyruvate, malonyl-CoA, and similar relations in the citrate cycle). Since the carboxyl group is the last oxidation step before carbon dioxide, the strategy of many metabolic conversions is simply that—to develop by reversible steps carboxyl groups in the vicinity of the acyl or phosphoryl group to be activated for transfer. By including the development of carbonyl groups to permit hydroxyalkyl (aldol) transfer, one can describe the meaning of very many metabolic conversions indeed.

In summary, catabolism of saccharides illustrates *the concentration of reaction tendencies from a stable evenly disseminated form in the sugars into energetically asymmetric molecules which develop in populations high probabilities for carboxyl-activated group transfer reactions.*

Differentiation of Structure along an Informational Pathway

The individual small molecule makes only a partial and uncertain contribution to the probability of reaction in a population of molecules. But we have seen that macromolecules are made up of many small units; they are in a sense a population in themselves. As such they show cooperative accumulation of probabilities either spatial (as for hydrogen bonding of two DNA strands, or cross-linking of proteins) or temporal (as for successive linear "reading" of base sequences in transcription). Therefore let us look upon template-controlled biosyntheses from the standpoint of a design to achieve probability for specific reaction.

The principal reactive sites in a DNA chain are the phosphate anions and the keto and amino groups. If we draw a section of native DNA structure showing these reactive groups but leaving space-filling groups as mere framework, we obtain something like Fig. 3. Since even the polyphosphate chain is undifferentiated, the singularities are principally of two kinds: (a) purine vs. pyrimidine or big-little, and (b) keto-amino. Especially to be noted is that the four-way modulation of a single chain (adenine-guanine-thymine-cytosine) is greatly diminished in the double-strand form. Not only are keto groups "neutralized" with opposed amino groups, but each big residue is balanced by a little residue. Since there is now only the subtlest difference between adenine-thymine and thymine-adenine and not even much between these and the other pairs, the already quiet four-way modulation of a single strand has been virtually reduced to a whispered two-way modulation having most of the reactive groups covered up. Each base is coupled in DNA with its "most opposite" type of base in another strand. Predominating over these softly whispered sounds are the strident rhythms of the multiple, negatively charged phosphate groups. In free nucleates, in simple solution (not organized by bases or histones), these latter cause the molecules to stay relatively independent and elongated, so that DNA especially takes up a rather simple conformation. These polyanionic repulsions are overcome by

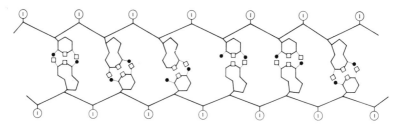

Fig. 3.   Diagram of a linear section of a pair of hydrogen-bonded polynucleotides, as in native DNA. The scheme emphasizes the principal distinguishing reactive centers (●, oxygen atoms, □, amino groups or ring nitrogen atoms, ⊖ phosphate anions). Merely space-filling groups are indicated only as lines; purines and pyrimidines simply by elongated or simple rings. Note the relative homogeneity of the double-strand molecule, even greater than that of its single strands.

internucleotide complex formation within the molecule, but hold the double molecules aloof and stable.

The relative sameness of the numerous specific polynucleotides is presumably responsible for the success of experimental generalizations such as the hydrolyses by specific DNase or RNase's, alkali lability or stability, effects of such agents as actinomycin, acridines, and certain dyes and ions, which do seem uniform for all DNA's, or RNA's, or sometimes both. Proteins have more unique sensitivities.

RNA, which seldom is supplied with its complementary strand, has the fourfold singularities of structure more exposed and greater consequent chemical reactivity and lability. This is commensurate with its role as active and working copy of the gene. We can see that the utilization of a four-symbol nucleotide modulation to determine a twenty-symbol amino acid message is more meaningful than just an economical mode of information storage and replication. It suppresses the chemical singularities that would lead to reactivity and instability in the information reservoirs and allows them to be revealed when needed for replication or translation. The polynucleotides, as intramolecular "populations" of relatively similar segments, have their statistical probabilities built in. What is lost in thermodynamic randomness, compared with a set of small molecules, is gained in structural definition in the polymer. But this is not equivalent to loss of entropy, for specific structure is more than *degree* of order, which is related to entropy and can be the same for many different sequences. Most important, a structural statement and prediction of reaction can be made about a single macromolecule of this kind, whereas entropy and energy functions only estimate average properties of sets of molecules.

How different the situation when the linear message is translated into protein! The few, much-alike (yet specific), and mutually repelling nucleotides bring about an assembly of the many, much-unlike amino acids. The polypeptide structure is studded with specifically interacting amino acid "side chains." In the proteins, the hydrophobic side chains can seek each other out and form complexes, the basic and acidic side chains can react either with each other or respond to the environment, the hydroxyl, imidazol, methylsulfide and other groups can fold in to form "active centers," and the sulfhydryl groups may lock the structure in enzyme-resistant form or loosen it, under the influence of oxidation-reduction control systems. That the final conformation in most proteins is a three-dimensional one has long been recognized (see Fig. 1).

At the polypeptide stage we see a process reminiscent of the biochemical principles discussed before. We saw that large units of the chemical energy of the almost uniformly structured glucose became mobilized successively at single carbon atoms. In the DNA-RNA protein system we have, not conversion, but transcription, of structures into each other. But with this copying, there is a similar mobilization of the dispersed information of the long nucleotide into "nodes" of information that "crystallize out" within the protein molecules as the highly specific active centers of three-dimensional enzymes.

Thus, the function of the metabolic pathways of the cell is to organize the small molecules in such a way as to concentrate their energy or mobilize their substance into forms which give probable group transfers. The function of the information pathways is to organize the stored macromolecular individuality of chemically simple and dispersed linear nucleic acids into the magnificent complexity and concentrated specificity of the proteins.

SUMMARY: OUT OF A LITTLE MONOTONY, MUCH VARIETY

The information transfers leading from DNA to RNA and protein depend upon the template control of biosyntheses of linear macromolecules which have both metabolically and topologically stable structures. These template processes are characterized by amplification steps rather than stoichiometric biochemical conversions. Templates, like enzymes, are used repeatedly. The multiplication factors of biosynthesis are basic parameters underlying growth, efficiency, differentiation, evolution, and pathology. Their quantitative evaluation would help to provide a theoretical basis for much that is empirical in biology today.

Qualitatively, the information pathways illustrate morphogenetic principles within macromolecules. Whereas small molecules have to be described in terms of average reactivities and energies, each macromolecule comprises a population of subunits leading to predictable reactivity within an individual structure. Double-stranded DNA has its delicate structural singularities all but suppressed into a relatively uniform, essentially two-fold modulation.

Much as intramolecular energy is mobilized by metabolic conversions of small molecules, from dispersed to concentrated form, by actual material conversion, the information of DNA is mobilized and, in addition, amplified. It is more uniform, more firm and ordered, more stable and less reactive, than RNA, accordingly gives rise to RNA, and is the dominant genetic determinant wherever both have been evolved. The spatial sequence of the polynucleotides is translated by a temporal sequence of syntheses in the polypeptides, with incorporation of a biochemically diverse series of subunits. In this way the stability of the delicately modulated four-symbol nucleotide messages becomes "crystallized" into the highly differentiated proteins, which can use their specific side chains to fold up into exquisitely specialized active structures. The process as a whole represents the concentration—with multiplication—of chemical diversity from a stable dispersed form into an elegantly organized and available active form.

REFERENCES

Anfinsen, C. B., Haber, E., Sela, M., and White, F. H. (1961). *Proc. Natl. Acad. Sci. U.S.* **47**, 1039.
Anson, M. L., and Mirsky, A. E. (1931). *J. Phys. Chem.* **35**, 185.
Anson, M. L., and Mirsky, A. E. (1934). *J. Gen. Physiol.* **17**, 393.
Crick, F. H. C. (1958). *Symp. Soc. Exptl. Biol.* **12**, 138-163.
Davis, B. D. (1958). *Arch. Biochem. Biophys.* **78**, 497.

Fox, M. S., and Hotchkiss, R. D. (1960). *Nature* **187**, 1002.

Hotchkiss, R. D. (1959). *Proc. 3rd Can. Cancer Res. Conference,* p. 3.

Kalckar, H. M. (1941). *Chem. Rev.* **28**, 71.

Lacks, S., and Hotchkiss, R. D. (1960). *Biochim. Biophys. Acta* **45**, 155.

Lipmann, F. (1941). *Advan. Enzymol.* **1**, 99.

Monod, J., Pappenheimer, A. M., Jr., and Cohen-Bazire, G. (1952). *Biochim. Biophys. Acta* **9**, 648.

Watson, J. D. (1965). "Molecular Biology of the Gene," 494 pp. Benjamin, New York.

Yoshikawa, H., and Sueoka, N. (1963). *Proc. Natl. Acad. Sci. U.S.* **49**, 559.

Problems of Synthesis and Purity of Macromolecules

John D. Gregory

During the two and one-half decades since the publication of Fritz Lipmann's clear-sighted paper on phosphate bond energy (Lipmann, 1941), very little reorientation of thought has been necessary in this field. New activated intermediates have come to light, of course, many through Lipmann's imaginative work, and new metabolic pathways have been found. But there has been no essential change in the principles of the production, transmission, and storage of energy in the form of metabolically useful group potential.

Logical extensions of the earlier ideas have, however, imposed striking new patterns on the general outlines of metabolism. In particular it has become evident that *in vivo* a great many molecules of all types, and especially macromolecules, are synthesized by reaction sequences different from those used for their breakdown. In addition, among macromolecules some types are evidently synthesized in a precise way by the use of templates, and others are not. From the latter situation certain problems arise that will be considered below.

CLASSIFICATION OF MACROMOLECULES

Macromolecular natural products may be formally classified in various ways, as in Scheme 1. Any such attempt is subject to criticism because a given type probably has several functions of varying importance depending upon its cellular or extracellular location and upon prevailing conditions. Lipids have not been included because for the purposes of this discussion they are not considered to be macromolecules.

SCHEME 1

Monodisperse { Nucleic acids } Information and
              { Proteins   } catalysis

              { Proteins
              { Cellulose, chitin, other glycans
              { Proteoglycans (mucoproteins)   } Structure
Polydisperse { Pectins, algins (polyuronides)
              { Cell wall components

              { Glycogen, starch, other glycans } Storage of energy
              { Polyphosphate   } and materials

BIOSYNTHESIS AND DEGRADATION

We now have considerable knowledge of the biosynthesis of almost all the types of compounds listed, and an outline of the pathways will be given. Nevertheless, any general scheme of intermediary metabolism, being a mosaic of information gathered from a great variety of organisms and tissues and often lacking confirmation in living cells, must be regarded with caution. The generalizations to be made here are intended to stimulate thought, not to be taken as universal.

As mentioned, the anabolic routes are different from the catabolic, and one reason for this is obvious in the light of our modern understanding of energetics. The synthetic pathways permit the utilization of more energy-rich linkages in forming the linkages of the polymer or macromolecule than would be possible by a reversal of the known degradative reactions. Substantial concentrations of polymer can thus be produced in an environment where the intermediates are dilute or scarce. Thus the energy originally present as group potential is utilized to produce and maintain concentration differences.

Another and speculative reason is that the cell may make use of the opportunity of separating synthetic and degradative pathways to different locations (metabolic compartments) by controlling the location of the enzymes. Chemical regulatory mechanisms, too, whether feedback or hormonal in nature, can function independently, for example, the several effects upon the activity of the glycogen-metabolizing enzymes (Ingram, 1965, p. 196).

Degradative reactions are very commonly hydrolytic and thus have equilibria that favor splitting. This applies generally to the classes of large molecules whose functions are information, catalysis, and structure. Those polymers that seem to have mainly, if not solely, storage functions are broken down not by hydrolysis, but in such a way that the linkage energy is not wholly lost. (This applies to their metabolic role and not to their digestion for the purpose of assimilation.) For example, the synthesis of starch or glycogen requires the expenditure of two energy-rich linkages per molecule of glucose, but phosphorolysis to glucose 1-phosphate permits some of this energy to be retained. The action of polynucleotide phosphorylase may possibly fall in this category.

The metabolic reactions of polyphosphate are less well understood, but it may serve for the storage of energy-rich phosphate much like the recognized phosphagens (Hoffmann-Ostenhof, 1962). The breakdown pathway may well be a reversal of the synthetic in this case.

Nucleic Acids

A simplification of the deoxyribonucleic acid (DNA) synthetic mechanism appears in Fig. 1. In this and in the other schemes, the activating

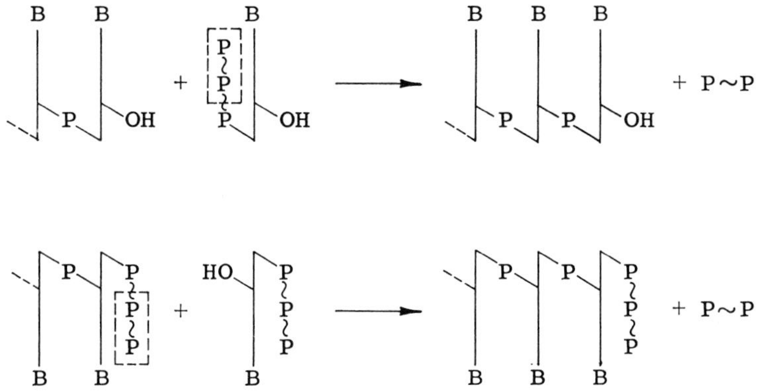

Fig. 1.   Chemical reactions in DNA biosynthesis. The upper equation is synthesis in the 5'- to 3'-direction. Purine and pyrimidine bases are represented by B.

group is outlined. Since the two strands of double-stranded DNA are antiparallel in orientation and are replicated simultaneously, it is necessary to postulate two reactions (Ingram, 1965, p. 49). In one strand the unit that is added carries the activating group for its own linkage; in the other the activating group is on the terminal member of the polymeric chain, and the added unit carries an activating group ready for the next step. Ribonucleic acid (RNA), at least messenger RNA, which is synthesized in the 5'- to 3'-direction (Bremer et al., 1965), must utilize the former reaction.

All of the enzymes that are known to degrade nucleic acids are hydrolytic in action except polynucleotide phosphorylase. This enzyme, which yields ribonucleoside disphosphates from RNA, may be involved in the turnover of metabolically active types of RNA, but its function in the cell has not yet been firmly established (Grunberg-Manago, 1963).

PROTEINS

The repetitive reaction in the assembly of amino acids into a protein chain is shown in Fig. 2, without any attempt to include the involvement of templates or ribosomes (Watson, 1965). Here again an activating group is found on the growing end of the polymer. The added unit also bears an activating group, but one not to be utilized (apart from its

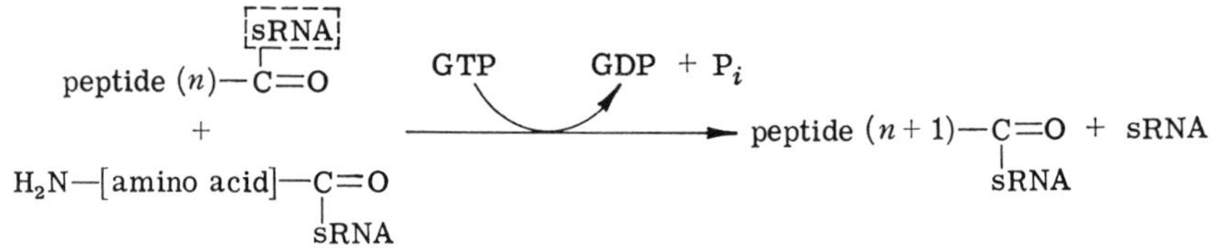

$$
\begin{array}{c}
\text{[sRNA]} \\
\text{peptide } (n)\text{—C=O} \quad\quad \text{GTP} \quad\quad \text{GDP} + \text{P}_i \\
+ \quad\quad\quad\quad\quad\quad\quad\longrightarrow \text{peptide } (n+1)\text{—C=O} + \text{sRNA} \\
\text{H}_2\text{N—[amino acid]—C=O} \quad\quad\quad\quad\quad\quad\quad \text{sRNA} \\
\text{sRNA}
\end{array}
$$

Fig. 2. Chemical reaction in protein biosynthesis. Soluble RNA, sRNA; inorganic phosphate, P$_i$; guanosine 5′-diphosphate, GDP; guanosine 5′-triphosphate, GTP.

coding function) until the addition of the next unit. The degradation of proteins apparently proceeds entirely through hydrolytic reactions catalyzed by the great diversity of proteases and peptidases.

HOMOPOLYSACCHARIDES

Intracellular synthesis and degradation of glycogen are diagrammed in Fig. 3 (Manners, 1962). Starch is made similarly, except that the activating group is adenosine 5′-diphosphate (ADP) instead of uridine 5′-diphosphate (UDP), and the phosphorolytic breakdown is analogous.

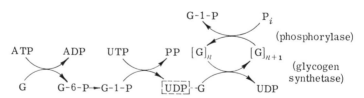

Fig. 3. Biosynthesis and degradation of glycogen. Glucose, G; glucose 1-phosphate, G-1-P; glucose 6-phosphate, G-6-P; uridine 5′-triphosphate, UTP; pyrophosphate, PP.

The precursor of cellulose is UDPG*, or prehaps GDPG†, but it is considered a structural rather than a storage polymer and is degraded by hydrolytic reactions. As seems to be the case in all polysaccharides, addition of units is made to the nonreducing end of the chain or to what may be thought of as the "tail" of the polymer. There is less evidence concerning the many other homoglycans of plants and animals (chitin, algins, pectins, fructans, mannans, galactans, etc.), but no type of activated intermediate has been shown other than nucleoside derivatives of sugars (Neufeld and Hassid, 1963).

Heteropolysaccharides

Available information on the synthesis of heteropolysaccharides, such as glycosaminoglycans (hyaluronic acid and chondroitin sulfates) (Dorfman, 1962) and bacterial polysaccharides and lipopolysaccharides (Osborn *et al.*, 1964), is also far from complete. When carbohydrate intermediates have been identified, however, they are again nucleoside diphosphate-activated units, and this is true for the bacterial glycerol and ribitol polyphosphates as well (Glaser, 1963). The biosynthesis of

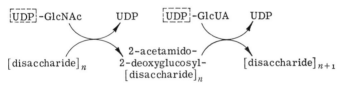

FIG. 4. Biosynthesis of hyaluronic acid. Uridine diphosphate N-acetylglucosamine, UDP-GlcNAc; uridine diphosphate glucuronic acid, UDP-GlcUA.

hyaluronic acid (Fig. 4) may be formulated as an example. The units are alternately added to the "tail" of the chain from the activated intermediates UDP-*N*-acetylglucosamine and UDP-glucuronic acid. This is consistent with the fact that most heteropolysaccharides are attached to protein or peptide by means of a glycosidic linkage at the "head" or reducing end, at least at some time during their existence. It is possible that they are normally synthesized in this state and that some types are then liberated by a later reaction.

Cell wall mucopeptides of bacteria, although they contain peptide sequences, seem not to be constructed in the same way as most proteins

---

* UDPG, uridine diphosphate glucose.
† GDPG, guanosine diphosphate glucose.

in that nucleic acid control is not involved (Perkins, 1963; Matsuhashi *et al.*, 1965).

COMPARISON OF MACROMOLECULES

The fact that proteins and nucleic acids are the only macromolecules that are synthesized with template control leads to the conclusion that they are the only ones in which we may expect to find monodispersity. In molecular populations of polysaccharides and also of other polymers that we are accustomed to regard as single species, the chain lengths may show more or less variation. Since the variety of components even in a heteropolysaccharide is relatively limited and the structure is partly repetitive, there is apparently no need for a template to guide the synthesis. The effects of several enzymes, whose specificity controls their order of action, seem to be sufficient to define the structure. There is no evidence to the contrary despite the fact that considerable specificity of structure, apart from the simple repetitive chain, has appeared in some cases such as the linkage area of acid glycosaminoglycans with protein in cartilage mucoproteins (Gregory *et al.*, 1964; Rodén and Armand, 1966). The presence of xylose in this particular structure has been related to a possible metabolic control mechanism for the synthesis of these mucoproteins (Neufeld and Hall, 1965).

THE CONCEPT OF "PURITY"

Problems of isolation and purification are enormously increased when polydispersity exists. In some cases, however, such as glycogen, the natural products are found in large concentration in the tissue and can be isolated relatively "pure" without difficulty. This is aided by the apparent absence of closely related species of molecules having differences of structure or composition other than molecular size.

In most cases the situation is far more complex. Starch, for instance, contains amylose, amylopectin, and sometimes a third component (Manners, 1962); agar consists of agarose and agaropectin, which differ in composition as well as structure (Horton and Wolfrom, 1963); the chondroitin sulfates and other glycosaminoglycans are a family that have small variations in constituents or in configuration (Brimacombe and Webber, 1964). In these particular examples, methods have been found for separating the molecular types because the chemical differences could be made use of and because these differences affected the physical properties enough to overshadow the effects of polydispersity. In other words, they are favorable situations.

Thus we must face the possibility that in the isolation and purification of macromolecules their polydispersity may sometimes mask the presence of mixtures of molecules that can legitimately be called different species. The choice of more appropriate fractionation methods can help, as illustrated in the work of Laurent on the separation of corneal muco-polysaccharides (Anseth and Laurent, 1961).

We must now look to our definitions of "purity" and consider what we will settle for in the area of polydisperse macromolecules. We clearly cannot arrive at an absolute definition of purity that is of any practical interest. If we wish to speak of "purification" at all, however, we should define our goals and our means of knowing whether we have made progress. "Where biologically active substances are concerned, the evidence required for reaching a reasonable judgment [of purity] must come from the biologist, the organic chemist, and the physical chemist. Purity should then be defined in operational terms, the more evidence the better" (Shedlovsky, 1943).

Even in the case of the monodisperse classes of compounds, it may not be sufficient for the biochemist to aim for "molecular species" in which all of the molecules have the same primary and secondary structures. Conformational changes in enzymes, for example, may be detectable on the basis of biochemical activity, and double strands of nucleic acids can be dissociated and recombined with other partners. When separation is possible because of conformational differences or associations that are ultimately reversible, purity must be judged in terms of the practical consequences. And, of course, functionally and operationally named substances, such as messenger and soluble RNA, are being resolved from day to day and will receive precise names as their structures are established.

In the area of polydisperse macromolecules we can never look forward to having completely homogeneous materials to work with. If separation methods of high resolution are available, it may be possible to divide a natural polysaccharide, for example, into a multitude of distinguishable fractions. But this is important only if it can be shown that they differ in metabolic activity or function. Unless this is so, there is no need to debate the "purity" of such a mixture; obviously any evaluation will depend on the interest of the moment and the sensitivity of methods of characterization. When a polymer, however, consists of the same units in the same arrangement, whether or not it varies in extent, we are justified in treating it as a molecular species and in giving it a name. It is essential therefore to look for fractionation methods that depend least on molecular size and that take advantage of chemical and charge characteristics.

Thus we find that as a consequence of knowledge accumulated from many years of studies on activated compounds in intermediary metabolism, we begin to appreciate the forces that govern the shape and extent of biological polymers. With these realizations we can start to formulate the general problems that will face the student of macromolecules in the future.

REFERENCES

Anseth, A., and Laurent, T. C. (1961). *Exptl. Eye Res.* **1**, 25.

Bremer, H., Konrad, M. W., Gaines, K., and Stent, G. S. (1965). *J. Mol. Biol.* **13**, 540.

Brimacombe, J. S., and Webber, J. M. (1964). "Mucopolysaccharides," 181 pp. Elsevier, Amsterdam.

Dorfman, A. (1962). *Federation Proc.* **21**, 1070.

Glaser, L. (1963). *Biochim. Biophys. Acta* **71**, 237.

Gregory, J. D., Laurent, T. C., and Rodén, L. (1964). *J. Biol. Chem.* **239**, 3312.

Grunberg-Manago, M. (1963). *Progr. Nucleic Acid Res.* **1**, 93.

Hoffmann-Ostenhof, O. (1962). *In* "Acides Ribonucléiques et Polyphosphates," p. 641. C.N.R.S., Paris.

Horton, D., and Wolfrom, M. L. (1963). *In* "Comprehensive Biochemistry" (M. Florkin and E. H. Stotz, eds.), Vol. 5, p. 189. Elsevier, Amsterdam.

Ingram, V. M. (1965). "The Biosynthesis of Macromolecules." Benjamin, New York.

Lipmann, F. (1941). *Advan. Enzymol.* **1**, 99.

Manners, D. J. (1962). *Advan. Carbohydrate Chem.* **17**, 371.

Matsuhashi, M., Dietrich, C. P., and Strominger, J. L. (1965). *Proc. Natl. Acad. Sci. U.S.* **54**, 587.

Neufeld, E. F., and Hall, C. W. (1965). *Biochem. Biophys. Res. Commun.* **19**, 456.

Neufeld, E. F., and Hassid, W. Z. (1963). *Advan. Carbohydrate Chem.* **18**, 309.

Osborn, M. J., Rosen, S. M., Rothfield, L., Zeleznick, L. D., and Horecker, B. L. (1964). *Science* **145**, 783.

Perkins, H. R. (1963). *Bacteriol. Rev.* **27**, 18.

Rodén, L., and Armand, G. (1966). *J. Biol. Chem.* **241**, 65.

Shedlovsky, T. (1943). *Ann. N.Y. Acad. Sci.* **43**, 259.

Watson, J. D. (1965). "Molecular Biology of the Gene," p. 335. Benjamin, New York.

On Protein Structure[*]

Gertrude E. Perlmann

A few recollections may not be out of place in a volume like this. In 1937 a lucky accident took me to the Carlsbergfondets Biologiske Institut in Copenhagen. Here is where I first met Fritz Lipmann. However, our acquaintance actually started later through a curious incident. One day I had left a flask with a milky suspension on the laboratory bench, a crime no protein chemist would dare to commit today. When confronted by the question, what did it contain, my reply was "protein metaphosphate crystals." My own astonishment, however, exceeded that of others when it was discovered that the flask contained, indeed, "earnest" crystals of ovalbumin with four metaphosphates per mole attached. Moreover, the metaphosphate had reacted with basic amino acid residues and was not linked to serine. Thus this incident led to a much cherished friendship. It was Fritz Lipmann who introduced me to phosphoserine, which he discovered in 1932, and subsequently to phosphoproteins, a subject that has occupied us for many years. Yet, as it sometimes happens in research, an apparently insignificant observation unexpectedly changes the whole direction of the scientific thought of an individual.

This was actually the case when, in 1953, we investigated the question whether the one phosphorus atom in pepsin and pepsinogen (1) is a constituent essential for the proteolytic activity of pepsin or the activation of the zymogen to the enzyme. To answer this question we used phosphatases of various origins to remove the phosphate group enzymatically, thereby leaving the protein relatively intact (2). The result was disappointing. Although the two proteins could be readily dephos-

* Supported in part by the United States Public Health Service Grant AM-02449 and by the National Science Foundation Grant GB-2419.

phorylated, the removal of the phosphorus produced no measurable effect on the proteolytic activity of pepsin if assayed with the protein substrate, hemoglobin, nor was the rate of hydrolysis of the dipeptide, N-acetylphenylalanyl-DL-diiodotyrosine, affected. It was possible, however, to demonstrate that this one atom of phosphorus is present as a diester and serves to link two sites of the single polypeptide chain of these two proteins in a cyclic loop (3).

Although the phosphorus turned out to be unessential for the proteolytic activity as well as for the activation of pepsinogen to pepsin, the rate of autodigestion of the phosphorus-free enzyme had increased considerably. It seemed as if on removal of the phosphorus a few peptide bonds, hitherto not accessible to enzymatic hydrolysis, were exposed and were rapidly hydrolyzed by the enzyme itself. That a slight loosening of the macromolecular configuration of the protein can affect the stability of the molecule is best demonstrated by a comparision of the effect of pH on the rate of the spontaneous inactivation of phosphorus-free pepsin and its parent protein. As is known, pepsin is rapidly inactivated above pH 6.0. In the case of the phosphorus-free enzyme, the upper pH of the stability range of the phosphorus-free pepsin is lowered from pH 6.0 to 5.2, whereas in the acid pH range the protein already becomes unstable at pH 2.8. In the presence of 8.0 M urea the range of maximum stability of the phosphorus-free pepsin is narrowed to the apparent pH range of 3.5 to 4.0 (4, 5). Thus these observations immediately led to several questions of a more general nature: (1) "What are the forces that govern the molecular conformation of pepsin and determine the specific folding of the polypeptide chain that confers biological activity on the molecule?" (2) "What are the features that are essential in stabilizing the zymogen and locking it into its most stable conformation, even at pH 7.0 where the enzyme per se is rapidly denatured?"

These questions can, of course, be approached from many angles. Although it appears at present that X-ray analysis is the technique of choice which offers a chance of success in defining accurately the structure of molecules as complex as proteins, the early work of Bernal and Crowfoot (6), who determined the unit cell in pepsin crystals, has not been pursued any further. However, indirect methods (optical rotatory dispersion, hypochromicity, fluorescence, hydrodynamic behavior), if brought into proper context with one another, may lead to answers of some of the points raised above. It is along these lines that our research on pepsin and pepsinogen, which emerged as a consequence of the dephosphorylation experiments, has been developed during the past years.

Let us sum up what may be considered as established facts concerning the relation of structure and function of the pepsin-pepsinogen system.

We reported in 1958 that in contrast to most globular proteins, the optical rotatory dispersion of pepsin, its hydrodynamic properties, and enzymatic activity remain unchanged if the protein is dissolved in concentrated urea or guanidine hydrochloride or if the solution is heated to 60°C (7, 8). Although hydrogen bonds of the type

$$\overset{|}{C} = O \ldots H - \overset{|}{N}$$

and those involving the phenolic hydroxyls of tyrosine and the carboxylate ions of the acidic amino acid residues, i.e.,

have been shown to exist in pepsin (9), they must be relatively unimportant in maintaining the conformation necessary for the proteolytic activity of this protein. From these studies and from the fact that 70% of the molecule is made up of nonpolar amino acids which must be in van der Waals contact with their neighbors, we concluded that the fraction of amino acid residues present in α-helical configuration must be very *low* and almost *negligible*. This "apparent lack" of helicity further follows from the fact that pepsin has a high content of dicarboxylic acids which in the pH range of greatest stability of the enzyme, i.e., pH 4.0–5.5, are ionized. Therefore, electrostatic repulsion would also prevent helix formation. Similarly, the seventeen proline residues, if distributed statistically along the peptide chain, would counteract a helical conformation. *Thus pepsin is essentially stabilized by hydrophobic interactions* (8). It is of interest, however, that on heating of pepsin solutions above 60°C conformational transitions are observed of a type which hitherto has not yet been described. These are reflected by an *increase* of the rotatory dispersion constant, λ_c, from 216 to 236 mμ, a phenomenon contrary to the decrease of λ_c usually observed on denaturation of proteins (10). Thus it should be emphasized that if a change in the specific rotation of proteins with temperature occurs similar to that observed with pepsin, it may involve a conformational pattern such as a β structure → coil transition. The unusually large amounts of serine and threonine in this protein may well favor a conformation of this type (11).

That the macromolecular conformation of pepsinogen differs from that of pepsin was foreshadowed by the difference in the amino acid distribution of the two proteins. During the activation process, peptides from the N-terminal portion of the polypeptide chain are released (12), and the number of basic amino acids is reduced from eighteen (11 lysines, 3 histidines, 4 arginines) to four (1 lysine, 1 histidine, 2 arginines) (13, 14). Therefore, it had to be anticipated that these amino acids, all

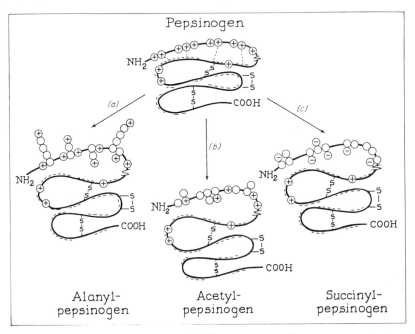

FIG. 1. Schematic diagram of modified pepsinogen. The native protein is reacted with: (a) N-carboxyanhydride of alanine to form alanylpepsinogen, (b) acetylimidazole to form acetylpepsinogen, and (c) succinic anhydride to form succinylpepsinogen.

clustered within a relatively small part of the molecule, must considerably influence the structural pattern of pepsinogen. As reported elsewhere, changes in the optical rotatory dispersion, and, similarly, hypochromicity and the hydrodynamic properties upon heating a pepsinogen solution or transferring the protein to concentrated urea, reflect a configurational transition similar in sharpness to the transition from an α helix to random coil. Furthermore, as the pH of the protein solution is increased to pH 12.0, sharp transitions are observed with a midpoint at pH 10.0, a value slightly lower than the pK of the ε-amino group of lysine. Hence it appears that the lysyl residues of pepsinogen function as *conformational determinants* and stabilize the protein by side-chain interaction with some of the carboxyl groups of the aspartic and glutamic acids of the pepsin moiety (*15*). This view is sustained by experiments on modified pepsinogens in which the basic ε-amino groups of the lysine residues are replaced by the less basic α-amino groups of an amino acid or a small peptide attached in peptide linkage, thus altering the net charge of the protein (Fig. 1*a*) (*16*). For instance, in the case of alanylpepsinogen the midpoint of the pH transition curve of the specific optical rotation [α] is shifted from pH 10.0 to 8.7, thus being closer to the p*K* value of the α-amino groups. In other modifications the ε-amino groups are trans-

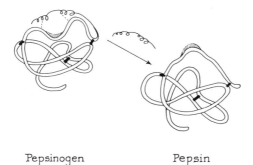

Pepsinogen   Pepsin

FIG. 2. Schematic diagram of the conformational changes on activation of pepsinogen to pepsin.

formed into uncharged or acidic side chains (Fig. 1*b,c*) (*17, 18*). In each case the alteration of the conformational characteristics of each modified pepsinogen is reflected in a decrease of the rotatory dispersion constant, λ_c, from 236 mμ to a value similar to the $\lambda_c = 216$ mμ of pepsin. Furthermore, the sharp transitions of the specific optical rotation in urea have disappeared. We believe that these results corroborate the existence of side-chain interaction of electrostatic nature in stabilizing the pepsinogen molecule in such a way as to lock it into its most thermodynamically stable conformation. This does not exclude the fact that the peptide chain segment which is removed on activation may have a structure, e.g., an α-helix, which is different and independent of the remainder of the pepsinogen molecule; however, it is the pattern of the cross-links introduced by side-chain interaction that is the essential conformational feature and directs an over-all structural pattern in the zymogen (Fig. 2) which is not present in the enzyme.

The conformational characteristics of the pepsin-pepsinogen system described thus far are well supported by experimental results, and we should like to consider them as established. Turning now to the question of a β structure in these two proteins the following observations are noteworthy. Using circular dichroism and optical rotatory dispersion in the far ultraviolet region, it was found that both proteins have a negative trough of the Cotton effect at 226 to 227 mμ which, in the case of pepsinogen but not with pepsin, is abolished in the presence of urea.* On heating the solution or altering the pH of the pepsinogen solution, the minimum of the trough is shifted to 232 mμ (*19, 20*). It returns to 226 mμ on cooling or on reversing the pH of the pepsinogen solution to neutrality. A similar result is obtained if a pepsin solution of pH 4.6 is heated to 60° or 65°C. Thus we have a phenomenon which is shared by *both* proteins and which differs from that hitherto described for α-helical molecules (*21*). Since pepsin and pepsinogen have the same content of hydroxy-amino acids, interactions as those suggested by Kendrew could well take place if these residues are "buried" into the interior of the molecule (*22*): (*a*) a hydrogen bond between the serine or threonine hydroxyl and a carbonyl group, or (*b*) interaction of the hydroxyl with a NH group of the backbone of the polypeptide chain. Thus inaccessible groups internally bonded may stabilize a β-type structure or create an as yet undefined conformation. This would, of course, necessitate the occurrence in these two proteins of recurring sequences of certain types of amino acids. Needless to say, this is speculation, but sequence studies or work with model substances may perhaps lead to an answer to these points.†

What, however, is the relation of the macromolecular conformation to the biological activity, and why does pepsin hydrolyze peptide bonds in such a specific manner at an acid pH? It is clear that a certain critical conformation of the active site has to be established and maintained. Thus the alignment of the amino acids along the polypeptide chain and the spatial arrangements of charges relative to the chromophores is critical and must be such as to ensure a three-dimensional structure of the

---

* The author would like to acknowledge the help of Dr. S. Beychok in the dichroism experiments.

† To effect this point we have initiated a study of the characterization of peptides derived from tryptic hydrolyzates of reduced carboxymethylated pepsinogen and pepsin (*23*). Thus we have demonstrated that in the polypeptide chain segment which is released on activation of the zymogen to the enzyme, fourteen basic amino acids are all clustered within a short distance close to the peptide bond that is hydrolyzed on activation (*24*). Furthermore, a peptide fraction common to pepsin and pepsinogen has been isolated which is rich in proline.

protein in solution which is associated with the lowest configurational free energy.** Since the enzymatic activity of pepsin is not affected by reagents known to bring about conformational changes (7, 8), this point was investigated in testing the susceptibility of pepsinogen to become activated to pepsin. It was found that only a rough relation exists between the conformational changes observed and the activation of the zymogen to the enzyme. The changes may, but do not always, parallel each other (15). Also, the degree of reversal differs. How varied this can be is illustrated in Fig. 3 which shows the result of an experiment in

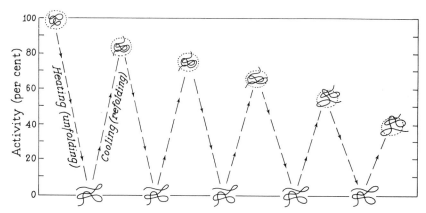

FIG. 3. Effect of heating and cooling on the conformation and "potential pepsin activity" of pepsinogen. Potential pepsin activity of pepsinogen refers to proteolysis of hemoglobin at pH 2.0 after activation in 0.1 N hydrochloric acid at 37°C for 10 minutes.

which a pepsinogen solution was heated to 60°C for 15 minutes followed by quenching to 25°C. If this cycle of heating-cooling is repeated several times, the protein is refolded sufficiently to restore the active site and to permit activation of the zymogen to the enzyme. However, the potential pepsin activity decreases progressively. Thus it is clear that metastable macromolecular states exist and that the biological activity of the molecule will depend on these "crystalline domains" within the macromolecular structure. Therefore, more effort should be directed toward a better definition of metastable states in proteins, the conditions under which they may occur, and most of all, their relation to the biological function of macromolecules.

** The aromatic amino acid residues, tyrosine and tryptophan, and a few dicarboxylic acids have been shown to be functional determinants of pepsin (1, 17, 25).

The question raised by us in 1953, i.e., what determines the proteolytic activity of pepsin, is as yet unanswered, and only unrelated observations are discussed here. However, they have led to the discernment of some of the macromolecular features of the enzyme and its zymogen.

REFERENCES

1. Northrop, J. H., and Herriott, R. M., in "Crystalline Enzymes," 2nd ed., pp. 28, 77. Columbia Univ. Press, New York, 1948.
2. Perlmann, G. E., Advan. Protein Chem. 10, 1 (1955).
3. Perlmann, G. E., J. Gen. Physiol. 41, 441 (1958).
4. Blumenfeld, O. O., Léonis, J., and Perlmann, G. E., J. Biol. Chem. 235, 379 (1960).
5. Glover, E. L., unpublished observations (1961).
6. Bernal, J. D., and Crowfoot, D., Nature 133, 794 (1934).
7. Perlmann, G. E., Proc. Intern. Cong. Biochemistry, 4th, Vienna, 1958 8, 32 (1960).
8. Perlmann, G. E., Proc. Natl. Acad. Sci. U.S. 42, 596 (1959).
9. Blumenfeld, O. O., and Perlmann, G. E., J. Gen. Physiol. 42, 563 (1959).
10. Linderstrøm-Lang, K., and Schellman, J. A., Biochim. Biophys. Acta 15, 203 (1955).
11. Fasman, G. D., and Blout, E. R., J. Am. Chem. Soc. 82, 2262 (1960).
12. Van Vunakis, H., and Herriott, R. M., Biochim. Biophys. Acta 23, 600 (1957).
13. Arnon, R., and Perlmann, G. E., J. Biol. Chem. 238, 563 (1963).
14. Blumenfeld, O. O., and Perlmann, G. E., J. Gen. Physiol. 42, 553 (1959).
15. Perlmann, G. E., J. Mol. Biol. 6, 452 (1963).
16. Becker, R. R., and Stahmann, M. A., J. Biol. Chem. 204, 745 (1956).
17. Perlmann, G. E., J. Biol. Chem. 241, 153 (1966).
18. Gounaris, A. D., and Perlmann, G. E., Federation Proc. (1966).
19. Perlmann, G. E., in "Ordered Fluids and Liquid Crystals," A.C.S. Monograph, in press.
20. Blout, E. R., Pollock, E. J., and Parrish, J. R., Abstr. 150th Natl. Meeting Am. Chem. Soc. p. 23C (1965).
21. Simmons, N. S., Cohen, C., Szent-Györgyi, A. G., Wetlaufer, D. B., and Blout, E. R., J. Am. Chem. Soc. 83, 4766 (1961).
22. Kendrew, J. C., Brookhaven Symp. Biol. 15, 216 (1962).
23. Koehn, P. V., Oestreicher, A. B., and Perlmann, G. E., Federation Proc. 25, (1965).
24. Press, E. M., unpublished observations (1963).
25. Herriott, R. M., J. Cellular Comp. Physiol. 47 (Suppl.), 239 (1956).

Strain and Conformation
Change in Enzymatic Catalysis[*]

William P. Jencks

INTRODUCTION

Relatively complex reactions, such as those of carbonyl, acyl, and phosphoryl groups, are particularly satisfying to those who are interested in the mechanism of enzymatic catalysis, because it is easy to speculate about possible means by which enzymes could accelerate such reactions by appropriate electron pushing and pulling and by the use of unusually reactive nucleophilic and electrophilic groups in the active site. However, enzymes also catalyze much simpler reactions, such as the transfer of a methyl group from a sulfonium ion (e.g. S-adenosylmethionine) to a thioether (e.g. methionine) to form a new sulfonium ion and thioether [eq. (1)] (Greene and Davis, 1960). It would not be expected that a simple displacement reaction of this kind would be susceptible to general

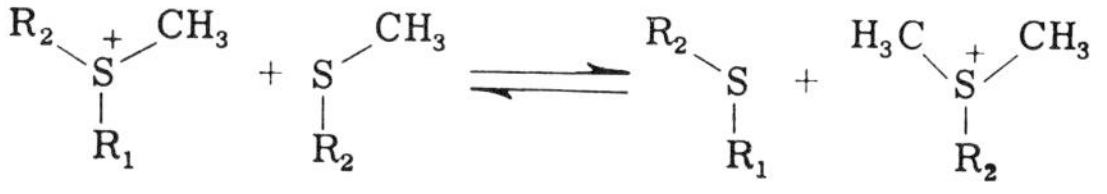

$$
\underset{R_1}{\overset{R_2}{\underset{|}{S}}}{}^{+}\!\!\diagdown\!CH_3 \; + \; \underset{R_2}{\overset{CH_3}{\underset{|}{S}}} \; \rightleftharpoons \; \underset{R_1}{\overset{R_2}{\underset{|}{S}}} \; + \; \underset{R_2}{\overset{H_3C}{\underset{|}{S}}}{}^{+}\!\!\diagdown\!CH_3 \tag{1}
$$

acid-base catalysis and there are probably no groups in enzymes which would be more effective as a nucleophilic reagent than the acceptor thioether itself and which could give an intermediate reactive enough to donate the methyl group to the acceptor. A nonpolar environment in the active site might cause some rate enhancement if there is dispersal of charge in the transition state, but would not be expected to have a

[*] Contribution No. 439 from the Graduate Department of Biochemistry, Brandeis University, Waltham, Massachusetts.

273

large influence on a reaction in which the transition state has the same net charge as the reactants and the nucleophile is a weak base. Binding of the two reactants next to each other at the active site might also be expected to lead to some rate enhancement in dilute solutions (Koshland, 1956, 1962; Westheimer, 1962), but could hardly in itself account for the large rate accelerations brought about by enzymatic catalysis of this and other reactions which occur sluggishly, if at all, in the absence of such catalysis. One is led to suppose that there must be some means other than simple approximation of the reactants and induced electron displacements by which enzymes can decrease the energy of activation and increase the specific rate constants of the reactions which they catalyze. The most obvious mechanism by which this might be brought about, which is also probably the most venerable proposal for the mechanism of action of enzymes, is the induction of some sort of strain or distortion into the substrate.

Some of the facts and theories which may be pertinent to this hypothesis are discussed in this paper. It should be emphasized at the outset that few, if any, of these basic ideas have not been discussed previously. The reader is referred to the reviews by Lumry (1959), Linderstrøm-Lang and Schellman (1959), Hammes (1964), Wilson (1964), and Jencks (1963) and the references therein, especially the papers by Smith (1949), Laidler (1954), Lumry and Eyring (1954), London et al. (1958), Bender et al. (1964) and Epand and Wilson (1964).

The several binding forces which may exist between an enzyme and its substrates, that are presumably due in large part to hydrophobic and hydrogen bonds, are individually weak, but when taken together may involve a very considerable free energy. The problem, then, is how this free energy can be utilized to lower the free energy of activation of the reaction which is to be catalyzed, i.e., to bring the substrates part way along the path to the transition state or to make them resemble the transition state (Fig. 1). The first way in which this can be done, as noted above, is simply by bringing reacting molecules together from dilute solution at the active site. This process, which is an entropy effect, can provide considerable assistance to the reaction in some experimental situations, but provides little or no help in others (Koshland, 1956, 1962; Westheimer, 1962). A second mechanism is by orienting the reactants properly in respect to each other, so that of the large number of possible conformations and positions which could be assumed in solution, only those which will lead to reaction are permitted when a "good" substrate is bound at the active site (Koshland, 1962; Hein and Niemann, 1962;

Bernhard and Gutfreund, 1958; Spencer and Sturtevant, 1959; Bender *et al.*, 1964). This type of explanation, in terms of confinement of the reacting groups to profitable rotamer distributions, has been used as an explanation for the rapid rate of some intramolecular reactions, compared to the corresponding bimolecular reactions (Bruice and Pandit, 1960). This mechanism is also primarily an entropy effect. However, it seems probable to the writer that in many intramolecular and enzymatic reactions such orientation effects are insufficient to explain the large observed rate enhancements and that there may be, in addition, some changes in bond lengths and angles which may be called strain or distortion and which increase the specific rate constant within the reacting

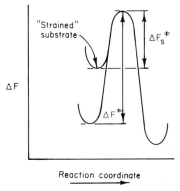

FIG. 1. Diagrammatic representation of the induction of strain or distortion in a substrate to bring it part way along the reaction coordinate to the transition state.

complex. This process should cause a lowering of the energy of activation, which probably occurs in many enzyme-catalyzed reactions in comparison with their nonenzymatic counterparts (Laidler, 1958). There is, however, no absolute distinction which can be made between these mechanisms. Experimentally, the determination of the energy and entropy of activation does not provide a definitive distinction, because the measured energy of activation may not correspond to the true potential energy of activation (Hammett, 1940) and interpretations of these quantities are particularly difficult in the face of the many processes which may be involved in an enzymatic reaction. Even theoretically it is difficult to draw a firm dividing line, because the distortion of a substrate, for example, is simply a forcing of the substrate into one of the several possible relative configurations of the component atoms for that substrate. This configuration must represent one of the possible configurations for that particular substrate in solution, although perhaps a very unlikely one. For example, the increase in the rate of lactonization of 2-(hydroxy-methyl)benzoic acids which is caused by *ortho* substituents has been reasonably explained in terms of forcing the starting material into an average conformation which resembles the transition state, but appears entirely as a change in the enthalpy of activation (Bunnett and Hauser, 1965). In this paper the terms "strain" and "distortion" will be used primarily to describe situations in which changes in bond angles and bond lengths occur, but it should be kept in mind that other types of free energy change are also significant and much of the discussion refers also to situations in which there is a lowering of the free energy of activation by mechanisms which are primarily entropic in character. In other words, the entropic "distortion" of a substrate is the fixing of the substrate into a single conformation, compared to the many conformations in which it exists in solution.

The first reason that it appears desirable to consider a strain or distortion mechanism as a partial explanation for enzyme catalysis is the difficulty in accounting for catalysis of certain reactions by other mechanisms, as described above. The second reason is the fact that the specificity of enzymes for good substrates is often manifested in rapid maximal rates of catalysis rather than in tight binding. A particularly good example is provided by Hofstee's demonstration that, within certain limits, the faster hydrolysis of long-chain than of short-chain fatty acid esters by esterase and chymotrypsin is a manifestation of a favorable maximal velocity rather than a favorable Michaelis constant for the long-chain compounds (Hofstee, 1954a,b; Lumry, 1959). The difference in the free energy of activation amounts to 550–650 cal per mole for each methylene group added to the fatty acid chain, which is approximately the increase in the strength of a hydrophobic bond brought about by the addition of a methylene group. This suggests that practically all of the binding energy, which would ordinarily be expected to cause a tighter binding of the longer chain compounds, is instead utilized to reduce the free energy of activation of the reaction. There are many other examples in which good and bad substrates have similar Michaelis constants, but different maximal velocities, and it seems eminently reasonable that an enzyme should utilize the several types of weak and rapidly reversible binding forces available to it to reduce activation energy as well as to promote specific binding. The situation is illustrated diagrammatically in Fig. 2. Take the binding energy of some substrate, A, to be ΔF_A. A better substrate, B, may interact with the enzyme through a number of additional weak binding forces, ΔF_{B_1}, ΔF_{B_2}, ΔF_{B_3} which involve hydrophobic bonds, hydrogen bonds, and other forces, with a total free energy, ΔF_B. If this energy is used to give tighter binding, the binding enery for this substrate is then $\Delta F_A + \Delta F_B$. However, if the binding sites on the enzyme are so positioned that the substrate does not fit perfectly into them, the substrate, the enzyme, or both may undergo deformation in order that binding may take place. The strain energy required for this deformation is ΔF_{B_S}. The observed binding energy will be the difference between the potential binding energy, ΔF_B, and the strain energy, ΔF_{B_S}. If these two quantities should be equal, they will balance each other and the observed

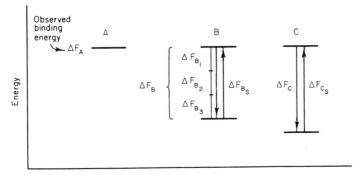

Fig. 2.   Scheme to show how enzyme-substrate binding forces may be utilized to induce strain in the enzyme-substrate complex.

binding of substrate B will be the same as that of substrate A. Similarly, for a substrate C with even more potential binding energy, ΔF_C, the strain energy, ΔF_{C_S}, which may be realized upon formation of the enzyme-substrate complex, will be even greater.

A related fact which requires explanation is that enzymes frequently react very slowly or not at all with small substrates which must be able to fit into the active site and would be expected to do so in a proper conformation to at least a small extent. This is especially evident in the very small reactivity of water in many reactions which involve group transfer to alcohols; the adenosinetriphosphatase (ATPase) activity of hexokinase, for example, is only 5×10^{-6} as large as the rate of phosphate transfer to glucose (Trayser and Colowick, 1961). This manifestation of enzyme specificity has been explained in terms of a requirement for an induced fit of the enzyme in the case of the larger specific substrate (Koshland, 1960), but could also be explained in terms of a requirement for the induction of strain in the enzyme-substrate complex, which may only be possible if the binding forces of the larger, specific substrate are utilized.

It is sometimes observed that the rate of reaction of substrates which contain an aromatic group is increased by the addition of a substituent on the aromatic ring, regardless of whether the substituent is electron-donating or electron-withdrawing. Such behavior is not easily explained by polar effect of the substituents, but would be expected if the substit̃uent makes possible a stronger interaction with the enzyme with the consequent induction of a larger strain energy. One example of this type of behavior is seen in the hydrolysis of acylanilides catalyzed by an enzyme from chick kidney (Nimmo-Smith, 1960). The rate of hydrolysis is increased by both electron-donating and electron-withdrawing substitu-

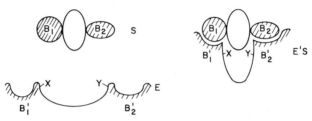

Fig. 3. The induced fit mechanism, in which binding of substrate through groups B_1 and B_2 causes a change in the conformation of the enzyme so that the groups X and Y in the active site, which are required for catalysis, are properly positioned relative to the substrate.

ents, and the limited data available suggest that the increased rate results from an increase in maximal velocity as well as a decrease in K_m with the substituted compounds.

The enzyme 2-keto-3-deoxy-6-phosphogluconic aldolase provides an interesting example in which even the formation of a covalent complex of the substrate and enzyme is insufficient for catalysis to occur, unless the substrate has attached to it a "handle," which might be utilized to induce strain (Ingram and Wood, 1966). Both the normal substrate and the dephospho analog bind to the enzyme at low concentrations to form an imine intermediate with an amino group on the enzyme, which can be stabilized by reduction with borohydride. The fact that the dephospho compound is not cleaved, in spite of the fact that it is otherwise structurally and electronically similar to the normal substrate, indicates that an interaction of the enzyme with the phosphate group, presumably electrostatic in nature, is a necessary part of the normal catalytic process.

The two alternative explanations for the manifestation of enzymatic specificity in maximal velocities rather than in binding or Michaelis constants are the occurrence of "induced fit" and nonproductive binding. It is possible, as suggested by Koshland (1958), that the groups in the active site of the enzyme (X and Y in Fig. 3) which have some electron pushing or pulling role in catalysis are not properly positioned to exert such effects in the free enzyme, but that upon combination with the substrate the enzyme undergoes a change in conformation to bring these groups into a position in which they can be catalytically active. This hy-

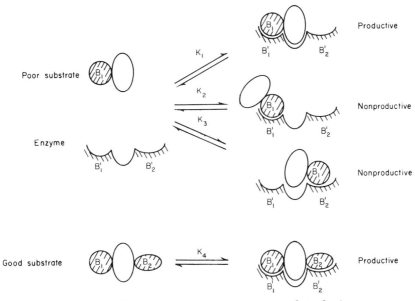

Fig. 4. Productive and nonproductive binding of poor and good substrates.

pothesis will be considered in more detail later. Alternatively, it is possible for a substrate to bind to the various parts of the active site in a number of different configurations, only one of which may be catalytically active (Fig. 4). The wrong or "nonproductive" modes of binding will contribute to the observed binding constant, but will not contribute to catalysis. The apparent dissociation constant, K_m, in such a situation is smaller than the dissociation constant for the productive mode according to the relationship $K_m = 1/(1/K_1 + 1/K_2 + 1/K_3)$. A "good" substrate will have several binding areas to correspond to the binding sites on the enzyme and will consequently bind in the correct configuration more often than the poor substrate. Consequently, it will exhibit a more favorable maximal velocity than the poor substrate, even though its apparent binding constant may not be more favorable (Bernhard and Gutfreund, 1958; Bernhard, 1959; Spencer and Sturtevant, 1959; Hein and Niemann, 1962; Zeller et al., 1965). In the example shown in Fig. 4, there are two binding sites, B_1 and B_2. The difference in the probability of productive and non-productive binding for good and poor substrates would be expected to be even greater with three or more binding sites. The competitive inhibition of amylase by portions of the substrate molecule reported by Thoma and Koshland (1960) may be interpreted in a similar manner. Bender and co-workers (1964) have recently reported that the slow rates of de-acylation of acyl chymotrypsins which are formed from "poor" substrates reflect an unfavorable entropy, rather than energy of activation, and this observation is interpretable in terms of a more favorable orientation of the good substrate in the active site of the acyl enzyme. These situations may be regarded as the induction of "entropic strain" in the enzyme-sub-strate complex. The "induced-fit" and nonproductive binding hypotheses very probably describe the real situation in some cases, but it seems probable to the writer that they do not account for all examples of the manifestation of enzyme specificity in maximal reaction rates. It is difficult to account for the very large rate enhancements which are observed with large specific substrates compared to small ones, such as water, by the nonproductive binding theory and it would be somewhat surprising if either the nonproductive binding or the induced fit mechanisms gave rise to the regular, progressive increase in hydrolysis rate with increasing chain length of the substrate, which is observed with chymotrypsin and esterase.

There is ample chemical precedent for the acceleration of reaction rates by strain or distortion. One of the clearest examples (Kumamoto et al., 1956; Haake and Westheimer, 1961; Kaiser et al., 1963) is the alkaline

(I)   (II)

hydrolysis of ethylene phosphate (I) with P—O cleavage, which occurs at least 10^8 times faster than the same reaction with the structurally similar compound, dimethyl phosphate (II). This rate acceleration is of the order of magnitude that one would like in a model for enzymatic catalysis. The detailed reason for the rapid reaction of ethylene phosphate is still not entirely clear, but it seems certain that it must result from some distortion or destabilization introduced by the ring structure which brings the energy and structure of the starting material part way along the path to the energy and structure of the transition state, compared to the open-chain compound. This reaction is particularly interesting because the rate-accelerating factor(s) increase the rate of ^{18}O exchange from labeled water as well as the rate of hydrolysis (Haake and Westheimer, 1961). The exchange reaction is a sort of transfer reaction and indicates that the molecule is activated for more than one kind of reaction, i.e., the destabilization induced by the ring structure makes it comparatively easy for the ring compound to reach any of several transition states and is not a simple "pulling apart" of the bonds which facilitates only the ring-opening reaction.

As in all discussions of enzyme mechanism, it is important to emphasize that the action of an enzyme is almost certainly not accounted for by a single mechanism. In particular, other factors, such as electronic effects, must be invoked to explain the specificity of bond cleavage in the strained enzyme-substrate complex, because strain alone might cause bond cleavage to occur at a position different from the observed position (Koshland, 1956).

With this introduction we will examine some of the models which may be useful in considering the strain hypothesis in greater detail.

CASE I: THE RIGID ENZYME

The simplest situation is that in which the enzyme is assumed to be in the same conformation in the free and bound states. The binding sites are displaced slightly from the position which would be required for the most stable binding of the substrate, so that the substrate must undergo distortion in order to bind. In Eq. (2), K_1 and its associated standard

$$E + S \underset{K_1}{\overset{}{\rightleftharpoons}} ES' \quad (2)$$
$$K_2 \diagdown \quad {\pm E} \diagup K_3$$
$$S'$$

free energy, ΔF_1, refer to the observed substrate binding. For purposes of calculation, the binding can be thought of as occurring in two steps: K_2 and ΔF_2 refer to the distortion of the substrate to a conformation of higher energy and K_3 and ΔF_3 refer to the binding of this distorted substrate to the enzyme. The quantity ΔF_3 represents the maximal energy which is potentially available from the binding forces between enzyme and substrate and the difference between this quantity and the observed energy of binding, ΔF_1, represents the free energy, ΔF_2, which has been utilized to induce distortion in the bound substrate and which may partially overcome the free energy of activation of the reaction catalyzed by the enzyme.

If S' resembles the transition state, maximal binding would be expected for molecules which resemble the transition state and this binding would be expected to be tighter than the binding of the normal substrate, which must undergo distortion before it can bind. A possible example of this situation is found in the enzyme proline racemase. Pyrrole-2-carboxylic acid (III) is an inhibitor of this enzyme which causes 50% inhibition at

a concentration 160 times smaller than that of proline (IV). Furan-2-carboxylic acid (V) and thiophene-2-carboxylic acid (VI) are also potent inhibitors, but tetrahydrofuran-2-carboxylic acid (VII) is not. It is probable that the transition state for this reaction involves the removal of hydrogen from the $\alpha\text{-}sp^3$ tetrahedral carbon atom of proline and approaches a planar structure with sp^2 hybridization of this carbon atom. It might be supposed, then, that the planar inhibitors bind tightly because they resemble the transition state and that the difference between the binding energies of the inhibitor and substrate reflects the utilization of binding energy to distort the substrate toward a planar configuration; for a 160-fold difference in binding constants this would amount to 3000 cal per mole (Cardinale and Abeles, 1965).

Similarly, the value of K_i for the inhibition of Δ^5-3-ketoisomerase by 17-β-dihydroequilinin (VIII) is 6.3×10^{-6} M, which is much smaller than the K_m value of 3.2×10^{-4} M for the active substrate Δ^5-androstene-3,17-dione (IX) (Wang et al., 1963). This reaction involves the removal of a proton from the tetrahedral sp^3 carbon atom at position 4 of the steroid and also presumably has a near-planar transition state in which this carbon atom approaches sp^2 hybridization. Furthermore, substrates which undergo isomerization with maximal reaction rates which are less than that of (IX) exhibit approximately tenfold *smaller* values of K_m.

(VIII)   (IX)

The strong inhibition by (VIII) and by related inhibitors may, then, reflect their structural similarity to the near-planar transition state, and the larger K_m values for (IX), compared to inhibitors and to less effective substrates, may reflect the larger conversion of binding into distortion energy as (IX) is bound to the enzyme. In neither case has it been definitely established that the K_m values for the substrates of these enzymes represent true enzyme-substrate dissociation constants, but the observed deuterium isotope effects suggest tentatively that the true dissociation constants probably do not differ greatly from the observed K_m values (Cardinale and Abeles, 1965; Malhotra and Ringold, 1965).

An interesting model system for this type of catalysis has been reported by Lovrien (1964), who has shown that chemically inert polymers, such as 10^{-3} M poly(vinylpyrrolidone), catalyze the *cis-trans* isomerization of the water-soluble azo dye, chrysophenine. This catalysis presumably involves adsorption of the dye onto the polymer in a conformation which resembles the transition state for isomerization, because no catalysis is observed in concentrated solutions of the monomer, vinylpyrrolidone.

CASE II: THE RIGID SUBSTRATE

One formulation of this case corresponds to the "induced fit" hypothesis (Koshland, 1958). In Eq. (3), the substrate binds to the enzyme, E, with the equilibrium constant K_1 and free energy ΔF_1. However, the groups

$$
\begin{array}{ccc}
E + S & \xrightarrow{K_1} & ES \\
K_4 \Big\updownarrow & & \Big\updownarrow K_2 \\
E' + S & \xrightleftharpoons[K_3]{} & E'S
\end{array}
\qquad (3)
$$

in the enzyme which are to bring about the catalytic process are not properly arranged in E and must undergo a substrate-induced conformation change to E′ in order to take up their proper positions relative to the substrate before they can facilitate the movement of electrons and enzyme activity is manifested (Fig. 3). The free energy change of this enzyme rearrangement, ΔF_4, must be unfavorable, because the natural form of the free enzyme is the unrearranged form, E. Therefore, the conformation change in the presence of substrate must be "bought" at the expense of the binding energy of the substrate, ΔF_3, which is thereby made unavailable either for binding specific substrates at low substrate concentrations or for overcoming the activation energy of the reaction. From one point of view, then, this energy might be regarded as wasted, because one can always suggest that if the enzyme existed in the form E′ in the first place this rearrangement would not be necessary and the full binding energy would be available for other purposes. While this argument may be teleological, it would seem to be an objection to the "induced fit" theory if one wishes to speculate as to what properties an enzyme should have to exhibit maximal catalytic activity. On the other hand, the "induced fit" may have other usefulness, which may justify its energetic cost, in the control of enzyme activity and in preventing enzyme activity on those substrates which do not have the binding groups required to induce activity in the enzyme.

Experimentally, a necessary, but not a sufficient requirement for an "induced fit" mechanism is the demonstration that a change in enzyme conformation occurs upon combination with substrate and a great deal of effort has been expended in an attempt to demonstrate such a conformation change. Although it is difficult to detect the small changes in conformation about the active site which might be expected upon combination with substrate, there is now a good deal of physical and chemical evidence that such changes do take place. One especially simple and unequivocal type of evidence for such a change, which has been available for some time, is the demonstration of changes in enzyme activity with time in the presence of substrate. It is difficult to imagine a mechanism for such a change in activity which does not involve a change in enzyme conformation, provided, as is usually the case, that the dissociation and reassociation of enzyme subunits are considered to be special cases of conformation change. A clear example of this phenomenon is the glutamic dehydrogenase from a *Neurospora* mutant studied by Fincham (1957). This enzyme undergoes a temperature-dependent reversible inactivation and shows an enhanced rate of reactivation in the presence of substrate.

There are a number of other examples of enzymes which show a time-dependent increase or decrease in activity which is dependent on the presence of substrate and which must reflect a substrate-induced conformational change (Grisolia, 1964; Worcel et al., 1965; Kearney, 1957; Sundaram and Fincham, 1964; Wang et al., 1965).

One of the important questions in regard to the "induced fit" mechanism, however, is not whether substrate-induced changes in enzyme conformation occur, but whether they occur each time a substrate molecule binds to the enzyme. The bonds which determine the conformation of a macromolecule are individually weak and are rapidly formed and broken, so that it is not surprising that the rates of change of the conformation of some polymers are extremely fast (Burke et al., 1965; Schwarz, 1965). On the other hand, other changes in macromolecule conformation, such as the time-dependent changes in enzyme activity noted previously, are extremely slow, presumably because energetically unfavorable prior equilibria must precede the rapid, but still rate-determining step which leads to the conformation change. Consequently, it cannot be predicted whether a substrate-induced conformation change in a given enzyme will proceed with sufficient rapidity to take place as a part of each catalytic act. Most of the experimental work which has been carried out on substrate-induced conformational changes involves experimental measurements over time periods which are long in comparison to the duration of the catalytic process and therefore do not provide an answer to this question. However, temperature jump and other techniques for the measurement of rapid reactions can provide information in the desired time scale and there already is some evidence for the occurrence of rapid isomerizations in enzymes, which may well represent conformational changes associated with the catalytic process (Hammes and Fasella, 1962; French and Hammes, 1965; Cathou and Hammes, 1965). If the rates of change of enzyme conformation [the steps which correspond to K_2 and K_4 in Eq. (3)] are not as fast as the catalytic process which leads to product formation, then the role of the substrate-induced conformation change will be restricted to the maintenance of control and specificity in the catalyzed reaction.

It is interesting to consider the case of Eq. (3a) in which the rates of interconversion of the two forms of the enzyme are slow relative to the rate of product formation, but fast relative to the time of observation of enzyme activity. Suppose ES decomposes relatively slowly to products with a rate constant k. It might be imagined that at low substrate concentration nearly all of the enzyme is in the form E (i.e., $K_4 > 1$) so that a molecule of ES will decompose to give products and E, and E will again combine with S without interconversion to E'. Under these conditions the observed specific activity of the enzyme would be that of the less active form, E. At high substrate concentration nearly all of the enzyme will be in the more active form, E'S $(K_2 > 1)$, so that a molecule of enzyme which has just dissociated from the products will combine with a substrate molecule to give E'S again before it has time to revert to the less active form, E; under these conditions the observed activity would be that of the active form E'S which reacts with the rate constant k'.

$$
\begin{array}{ccc}
\text{E} + \text{S} \xrightleftharpoons[\text{fast}]{K_1} & \text{ES} \xrightarrow{k} & \text{Product} + \text{E} \\[2mm]
k_4 \Big\updownarrow k_{-4} & k_2 \Big\updownarrow k_{-2} & \\[2mm]
\text{E}' + \text{S} \xrightleftharpoons[\text{fast}]{K_3} & \text{E}'\text{S} \xrightarrow{k'} & \text{Product} + \text{E}'
\end{array}
\tag{3a}
$$

Such a mechanism might account for activation of enzyme activity by substrate (or an activator) without postulating two binding sites. The difficulty with this mechanism is that it requires that equilibrium not be maintained between ES and E'S; if such equilibrium were maintained a constant specific activity of the enzyme-substrate complex would be observed. This is true regardless of whether the concentrations of ES and E'S are maintained by equilibrium or by steady-state mechanisms. The suggestion that such equilibrium not be maintained requires that steps 2 and 4 be practically irreversible and leads to a cyclic process in which the reactions shown in Eq. (3a) constantly proceed clockwise; this violates the principle of microscopic reversibility or detailed balance (Klein, 1955). This is probably sufficient to rule out such a mechanism, but perhaps the possibility should be kept in mind that the thermodynamic and kinetic considerations which are applied to simpler systems may not apply in the same way to enzymes; violations of microscopic reversibility may not be as serious as violations of more fundamental thermodynamic laws. Weber and co-workers have independently proposed a somewhat similar scheme to account for certain interaction effects in the binding of small molecules to proteins (Weber and Anderson, 1965; Anderson and Weber, 1965; Weber, 1965).

A mechanism by which changes in enzyme conformation may accelerate the reaction of a substrate will now be considered; this mechanism is quite different from that of an induced fit which serves only to orient catalytic groups in their proper position relative to the substrate.

The substrate-induced change in the conformation of the enzyme may itself serve to induce strain in the substrate and facilitate reaching the transition state. This situation may be described by Eq. (4). If the structure of the enzyme is such that the substrate binds only to a deformed,

$$
\begin{array}{c}
\text{E} \\
\Big\uparrow \text{fast} \\
\text{E}' + \text{S} \rightleftharpoons \text{E}'\text{S} \rightleftharpoons \text{ES}^* \rightleftharpoons \text{E} + \text{P}
\end{array} \qquad (4)
$$

high-energy state of the protein, E', the E'S complex will have a tendency to return to the undeformed state E and can facilitate reaction of the substrate during this process. In this case, as in case I, the binding energy of the substrate is utilized to partially overcome the activation energy of the reaction; the difference is that in case II movement of a portion of the

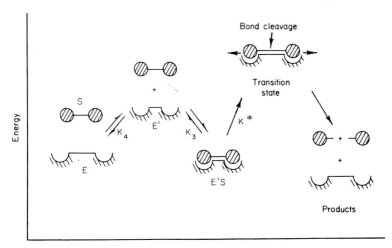

FIG. 5. Scheme to show how a substrate-induced conformation change in an enzyme may be utilized to facilitate reaction of the substrate by simply helping to pull it apart.

protein takes place as an integral part of the catalytic process. The induction of strain permits the free energy changes which are involved in the binding of substrate and the change in conformation of the enzyme to be utilized directly to accelerate the reaction; this is in contrast to the situation with "induced fit," in which these free energies are utilized only for control and specificity. One very crude representation of the strain mechanism for case II, in which the enzyme simply helps to pull apart the substrate, is shown in Fig. 5.

One experimental test of this hypothesis would be the demonstration, in the case of a multisubstrate enzyme, that the binding energy of one substrate is utilized to reduce the activation energy for the reaction of a second substrate with some small molecule that is not a normal substrate. A possible example of this situation is found in the luciferase-catalyzed hydrolysis of adenosine triphosphate (ATP) in the presence of luciferin, which can be explained in terms of case II by either the strain or "induced fit" hypotheses (DeLuca and McElroy, 1965). Normally this enzyme catalyzes the displacement of pyrophosphate (PP) from ATP by the carboxyl group of luciferin (L) to give luciferyl-AMP and the reverse displacement of luciferin from luciferyl-AMP by pyrophosphate to give ATP and luciferin [Eq. (5)].* In the absence of pyrophosphate-contain-

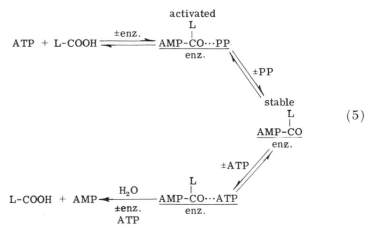

$$(5)$$

ing compounds, enzyme-bound (enz.) luciferyl-AMP is quite stable, but in the presence of a pyrophosphate-containing molecule the enzyme activates it in such a way that it reacts either with pyrophosphate itself, to form ATP, or with water, to give hydrolysis products, if ATP rather than pyrophosphate is the activating molecule. According to the strain hypothesis, then, the binding energy of the pyrophosphate group is utilized to induce a conformation change in the enzyme which induces strain in the luciferyl-AMP and facilitates its reaction with any nucleophilic reagent with which it can come in contact. An analogous interpretation may be made for the case of valyl-AMP bound to isoleucyl-RNA synthe-

---

* Adenosine monophosphate, AMP; ribonucleic acid, RNA.

tase, which undergoes breakdown in the presence of transfer RNA containing isoleucine-specific chains (Norris and Berg, 1964).

It has been suggested by Fernley and Walker (1965), based on the kinetic behavior of the enzyme, that calf-intestinal alkaline phosphatase exists in two conformations, of which only one combines with the substrate and only the other reacts to give inorganic phosphate. If this interpretation is substantiated by other experiments, this would be an example in which the conformation changes of case II are of kinetic significance in the catalytic process. More direct evidence for this type of behavior has been obtained in temperature-jump experiments with ribonuclease, which in the presence of cytidine 3′-phosphate undergoes an isomerization at a faster rate than this substrate is converted to cytidine 2′,3′-phosphate (Cathou and Hammes, 1965).

DISTORTION IN BOTH ENZYME AND SUBSTRATE

While the assumption of a rigid enzyme or substrate (cases I and II) is useful for purposes of illustration and discussion, neither of these assumptions is likely to correspond precisely to reality because neither the enzyme nor the substrate is completely rigid and the induction of strain in one will tend to induce a complementary strain in the other. The scheme for this more complicated situation is shown in Eq. (6), in which

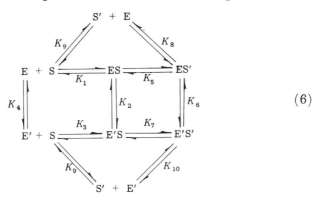

$$(6)$$

the symbols have the same meaning as in the previous equations. Although Eq. (6) is complex, the situation is understandable as a combination of cases I and II in which the final strain energy in E′S′ is the sum of the individual strain energies in E′ and S′ caused by their distortion to the same conformations which exist in E′S′ in the (hypothetical) separate equilibria K_4 and K_9. We need not be concerned here with the pathway by which E and S reach E'S' except to note that distortions of both E and S over only very small distances are necessary and any conformational changes which do take place must be at least as fast as the observed rate of reaction.

The Reverse Reaction

It is important to keep in mind that any complete mechanism for enzyme action must account for rate accelerations in the reverse as well as in the forward direction. If strain is to accelerate the reaction in both directions, the nature of any strain or distortion that can take place is severely limited because many types of distortion, such as binding to an enzyme in a way which will tend to pull apart the substrate, will accelerate the reaction in only one direction. Stated more precisely, the requirement is that *both* the substrate and the product, in their respective complexes with the enzyme, be distorted in such a way that they resemble the transition state. It is not always easy to imagine just what kind of change this involves, but, for example, in the case of a hydrolysis or transfer reaction of an acyl compound it could involve a bending of the molecule so that the planar bonds of the sp^3-hybridized carbonyl carbon atom are brought toward the bond angles of the tetrahedral configuration of the transition state, which presumably resembles a tetrahedral addition compound. For a bimolecular displacement [e.g., Eq. (1)] it could involve compression of the reacting molecules against each other to partially overcome the van der Waals repulsion forces.

From a consideration of the reaction in both directions it can be argued that strain or distortion *must* be a significant factor in many enzymatic reactions. Consider (Fig. 6) a molecule AB with the internuclear distance

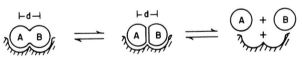

Fig. 6.   If the molecule AB is bound to an enzyme without strain, there will be strain in the complex of A and B with enzyme after bond cleavage.

"d" between two atoms which are to undergo reaction, and assume that this molecule binds to a rigid enzyme without strain. After cleavage or substitution of the AB bond, the products, A and B are bound to the same sites in the same positions by the same binding forces. However, there will now be repulsion between the products, which will be closer to each other than the sum of their van der Waals radii, and this repulsion will give rise to a strain energy, compared to the dissociated products A and B. In the reverse reaction, this strain would cause an acceleration of the reaction. Conversely, if the products A and B were bound to sites in a rigid enzyme without strain, strain would generally be induced upon the formation of AB, because the lowest energy state of AB has the internuclear distance d; some compromise must be reached between breaking the bonding forces to the enzyme and stretching the A—B bond. The strain energy in this case would facilitate the cleavage of AB. Essentially the same argument may be made for the case of the flexible enzyme (case II) in which some distortion of the enzyme, which will lead to strain in the substrates, must take place in the binding of either AB or of A and B. In general, there will be a tendency for the introduction of strain in one or the other or both directions of the reaction, because differences in the geometries of the substrate and product will usually lead to strain or distortion in the binding of one or both. If the geometry of the active site is intermediate between that required to fit the substrate and product, there will be a tendency to induce strain in both which may facilitate the reaction in both directions. The requirements that the active-site region of the enzyme have a definite geometry for the several weak bonding forces which interact with the substrate, that there be a defined change in free energy upon distortion of this geometry, and that the free energy changes from distortion of the enzyme and substrate are involved in the catalytic process itself follow as corollaries of these considerations. These requirements, in turn, provide one plausible explanation for the fact that enzymes are large molecules, because it would not be expected that a small catalyst molecule would be likely to have available to it the structural features necessary to satisfy these requirements.

This point of view may be summarized by the simple statement that an enzyme will tend to bind the transition state more firmly than either the substrate or the product; because of this there will be a tendency for the substrate and the enzyme to undergo changes in structure to approach the structure of the transition state. The concept of an equilibrium binding of catalyst to substrate has been used by Kurz (1963) in a somewhat different sense to describe nonenzymatic catalyzed reactions.

Consider the reaction of Eq. (7) and the special case of the Haldane relationship shown in Eq. (8) in which K_S and K_P are dissociation constants for the enzyme-substrate and enzyme-product complexes, respectively. The induction of strain in the forward direction will result in an increase in the value of K_S to a value larger than that which would be obtained if the enzyme and substrate fitted each other perfectly without distortion.

If this strain is utilized to lower the free energy of activation of the catalyzed reaction, there will be a corresponding increase in k_f. The same considerations hold, in theory, for the reverse reaction in respect to K_P and k_r. However, as noted above, any such facilitation by strain in the

$$E + S \underset{K_S}{\rightleftarrows} ES \underset{k_r}{\overset{k_f}{\rightleftarrows}} EP \overset{K_p}{\rightleftarrows} E + P \qquad (7)$$

$$K_{eq.} = \frac{1}{K_S} \frac{k_f}{k_r} K_p = \frac{[P]}{[S]} \qquad (8)$$

reverse direction is limited by the structures of the substrate, transition state, product, and enzyme in that distortion of *both* substrate and product must be in a direction such as to make them both resemble the transition state. If the enzyme simply "pulls apart" the substrate, the binding of the products for the reverse reaction will be "normal," and there will be either no facilitation or a hindrance of the reverse reaction.

There are a number of enzymes which appear to be partially unidirectional in that they catalyze reactions in one direction better than in the other direction, even if the over-all equilibrium constant is not unfavorable for reaction in the second direction. This may be caused by an unusually high affinity of the enzyme for products (small K_P) with a consequent reduction in k_r, according to the Haldane relation; such an explanation has been suggested, for example, for the difficultly reversible reaction catalyzed by the methionine-activating enzyme [Eq. (9)] (Mudd

$$ATP + S\underset{R}{\overset{CH_3}{<}} \;\;\rightleftharpoons\; adenosine-S\underset{R}{\overset{+CH_3}{<}} \cdots PPP\cdots Enz. \longrightarrow PP + P + Enz. \qquad (9)$$

and Mann, 1963). (The alternative explanation for this situation is an unusually large value of K_S; an argument similar to that below may be developed for this case.) In terms of the strain hypothesis, this situation would arise if binding energy were utilized to induce strain and lower the activation energy in the forward direction, but did so to a much smaller extent in the reverse direction. The result would be a rapid rate in the forward direction and a slower rate, but a tighter binding, in the reverse direction, because most of the binding energy would be utilized to induce binding rather than strain in this direction. It is noteworthy that in the case of the methionine-activating enzyme, the binding energy of just one product, inorganic triphosphate, has been estimated to be more than —9.4 kcal per mole (Mudd and Mann, 1963). If a considerable fraction of this energy, plus binding energy from other portions of the substrates, is utilized to lower the activation energy of the reaction in the forward direction, a considerable acceleration of the rate from the induction of strain could occur.

THE CASE OF THE OSCILLATING ENZYME

Oscillation of an enzyme between two conformations would provide an ideal and simple mechanism for enzyme catalysis if such oscillation could occur with some driving force in both directions. This is shown

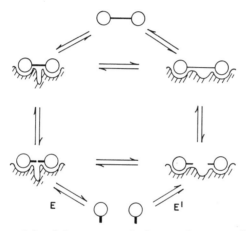

FIG. 7. Catalysis of bond formation and cleavage by an oscillating enzyme.

schematically in Fig. 7. Suppose an enzyme can exist in two states, E and E'. When the substrate is bound to the enzyme in state E' the bonds are distorted so that it is readily transformed to the product(s). When the products are bound to the enzyme in the state E, the molecules are compressed against each other so that bond formation occurs to give substrate. Now if the enzyme can oscillate with some driving force between states E and E', it can carry along the reactants and bring about the interconversion of substrates and products.

The requirement for such a mechanism is that there be some driving force to cause the interconversion between states E and E'. This could occur in either of two ways: E and E' may represent the extremes of a springlike oscillation of protein conformation and therefore be relatively high-energy states relative to a ground state with a structure intermediate between E and E' (Fig. 8A) or E and E' may represent two different stable states which undergo an oscillation of their free energies relative to each other (Fig. 8B).

The first mechanism requires that there exist a periodic, springlike vibration of the enzyme between the two states with an elastic restoring force and some force to set the process in motion. One example of such a proposed mechanism is the "critical seam" hypothesis for acid phosphatase which was proposed by London *et al.* (1958). The difficulty with such a mechanism lies in the specification of the forces which could set

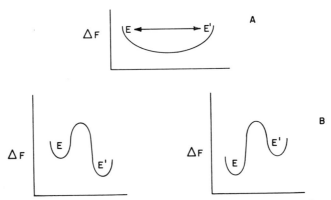

FIG. 8. Energy diagrams for a "springlike" oscillating enzyme and a situation in which the relative energy of two enzyme conformations undergoes an oscillation.

such an oscillation in motion and a mechanism to prevent the damping out of the oscillation by random collisions of small molecules with the protein and by energy transfer within the protein itself. No way around these difficulties is apparent to the writer at the present time.

The second mechanism requires that some free energy or force be fed into the system so that at one time state E' is more stable than state E and there is a tendency to convert bound substrate to products, and that at another time state E is more stable than state E' and there is a tendency to convert bound products to the original substrate. In a simple system, the only forces which would seem to be available with the proper time-dependence for such interconversions are the binding forces between the reactants and the enzyme. If these binding forces were very different for substrate and product, the binding of substrate to form E might provide the force necessary to favor conversion to form E' and the binding of product to form E' might provide the force necessary to favor conversion to form E. This seems to be possible in principle, but is difficult to imagine in practice because of the relatively large energies which would be required in order to provide significant catalysis and the fact that in most cases the binding areas of the substrate and products will be very similar, so that it is unlikely that the binding of each would favor a different protein conformation.

Another possible source of the energy for the interconversion of E and E′ is the binding of some activator molecule, which could be different from the substrate or could be a second molecule of substrate (substrate activation) which favors a change in enzyme conformation in the manner proposed for the so-called "allosteric" effect (Monod *et al.*, 1963, 1965). Binding of activator in a random order with similar binding constants to E and ES would not give a situation which is essentially different from that observed with substrate alone, but if the activator binds only to ES or binds much more firmly to ES than to E, as in a compulsory order mechanism, it can provide the driving force for a conformation change to E′S with an accompanying induction of strain in the substrate [Eq.

$$
\begin{array}{ccccc}
E + S \rightleftharpoons & ES & \xrightarrow{\pm A} & AES & \\
\updownarrow & \updownarrow & & \updownarrow & \\
E' + S \rightleftharpoons & E'S \rightleftharpoons & AE'S \rightleftharpoons & AE'P \rightleftharpoons & A + E' + P
\end{array} \tag{10}
$$

(10)]. In a mechanism of this kind it is unlikely that the same activator would significantly accelerate the reverse reaction, but a different activator might then be utilized. It would be desirable to obtain data on the effect of activators on rates of reaction in both the forward and reverse directions to provide further information relevant to this point.

The possibility should be considered that the change in conformation of the enzyme-substrate complex may be the rate-determining step in the over-all reaction (Hammes and Fasella, 1962). It is usually proposed that if the reactions of a number of substrates are catalyzed by an enzyme at the same rate, the reactions proceed through a common intermediate, such as an acyl enzyme or phosphoryl enzyme, but a rate-determining conformational change is a possible alternative explanation for such a result (Kirsch and Katchalski, 1965). Two cases should be considered: the synchronous and the consecutive. In the synchronous case [Eq. (11)],

$$
E + S \rightleftharpoons ES \xrightarrow{\text{rds}} E'P \tag{11}
$$

the conformational change is concerted with bond cleavage, so that both of these processes contribute to the rate-determining step and neither alone should be considered as wholly rate-determining. If the conformational change is utilized to overcome partially the activation energy of the reaction and this activation energy is different for different substrates, it is probable that the conformational change would occur at different rates with different substrates and that the free enzyme, which could change conformation without overcoming the activation energy for a reaction of the substrate, would be found to undergo conformational changes at a still different rate. In the consecutive case [Eq. (12)] the

$$E + S \Longrightarrow ES \underset{\xrightarrow{\hspace{1cm}}}{\overset{slow}{\Longrightarrow}} E'S \text{ or } E'S' \xrightarrow{fast} E'P \qquad (12)$$

conformation change occurs as the slow step and is followed by bond cleavage and formation in the substrates at a rate which will be different for different substrates, but fast compared to the conformational change. The rate of the conformational change will depend on the nature of the driving force by which it is brought about, and it is conceivable that it could occur at a rate which is independent of the nature of the substrate. However, if it is brought about by the binding forces between enzyme and substrate and if it causes a decrease in the activation energy for reaction of substrates, it is probable that its rate would be modified by the substrate and be different for different substrates. In the absence of substrate, ribonuclease undergoes an isomerization which probably represents a conformational change as measured by the temperature-jump technique in the presence of an indicator; in the presence of substrates or products, different relaxation times are observed (French and Hammes, 1965; Cathou and Hammes, 1965).

Experimental examination of the hypotheses discussed here is obviously difficult. It will be useful to obtain more data of the kind obtained by Hofstee, in which enzyme specificity is manifested in maximal rates rather than binding constants, with particular attention to obtaining kinetic constants which may be interpreted in terms of defined steps of the enzymatic reaction and to studying the reaction from both directions. With more complete information of this sort it may be possible to distinguish strain effects from the effects of nonproductive binding and induced fit. The problem of directly demonstrating strain or conformation changes which take place at rates sufficient to account for enzyme catalysis is difficult, but no longer impossible, with the development of modern techniques for the measurement of fast reactions. More extensive study of isotope effects should offer one promising approach. If a bond, to hydrogen, for example, is distorted in the enzyme-substrate complex relative to the starting materials, this may give rise to an isotope effect on the enzyme-substrate binding constant. Such an isotope effect would be strong evidence for the existence of deformation if it could be shown that the measured apparent binding constant does not contain significant kinetic constants and if the very small differences in the effective radius of hydrogen and deuterium do not affect binding for steric reasons.

REFERENCES

Anderson, S. R., and Weber, G. (1965). *Biochemistry* **4**, 1948.

Bender, M. L., Kézdy, F. J., and Gunter, C. R. (1964). *J. Am. Chem. Soc.* **86**, 3714.

Bernhard, S. A. (1959). *J. Cell. Comp. Physiol.* **54** (Suppl. 1), 256.

Bernhard, S. A., and Gutfreund, H. (1958). *Proc. Intern. Symp. Enzyme Chem., Tokyo Kyoto, 1957*, p. 124.

Bruice, T. C., and Pandit, U. K. (1960). *J. Am. Chem. Soc.* **82**, 5858.

Bunnett, J. F., and Hauser, C. F. (1965). *J. Am. Chem. Soc.* **87**, 2214.

Burke, J. J., Hammes, G. G., and Lewis, T. B. (1965). *J. Chem. Phys.* **42**, 3520.

Cardinale, G., and Abeles, R. (1965). Personal communication.

Cathou, R. C., and Hammes, G. G. (1965). *J. Am. Chem. Soc.* **87**, 4674.

DeLuca, M., and McElroy, W. D. (1965). *Biochem. Biophys. Res. Commun.* **18**, 836.

Epand, R. M., and Wilson, I. B. (1964). *J. Biol. Chem.* **239**, 4145.

Fernley, H. N., and Walker, P. G. (1965). *Biochem. J.* **97**, 95.

Fincham, J. R. S. (1957). *Biochem. J.* **65**, 721.

French, T. C., and Hammes, G. G. (1965). *J. Am. Chem. Soc.* **87**, 4669.

Greene, R. C., and Davis, N. B. (1960). *Biochim. Biophys. Acta* **43**, 360.

Grisolia, S. (1964). *Physiol. Rev.* **44**, 657.

Haake, P. C., and Westheimer, F. H. (1961). *J. Am. Chem. Soc.* **83**, 1102.

Hammes, G. G. (1964). *Nature* **204**, 342.

Hammes, G. G., and Fasella, P. (1962). *J. Am. Chem. Soc.* **84**, 4644.

Hammett, L. P. (1940). "Physical-Organic Chemistry," p. 118. McGraw-Hill, New York.

Hein, G E., and Niemann, C. (1962). *J. Am. Chem. Soc.* **84**, 4495.

Hofstee, B. H. J. (1954a). *Biochim. Biophys. Acta* **24**, 211.

Hofstee, B. H. J. (1954b). *J. Biol. Chem.* **207**, 219.

Ingram, J. M., and Wood, W. A. (1966). *J .Biol. Chem.* in press.

Jencks, W. P. (1963). *Ann. Rev. Biochem.* **32**, 639.

Kaiser, E. T., Panar, M., and Westheimer, F. H. (1963). *J. Am. Chem. Soc.* **85**, 602.

Kearney, E. B. (1957). *J. Biol. Chem.* **229**, 363.

Kirsch, J. F., and Katchalski, E. (1965). *Biochemistry* **4**, 884.

Klein, M. J. (1955). *Phys. Rev.* **97**, 1446.

Koshland, D. E., Jr. (1956). *J. Cell. Comp. Physiol.* **47** (Suppl. 1), 217.

Koshland, D. E., Jr. (1958). *Proc. Natl. Acad. Sci. U.S.* **44**, 98.

Koshland, D. E., Jr. (1960). *Advan. Enzymol.* **22**, 45.

Koshland, D. E., Jr. (1962). *J. Theoret. Biol.* **2**, 75.

Kumamoto, J., Cox, J. R., Jr., and Westheimer, F. H. (1956). *J. Am. Chem. Soc.* **78**, 4858.

Kurz, J. L. (1963). *J. Am. Chem. Soc.* **85**, 987.

Laidler, K. J. (1954). "Introduction to the Chemistry of Enzymes," Chap. 9. Mc-Graw-Hill, New York.

Laidler, K. J. (1958). "The Chemical Kinetics of Enzyme Action." Oxford Univ. Press, London and New York.

Linderstrøm-Lang, K. U., and Schellman, J. A. (1959). *In* "The Enzymes" (P. D. Boyer, H. Lardy, and K. Myrback, eds.), Vol. I, pp. 443, 466. Academic Press, New York.

London, M., McHugh, R., and Hudson, P. B. (1958). *Arch. Biochem. Biophys.* **73**, 72.

Lovrien, R. (1964). *Abstr. 148th Natl. Meeting, Am. Chem. Soc., Chicago, Illinois, 1964* p. 44C.

Lumry, R. (1959). *In* "The Enzymes" (P. D. Boyer, H. Lardy, and K. Myrback, eds.), Vol. I, p. 157. Academic Press, New York.

Lumry, R., and Eyring, H. (1954). *J. Phys. Chem.* **58**, 110.

Malhotra, S. K., and Ringold, H. J. (1965). *J. Am. Chem. Soc.* **87**, 3228.

Monod, J., Changeux, J-P., and Jacob, F. (1963). *J. Mol. Biol.* **6**, 306.

Monod, J., Wyman, J., and Changeux, J-P (1965). *J. Mol. Biol.* **12**, 88.

Mudd, S. H., and Mann, J. D. (1963). *J. Biol. Chem.* **238**, 2164.

Nimmo-Smith, R. H. (1960). *Biochem. J.* **75**, 284.

Norris, A. T., and Berg, P. (1964). *Proc. Natl. Acad. Sci. U.S.* **52**, 330.

Schwarz, G. (1965). *J. Mol. Biol.* **11**, 64.

Smith, E. L. (1949). *Proc. Natl. Acad. Sci. U.S.* **35**, 80.

Spencer, T., and Sturtevant, J. M. (1959). *J. Am. Chem. Soc.* **81**, 1874.

Sundaram, T. K., and Fincham, J. R. S. (1964). *J. Mol. Biol.* **10**, 423.

Thoma, J. A., and Koshland, D. E., Jr. (1960). *J. Am. Chem. Soc.* **82**, 3329.

Trayser, K. A., and Colowick, S. P. (1961). *Arch. Biochem. Biophys.* **94**, 161.

Wang, S., Kawahara, F. S., and Talalay, P. (1963). *J. Biol. Chem.* **238**, 576.

Wang, J. H., Shonka, M. L., and Graves, D. J. (1965). *Biochemistry* **4**, 2296.

Weber, G. (1965). *In* "Molecular Biophysics" (B. Pullman and M. Weissbluth, eds.). pp. 205-238. Academic Press, New York.

Weber, G., and Anderson, S. R. (1965). *Biochemistry* **4**, 1942.

Westheimer, F. H. (1962). *Advan. Enzymol.* **24**, 441.

Wilson, I. B. (1964). *In* "Comprehensive Biochemistry" (M. Florkin and E. H. Stotz, eds.), Vol. XII, p. 285. Elsevier, Amsterdam.

Worcel, A., Goldman, D. S., and Cleland, W. W. (1965). *J. Biol. Chem.* **240**, 3399.

Zeller, E. A., Ramachander, G., Fleisher, G. A., Ishimaru, T., and Zeller, V. (1965). *Biochem. J.* **95**, 262.

The Enzymatic Signifcance of the S-Acetylation and N-Acetylation of 3-Phosphoglyceraldehyde Dehydrogenase by Substrates *

Jane Harting Park

It is certainly a pleasure to submit an article in remembrance of the 1941 publication of Dr. Lipmann's ideas entitled "Phosphate Bond Energy." Actually, we feel obliged to observe a double celebration to include the second long chapter, "Acetyl Phosphate," which was published in the *Advances in Enzymology* in 1946. This paper, which might be considered as an experimental extension of the first article, detailed the discovery of acetyl phosphate and reported the initial observations on coenzyme A. These findings, of course, provided momentum and often reorientation for future investigations in many areas. The recent studies on the mechanism of the oxidation and phosphorylation reactions of 3-phosphoglyceraldehyde dehydrogenase, which originated in Warburg and Christian's discovery of 1,3-diphosphoglyceric acid (1), were certainly given a second forward thrust by Lipmann's work on the active 2-carbon fragments (2).

ACETYL PHOSPHATE AND 3-PHOSPHOGLYCERALDEHYDE DEHYDROGENASE

In 1950 acetyl phosphate was a very popular compound, and in this general context Dr. Velick and I attempted to catalyze the oxidation of acetaldehyde to acetyl phosphate with 3-phosphoglyceraldehyde dehy-

* This work has been supported by the U.S. Public Health Service, National Science Foundation, and the Muscular Dystrophy Association of America.

drogenase crystallized from rabbit muscle (3). The reaction [Eq. (1)] was carried out in the presence of DPN and inorganic phosphate. Momentarily we were quite enthusiastic about the positive result because this was the first clear-cut demonstration of the production of acetyl

$$\begin{matrix} CHO \\ | \\ CH_3 \end{matrix} + H_3PO_4 + DPN^+ \rightleftharpoons \begin{matrix} O \\ || \\ C \sim OPO_3H_2 \\ | \\ CH_3 \end{matrix} + DPNH + H^+ \quad (1)$$

phosphate in a mammalian system. Very shortly it became apparent that this oxidation was far too slow to be of physiological significance. Nevertheless the reaction was technically useful in studying the mechanism of the oxidation and phosphorylation reactions because the product, acetyl phosphate, could be readily prepared by the procedure of Stadtman and Lipmann (4) and used as a model substrate in place of the more labile 1,3-diphosphoglyceric acid. For example, the dehydrogenase was found to carry out ^{32}P exchange and arsenolysis reactions with acetyl phosphate as shown in Eq. (2) (5, 6).

$$\begin{matrix} O \\ || \\ C \sim OPO_3H_2 \\ | \\ CH_3 \end{matrix} \xrightleftharpoons{ESH_{(DPN)_4}} \begin{matrix} O \\ || \\ C \sim SE_{(DPN)_4} \\ | \\ CH_3 \end{matrix} \begin{matrix} \xrightarrow{^{32}PO_4} \begin{matrix} O \\ || \\ C \sim O^{32}PO_3H_2 \\ | \\ CH_3 \end{matrix} \\ \searrow_{AsO_4} \begin{matrix} O \\ || \\ C-OH \\ | \\ CH_3 \end{matrix} \end{matrix} \quad (2)$$

The enzyme is designated as $ESH_{(DPN)_4}$ to indicate the requirements of SH groups and DPN for these reactions. These two reactions suggested that the enzyme had a transacetylase activity and that an acetyl enzyme intermediate was involved in the over-all catalysis of the oxidation of acetaldehyde. The enzyme was shown to have transcetylase activity as the acetyl group of acetyl phosphate could be transferred to coenzyme A (CoA) (5). The formation of acetyl coenzyme A was verified in a coupled system using both the sulfanilamide-acetylating enzyme of Lipmann and his co-workers (7) and the crystalline condensing enzyme of Ochoa and associates (8) [Eq. (3)]. These experiments were made possible by Lipmann and Gregory who kindly sent us a large supply of coenzyme A.

The suggested acetyl enzyme complex was subsequently prepared by Racker and Krimsky (9) using acetyl phosphate as the acetylating substrate for the DPN-free dehydrogenase. With the hydroxamic acid procedure of Lipmann and Tuttle (10), it was possible to show quantitatively that 0.8–1.8 moles of acetyl groups were bound per mole of enzyme.

$$\underset{CH_3}{\overset{O}{\overset{\|}{C}}}\sim OPO_3H_2 \underset{}{\overset{ESH_{(DPN)_4}\quad +\quad CoASH}{\rightleftharpoons}} \underset{CH_3}{\overset{O}{\overset{\|}{C}}}\sim SCoA$$

$$+ \text{ OAA} \diagdown \qquad \diagup + \text{ sulfanilamide}$$

$$\text{Citric acid} \qquad \qquad \underset{\text{sulfanilamide}}{\text{Acetyl}} \qquad (3)$$

From these studies and related kinetic data (11, 12) the over-all mechanism for the oxidation of an aldehyde to an acyl phosphate could be written as a two-step reaction. The aldehyde is first oxidized in the presence of DPN to an acyl enzyme intermediate which is then phosphorylated to the acyl phosphate. In Eq. (4) the two-step oxidation of acetaldehyde to acetyl phosphate is catalyzed by 3-phosphoglyceraldehyde dehydrogenase (ESH) and proceeds via an acetyl enzyme intermediate.

$$\underset{CH_3}{\overset{CHO}{|}} + ESH \underset{DPNH}{\overset{DPN^+}{\rightleftharpoons}} \underset{CH_3}{\overset{O}{\overset{\|}{C}}}\sim SE + H_3PO_4 + \underset{CH_3}{\overset{O}{\overset{\|}{C}}}\sim OPO_3H_2 \qquad (4)$$

In the course of the transacetylase studies it was noted that a phosphatase activity appeared if the enzyme was incubated with acetyl phosphate in the absence of cysteine (13). This acetyl phosphatase activity was not the same as that studied by Lipmann and his associates (2) because the hydrolytic activity of the dehydrogenase was not heat stable and the cleavage occurred at a C—O bond rather than a P—O bond (14). The C—O cleavage was shown by the ^{18}O experiments carried out with Koshland and illustrated in Eq. (5). The enzyme is designated as $E_{(DPN)_4}$ to indicate a requirement for DPN but not for sulfhydryl groups.

$$CH_3\overset{O}{\overset{\|}{C}} \sim OPO_3H_2 + H_2^{18}O \xrightarrow{E_{(DPN)_4}} CH_3\overset{O}{\overset{\|}{C}}{}^{18}OH + H_3PO_4 \qquad (5)$$

The unique nature of this cleavage by a phosphatase at the C—O bond suggested that the dehydrogenase might possess an esterase activity similar to that of the proteolytic enzymes. In collaboration with Cunningham, Meriwether, and Olson the dehydrogenase was indeed shown to hydrolyze p-nitrophenyl acetate (15) and various derivatives of this substrate (16). Equation (5) shows that the esterase activity of the dehydrogenase (ESH) requires sulfhydryl groups but not DPN.

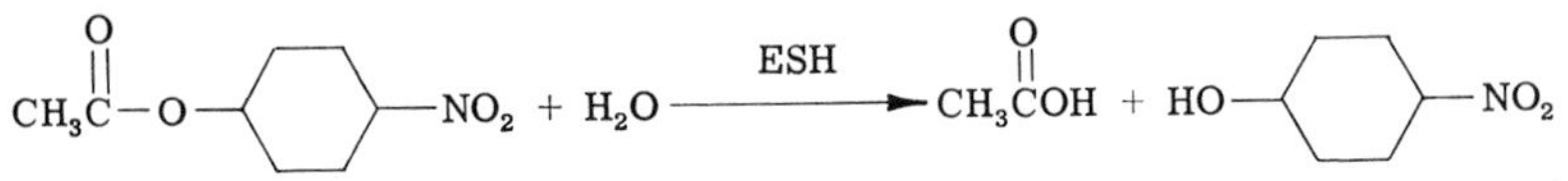

$$CH_3\overset{O}{\overset{\|}{C}}-O-\langle\rangle-NO_2 + H_2O \xrightarrow{\text{ESH}} CH_3\overset{O}{\overset{\|}{C}}OH + HO-\langle\rangle-NO_2$$

$$(6)$$

For the dehydrogenase, p-nitrophenyl acetate is a stronger acetylating agent than acetyl phosphate, and it is technically easier to form an acetyl enzyme complex with this substrate. In collaboration with Harris at Cambridge University we were able to show that p-nitrophenyl acetate acetylates a specific cysteine residue which is the active site for the dehydrogenase, transferase, and esterase activities. The sequence of the active center octadecapeptide is shown in Fig. 1 (17).

$$\overset{^{14}COCH_3}{|}$$

Lys-Ileu-Val-Ser-Asn-Ala-Ser-Cys-Thr-Thr-Asn-Cys-Leu-Ala-Pro-Leu-Ala-Lys

1   8   12   18

FIG. 1. The amino acid sequence around the active cysteine residue, number 8, in 3-phosphoglyceraldehyde dehydrogenase. The second cysteine moiety in position number 12 is not acetylated with p-nitrophenyl acetate or carboxymethylated with iodoacetic acid.

The active cysteine residue can also be acetylated with acetyl phosphate, but the reaction is much slower. This fact plus the numerous differences between p-nitrophenyl acetate and acetyl phosphate as substrates for the dehydrogenase [(Eqs. (2), (5), and (6)] prompted a more detailed investigation of the acetylation reactions. In the course of this comparative study, it was found that acetyl phosphate readily acetylates a second site, namely the ε-amino group of a lysine residue (18). The lysine moiety can also be acetylated by p-nitrophenyl acetate $(18, 19)$. The sequence of the tridecapeptide (20) containing the N-^{14}C-acetyl-lysine is given in Fig. 2.

This sequence is the same as that found by Harris and Polgar for an

N-acetylated peptide prepared with ^{14}C-p-nitrophenyl acetate and crystalline 3-phosphoglyceraldehyde dehydrogenase from pig muscle (21).

The N-^{14}C-acetyllysine moiety is not part of the octadecapeptide since the neighboring amino acids in this tridecapeptide differ from those of

$$HN^{14}COCH_3$$
$$|$$
Ala-Thr-Gln-Lys-Thr-Val-Asp-Gly-Pro-Ser-Gly-Lys-Leu
$$\quad\quad\quad\ 4 \quad\quad\quad\quad\quad\quad\quad\quad\quad\quad\quad\quad\ 12$$

FIG. 2. The amino acid sequence surrounding the lysine residue, number 4, which is specifically labeled by acetyl phosphate or p-nitrophenyl acetate.

the NH$_2$-terminal and COOH-terminal lysines of the active center. There are four identical S-acetyl sites on the enzyme (mol. wt. 140,000) and an equal number of identical N-acetyllysine sites (15, 17, 20, 22).

MECHANISMS FOR THE S-ACETYLATION AND N-ACETYLATION OF THE DEHYDROGENASE

The acetylation of the cysteine residue with p-nitrophenyl acetate proceeds by a direct nucleophilic attack of the sulfhydryl group on the carbonyl carbon of the acetate moiety as formulated by Olson and Park (16). Since acetyl phosphate acetylates the same cysteine residue it is reasonable to assume that the mechanism for thioester formation is identical to that with p-nitrophenyl acetate.

The properties of the N-acetylation of the enzyme, however, correspond closely to the characteristics for an intramolecular S—N transfer reaction of S-acetyl-β-mercaptoethylamine or S-acetyl-γ-mercaptopropylamine (23, 24). An S—N transfer reaction has actually been demonstrated with a purified S-acetyl enzyme in the following manner. The DPN-free dehydrogenase is incubated at pH 7.0 and 0°C with ^{14}C-p-nitrophenyl acetate which is the preferred substrate for preparing an S-acetyl enzyme in high yields (20). The ^{14}C-S-acetyl enzyme is then passed through a Sephadex G-25 column in order to separate it from the unreacted ^{14}C-p-nitrophenyl acetate and the reaction products, p-nitrophenol and ^{14}C-acetic acid. If this purified enzyme is maintained at 0°C and pH 7.0, it remains essentially in the S-acetyl form as shown by comparing the peptide patterns obtained from the pepsin digestions of the S-acetyl enzymes before and after Sephadex treatment (see peptides S1 to S7 of Fig. 3, *panels 1* and *2*). When the purified S-acetyl enzyme is incubated at pH 8.5 and room temperature there is an appearance of

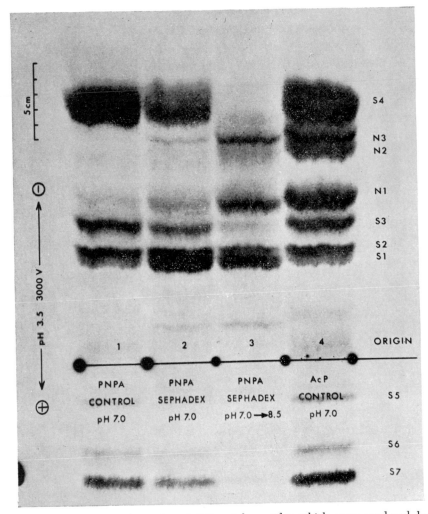

FIG. 3. The autoradiographs of ^{14}C-acetyl peptides which were produced by pepsin digestion of ^{14}C-acetyl enzymes and demonstrate an S—N acetyl transfer reaction. The control in *panel 1* shows the S-acetyl peptides, S1 to S7 obtained from the pepsin digestion of an acetyl enzyme labeled with *p*-nitrophenyl acetate at pH 7.0 and 0°C (*15*). These peptides are fragments of the active center octadecapeptide shown in Fig. 1. The control in *panel 4* shows both the S-acetyl and N-acetyl peptides from an enzyme labeled with ^{14}C-acetyl phosphate at pH 7.0 and room temperature. The N-peptides have been identified (*20*) as components of the N-acetylated tridecapeptide of Fig. 2. The peptides in *panels 2 and 3* were obtained from enzymes which were labeled with *p*-nitrophenyl acetate, purified on a Sephadex column, and then incubated for 15 minutes at pH 7.0 at 0°C and pH 8.5 at room temperature, respectively. PNPA, *p*-nitrophenyl acetate; AcP, acetyl phosphate.

[14]C-N-acetyl peptides, N1, N2, N3, which resulted from an S—N transfer reaction in the absence of substrate. The N-acetyl peptides in *panel 3* can be readily identified as the three known N-acetyl peptides in *panel 4* which are formed when the enzyme is acetylated with acetyl phosphate at pH 7.0 and room temperature (*20*). The rate of the S—N transfer is approximately equivalent to that of S-acetyl-γ-mercaptopropylamine (*23*). The studies to date indicate that the S—N transfer is the major reaction for the N-acetylation of the enzyme. This transfer reaction is interesting as an illustration of a migrating substrate and suggests a proximity of the sulfhydryl and the ε-amino groups. The difficulties encountered in acetylating both the cysteine and lysine moieties in a given monomer reinforce the idea of proximity and even steric hindrance (*30*). Since the two acetylated residues were not found in the active center octadecapeptide it must mean that the cysteine and lysine groups are approximated by a three-dimensional folding of the peptide chain. The implications of the S- and N-acetylation reactions in terms of enzyme catalysis and cell biology are discussed in the following sections.

In the course of these studies on the S—N transfer reaction the formation of a third acetyl enzyme complex was recently discovered by Park, Meriwether, and Earl. Close examination of Fig. 3 shows that after the S-acetyl enzyme is passed through Sephadex there is a somewhat diminished intensity of the distal S-4 peptide and an increase in the radioactivity in the area of band S-1 (*Panels 1* and *2*). This ^{14}C-acetyl group is in thioester linkage as the new peptides are performic acid labile. However, in the native enzyme these S-acetyl groups are more stable than those of the active site as indicated in *Panel 3*. When the pH is raised from 7.0 to 8.5, the S-acetyl bands of the active site, for example S-4, disappear whereas the new peptides in the S-1 area are still visible. Analysis of these peptides yielded a sequence for a pentapeptide given in Fig. 4. The acetylated cysteine of this peptide is neither cysteine number

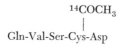

Gln-Val-Ser-Cys-Asp

Fig. 4. The amino acid sequence surrounding the cysteine residue in the third acetylated site of the enzyme.

8 nor *12* in the active center. The data indicate that the acetylation of the cysteine residue in the pentapeptide very likely occurs by an S—S transfer reaction of the ^{14}C-S-acetyl group from the active site to this moiety. The enzymatic significance of this site is currently under investigation.

THE EFFECTS OF DPN, PHOSPHATE, AND ARSENATE ON THE ACYLATION AND DEACYLATION REACTIONS OF THE ACETYL ENZYMES

In a catalytically oriented study of the acylation and deacylation of the enzyme, the effects of the reactants in the transferase activities, namely, DPN, phosphate, and arsenate, were examined. In the presence of DPN an acetyl enzyme complex cannot be prepared at pH 7.0 with either p-nitrophenyl acetate or acetyl phosphate. The DPN could prevent the isolation of the acetyl enzyme complex by (1) blocking the acetylation reaction or (2) accelerating the deacylation as indicated below:

$$\text{AcP + ESH} \underset{-P_i}{\overset{}{\rightleftharpoons}} \text{ES–Ac} \xrightarrow{+H_2O} \text{ESH + acetate}$$

Reaction:	Acylation	Deacylation	
DPN Effect:	(1) Inhibition	(2) Acceleration	(7)

The case with p-nitrophenyl acetate is relatively straightforward and is therefore presented first.

p-Nitrophenyl Acetate and the Active Site Cysteine

The effects of DPN on the acylation or deacylation step were separately examined in the following manner:

(1) To measure the effect of DPN on the acylation step, the DPN-free enzyme was incubated with DPN, ^{14}C-PNPA, and then added to the enzyme-(DPN)$_3$ complex; the amount of acetylation was quantitatively determined as the moles of ^{14}C-acetyl groups bound per mole of enzyme.

(2) To measure the effect of DPN on the deacylation step, the DPN-free enzyme was incubated with ^{14}C-PNPA to form the ^{14}C-acetyl enzyme complex, and DPN was subsequently added to effect, if possible, the removal of the bound ^{14}C-acetyl groups.

The results of such experiments are shown in Table I. The control value for the acetylation of the cysteine residues shows that 3.3 moles of ^{14}C-acetyl groups are bound per mole of enzyme, but in the presence of DPN only 0.3 mole of ^{14}C-acetyl groups is bound per mole of enzyme. If DPN is added to the preformed acetyl enzyme complex, there is only a slight reduction in the number of enzyme-bound ^{14}C-acetyl groups from 3.0 to 2.6. Thus DPN prevents acylation of the enzyme with ^{14}C-

p-nitrophenyl acetate but does not cause rapid deacylation. The DPN inhibition of the acylation reaction is confirmed by spectrophotometric determination, as indicated in the last column. Inorganic phosphate alone has no effect on the acylation or deacylation. However, a combination

TABLE I

EFFECT OF DPN AND/OR PHOSPHATE ON THE ACETYLATION OF DEHYDROGENASE
WITH *p*-NITROPHENYL ACETATE AND THE DEACYLATION
OF THE S-ACETYL ENZYME COMPLEX

Additions	Moles of ^{14}C-acetyl groups bound per mole of enzyme		Spectrophotometric determination of bound acetyl residues[a]
	Acylation[b]	Deacylation[c]	Acylation
None	3.3	3.0	3.1
DPN	0.3	2.6	0.1
PO$_4$	3.0	3.4	3.1
DPN + PO$_4$	0.3	0.5	0.1

[a] *Acetylation of the enzyme:* The dialyzed, DPN-free dehydrogenase (0.1 μmole) was preincubated with DPN (1.0 μmole) and/or phosphate (2.0 μmoles) for 10 minutes at room temperature, pH 7.0. The tubes were cooled to 0°C, and *p*-nitrophenyl acetate (2.0 μmoles) were added; total volume, 1.2 ml. The reaction was terminated after 15 minutes, and the number of enzyme-bound ^{14}C-acetyl groups was determined as previously described (15).

[b] *Deacylation of the acetyl enzyme complex:* An acetyl enzyme complex was formed by incubating the DPN-free dehydrogenase (0.1 μmole) with [14]C-*p*-nitrophenyl acetate (2.0 μmoles) for 15 minutes at 0°C, pH 7.0. The DPN (1.0 μmole) and/or phosphate (2.0 μmoles) were added, and the incubation continued for 10 minutes. The reaction was then terminated and the number of enzyme-bound ^{14}C-acetyl groups was determined.

[c] *Spectrophotometric measurements of the formation of the acetyl enzyme complex:* Measurements of the acylation of the enzyme were made according to the procedure of Hartley and Kilby (25). When *p*-nitrophenyl acetate was added to a large amount of the dehydrogenase, there was an initial burst of *p*-nitrophenol liberation which represented the formation of the acetyl enzyme. The burst was followed by a slow continuing *p*-nitrophenol release caused by the breakdown and reformation of the acetyl enzyme complex. By extrapolation of the curves the moles of acetyl group bound per mole of enzyme were determined as previously detailed (15).

of DPN and phosphate inhibits acylation but promotes a deacylation of the acetyl enzyme complex. Clearly, DPN is required for the transfer of the acetyl group from the enzyme to inorganic phosphate. These data are consistent with the previous enzymatic findings that DPN inhibits acylation with *p*-nitrophenyl acetate but is required for phosphate transfer reactions (5, 6, 15).

Acetyl Phosphate and the Active Site Cysteine

Experiments on the effect of DPN on the acylation and deacylation reactions are technically more complicated with acetyl phosphate as the substrate than with p-nitrophenyl acetate. First, the effects of DPN *alone* could not be tested because inorganic phosphate is always present in the reaction mixture as a contaminant of the ^{14}C-acetyl phosphate and as a product of the enzyme acetylation reaction. Therefore, those experiments in which only DPN is added are actually a combination of DPN *and* inorganic phosphate. The phosphate contamination is about equivalent to the amount added in the PNPA experiment of Table 1. A second complication is that there is no convenient spectrophotometric method for measuring the acylation of the enzyme with acetyl phosphate. Consequently, one must look at the over-all disappearance of acetyl phosphate and infer from the hydroxamic acid analysis whether there was acetylation or not. Insofar as possible, these factors were taken into account.

The experimental data showing the effects of DPN on the acetylation of the dehydrogenase with acetyl phosphate are presented in Table II. The first line shows the control values of 2.0 moles of ^{14}C-acetyl groups bound for the periods of acylation and deacylation, respectively. Under these particular conditions the acylation gives predominantly an S-acetyl enzyme. During the incubation 1.2 μmoles of acetyl phosphate disappeared. This value represents the turnover of the acetyl groups on the active site. When DPN is added there is no apparent acylation, a significant deacylation, and an over-all disappearance of 1.1 μmoles of acetyl phosphate. The deacylation is probably not caused by DPN alone but is due to the combined effect of DPN and the phosphate present as a contamination. Such an explanation involving a transfer reaction is consistent with the data of Table I and the hydroxamic acid analysis.

The disappearance of acetyl phosphate, which represents the breakdown of the acetyl enzyme complex during the incubation, was not due to the previously discussed phosphatase activity (13) because the phosphatase reaction was inhibited by the 2.0 μmoles of added cyanide. Moreover, the hydrolysis of acetyl phosphate under the conditions described in Table II occurs in the absence of DPN and requires sulfhydryl groups, whereas the phosphatase activity is just the reverse in requiring DPN as a coenzyme and oxidized sulfhydryl groups. The hydrolysis, as originally described for the phosphatase reaction (13), is at least 20 times faster than the disappearance of acetyl phosphate shown in Table II. When the more favorable conditions of Colowick and Ehring are used for the sys-

TABLE II

Effect of DPN and/or Arsenate on the Acylation of 3-Phospho-
glyceraldehyde Dehydrogenase with Acetyl Phosphate and
on the Deacylation of the Acetyl Enzyme Complex

Additions	Moles of ^{14}C-acetyl bound per mole of enzyme		Disappearance of acetyl phosphate (μmoles)
	Acylation[a]	Deacylation[b]	Acylation and deacylation[c]
None	2.0	2.0	1.2
DPN	0.4	0.3	1.1
AsO$_4$	1.5	1.6	1.5
DPN + AsO$_4$	0.0	0.4	4.0

[a] *Acetylation of the enzyme:* The dialyzed, DPN-free enzyme (0.1 μmole) was preincubated for 10 minutes with DPN (1.0 μmole) and/or arsenate (2.0 μmoles). In order to inhibit the contaminating phosphatase activity of the enzyme, cyanide (2.0 μmoles) was added to each tube. The acetylating substrate, 4.0 μmoles of acetyl phosphate, was then added and the incubation continued for 30 minutes at room temperature and pH 7.0. In these experiments with acetyl phosphate there is always some inorganic phosphate present as a product of the acetylation reaction and as an impurity in the ^{14}C-acetyl phosphate. The reactions were stopped and the amount of bound ^{14}C-acetyl groups was then determined as reported previously (15).

[b] *Deacylation of the acetyl enzyme complex:* An acetyl enzyme complex was formed by incubating the DPN-free enzyme (0.1 μmole) with ^{14}C-acetyl phosphate (4.0 μmoles) in the presence of cyanide (2.0 μmoles) for 30 minutes at room temperature, pH 7.0. The additions were then made, and after 10 minutes the reactions were terminated.

[c] *Combined measurement of acetylation and deacetylation:* The measurement of the disappearance of acetyl phosphate under a given set of experimental conditions represents the over-all process of acylation and deacylation of the enzyme. For these determinations the DPN-free dehydrogenase (0.1 μmoles) was preincubated for 10 minutes with cyanide (2.0 μmoles) and the compounds listed in the additions column of the table. Acetyl phosphate (4.0 μmoles) was added, and after 30 minutes the disappearance of the acetyl phosphate was determined with the hydroxamic method of Lipmann and Tuttle (10).

tematic oxidation of the enzyme with iodosobenzoate (26), the rate of the phosphatase activity is then about 2000 times faster than the turnover of the active site thioester bond in Table II. Since the rate of turnover of acetyl phosphate at the active site is about 0.04 μmole of acetyl phosphate disappearing per 0.1 μmole of enzyme per minute (Table II), one is certainly on the borderline between catalytic and chemical breakdown of the thioester bond.

These data then show that the added DPN promotes deacylation, but it is impossible to state with certainty whether DPN blocks the formation of the acetyl enzyme complex. The disappearance of acetyl phosphate in the presence of DPN is only presumptive evidence for the turnover of an acetyl enzyme complex.

The next set of experiments on the arsenolysis of acetyl phosphate definitely shows that DPN does not inhibit acylation but rather accelerates deacylation. Low concentrations of arsenate (2.0 μmoles) did not significantly affect the acylation or deacylation of the enzyme. However, with arsenate and DPN there was no "apparent" acylation and a definite deacylation. The acetyl phosphate (4.0 μmoles) was completely hydrolyzed. Since the possibility of phosphatase activity is ruled out by the presence of cyanide and the transfer of acetyl groups to inorganic phosphate would not change the hydroxamic acid value, the most reasonable explanation for the disappearance of the acetyl phosphate is that the formation of the acetyl enzyme was followed by a rapid, irreversible arsenolysis reaction.

There is therefore a very real difference between the acetylation by acetyl phosphate, which occurs in the presence or absence of DPN, and the acetylation by p-nitrophenyl acetate, which is strongly inhibited by DPN. The properties of the deacylation of the acetyl enzymes formed by these two substrates at pH 7.0 are, of course, identical since they acetylate the same cysteine moiety. These observations are again consistent with the requirement of DPN for the reactions of acetyl phosphate in the ^{32}P exchange, arsenolysis, and acetyl CoA formation catalyzed by the dehydrogenase (5, 6).

It is worthy of note that the S-acetyl enzyme, produced from the reaction of acetyl phosphate with the enzyme in the absence of DPN, can apparently be made to regenerate acetyl phosphate simply by the addition of DPN. This suggests that the following equilibrium

$$\text{Acetyl phosphate} + \text{E} \rightleftharpoons \text{acetyl-E} + \text{phosphate}$$

is actually shifted to the left by the addition of DPN. This would be expected to occur if DPN were bound more tightly by E than by acetyl-E. Such a shift in equilibrium would mean that the acetyl enzyme bond becomes more "energy-rich," in the Lipmann sense (27), when DPN is bound.

ACETYL PHOSPHATE AND THE ACETYLATED LYSINE RESIDUE

The comparison between the enzymatic reactivity of the S-acetyl enzyme and the N-acetyl enzyme is shown in Table III. The S-acetyl and

N-acetyl enzymes were prepared by acetylating with acetyl phosphate at pH 7.0 and 8.5, respectively. The control values indicate that 2.5 and 2.2 moles of ^{14}C-acetyl groups were bound per mole of enzyme. When 2.0 µmoles of arsenate were added to the acetyl enzyme complexes there was a 10–20% deacylation of the enzyme. In the presence of arsenate and DPN there is almost complete deacylation of the S-acetyl enzyme complex but an insignificant effect on the N-acetyl complex. The S-acetyl enzyme is the catalytically active intermediate, whereas the N-acetyl group appears to be stable.

TABLE III

EFFECT OF DPN AND ARSENATE ON THE DEACYLATION OF THE
S-ACETYL AND N-ACETYL ENZYME COMPLEXES OF
3-PHOSPHOGLYCERALDEHYDE DEHYDROGENASE[a]

Additions (µmoles)	Moles of ^{14}C-acetyl groups bound per mole of enzyme	
	S-Acetyl enzyme pH 7.0	N-Acetyl enzyme pH 8.5
None	2.5	2.2
AsO$_4$, 2.0	2.0	2.0
AsO$_4$, 2.0; DPN, 1.0	0.2	2.1
AsO$_4$, 40.0	0.3	1.9

[a] The S-acetyl and N-acetyl enzyme complexes were formed by incubating the DPN-free enzyme (0.1 µmole) with ^{14}C-acetyl phosphate (4.0 µmoles) for 30 minutes at pH 7.0 and 8.5, respectively. Additions were then made, and the incubation continued for 10 minutes. The reactions were stopped by the addition of acetone-ether-1 N HCl mixture. The effects of the arsenate and DPN on the acetyl enzyme complexes could be appraised from the quantitative determinations of the bound ^{14}C-acetyl groups.

The stability of the N-acetyl complex could be due to the fact that DPN, which is required for arsenolysis (5, 6) is not bound to the N-acetylated enzyme (20). The arsenolyses would thereby be inhibited because of the reported inhibition of DPN binding. The last experiment was designed to test the possibility of an arsenolysis reaction that would be independent of DPN. Table III shows that a high arsenate concentration (40.0 µmoles) can cause a deacylation of the S-acetyl enzyme but not the N-acetyl enzyme. A DPN-independent arsenolysis has not previously been noticed with the dehydrogenase. Since thioesters are not thought to be unstable in the presence of arsenate, this arsenolysis is a characteristic for the enzyme thioester bond. The possibility that trace amounts of bound DPN might effect this arsenolysis has not been rigorously excluded.

As yet it has not been possible to remove the N-acetyl group with high concentrations of arsenate, DPN, and phosphate or exchange it with ^{12}C-acetyl phosphate (20). However, there could be a reversal of the S—N transfer reaction via a modified type of thiazoline ring intermediate:

$$\text{Cysteine-S—C—NH}_2^+\text{-Lysine}$$
$$\text{H}_3\text{C} \qquad \text{O}^-$$
$$\text{Peptide chain}$$

The equilibrium as judged by studies on model compounds will be far to the side of the N-acetyl derivative (28).

THE CATALYTIC IMPLICATIONS OF N-ACETYLATION

Thus N-acetylation appears to be the enzymatic counterpart to "a dead end street." However, the lysine residue has been implicated in another manner—not as a transferase site but rather as a DPN-binding site. It has been shown that DPN binding was reduced approximately in proportion to the N-acetylation of the enzyme (20); DPN binding was not reduced at pH 4.5 where only S-acetylation occurred. Coenzyme binding was moderately to markedly reduced with N-acetylation of the enzyme at pH 7.0 and 8.5. Previously bound DPN, however, could not be displaced by exposure to acetyl phosphate. The N-acetylated enzyme was inactive when assayed as a dehydrogenase with glyceraldehyde-3-phosphate, DPN, and arsenate. Since DPN prevented N-acetylation, it thereby protected against the inactivation by acetyl phosphate. These observations suggest a competition between acetyl phosphate and DPN for the lysine residue. Alternative explanations such as conformational changes in the enzyme are also possible.

Since N-acetylation inactivates the enzyme, the biological consequences of this inhibition must be taken into consideration. It appears as if the enzyme has a built-in defense against this inactivation by virtue of its coenzyme, DPN, which prevents N-acetylation. It is interesting in this regard that 3-phosphoglyceraldehyde dehydrogenase binds DPN very tightly, and is unique among the dehydrogenases in having a higher binding constant for DPN than DPNH and crystallizing with three moles of DPN bound per mole of enzyme. In yeast cells, the spectrophotometric measurements indicate that DPN is bound to the enzyme *in vivo* (29). The DPN concentration in many types of cells is about fifteen times greater than the DPNH. These conditions are such that when the enzyme-bound DPN is reduced by the oxidation of 3-phosphoglyceraldehyde to 1,3-diphosphoglyceric acid the newly formed DPNH is readily replaced by DPN. Thus the enzyme appears to be well protected in the cellular cytoplasm.

A certain proximity of the cysteine and lysine moieties is indicated by the S—N transfer and the difficulties encountered in acetylating both the cysteine and lysine moieties in a given monomer (30). This suggested proximity would fit well with the known facts of a direct H transfer from the aldehyde to the DPN during the oxidation reaction (31). The acetylated lysine and cysteine residues are not found in the same peptide, and it appears that the three-dimensional folding of the molecule must account for the proximity. There are, of course, many precedents for this type of folding—notably, ribonuclease (32) and chymotrypsin (33). Thus the picture one derives from studies with model compounds, acetyl phosphate and p-nitrophenyl acetate, is wholly compatible with conditions that might be required for the enzyme to function maximally.

SUMMARY

Acetyl phosphate and p-nitrophenyl acetate have been employed as substrates to demonstrate the versatility of 3-phosphoglyceraldehyde dehydrogenase as a transferase, esterase, and phosphatase. At pH 7.0 both these substrates form an S-acetyl enzyme complex which is the intermediate for the dehydrogenase, transferase, and esterase activities. DPN inhibits the S-acetylation of the enzyme with p-nitrophenyl acetate but not with acetyl phosphate. The S-acetyl group may be transferred in the presence of DPN to inorganic phosphate or arsenate. A new DPN-independent arsenolysis of the S-acetyl enzyme complex is also postulated.

A second ^{14}C-acetyl enzyme complex is formed at pH 8.5 when the ε-amino group of a lysine moiety is acetylated by an intramolecular S—N transfer reaction. The coenzyme, DPN, prevents this S—N transfer reaction. The lysine residue does not participate in transfer reactions but may be involved in DPN binding.

A third ^{14}C-acetyl enzyme complex, involving a cysteine other than the active site cysteine, has been described. DPN prevents the acetylation of this cysteine residue, which is outside the active center octadecapeptide, as well as the lysine moiety. Thus DPN may have an unexpected role in properly orienting the substrates and forestalling the acetylation of "incorrect moieties" on the enzyme.

REFERENCES

1. Warburg, O., and Christian, W., *Biochem. Z.* **303**, 40 (1939).
2. Lipmann, F., *Advan. Enzymol.* **6**, 231 (1946).
3. Harting, J., and Velick, S. F., *Federation Proc.* **10**, 195 (1951); *J. Biol. Chem.* **207**, 857 (1954).
4. Stadtman, E. R., and Lipmann, F., *J. Biol. Chem.* **185**, 549 (1950).
5. Harting, J., and Velick, S. F., *Federation Proc.* **11**, 226 (1952); *J. Biol. Chem.* **207**, 867 (1954).
6. Racker, E., and Krimsky, I., *Nature* **169**, 1043 (1952).
7. Chou, T. C., Novelli, G. D., Stadtman, E. R., and Lipmann, F. *Federation Proc.* **9**, 160 (1950).
8. Ochoa, S., Stern, J. R., and Schneider, M. C., *J. Biol. Chem.* **193**, 691 (1951).
9. Racker, E., and Krimsky, I., *Science* **122**, 319 (1955).
10. Lipmann, F., and Tuttle, L. C., *J. Biol. Chem.* **159**, 21 (1945).
11. Segal, H. L., and Boyer, P. D., *J. Biol. Chem.* **204**, 265 (1953).
12. Velick, S. F., and Hayes, J. E., *J. Biol. Chem.* **203**, 545 (1953).
13. Park, J. H., and Koshland, D. E., *J. Biol. Chem.* **233**, 986 (1958).
14. Bentley, R., *J. Am. Chem. Soc.* **71**, 2765 (1949).
15. Park, J. H., Meriwether, B. P., Clodfelder, P., and Cunningham, L. W., *J. Biol. Chem.* **236**, 136 (1961).
16. Olson, E. J., and Park, J. H., *J. Biol. Chem.* **239**, 2316 (1964).
17. Harris, J. I., Meriwether, B. P., and Park, J. H., *Nature* **197**, 154 (1963).
18. Mathew, E., and Park, J. H., *Federation Proc.* **24**, 350 (1965).
19. Polgar, L., *Acta Physiol. Acad. Sci. Hung.* **25**, 1 (1964).
20. Mathew, E., Agnello, C. F., and Park, J. H., *J. Biol. Chem.* **240**, PC 3233 (1965).
21. Harris, J. I., and Polgar, L., *J. Mol. Biol.* **14**, 630 (1965).
22. Harris, J. I., and Perham, R., *J. Mol. Biol.* **13**, 876 (1965).
23. Wieland, T., and Hornig, H., *Ann. Chem.* **600**, 12 (1956).
24. Martin, R. B., and Hedrick, R. I., *J. Am. Chem. Soc.* **84**, 106 (1962).
25. Hartley, B. S., and Kilby, B. A., *Biochem. J.* **50**, 672 (1952).
26. Ehring, R., and Colowick, S. P., *Federation Proc.* **23**, 424 (1964).
27. Lipmann, F., *Advan. Enzymol.* **1**, 99 (1941).
28. Martin, R. B., and Hedrick, R. I., *J. Am. Chem. Soc.* **84**, 106 (1962).
29. Chance, B., *in* "The Mechanism of Enzyme Action" (W. D. McElroy and H. B. Glass, eds.), p. 445. Johns Hopkins Press, Baltimore, Maryland, 1954.
30. Park, J. H., Agnello, C. F., and Mathew, E., unpublished experiments. (1965).
31. Levy, H. R., and Vennesland, B., *J. Biol. Chem.* **228**, 85 (1957).
32. Crestfield, A. M., Stein, W. H., and Moore, S., *J. Biol. Chem.* **238**, 2423 (1963).
33. Hartley, B. S., *Nature* **201**, 1284 (1964).

Fungal Degradation of Pine Bark Lignin*

F. F. Nord and Katsumi Hata†

> It is certain that all bodies whatsoever, though they have no sense,
> yet they have perception; for when one body is applied to another,
> there is a kind of election to embrace that which is agreeable, and
> to exclude or expel that which is ingrate; and whether the body be
> alterant or altered, evermore a perception precedeth operation; for
> else all bodies would be like one to another.
>
> *Francis Bacon (1623)*

INTRODUCTION

At about the turn of the century there were three domains in the
sphere of biochemistry which promised sweeping developments.

I.

In the field of the degradation of carbohydrates the pathway to the
final destination has been fraught with difficulties, frustrations, and many
scientific arguments which naturally led to the proposal of different hypotheses.

Many varied approaches to the problem were attempted to gain an
insight into the detailed mechanism of yeast fermentation. The type of
experiments depended on the era and the state of biochemical knowledge at that time. For example, the earliest workers were mainly interested in the quantitative aspects of this process. Thus, the basic
chemical equation expressing the changes that occurred during the dissimilation of carbohydrate was first put forward by Gay-Lussac in 1815.

The next stage began when the Buchners and M. Hahn prepared the
first yeast juice and showed that fermentation without intact yeast cells
was possible. This discovery made the application of modern enzymolog-
ical techniques to yeast juices feasible, so that individual enzyme systems

* Contribution No. 403 from the Laboratory of Organic Chemistry and Enzymology, Fordham University.
† Visiting scientist from Kagawa University, Japan.

could be isolated, purified, and studied. As a consequence of these *in vitro* investigations, a series of enzymatic reactions representing the dissimilation of sugar to alcohol was proposed, in which the participation of phosphorus was considered as indispensable. So great was the emphasis placed on this phase sequence, that it soon appeared to be the *sole* pathway for carbohydrate breakdown in yeast cells (Meyerhof, 1948).

However, even during this particular era, strong arguments were advanced against such a claim. That these investigators were correct in their viewpoint for the existence of multiple and even nonphosphorylating pathways in microorganisms is amply justified by recent experiments. For with the advent of radioactive tracer techniques, it has been possible to delve more easily into the complex reaction mechanics of living organisms with the result that today the existence of alternate pathways is a generally accepted fact. Moreover, it is now solidly established that the Embden-Parnas-Meyerhof route is *not* an exclusive universal process, since, for example, certain microorganisms can ferment glucose by a nonphosphorylating pathway, whereas others cleave the carbohydrate molecule in a manner different from normal glycolysis (Nord, Horecker). Cremer (1899) demonstrated the occurrence in yeast of enzymes capable of breaking down and synthesizing glycogen. Further work showed that glycogen in these reactions was phosphorylated to a mixture of glucose 6-phosphate and fructose 6-phosphate (Cremer-Cori ester), that contained a new type of energy-rich phosphate bond.

These few experimental facts represent the spine of the concept which then led Lipmann to postulate that during fermentation reactions occur in the cell with the purpose of making available "the 12 kg.-cal. phosphate bond as a circulating energy unit."

II.

The work of some men appears to be immortal and forever new, because it rests upon approaches and procedures which men of science recognize as truly valid, namely: (*a*) the proposal of the problem in clear terms, (*b*) the conduct of the experimental solution by disciplined techniques, and (*c*) the interpretation of the results obtained with imaginative insight.

A little more than three decades ago, Hans Spemann transformed embryonic cells, that would have become skin, into brain tissue, testing in this manner whether men can both preserve and enlarge life. He achieved the transformation by moving a patch of preskin cells on a growing embryo to a region from which the brain would later develop.

The implications of these experiments were threefold. To biologists of that time it meant that environmental factors were important: first, in controlling the process of embryological development; second, on the basis of recent discoveries in genetics, Spemann's finding could be understood as indicating that all cells of a developing organism possess complete sets of all genes, and that only a certain number of these function in a given kind of cell, the rest of them being "turned off"; third, it appeared that genes could be turned on and off through an agent similar to the environmental factor for development control. However, more than 30 years after Spemann's discovery, genetic regulation remains the central problem in developmental biology.

III.

The direction of the studies on intermediary metabolism has been recently diverted significantly toward biosynthetic processes. The opportunity for an experimental approach to the general problem of aromatization arose from the isolation of aromatic polyauxotrophs of the microorganisms *Escherichia coli* and *Neurospora*.

The researches of B. D. Davis, M. Katagiri, and E. L. Tatum on the mutants of these organisms which require a supplementary mixture of aromatic compounds for their metabolic activities have established a partial pathway for the biosynthesis of phenylalanine and tyrosine from carbohydrate precursors. Through the enzymes of these bacteria, β-D-glucose is converted via the well-known D-sedoheptulose into a glucoheptonic acid. This acid supplies the carbon atoms for the two aromatic acids which via several intermediary steps form shikimic acid. The easy transition of the latter into aromatic rings *in vitro* had already been observed by Eykman in 1891.

Shikimic acid also plays an important role in fungi and, accordingly, these investigations then suggested that other aromatic compounds, such as lignin, may also be formed via a similar pathway.

This assumption proved to be correct and as an introduction to future microbiological investigations we will report in this chapter the results of a comparative study on the fungal degradation of bark lignin and wood lignin.

IV.

Bark has been considered to be very resistant to the destroying action by microorganisms and to act as a protector of wood tissue. However, in nature, after a tree is felled, the bark is gradually degraded by the action of fungi and soil bacteria in the forest.

TABLE I
ANALYSIS OF BARK AND WOOD DECAYED BY VARIOUS FUNGI[a]

Fungus	Loss of weight[b]	Alcohol-benzene extract	Lignin	Loss of lignin[c]	% Change of lignin content[d]
Mycena epipterygia M143	7.6	0.15	33.34	8.7	+ 1.2
	5.3	0.18	53.37	6.9	+ 1.7
Coniophora cerebella K30	7.8	0.16	32.92	10.1	+ 2.4
	5.5	0.18	54.86	6.3	− 1.1
Lenzites saepiaria B719	8.9	0.17	32.50	12.3	+ 3.7
	6.5	0.19	53.98	7.0	+ 0.5
Stereum hirsutum N211	9.2	0.19	32.81	11.7	+ 2.8
	6.0	0.19	54.56	5.5	− 0.5
Fomes ignarius 86391	9.4	0.18	34.28	7.9	− 1.6
	6.2	0.19	54.32	6.1	− 0.1
Ganoderma applanatum H79	10.2	0.18	32.89	12.5	+ 2.5
	8.6	0.21	53.66	9.6	+ 1.1
Fomes fomentarius	10.5	0.17	34.25	9.1	− 1.5
	9.6	0.21	54.90	8.5	− 1.2
Pholiota mutabilis H-14	10.9	0.20	33.88	10.6	− 0.4
	6.9	0.21	55.18	5.3	− 1.7
Lepiota procera R-1	11.5	0.21	33.14	13.1	+ 1.8
	7.0	0.18	53.68	8.0	+ 1.1
Polyporus hirsutus 56479-S	11.8	0.20	33.61	12.2	+ 0.4
	8.9	0.22	53.67	9.9	+ 1.1
Trametes suaveolens 71404-S	11.8	0.19	33.28	13.0	+ 1.4
	8.9	0.21	54.30	7.9	− 0.1
Fomes annosus 58548-S	13.1	0.22	33.10	14.8	+ 1.9
	9.3	0.22	53.54	10.5	+ 1.4
Collybia velutipes	15.1	0.27	37.31	6.1	−10.6
	9.3	0.21	53.82	10.0	+ 0.8
Schizophyllum commune 56473-S	15.3	0.26	33.97	14.7	− 0.7
	7.5	0.19	54.59	7.0	− 0.6
Polystictus sanguineus 25	29.1	0.43	31.04	34.08	+ 8.0
	10.2	0.23	52.14	13.7	+ 3.9
Collybia butyracea M117	30.0	0.87	21.26	55.9	+37.0
	21.1	0.65	47.22	31.3	+13.0
Poria subacida B11	31.4	0.55	30.32	38.4	+10.1
	10.8	0.24	53.98	11.3	+ 1.1
Polyporus versicolor	43.5	0.74	33.70	43.5	+ 0.1
	13.7	0.27	53.83	14.4	+ 0.8

[a] First value given is for wood, second value is for bark. All values given as per cent.

Until now, many investigations have been carried out on the decay of wood, but studies on the decay of bark are practically nonexistent. Studies on the chemistry of bark decay are important not only in regard to the chemistry of bark constituents, but also in connection with the physiology of trees and the utilization of bark.

Accordingly, some investigations, using Western white pine bark, were carried out concerning the rate at which bark can be degraded by white-rot fungi as compared with wood and regarding the mechanism by which the constituents of bark, especially lignin, decompose in the course of degradation by fungi.

1. DEGRADATION OF PROTOLIGNIN AND RELATED COMPOUNDS PRESENT IN BARK BY WHITE-ROT FUNGI

The outer bark was exposed to 18 species of fungi, and the extent of change in bark components, especially lignin, was studied in comparison with those of wood.

The outer bark and wood meals of Western white pine were extracted successively with ethanol-benzene, 95% ethanol, and hot water. Nine grams of the extractive-free samples were divided into six Erlenmeyer flasks with the nutrient solution (Ishikawa *et al.*, 1962, 1963) which did not contain glucose. The ratio of sample to nutrition solution was 1:23. The medium was sterilized at 100°C by the intermittent method, inoculated with a mycelial suspension of the fungus, and incubated at 26°–28°C for 5 months. The decayed samples were filtered, washed with water, air-dried, freed from the lumps of the mycelium by the use of a screen, and the loss of weight, solubility in ethanol-benzene, and the lignin content determined. The results are recorded in Table I. Accordingly, the degradation of samples was generally poor even for the wood medium in comparison with the results reported by Erdtman *et al.* (1951) and Higuchi *et al.* (1955) for experiments in media containing sugar and starch. However, *Polyporus versicolor, Polystictus sanguineus* 25, *Poria subacida* B11, and *Collybia butyracea* M117 degraded wood fairly intensely, whereas bark was decomposed only slightly by these species of fungi. The per cent change of lignin content becomes positive

---

[b] Per cent calculated on the basis of the absolutely dry weight of the extractive-free samples.

[c] Calculated on the basis of the amount of lignin present in the samples prior to decay. Lignin content was 33.74% for wood and 54.27% for bark.

[d] Calculated on the basis of the formula

$$\frac{(\% \text{ lignin of undecayed sample}) - (\% \text{ lignin of decayed sample})}{(\% \text{ lignin of undecayed sample})} \times 100$$

when lignin is degraded more selectively than carbohydrate. This is the usual case with the white-rot fungi. However, in some cases the per cent change was negative. We exposed samples to the enzymatic activities of the fungi only for 5 months. If we did so for a longer period, the per cent change would probably become positive in all cases. As indicated by the per cent change of C. butyracea M117, this fungus decomposed lignin most selectively in bark as well as in wood.

We used extractive-free bark and wood as samples for the medium and thoroughly washed the decayed sample with water. Therefore, the alcohol-benzene extracts of the decayed sample were mainly composed of the lignin degradation products which are insoluble in water. The amount of the extractives was below 1% even for the extensively decayed samples.

The samples decayed by the four fungi were analyzed for holocellulose and cellulose by a modification of the TAPPI standard method (1954). The results are recorded in Table II.

TABLE II

HOLOCELLULOSE AND CELLULOSE CONTENT OF DECAYED BARK AND WOOD[a]

Sample	Holo-cellulose	Loss of holo-cellulose[b]	Cellulose	Loss of cellu-lose[b]	Lignin + holo-cellulose
Before decay	66.24	0.0	51.04	0.0	99.98
	45.58	0.0	33.88	0.0	99.85
Decayed by P. sanguineus	61.17	34.5	51.03	29.1	92.21
	45.31	10.7	33.74	10.6	97.45
Decayed by C. butyracea	68.26	27.9	61.22	16.1	89.52
	51.57	10.7	39.52	8.0	98.79
Decayed by P. subacida	63.47	34.3	53.42	28.2	93.79
	45.30	11.3	33.20	12.6	99.28
Decayed by P. versicolor	61.52	47.5	50.01	44.6	95.22
	44.60	15.6	32.47	17.3	98.43

[a] All values given as per cent. First value given is for wood, second value for bark.
[b] Calculated on the basis of the amount of holocellulose and cellulose present in the extractive-free samples before decay.

As indicated in the case of the loss of cellulose and holocellulose, white-rot fungi attacked not only lignin but also cellulose and hemicellulose fairly extensively.

The sum total of lignin plus holocellulose should be 100%, and that of the samples before decay was almost 100% for bark as well as for wood. However, in the case of decayed samples, it was considerably less than 100%. This indicates that some portions of holocellulose or/

and lignin of the decayed samples were decomposed and lost during the treatment. These decomposed portions are probably the transformed and depolymerized fractions from cellulose, hemicellulose, and lignin. The decreasing amount of the sum total is less in the decayed bark than in the decayed wood. This is due to the fact that the extent of the degradation of bark was less than that of wood.

The samples, decayed by the same four species of fungi as mentioned above, were treated with hot 1% sodium hydroxide and the residual samples were analyzed for lignin content. From the analytical results, the amounts of 1% sodium hydroxide-extractable lignin and 1% sodium hydroxide-unextractable lignin of the samples were calculated. The results are shown in Table III.

TABLE III

SOLUBILITY IN 1% SODIUM HYDROXIDE, LIGNIN CONTENT,
AND METHOXYL CONTENT[a]

Sample	Solubility in 1% NaOH	1% NaOH-unextractable lignin[b]	1% NaOH-extractable lignin[c]	CH_3O of 72% H_2SO_4 lignin
Before decay	15.15	30.89	2.85	14.6
	39.05	28.48	25.79	7.2
Decayed by P. sanguineus	31.00	22.15	8.89	12.5
	38.31	30.30	21.84	6.3
Decayed by C. butyracea	37.89	9.68	11.58	13.2
	34.91	29.78	17.44	6.5
Decayed by P. subacida	31.40	20.45	9.67	12.8
	36.95	30.92	23.06	6.2
Decayed by P. versicolor	27.05	24.91	8.79	13.1
	39.26	29.46	24.37	7.2

[a] All values given as per cent. First value given is for wood, second value for bark.

[b] Based on the dry weight of samples and calculated from the lignin content of the residual samples after the extraction with 1% sodium hydroxide.

[c] Based on the dry weight of samples and calculated by subtracting 1% sodium hydroxide-unextractable lignin from the lignin content of the samples.

Bark contains considerable amounts of characteristic phenolic acids which are easily soluble in dilute alkali (Kiefer and Kurth, 1953; Hata and Sogo, 1958). Accordingly, the solubility in 1% sodium hydroxide and the 1% sodium hydroxide-extractable lignin content of bark are very high.

In the case of wood, the solubility in 1% sodium hydroxide and the amount of 1% sodium hydroxide-extractable lignin increased very much after decay. This may be due to the fact that the 1% sodium hydroxide-extractable lignin has a smaller molecular weight than the 1% sodium hydroxide-unextractable lignin. The increase of the former in the decayed wood probably results in the degradation of the lignin by the enzyme actions of the fungi. In the case of bark, the solubility in 1% sodium hydroxide and the amount of 1% sodium hydroxide-extractable lignin did not increase or were somewhat decreased by decay. This is probably due to the fact that the degradation of bark lignin was slight and that the bark phenolic acids could also be degraded.

Seventy-two per cent sulfuric acid-lignin of bark contains many bark phenolic acids which possess a 3,4-dihydroxyphenyl unit in their molecules and only a small amount of methoxyl. Therefore, the sulfuric acid-lignin of bark has a low concentration of methoxyl. For bark as well as for wood, the methoxyl content of lignin in the decayed sample was somewhat smaller than that of lignin in the same sample prior to decay. This indicates that the lignin remaining in the decayed sample is also changed in structure.

2. DEGRADATION OF BARK PHENOLIC ACIDS AND ISOLATED LIGNIN

Bark phenolic acids have been considered protectors of bark tissue against microorganisms. However, this consideration is lacking experimental confirmation. Concerning the claim that there are differences between bark lignin and wood lignin with respect to their resistance against wood-destroying fungi, experimental evidence is not available. Therefore, bark phenolic acids and Björkman lignin (MW lignin) from bark and wood were exposed to the enzymatic activities of three species of white-rot fungi, and the progress of their degradation was compared.

Bark phenolic acids were prepared by treating the extractive-free bark with 1% sodium hydroxide at 30°C and purified by a modification of the method of Kurth *et al.* (1948). MW lignin was prepared from the extractive-free bark and wood (Björkman, 1956). Bark phenolic acids gave negative results for the color reaction with phloroglucinol and hydrochloric acid, whereas MW lignins from bark and wood gave positive results.

The medium was prepared by applying a modification of the Van Vliet method (1954). It contained 1% bark phenolic acids or MW lignin together with 0.5% glucose. In this case, acetone-water (1:1, v/v) and dioxane-water (25:1, v/v) were used as solvents, respectively, for bark phenolic acids and MW lignin. The medium was inoculated with a 10-day-old mycelial pellet suspension of the fungus and incubated at 26°–28°C for 14 days. After the incubation, the residual bark phenolic acids and MW lignin were recovered and weighed. The loss in weight is recorded in Table IV.

TABLE IV
LOSS IN WEIGHT OF BARK PHENOLIC ACIDS AND MW LIGNIN BY WHITE-ROT FUNGI

	Weight loss (%)		
Sample	Polyporus versicolor	Poria subacida B11	Fomes fomentarius
Bark phenolic acids	7.5	6.2	5.4
Bark MW lignin	45.9	28.9	19.5
Wood MW lignin	49.7	31.1	20.2

The degradation of bark phenolic acids was very difficult, whereas that of bark MW lignin was comparatively easy. The fungi grew on the medium containing bark phenolic acids also, even though the growing of mycelium was somewhat slower than that on the medium containing MW lignin. The bark phenolic acids do not seem to be particularly poisonous to the fungi. Their high resistance toward fungal degradation may result from the difficulty arising in the utilization of the carbon source by the fungi.

As can be seen from the results in Table I, bark has a very high resistance toward wood-destroying fungi, even after it has been freed from the extractives. This ability of the bark may mainly be due to the presence of the bark phenolic acids that are present to a large extent in the bark and cover the cellulose, hemicellulose, and lignin. Bark, prior to the extraction with organic solvents, namely bark in the natural state, contains several kinds of extractives such as tannin, wax, and pigments, in addition to the bark phenolic acids (Kurth and Kiefer, 1950; Hata and Sogo, 1956; Nickles and Rowe, 1962). These extractives probably also protect the bark tissues against microorganisms.

3. FUNGAL DEGRADATION PRODUCTS OF BARK LIGNIN

To obtain some information concerning the mechanism of the fungal degradation of bark lignin, the intermediate degradation products of the action of Fomes annosus 58548-S on bark lignin were studied in comparison with those from wood lignin.

To 360 gm of the extractive-free bark and 360 gm of wood meals was added the nutrient solution containing 0.2% glucose; the solution had been sterilized, inoculated with this fungus, and incubated at 26°–28°C for 3 months.

The decayed bark and wood were filtered and washed with water.

The filtrate and washings were combined, acidified with sulfuric acid to pH 2.0, and extracted with ether. These ether extracts were combined, concentrated to a small volume *in vacuo* under nitrogen, and used as sample *A* for thin-layer chromatography. The residual samples of the ether extraction were extracted with acetone-water (9:1, v/v). After recovering the acetone from solution, ammonium sulfate was added to the aqueous phase until it became half-saturated, and the degraded lignin obtained from the solution was removed by filtration. The filtrate was acidified to pH 2.0 and extracted with ether. The ether solution was concentrated and used as the sample *B* for thin-layer chromatography.

The chromatography was carried out on a 0.5-mm thickness of Adsorbosil-2 using the following solvent systems: butanol saturated with 3% ammonium hydroxide (w/v); dimethylformamide-carbon tetrachloride (2:9, v/v). The degradation products were identified by a comparison of their R_f values with those of authentic samples, color reactions, fluorescence under ultraviolet light, and the ultraviolet absorption spectrum of their ethanol solution. The results are recorded in Table V.

TABLE V

DEGRADATION PRODUCTS DETECTED BY THIN-LAYER CHROMATOGRAPHY FROM
BARK AND WOOD MEDIA DECAYED BY *F. annosus*

Product	From bark medium[a]		From wood medium[a]	
	A	B	A	B
Vanillic acid	+	−	+++	±
Protocatechuic acid	+++	±	−	−
p-Hydroxybenzoic acid	+	−	+	−
p-Hydroxycinnamic acid	+	−	+	−
Protocatechuic aldehyde	±	−	−	−
Vanillin	±	−	+	−
Coniferyl aldehyde	+	−	++	−
Guaiacylglycerol-β-coniferyl ether	±	±	+	+

[a] Key: +, ++, and +++, degrees of intensity of observed spots; ±, very faint spots; −, not observed.

In the wood medium, vanillic acid (I) was found in large amounts, whereas in the bark medium extensive amounts of protocatechuic acid (II) were present. It has been thought that (II) can be formed from (I) and isovanillic acid by soil bacteria as a transformation product (Sundman, 1964). Recently, Hata *et al.* (1966) studied the fungal degradation of bark phenolic acids and MW lignin from bark and wood and

CHO structures (I) and (II) shown

found that (II) is an intermediate degradation product of bark phenolic acids only. Therefore, (II) is a degradation product from bark phenolic acids that were present in the bark. From the observation that much more (II) was found than (I) in the bark medium, it is believed that bark phenolic acids cover and protect lignin and other components so that, at an earlier stage of degradation, the enzymes of the white-rot fungi react mainly with bark phenolic acids.

Vanillin (III) and coniferyl aldehyde (IV) were identified from wood medium in correspondence with the results obtained by Higuchi *et al.*

Structures (III), (IV), (V) shown

(1955). A small amount of these compounds could be found in the bark medium too. A slight amount of protocatechuic aldehyde (V) was detected in the bark medium.

Guaiacylglycerol-β-coniferyl ether (VI) was identified clearly in the wood medium but only faintly in the bark medium. Fukuzumi (1960) and Ishikawa *et al.* (1962, 1963) detected (VI) as an enzymatic degradation compound of softwood lignin. Nimz (1965) isolated (VI) in crystalline form from spruce wood by treating it with 2% aqueous acetic acid. Recently, Hata *et al.* (1966) detected (VI) in the fungal degradation products of bark MW lignin as well as of wood MW lignin, but could not find it in the fungal degradation compounds of bark phenolic acids.

p-Hydroxybenzoic acid (VII) and *p*-hydroxycinnamic acid (VIII) were identified in the bark medium as well as in the wood medium. It was reported (Ishikawa *et al.*, 1962, 1963) that these compounds were produced by some white-rot fungi not only from the medium containing lignin but also from the medium which did not contain lignin. Therefore, it is uncertain whether these compounds are the degradation products of lignin or not.

(VI)   (VII)   (VIII)

Bark lignin is probably decomposed by the white-rot fungi through the pathway that is similar to that of wood lignin, whereas the mode of the fungal degradation of bark phenolic acids is different from that of lignin.

4. Degraded Lignin Obtained from Bark and Wood Decayed by *Fomes annosus* 58548-S

As mentioned in the section above, a small amount of degraded lignin was obtained from the decayed bark and wood by extracting with acetone-water (9:1, v/v). The degraded lignin was dissolved with dioxane containing a small amount of water and filtered. The filtrate was added dropwise to ether to form a precipitate of degraded lignin. This precipitate was washed with ether and then with petrol ether. The purification was repeated once more.

The appearance of the degraded lignin of bark and wood was similar to MW lignin of bark and wood. The yields were approximately 0.2% from decayed bark and 0.4% from decayed wood. The degraded bark lignin was weakly positive toward the color reaction with phloroglucinol and hydrochloric acid just as the degraded wood lignin was. They were soluble in ethanol, methanol, acetone, and dioxane, and one part of them was soluble in water, but insoluble in ether, petrol ether, and benzene. They showed higher solubility in most solvents than MW lignin did, so that they seem to be smaller in molecular weight than MW lignins. The infrared absorption spectra of MW lignin and degraded lignin were obtained using KBr as phase and Fig. 1 shows a comparison

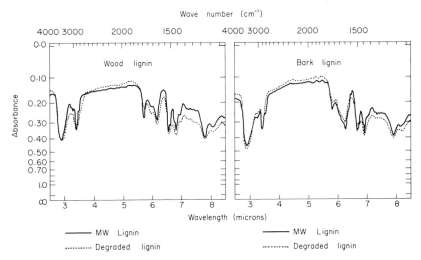

Fig. 1.   Infrared absorption spectra of MW lignin and degraded lignin of wood and bark.

of these spectra. Bark MW lignin gave a spectrum which was very similar to that of wood MW lignin. The difference in the spectrum between the degraded lignin and MW lignin was very little. However, the former showed somewhat more carbonyl groups at the wave number of 1700 cm^{-1} as compared with that of MW lignin.

The bark and wood meals prior to decay were thoroughly extracted with alcohol-benzene and then 95% alcohol, so that Brauns' native lignin did not remain in the samples. Therefore, the degraded lignin mentioned above was the newly formed fraction originating in the proto-lignin.

Fukuzumi (1960) obtained decayed lignin from decayed softwood by extracting it with acetone-water. His decayed lignin showed negative results for the color reaction with phloroglucinol and hydrochloric acid, and its infrared spectrum showed the existence of many carbonyl groups.

Probably it was transformed more extensively than the degraded lignin which we obtained.

CLASSIFICATION OF DEGRADED LIGNIN AND LIGNIN DEGRADATION PRODUCTS

From the results mentioned in previous sections we can classify the lignin remaining in the decayed bark and wood and the lignin degradation products as follows: A, 1% NaOH-unextractable degraded lignin; B, 1% NaOH-extractable degraded lignin, except C and D; C, acetone-water extractable degraded lignin, except D; D, water soluble degraded lignin; E, lignin degradation compounds, such as guaiacylglycerol-β-coniferyl ether, coniferyl aldehyde, etc., and F, loss as gas.

As shown from the per cent of alcohol-benzene extract in Table I and in the results described in previous sections, the amount of C, D, and E seems to be very small. In the course of degradation of lignin by white-rot fungi, giant molecules of protolignin are degraded gradually to become smaller and smaller, and the degraded lignin of lower molecular weight decomposes faster to degradation compounds, such as guaiacyl-glycerol-β-coniferyl ether, coniferyl aldehyde, etc. However, at the same time, probably the enzyme breaks the linkage which combines a dimeric or a monomeric phenylpropane unit to the main body of the large molecule, and the dimeric or monomeric degradation compound can be liberated directly from the surface of the large molecule of lignin.

SUMMARY

The outer bark of Western white pine was exposed to the enzymatic activity of 18 species of white-rot fungi, and the change in the amount of bark components, especially lignin, was studied in comparison with those components of wood. The degradation of the bark was very difficult even after preparing an extractive-free sample. *Collybia butyracea* M117 decomposed lignin in bark as well as in wood.

Bark phenolic acids could hardly be degraded by the fungi, whereas bark MW lignin was degraded as easily as wood MW lignin. However, fungi grew on the medium containing bark phenolic acids also, even though the growth rate of the mycelium was slower than on that of the MW lignin-containing medium.

The degradation compounds from the decayed bark and wood medium were studied by thin-layer chromatography. Vanillic acid was identified from the wood medium, and protocatechuic acid, extensively, from the bark medium, indicating that at the earlier stage of degradation of bark the fungus destroys mainly bark phenolic acids that are covering lignin and other components of bark. Bark lignin seems to have guaiacylglycerol-β-coniferyl ether units as does wood lignin.

ACKNOWLEDGMENTS

The original cultures used in this study were obtained through the courtesy of Dr. A. Hervey of the New York Botanical Garden. Some samples of certain authentic compounds used for thin-layer chromatography were received through the courtesy of Dr. H. Ishikawa of Ehime University, Japan, Dr. A. Sakakibara of Hokkaido University, Japan, and Dr. J. C. Pew of the Madison Forest Products Laboratory. This work has benefited from suggestions made by our colleagues Dr. D. D. Clarke, Dr. M. J. Reale, and Dr. Walter J. Schubert. The investigation was carried out in part with the support of the National Science Foundation.

REFERENCES

Apenitis, A., Erdtman, H., and Leopold, B. (1951). *Svensk Kem. Tidskr.* **63**, 195.

Björkman, A. (1956). *Svensk Papperstid.* **59**, 477.

Cremer, M. (1899). *Ber. D. Chem. Ges.* **32**, 2062.

Eykman, B. B. (1891). *Ber. D. Chem. Ges.* **24**, 1278.

Fukuzumi, T. (1960). *Bull. Agr. Chem. Soc. Japan* **24**, 728.

Hata, K., and Sogo, M. (1956). *Nippon Ringaku Kaishi* **38**, 473.

Hata, K., and Sogo, M. (1958). *Nippon Mokuzai Gakkaishi* **4**, 5.

Hata, K., Schubert, W. J., and Nord, F. F. (1966). *Arch. Biochem. Biophys.* **113**, 250.

Higuchi, T., and Kawamura, H. (1955). *Nippon Ringaku Kaishi* **37**, 298.

Higuchi, T., Kawamura, I., and Kawamura, H. (1955). *Nippon Mokuzai Gakkaishi* **37**, 547.

Ishikawa, H., Schubert, W. J., and Nord, F. F. (1962). *Life Sci.* No. 8, 365.

Ishikawa, H., Schubert, W. J., and Nord, F. F. (1963). *Arch. Biochem. Biophys.* **100**, 131.

Kiefer, H. J., and Kurth, E. F. (1953). *Tappi* **36**, 14.

Kurth, E. F., and Kiefer, H. J. (1950). *Tappi* **33**, 183.

Kurth, E. F., Hubbard, J. K., and Humphrey, J. D. (1948). *Forest Prod. Res. Soc. Preprint* **39**, 7.

Nickles, W. C., and Rowe, J. W. (1962). *Forest Prods. J.* **12**, 374.

Nimz, H. (1965). *Chem. Ber.* **98**, 533.

Nord, F. F. (1965). *Bull. Inst. Politeknic Iasi* [11] **15**, (35).

Sundman, V. (1964). *J. Gen. Microbiol.* **36**, 171.

Tappi (1954). T 9m-54.

Van Vliet, W. F. (1954). *Biochim. Biophys. Acta* **15**, 211.

Cellular Composition and 0-Antigen Synthesis of a Thymine-Requiring Strain of *Salmonella anatum*

Berma M. Kinsey and P. W. Robbins

In his classic discussion of "phosphate bond energy" Lipmann (1941) predicted that many biosynthetic reactions would be found to be coupled to the hydrolytic cleavage of "energy-rich" phosphate anhydrides. This prediction has been borne out strikingly by recent work on polysaccharide synthesis that has shown the involvement of the "energy-rich" Leloir nucleotide sugar derivatives in the enzymatic synthesis of homopolysaccharides, such as glycogen and starch, and heteropolysaccharides, such as hyaluronic acid. Recently, considerable attention has centered on the heteropolysaccharide 0-antigen of the enteric bacteria in the synthesis of which the Leloir nucleotides have proven to be major precursors. Synthesis of the 0-antigen appears to involve the interaction of the nucleotide sugar derivatives, uridine diphosphate galactose (UDP-galactose), thymidine diphosphate rhamnose (TDP-rhamnose), and guanosine diphosphate mannose (GDP-mannose), with a lipidlike coenzyme or carrier (Wright *et al.*, 1965; Weiner *et al.*, 1965).

In a thymineless strain (Th-2) of *Salmonella anatum* (A_1) the composition of the cells was found to vary with the thymine concentration in the growth medium. Since thymidine diphosphate rhamnose is a major precursor of the antigen, we were interested in studying the relationship between 0-antigen synthesis and the thymine nucleotide pool of the cell. We report in this paper the results of studies on the deoxyribonucleic acid (DNA), ribonucleic acid (RNA), 0-antigen, and protein content of Th-2, as related to the thymine nucleotide pool, under various conditions of growth.

MATERIALS AND METHODS

GROWTH OF BACTERIA AND ISOLATION OF MUTANTS

Unless otherwise stated, experiments were carried out at 37°C with aeration and the indicated supplements of thymine in the following minimal medium: in 1 liter, 4.68 gm NaCl, 1.5 gm KCl, 1.08 gm NH$_4$Cl, 14.52 gm Trizma base (Sigma) 0.20 gm MgCl$_2$·6H$_2$O, 0.35 gm Na$_2$SO$_4$, 0.2 ml of 1.0 M CaCl$_2$, and 0.2 ml of 0.01 M FeCl$_3$ adjusted to pH 7.5 with HCl. Phosphate and glucose were added to final concentration of 0.01 M and 0.5%, respectively. The broth used on appropriate occasions consisted of 10 gm Difco Tryptone, 5 gm Difco yeast extract, 5 gm NaCl and 0.5 ml of 2 N NaOH in 1 liter of water. Thymine-C^{14}, uracil-C^{14}, and thymine-H^3 were purchased from New England Nuclear Corp. For isolation of mutants a culture of S. *anatum*, grown to the stationary phase in 2 ml of minimal medium, was harvested and resuspended in the same volume of medium containing 30 μl of ethylmethane sulfonate. After standing at 37°C for 3 hours, 0.5 ml of the cell suspension was transferred to 5 ml of minimal medium supplemented with 10 μg of thymidine per milliliter and 500 μg of aminopterin per milliliter (Okada *et al.*, 1960). After 48 hours the full-grown culture was diluted and plated on thymidine-supplemented medium. Thymidine-requiring colonies were selected by replica plating techniques and tested for the presence of the normal S. *anatum* 0-antigen by cross-streaking tests with the bacteriophage ε^{15}vir. One of the mutants so selected, designated Th-2, was used for most of the experiments described below. The mutants were unable to grow at a thymine concentration of 2 μg per milliliter and required 10 μg per milliliter for full growth. A strain designated Th-9 was isolated which was resistant to ε^{15}vir. This latter strain had a rough colony morphology and agglutinated spontaneously in broth.

ANALYTICAL METHODS

PROTEIN

The optical density at 650 mμ of an aliquot taken directly from the growth medium and diluted 1:3 with 1 N HCl was used as a measure of cell mass. Protein determinations (Lowry *et al.*, 1951) on washed whole cells grown at 5 or 50 μg of thymine per milliliter gave a value of 0.4 mg of protein per optical density unit.

DNA

An aliquot of cells (9 ml total volume) was added to 1 ml of 50% TCA (trichloroacetic acid) and the precipitate was chilled, centrifuged, washed twice with 5 ml of cold 5% TCA, suspended in 0.33 ml of 0.05 N NaOH, and reprecipitated with 0.67 ml of 7.5% TCA.

DNA was determined by the diphenylamine reaction (Burton, 1956). Calf-thymus DNA heated at 70°C for 15 minutes in 5% TCA was used as a standard. When radioactive thymine was used, 1 ml of cells was added to 1 ml of cold 10% TCA or 2 ml of 1 N HCl and the precipitate was collected on a 0.45-μ membrane filter and washed several times. The filters were either dissolved in 10 ml of Bray's scintillation fluid (Bray, 1960) or glued to a planchet for gas-flow counting. Since it was difficult to determine the absolute counting efficiency under these conditions, DNA was not estimated from the incorporation and specific activity of the thymine.

Acid-Soluble Nucleotide Pool

Ten ml of cells were chilled, centrifuged, washed twice with 5 ml of cold 0.9% NaCl and treated with 1 ml of hot 70% ethanol. After 4 minutes at 75°C, the precipitate was removed by centrifugation and the supernatant fluid was evaporated to dryness under a stream of nitrogen. The residue was redissolved in water with carrier UDP-glucose and thymidine triphosphate (TTP), and the mixture was subjected to hanging-strip electrophoresis on Whatman #31 paper in 0.15 M triethylammonium acetate buffer, pH 4, for 18 hours at 250 volts. The nucleotide region was eluted into scintillation vials, 1.0 to 1.5 ml being collected, and 10 ml of scintillation solution was added for counting.

Rhamnose and Heptose Determination

The determination of 6-deoxyhexose was carried out according to Dische (1955). Since rhamnose to protein ratios varied from one determination to the other, samples from as many different cultures as possible were analyzed at the same time. Heptose was determined with the same samples used for 6-deoxyhexose measurement (Osborn, 1963). It was necessary to read the heptose standards immediately before every two or three samples, since the values increased slowly with time even after 2 hours. If whole cells or crude lipopolysaccharide fractions were used, a blank without cysteine was prepared for each sample.

Preparation of LPS Fractions

Lipopolysaccharide (LPS) was prepared from whole cells by phenol extraction (Robbins and Uchida, 1962). The dialyzed preparation was evaporated to a small volume if necessary and centrifuged at 50,000 rpm for 90 minutes. The supernatant fluid was removed and the pellet was dissolved in water.

RESULTS

The experiments described below were carried out on *Salmonella anatum*-T⁻ (Th-2), *S. anatum* (A₁), and lysogenic derivatives of these strains grown in minimal medium supplemented as indicated with various concentrations of thymine.

THYMINE NUCLEOTIDE POOL, DNA, AND RNA

The size of the pool and amount of acid-precipitable thymine-^{3}H per unit of protein is clearly different when Th-2 is grown in thymine-^{3}H at concentrations of 5 and 50 µg per milliliter (Fig. 1) even though the generation time is exactly the same under these two sets of conditions. At

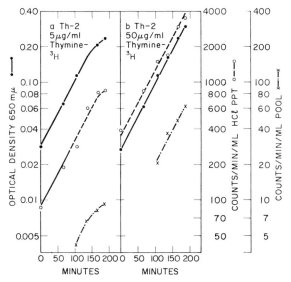

FIG. 1. Pool size and acid-precipitable counts for Th-2 grown in 5 µg (*a*) and 50 µg (*b*) of thymine-^{3}H per milliliter. The cells were grown in minimal medium with the indicated supplement of thymine-^{3}H (16,400 cpm/µg). At intervals, 1 ml of culture was added to 2 ml of 1 *N* HCl, and the O.D. at 650 mµ was determined. The precipitate was then collected on a 0.45-µ membrane filter and washed four times with water. The filter was dissolved in 5 ml of Bray's scintillation solution for counting. For pool determination, a 10-ml sample was withdrawn and treated as described under "Methods." ●——●, Optical density at 650 mµ; ○ – – ○, HCl-precipitable material; X-··-X, pool.

5 µg per milliliter, the pool is smaller by a factor of 5 and the acid-precipitable counts by a factor of 4. In order to correlate the difference in
amount of acid-precipitable counts with cell number, cultures of Th-2 at 5
and 50 µg of unlabeled thymine per milliliter and A₁, without thymine,
were compared with respect to optical density, viable count, and DNA
content (Fig. 2). Here the difference in DNA content is strikingly apparent. The respective values for Th-2 with 5 and 50 µg of thymine per
milliliter, and for A₁, without thymine, are 15, 25, and 32 µg of DNA per

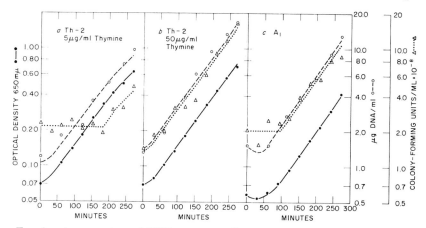

FIG. 2. A comparison of DNA content, cell mass, and viable count for Th-2 at
5 µg (*a*) and at 50 µg (*b*) of thymine per milliliter, and A₁ (*c*). The medium was
innoculated from a culture grown with 10 µg of thymine per milliliter, and samples
were taken for analysis as described in "Methods" after 1 hour. Viable count was
determined with one plate for each point after dilution into LB broth. ●——●,
Optical density; ○－－○, DNA; △....△ viable count.

optical density unit. The average for three separate experiments was
11.5 µg of DNA per optical density unit for Th-2 at 5 µg per milliliter and
22.8 µg of DNA per optical density unit at 50 µg per milliliter or 29 and
57 µg of DNA per milligram of protein, respectively. The media for this
experiment were innoculated with a culture of Th-2 that had reached full
growth with 10 µg of thymine per milliliter. The generation time of A₁
was the same as that of Th-2 at 5 or 50 µg of thymine per milliliter. Examination of stained cells under the microscope revealed that whereas
cells of A₁ and Th-2 grown at 50 µg of thymine per milliliter were seen
mostly as chains of two units, Th-2 grown at 5 µg of thymine per milliliter
formed chains of six units. This agrees very well with the viable counts
of 21×10^8, 7.5×10^8, and 22.5×10^8 colony-forming units per optical

density unit for A_1 and Th-2 grown at 5 and 10 μg of thymine per milliliter.

When uracil-^{14}C was used as the label for cells of Th-2, no significant difference was observed in the amount of acid-precipitable label when cells were grown with 5 or 50 μg of thymine per milliliter (Fig. 3). Presumably the acid-precipitable counts represent the level of RNA synthesis in the cells.

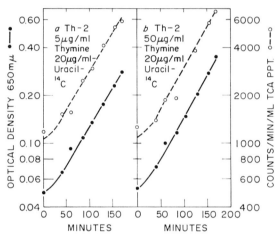

Fig. 3. Acid-precipitable counts and cell mass of Th-2 grown in uracil-^{14}C with 5 μg (a) and 50 μg (b) of thymine per milliliter. Cells were grown in 20 μg of uracil-[14]C (0.5 μc/μg) per milliliter with the indicated thymine supplement. For optical density measurement, 0.3 ml of culture was added to 0.6 ml of 1 N HCl. A 1-ml sample was centrifuged, washed with cold saline, resuspended in saline, treated with an equal volume of cold 10% TCA. The precipitated material was collected on a membrane filter and washed four times with cold 5% TCA. The filter was glued onto a planchet for gas-flow counting. ●——●, Optical density; ○--○, TCA-precipitable material.

When Th-2 in the logarithmic growth phase is transferred from a medium containing 10 μg of thymine-^{14}C per milliliter to one with 5 μg per milliliter, a slower rate of formation of acid-precipitable label was observed which lasted until the ratio of incorporated ^{14}C to optical density had reached the level characteristic of that external concentration of thymine, at which point the normal rate was resumed (Fig. 4). No change in rate was observed in going from 10 to 50 μg of thymine per milliliter.

When the thymine concentration of a culture of Th-2 was altered suddenly from 50 to 5 μg per milliliter, striking changes took place in the DNA and nucleotide pool contents of the cells, as seen in Fig. 5. In a culture with a mass doubling time of 60 minutes, the pool dropped to one-sixth of its former value within 20 minutes after a 10-fold dilution of external thymine concentration. The rate of formation of TCA-precipitable label slowed down, but after 140 minutes it had resumed its former doubling time with the DNA to protein ratio 2.4 times lower than the initial rate. The events which took place on restoration of the higher thymine concentration were not as clear-cut, although it is evident that the pool increased to a higher level within 10 minutes and the rate of

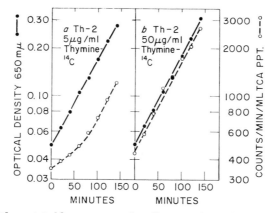

FIG. 4. Acid-precipitable counts and cell mass for Th-2 transferred during logarithmic growth from 10 µg of thymine-14C per milliliter to 5 µg (*a*) and 50 µg (*b*) of thymine-14C per milliliter. One ml of a culture of Th-2 (optical density 0.55) at 10 µg of thymine-14C per milliliter (10,000 cpm/µg) was transferred to 10 ml of prewarmed medium containing 5 or 50 µg of thymine-14C per milliliter of the same specific activity. Samples were taken beginning immediately as described for Fig. 3. ●——●, Optical density; ○ – – ○, TCA-precipitable material.

DNA synthesis increased so that within 40 minutes the DNA to protein ratio was restored to that previously characteristic of 50 µg of thymine per milliliter, after which the rate of DNA synthesis again became the same as the growth rate. The failure of the growth rate to remain constant after enrichment of thymine in this experiment may have been caused by a small change in the growth conditions or by initiation of some degree of periodicity in cell division (cf. Lark, 1961). The pool appeared to be larger than formerly at 50 µg per milliliter, but this may have been a result of the same factors. It is clear, however, that the pool size and the DNA content of Th-2 are very sensitive to external thymine concentration (see Figs. 2 and 4). Changes in pool size begin immediately after changes in thymine concentration and rapidly reach the level characteristic of the new concentration. Changes in DNA content also begin immediately and in the case of enrichment of thymine are completed within one mass doubling time. After dilution of thymine, about two generations are required before the appropriate level is reached.

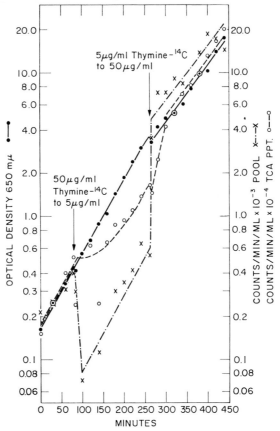

Fig. 5.   Acid-precipitable counts, cell mass, and acid-soluble thymine pool for Th-2 transferred from 50 μg of thymine-^{14}C per milliliter to 5 μg/ml and back to 50 μg/ml. Optical density, pool size, and acid-precipitable counts were determined as described in "Methods." At 80 minutes, 13 ml of culture growing at 50 μg of thymine-^{14}C (11,800 cpm/μg) per milliliter was transferred to 117 ml of prewarmed medium with no added thymine. After 180 minutes at 5 μg of thymine per milliliter, 12 ml of culture was added to 108 ml of prewarmed medium containing 50 μg of thymine per milliliter of the same specific activity. The optical density and counts have been corrected for the tenfold dilution. ●——●, Optical density; ○– –○, TCA-precipitable material; X-··-X, pool.

COMPOSITION OF LIPOPOLYSACCHARIDE

Most of the rhamnose in the cell is associated with the polysaccharide 0-antigen, thus its concentration may be estimated roughly by measuring the rhamnose content of cells (Robbins *et al.*, 1965). The rhamnose to protein ratios of whole cells of various strains grown at different thymine concentrations are compared in Table I. It is clear that the rhamnose to

TABLE I

RHAMNOSE TO PROTEIN RATIOS OF WHOLE CELLS OF S. *anatum* STRAINS

Organism:			Th-2			A_1
Thymine or thymidine concentration (μg/ml):	5	10	50	100	1000	0
Rhamnose to protein ratio	14	—	77	—	—	—
(mμmoles/mg)	—	56.5	—	92	100	—
	—	32[a]	—	—	—	116[a]
	—	42,[a] 43.5	—	76,[a] 100	—	128[a]
Average of 4–7 separate determinations	—	55.4	—	112	—	163.5

[a] Organisms grown in LB broth; all others grown in Tris minimal medium as described in "Methods."

protein ratio of Th-2 cells increases significantly if the thymine or thymidine concentration of the growth medium is increased, although the rhamnose to protein ratio of Th-2, even at 1 mg of thymine per milliliter, was always somewhat lower than that of A_1.

An analysis of the amount and composition of the Th-2 lipopolysaccharide prepared from cells grown at 5 and 50 μg of the thymine per milliliter is presented in Table II. The material analyzed in each case was the 50,000 rpm pellet fraction, high molecular weight lipopolysaccharide. In the case of Th-2 (5 μg of thymine per milliliter) about 63% of the rhamnose and 84% of the heptose were recovered in the pellet fraction, whereas for Th-2 (50 μ of thymine per milliliter) 56% of the rhamnose and 67% of the heptose were precipitated in the ultracentrifuge. The heptose per milligram of cellular protein in the lipopolysaccharide fraction was about the same in the two preparations, but the rhamnose was 2.5 times higher in the material from Th-2 grown with 50 μg of thymine per milliliter. The effect is clearly seen in the calculated ratios of polysaccharide rhamnose to heptose shown in the last column of Table II. Experiments which showed that carbon source and generation time have no influence on the rhamnose to protein ratio are summarized in Table III.

TABLE II

ANALYSIS OF LIPOPOLYSACCHARIDE FROM TH-2 GROWN WITH THYMINE[a]

Amount of thymine added to Th-2 (μg/ml)	Total Rhamnose[b]	Total heptose[b]	μmoles Rhamnose per μmole heptose
5 (preparation 1)	32.0	95.0	0.33
5 (preparation 2)	32.0	108.0	0.30
50 (preparation 1)	76.0	89.0	0.85
50 (preparation 2)	83.0	100.0	0.83

[a] Lipopolysaccharide was isolated and analyzed as described in "Materials and Methods." The total rhamnose and heptose values are corrected for losses. The rhamnose and heptose per milligram of protein calculations are based on the final optical density of the culture, assuming 0.4 mg protein/ml/optical density unit (650 mμ). This calculation corrects the yield of lipopolysaccharide rhamnose and heptose for the different weights of cells used for each lipopolysaccharide preparation.

[b] Values given as mμmoles per milligram of protein in cells.

TABLE III

COMPARISON OF GENERATION TIME AND RHAMNOSE TO PROTEIN RATIO

Strain	Carbon source	Doubling time (minutes)	Rhamnose to protein ratio
A_1	Broth	35	158
A_1	Glucose	60	183
A_1	Citrate	90	147
A_1	Succinate	150	180
Th-2	Broth[a]	35	60
Th-2	Glucose[a]	65	59
Th-2	Citrate[a]	250	53
Th-2	Succinate[a]	450	70

[a] Supplemented with 10 μg of thymidine per milliliter. The glucose, citrate, and succinate were added to Tris minimal medium in the following final concentrations: glucose, 0.5%; citrate, 0.5%; succinate, 0.5%.

DISCUSSION

From the experiments described above, it seems clear that in S. anatum-Th-2, the level of the thymidine nucleotide pool is directly related to the external thymine concentration. The fact that the cells could not survive at 1 μg of thymine per milliliter, which represents more total thymine in the culture than the cells would contain at full growth, indicates that the limiting factor must involve transport or utilization of thymine. Thymineless mutants obtained by the aminopterin method differ from known thymineless mutants of E. coli which require less than 2 μg of thymine per milliliter for full growth (Pritchard and Lark, 1964). The reason for these differences may become clear when the pathway for incorporation of thymine into DNA is elucidated.

It is known (Klenow, 1962; Reichard *et al.*, 1961; Morris *et al.*, 1963; Lark, 1960) that the level of various nucleotides may have an influence on DNA synthesis. We find that there is a correlation between the thymidine nucleotide pool and the level of DNA in the cells of S. *anatum*-Th-2. Further, a decrease in the thymidine nucleotide pool and DNA caused by low external thymine concentration does not seem to bring about a measurable decrease in the rate of RNA or protein synthesis, although the rate of cell division may decrease. Possibly the high steady-state rate of RNA and protein synthesis require the presence of only a single genome within the cell if conditions of growth are otherwise adequate.

The decrease in the rhamnose to protein ratio of the cells with a decrease in the thymine nucleotide pool suggests the simple relationship that a lower intracellular concentration of TDP-rhamnose causes a slower rate of polysaccharide synthesis. The hypothesis that low concentrations of thymidine diphosphate sugars may limit the rate of polysaccharide synthesis under some conditions should be tested in other ways. Since the *in vitro* antigen-synthesizing system has a high affinity for TDP-rhamnose (Wright *et al.*, 1965) it is possible that one of the enzymes that converts TDP-glucose to TDP-rhamnose becomes rate-limiting because of low substrate affinity. Finally, the change in lipopolysaccharide composition could be a secondary effect unrelated to the polysaccharide precursor concentration. If this latter possibility proves to be true, more detailed analysis might reveal new interrelationships between the synthesis of lipopolysaccharide and other cellular components.

REFERENCES

Bray, G. A. (1960). *Anal. Biochem.* 1, 279.

Burton, K. (1956). *Biochem. J.* 62, 315.

Dische, Z. (1955). *Methods Biochem. Analy.* 2, 313.

Klenow, H. (1962). *Biochim. Biophys. Acta* 61, 885.

Lark, K. G. (1960). *Biochim. Biophys. Acta.* 45, 121.

Lark, K. G. (1961). *Biochim. Biophys. Acta.* 51, 107.

Lipmann, F. (1941). *Advan. Enzymol.* 1, 99.

Lowry, O. H., Rosebrough, N. J., Farr, A. L., and Randall, R. J. (1951). *J. Biol. Chem.* 193, 265.

Morris, N. R., Reichard, P., and Fischer, G. A. (1963). *Biochim. Biophys. Acta.* 68, 93.

Okada, T., Yanagisawa, K., and Ryan, F. J. (1960). *Nature* 188, 340.

Osborn, M. J. (1963). *Proc. Natl. Acad. Sci. U.S.* 50, 499.

Pritchard, R. H., and Lark, K. G. (1964). *J. Mol. Biol.* **9**. 288.

Reichard, P., Canellakis, Z. N., and Canellakis, E. S. (1961). *J. Biol. Chem.* **236**, 2514.

Robbins, P. W., and Uchida, T. (1962). *Biochemistry* **1**, 323.

Robbins, P. W., Keller, J. M., Wright, A., and Bernstein, R. L. (1965). *J. Biol. Chem.* **240**, 384.

Weiner, J. M., Higuchi, T., Rothfield, L., Saltmarsh-Andrew, M., Osborn, M. J., and Horecker, B. L. (1965). *Proc. Natl. Acad. Sci. U.S.* **54**, 228.

Wright, A., Dankert, M., and Robbins, P. W. (1965). *Proc. Natl. Acad. Sci. U.S.* **54**, 235 (1965).

Biosynthesis of Thiamine and Its Inhibition by Aminothiazole*

Yoshitsugu Nose and Akio Iwashima

Although growing microorganisms are capable of synthesizing thiamine *de novo*, the addition of hydroxymethylpyrimidine and thiazole moieties of thiamine to the medium causes a rapid increase of thiamine in growing and resting cells of the organisms. This fact aided in the clarification of the thiamine biosynthetic pathway from hydroxymethylpyrimidine and thiazole. The mechanism of thiamine synthesis is an ATP-dependent reaction in which hydroxymethylpyrimidine and thiazole are both activated enzymatically by ATP; this activation is followed by the condensation of the two intermediates.

Aminothiazole, which has a structure very closely related to the thiazole of thiamine, can be incorporated into the thiamine-synthesizing system of the microorganism and phosphorylated by ATP as well as thiazole. Consequently, aminothiazole shows a strong inhibitory action on the growth of the microorganism. However, the organism gains the ability to eliminate·the antimetabolite for its own protection. This procedure will be considered in this chapter.

THIAMINE SYNTHESIS FROM HYDROXYMETHYLPYRIMIDINE AND THIAZOLE

The mechanism of thiamine biosynthesis was clarified using the cell-free extract of baker's yeast by three independent groups (Camiener and Brown, 1960; Lewin and Brown, 1961; Leder, 1961; Nose *et al.*, 1959,

* Abbreviations used in this chapter are: hydroxymethylpyrimidine, hydroxymethyl-pyrimidine-P, and hydroxymethylpyrimidine-PP for 2-methyl-4-amino-5-hydroxymethylpyrimidine, its monophosphate and pyrophosphate esters, respectively; thiazole

1961). The reaction consists of two step reactions; the first reaction is the phosphorylation of both hydroxymethylpyrimidine and thiazole into hydroxymethylpyrimidine-PP and thiazole-P, respectively. This reaction belongs to a kinase type of group activation proposed by Lipmann (1957). The second reaction is a condensation of the two activated compounds with liberation of pyrophosphate. It is a transfer reaction involving the pyrimidyl radical and leads to the formation of thiamine monophosphate. The results of these studies are summarized by the following equations:

$$\text{Hydroxymethylpyrimidine} \xrightarrow{\text{ATP}} \text{hydroxymethylpyrimidine-P} \qquad (1)$$

$$\text{Hydroxymethylpyrimidine-P} \xrightarrow{\text{ATP}} \text{hydroxymethylpyrimidine-PP} \qquad (2)$$

$$\text{Thiazole} \xrightarrow{\text{ATP}} \text{thiazole-P} \qquad (3)$$

$$\text{Hydroxymethylpyrimidine-PP} + \text{thiazole-P} \rightleftharpoons \text{thiamine-P} + \text{PP} \qquad (4)$$

The enzymes that catalyze reactions (1)–(4) were named hydroxymethylpyrimidine kinase (EC 2.7.1.49), phosphomethylpyrimidine kinase (EC 2.7.4.7), hydroxyethylthiazole kinase (EC 2.7.1.50), and thiaminephosphate pyrophosphorylase (EC 2.5.1.3), respectively. It has been reported by Nose et al. (1964) that these reactions are responsible for the biosynthesis of thiamine in E. coli W and its mutants.

INHIBITION BY AMINOTHIAZOLE OF THIAMINE BIOSYNTHESIS

Inhibition of Bacterial Growth and Thiamine Synthesis

The inhibition by aminothiazole of the growth of E. coli was first described by Nakayama (1956). This compound completely inhibited the growth of the "wild strain" of E. coli ATCC 9637 at a medium concentration of 10^{-7} M and the inhibition was antagonized by 10^{-9} M thiazole. This inhibition was also observed in the growth of Saccharomyces cerevisiae by 10^{-6} M aminothiazole added to the Hayduck medium. These phenomena were thought to be caused by the inhibition by aminothiazole of thiamine synthesis in the microorganism. In order to clarify the inhibitory mechanism of aminothiazole, enzymatic studies were carried

and thiazole-P for 4-methyl-5-hydroxyethylthiazole and its monophosphate ester, respectively; thiamine-P for thiamine monophosphate; aminothiazole and aminothiazole-P for 2-amino-4-methyl-5-hydroxyethylthiazole and its monophosphate ester; ATP for adenosine triphosphate; EDTA for ethylenediaminetetraacetic acid.

out using the thiamine-synthesizing system obtained from baker's yeast extract. The enzyme preparations were obtained from this extract by treatment with protamine sulfate and fractionation with ammonium sulfate. As shown in Table I, the inhibitory effect by aminothiazole on thiamine synthesis from hydroxymethylpyrimidine, thiazole, and ATP was pronounced. The same concentration of compound as thiazole inhibited over 80% of the enzymatic synthesis of thiamine. From the structural

TABLE I

INHIBITION BY AMINOTHIAZOLE OF ENZYMATIC SYNTHESIS OF THIAMINE FROM
HYDROXYMETHYLPYRIMIDINE AND THIAZOLE[a]

Aminothiazole added (mμmoles)	Aminothiazole/ Thiazole	Thiamine formed (mμmoles)
50[b]	—	0.09
0	0	2.94
5	0.1	2.37
20	0.4	0.76
50	1	0.48
50[c]	0.1	2.09
500	10	0.19
5000	100	0.09

[a] Reaction mixtures (5 ml) contained: Tris-maleate buffer (pH 7.0), 100 μmoles; hydroxymethylpyrimidine, 50 mμmoles; thiazole, 50 mμmoles; ATP, 10 μmoles; MgCl$_2$, 10 μmoles, and enzyme protein, 0.9 mg. The mixtures were incubated for 2 hours at 38° C and analyzed for thiamine by the thiochrome method.

[b] No thiazole added.

[c] Thiazole (500 mμmoles) added.

similarity of aminothiazole and thiazole, the inhibition point was assumed to be in the thiazole kinase reaction step. When hydroxymethylpyrimidine-PP, thiazole, and ATP were used as the substrates and the effect of aminothiazole on the thiazole kinase reaction was tested, the Lineweaver-Burk plot demonstrated the competitive nature of the inhibition as shown in Fig. 1. Further, from the autobiographical data using a thiazole-less mutant strain of E. coli which responded to the thiazole phosphate spot on the paper chromatogram of the reaction mixture, the reduction of thiazole phosphate formation was observed.

ENZYMATIC FORMATION OF AMINOTHIAZOLE PHOSPHATE

As seen in the case of inhibition by deoxypyridoxine of pyridoxal kinase reaction in yeast (Hurwitz, 1952), it was expected that aminothiazole inhibition might be accompanied by phosphorylation of the compound by ATP as well as thiazole. The aminothiazole-P enzymatically synthesized in the reaction mixture, which had been incubated with aminothiazole and ATP, was isolated by chromatography on a Dowex 1 column. The compound thus obtained was identical with an authentic sample of aminothiazole-P, tested by both paper chromatography and

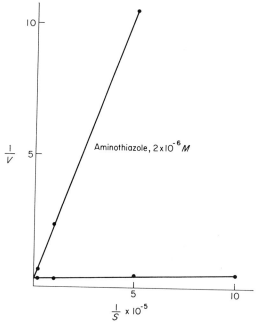

Fig. 1. A Lineweaver-Burk plot showing the inhibition of thiazole kinase reaction by aminothiazole. Reaction mixture (5 ml) contained: Tris-maleate buffer (pH 7.0), 100 μmoles; hydroxymethylpyrimidine-PP, 50 mμmoles; ATP, 10 μmoles; $MgCl_2$, 10 μmoles, and the concentration of thiazole was varied as shown. Aminothiazole, 10 mμmoles, was added. Incubation was carried out for 30 minutes at 38°C.

ultraviolet absorption spectroscopy. Aminothiazole-P also inhibited the condensation step of hydroxymethylpyrimidine-PP and thiazole-P. The K_m for thiazole-P and K_i for aminothiazole-P were 5.0×10^{-7} and 2.0×10^{-8} M, respectively.

In conclusion, the inhibition by aminothiazole of thiamine synthesis can be explained by two step inhibitory reactions as summarized in Fig. 2. Aminothiazole was ingeniously placed in the thiamine-synthesizing system and inhibited the growth of the microorganism.

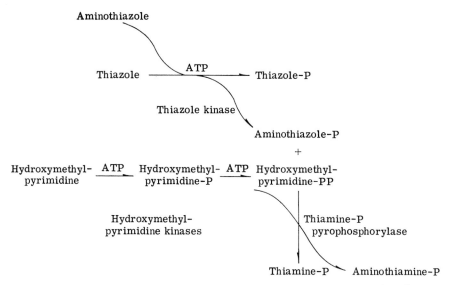

Fig. 2.   Inhibition mechanism of thiamine biosynthesis by aminothiazole.

RESISTANCE OF *ESCHERICHIA COLI* TO AMINOTHIAZOLE

It is of interest that an antimetabolite can produce an impediment toward growth in a microorganism, but the microorganism can gain the ability to protect itself against such an attack. An aminothiazole-resistant strain of E. coli W ATCC 9637 was obtained after four successive incubations in the presence of aminothiazole. The growth of the resistant strain was inhibited by 10^{-2} M aminothiazole in the medium, whereas the sensitive strain was inhibited by 10^{-6} M as shown in Fig. 3.

THIAMINE SYNTHESIS BY SENSITIVE AND RESISTANT STRAINS OF *E. coli*

The amount of thiamine synthesized in the cells of the resistant strain grown in the basal medium was almost equal to that of the sensitive strain. The growing and resting cells of *E. coli* W are both able to synthesize thiamine from media to which hydroxymethylpyrimidine and thiazole have been added as described above. However, the synthesizing ability of thiamine in the resistant strain is fairly low compared with that of the sensitive (wild) one. Table II shows a comparison of the thiamine content synthesized by cell suspensions of both strains in a medium containing a concentration of 10^{-5} M hydroxymethylpyrimidine and thiazole with glucose. The sensitive strain synthesized thiamine

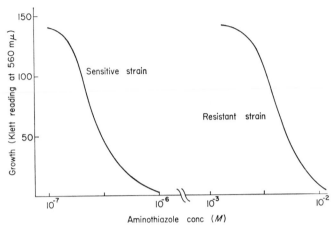

Fɪɢ. 3.   Inhibition by aminothiazole of growth of *E. coli* sensitive and resistant to aminothiazole.

in good yield and the synthesis was inhibited by aminothiazole. On the other hand, no thiamine synthesis of the resistant strain was observed under this condition. The thiazole-P formation in the cells of the sensitive strain was 3.3 mμmoles per reaction tube, whereas the resistant strain failed to produce any ιhiazole-P. This fact suggests that the latter had lost the ability to form thiazole-P which is essential for thiamine synthesis. This phenomenon was also observed in the protoplasts of both strains that were prepared with eggwhite lysozyme and EDTA treatments according to Mahler and Fraser (1956). In the protoplast experiment, the sensitive strain produced 2.7 mμmoles of thiamine per reaction tube, whereas the resistant strain yielded only 0.2 mμmole.

TABLE II

Tʜɪᴀᴍɪɴᴇ Fᴏʀᴍᴀᴛɪᴏɴ ғʀᴏᴍ Hʏᴅʀᴏxʏᴍᴇᴛʜʏʟᴘʏʀɪᴍɪᴅɪɴᴇ ᴀɴᴅ Tʜɪᴀᴢᴏʟᴇ ʙʏ Cᴇʟʟ
Sᴜsᴘᴇɴsɪᴏɴs ᴏғ *E. coli* Sᴇɴsɪᴛɪᴠᴇ ᴀɴᴅ Rᴇsɪsᴛᴀɴᴛ ᴛᴏ Aᴍɪɴᴏᴛʜɪᴀᴢᴏʟᴇ[a]

Thiamine formed (mμmoles)	
Sensitive strain[b]	Resistant strain
10.2 (1.6)	0
23.2 (5.4)	0

[a] Reaction mixtures contained 200 μmoles of Tris-maleate buffer (pH 7.0), 100 mμmoles each of hydroxymethylpyrimidine and thiazole, 2 ml of cell suspension, 2 ml of 10% glucose, 1.6 ml of 4.5% NaCl for a total volume of 10 ml. While shaking the mixtures were incubated at 37° C for 1 hour.

[b] Numbers in parentheses indicate the amount of thiamine formed in the presence of 10 μmoles of aminothiazole.

Activities of Thiazole Kinase and Thiamine-P Pyrophosphorylase of the Sensitive and Resistant Strains

The activities of thiazole kinase prepared by sonic extraction from both strains were estimated and plotted for thiazole concentrations in the presence of 10^{-5} M hydroxymethylpyrimidine-PP according to the method of Lineweaver and Burk. The K_m for thiazole and the K_i for aminothiazole of the resistant strain were 6×10^{-4} and 3×10^{-4} M, respectively, these values were very close to those of the sensitive strain

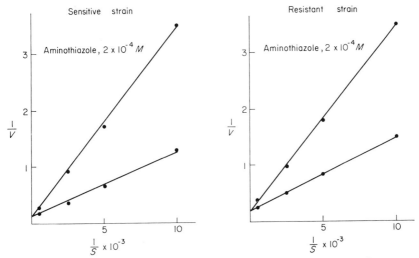

Fig. 4. Lineweaver-Burk plots of thiazole kinase activity of *E. coli* sensitive and resistant to aminothiazole. The reaction mixtures were similar to those described in Fig. 1. Aminothiazole, 1 μmole, was added.

(Fig. 4). Thiamine-P pyrophosphorylase obtained from both strains gave almost the same activities for several substrate concentrations. These findings led to the assumption concerning the alteration of cell membrane permeability for thiazole and aminothiazole a derivative of thiazole which is structurally very similar to it, rather than the alteration of the enzyme characteristics responsible for thiamine synthesis.

When the amount of thiamine synthesized by the whole cells of both strains in various concentrations of thiazole in the presence of 10^{-5} M hydroxymethylpyrimidine was estimated, a relationship between both strains was obtained, as shown in Fig. 5. It indicated that the resistant strain having 100–200 times the amount of thiazole as the sensitive one and the sensitive strain synthesized almost equal amounts of thiamine.

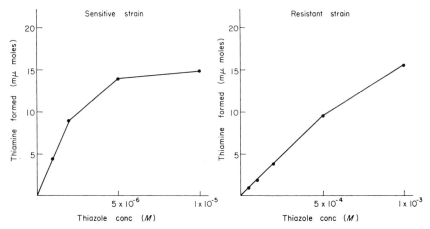

FIG. 5. Effect of various concentrations of thiazole on thiamine synthesis by cell suspensions of *E. coli* sensitive and resistant to aminothiazole.

The "K_m" for [thiazole]/thiamine synthesis of whole cells (usage adopted for the sake of comparison) had a value of 1.5×10^{-6} M for the sensitive strain and 4.8×10^{-4} M for the resistant strain which is reasonably close to the value of 6×10^{-4} M for the K_m of the thiazole kinase (Fig. 4).

Although other possibilities cannot be excluded, a decrease in cell membrane permeability to thiazole, namely, aminothiazole, might be responsible for resistance in the resistant strain studied.

ACKNOWLEDGMENTS

We wish to thank Dr. Akiji Fujita for his kind encouragement and revisions. We are also indebted to Dr. Shojiro Yurugi for a gift of aminothiazole and related compounds.

REFERENCES

Camiener, G. M., and Brown, G. M. (1960). *J. Biol. Chem.* **235**, 2404, 2411.

Hurwitz, J. (1952). *Biochim. Biophys. Acta* **9**, 496.

Leder, I. G. (1961). *J. Biol. Chem.* **236**, 3066.

Lewin, L. M., and Brown, G. M. (1961). *J. Biol. Chem.* **236**, 2768.

Lipmann, F. (1957). *In* "Metabolism of the Nervous System," p. 327. Macmillan (Pergamon), New York.

Mahler, H. R., and Fraser, D. (1956). *Biochim. Biophys. Acta* **22**, 197.

Nakayama, H. (1956). *Bitamins* **11**, 20.

Nose, Y., Ueda, K., and Kawasaki, T. (1959). *Biochim. Biophys. Acta* **34**, 277.

Nose, Y., Ueda, K., Kawasaki, T., Iwashima, A., and Fujita, T. (1961). *J. Vitaminol.* (*Kyoto*) **7**, 92, 98.

Nose, Y., Tokuda, Y., Hirabayashi, M., and Iwashima, A. (1964). *J. Vitaminol.* (*Kyoto*) **10**, 105.

Some Aspects of Sugar Nucleotide Metabolism

W. Z. Hassid

Lipmann's (1941) introduction of the concept "energy-rich" phosphorus bonds proved to be a major contribution to the understanding of how energy liberated in oxidative reactions and stored in adenosine triphosphate (ATP) could be used to form new linkages in a succession of transfer reactions, resulting in the synthesis of complex saccharides, such as glycogen, cellulose, and various oligosaccharides.

The general process for synthesis of complex saccharides (oligosaccharides, glycosides, and polysaccharides) is that of transglycosylation. In this process the glycosyl donor may be a sugar phosphate, sugar nucleotide, oligosaccharide, or polysaccharide.

Cori and Cori (1936, 1937) discovered that α-D-glucose 1-phosphate is the first degradation product of glycogen and demonstrated that glycogen can be synthesized *in vitro* by the reverse reaction from the same sugar phosphate (Cori and Cori, 1940). It was soon shown that starch could be synthesized from α-D-glucose 1-phosphate by a phosphorylase from the potato (Hanes, 1940, 1941) and sucrose by a phosphorylase from *Pseudomonas saccharophila* with the same phosphorylated sugar and D-fructose. It was, therefore, assumed that the general pattern for complex saccharide formation occurred via sugar 1-phosphate. However, it is now believed that formation of these compounds from α-D-glucose 1-phosphate is not a normal physiological process and that phosphorylases act mainly as degradative enzymes. In fact, only six enzymes of this type are known: glycogen phosphorylase (Cori and Cori, 1940), starch phosphorylase (Hanes, 1940), sucrose phosphorylase (Hassid *et al.*, 1944), maltose phosphorylase (Fitting and Doudoroff, 1952), cellobiose phosphorylase (Ayers, 1959), and laminaribiose phosphorylase (Marechal and Goldemberg, 1963). The number of enzymes that lead to the formation of polysaccharides from a disaccharide is also restricted. The

351

two best known enzymes that form polysaccharides from sucrose are the dextran synthesized by cultures of *Leuconostoc mesneteroides* (Stacey and Barker, 1960*a*) and related microorganisms and the levan synthesized from the same substrate by *Acetobacter levanicum* (Hestrin *et al.*, 1956), *Bacillus subtilis* (Dedonder, 1960), and other species. Certain strains of *Escherichia coli* also produce amylosaccharides from maltose (Stacey and Barker, 1960*b*).

Recent investigations indicate that *in vivo* complex saccharides are synthesized from sugar nucleotides. From the thermodynamic point of view, sugar nucleotides are superior glycoside donors to the sugar 1-phosphates for such syntheses.

The free energy of hydrolysis (ΔF) of compounds containing glycosidic linkages varies considerably, but the sugar nucleotides have the highest glycosyl transfer potential. The ΔF values reported for hydrolysis of the glycosidic linkages of a number of compounds are as follows: UDP-D-glucose (pH 7.4), —7600 cal; sucrose, —6600 cal[*]; α-D-glucose 1-phosphate (pH 8.5), —4800 cal; trehalose, —4400 cal; glycogen (α-D-glucose 1,4-linkages), —4300 cal; maltose, —4600 cal; levan (β-D-2,6-fructose linkages), —4000 cal; inosine (C—N linkage), —4000 cal; dextran (α-D-glucose 1,6-linkages), —2000 cal. [For references to ΔF values of glycosidic linkages to the various compounds, see Hassid and Neufeld (1962).]

With the exception of α-D-glucose 1-phosphate and sucrose, these ΔF values are only approximate, because of certain assumptions made in calculating the free energy changes and also on account of the experimental difficulties in determining the equilibrium constants.

Although the relatively high ΔF value of —7600 cal applies only to the one sugar nucleotide, UDP-D-glucose, it is assumed that sugar diphosphate nucleosides, containing other glycosyl moieties than D-glucose and bases besides uridine, have approximately the same high ΔF values.

OCCURRENCE OF NUCLEOSIDE DIPHOSPHATE SUGARS

Leloir's discovery (1951) of uridine diphosphate (UDP) D-glucose from yeast was followed by isolation of a number of other uridine di-

---

[*] Neufeld calls attention to the fact that the value of —4800 cal for the $\Delta F°$ of hydrolysis of a α-D-glucopyranosyl phosphate was obtained at pH 8.5. If a correction to pH 6.6 is applied, the $\Delta F°$ of hydrolysis of α-D-pyranosyl phosphate becomes —5200 cal, and that of sucrose would be —7000 cal. Taking this into consideration the $\Delta F°$ of hydrolysis of the D-glycosidic bond of UDP-D-glucose at pH 6.6 is approximately —8000 cal.

phosphate nucleotides containing glysoyl residues from microorganisms, plant and animal tissues. Thus, UDP-D-galactose, UDP-D-glucuronic acid, UDP-D-xylose, UDP-L-arabinose, UDP-D-N-acetyl-D-glucosamine, and others were isolated from natural sources (Leloir, 1956; Hassid *et al.*, 1959). It was, therefore, assumed that the base of the sugar diphosphate nucleoside must always be uracil. But soon followed the discovery of sugar diphosphate nucleosides containing guanosine, thymidine, cytidine, or adenosine as the constituent of the molecule.* Examples of such compounds isolated from various sources are the following: D-glucose, D-fructose, L-fucose, 3,6-dideoxy-L-*xylo*-hexose (colitose) (Heath and Elbein, 1962); L-galactose derivatives of GDP; D-glucose, 3,6-dideoxy-D-*arabino*-hexose (tyvelose) (Nikaido and Jokura, 1961); glycerol and ribitol derivatives of CDP; D-glucose derivatives of ADP; D-glucose, D-galactose, D-ribose, and N-acetyl-D-glucosamine derivatives of TDP (Neufeld and Hassid, 1963); and GDP-D-mannuronic acid and GDP-L-guluronic acid from brown algae (Lin, 1965). One sugar nucleotide, cytosine monophosphate N-acetylneuraminic acid, was found which does not contain a pyrophosphate linkage (Roseman, 1962a).

The concentration of sugar nucleotides in different organisms may vary considerably. For example, a relatively high value of 370 µmoles of UDP-D-glucose per kilogram of wet weight was isolated from yeast (Neufeld and Hassid, 1963) and only 0.1 µmole of UDP-D-galactose per kilogram was found in mung bean seedlings. However, the presence of a sugar nucleotide in trace amounts does not necessarily indicate that it is of a minor metabolic importance; on the contrary, a low concentration may signify that this compound is being utilized at a rapid rate for the synthesis of a complex saccharide or in other metabolic reactions.

The highest concentrations of sugar diphosphate nucleosides may be encountered in microorganisms in cases where there is a block caused by a deficiency involved in the utilization of the glycosyl nucleotide. This is found in mutants of *Escherichia coli* or *Salmonella* which are able to incorporate D-galactose into UDP-D-galactose, but are unable to use this sugar diphosphate nucleoside because it lacks the UDP-D-galactose

---

* Abbreviations used in this chapter: ADP, adenosine diphosphate; CDP, cytidine diphosphate; TDP, thymidine diphosphate; GDP, guanosine diphosphate; CMP, cytidine monophosphate; NAD, nicotinamide adenine dinucleotide; NADH, reduced NAD, NADP$_2$H, reduced form of nicotinamide adenine dinucleotide phosphate; PP, pyrophosphate; P$_i$, orthophosphate; ITP, Inosine triphosphate; UMP, uridine monophosphate; TTP, thymidine triphosphate; dUDP, deoxy uridine diphosphate; dTDP, thymidine diphosphate; IDP, inosine diphosphate.

4-epimerase enzyme (Nikaido, 1962; Wiesmeyer and Jourdian, 1961). When cells of such mutants of *E. coli* are incubated with D-galactose, concentrations as high as 20 mmoles of UDP-D-galactose may accumulate per kilogram of cells.

High concentrations of sugar nucleotides may also occur under conditions in which the utilization of these compounds is blocked by a drug. In penicillin-inhibited *Staphylococcus aureus* an accumulation of 5000 μmoles of the muramic acid-peptide derivative of uridine diphosphate was found per kilogram of cells (Park, 1952).

SYNTHESIS OF NUCLEOSIDE DIPHOSPHATE SUGARS

The synthesis of nucleoside diphosphate sugars involves the transfer of a nucleotidyl group from a nucleoside triphosphate to a sugar 1-phosphate with the simultaneous release of pyrophosphate according to the following general reaction (Munch-Petersen *et al.*, 1953; Leloir, 1964a):

Nucleoside triphosphate + sugar 1-phosphate

$\Updownarrow$ pyrophosphorylase
nucleoside diphosphate suger + inorganic pyrophosphate

Many nucleoside diphosphate sugars containing different bases and different sugar moieties were found to be synthesized by this enzymatic process.

A similar reaction (Roseman, 1962a; Warren and Blacklow, 1962) leads to the synthesis of a nucleoside monophosphate sugar which occurs as follows:

CTP + neuraminic acid → CMP-neuraminic acid + pyrophosphate

INTERCONVERSION OF NUCLEOSIDE DIPHOSPHATE SUGARS

The glycosyl moiety of the nucleoside diphosphate sugars formed by the pyrophosphorylase reaction is capable of undergoing a number of transformations. The first of these reactions to be studied was the 4-epimerization of UDP-D-glucose to UDP-D-galactose (Leloir, 1951). In spite of the assiduous study of this reaction (Maxwell *et al.*, 1958; Maxwell and de Robichon-Szulmajster, 1960), it is not well understood. The reaction requires catalytic amounts of NAD and presumably takes place through an oxidized intermediate in which the asymmetry at the 4-position is lost. However, attempts to trap such an intermediate have not been successful. It is considered that such an intermediate may exist as a transiently enzyme-bound compound. De Robichon-Szulmajster (1961) suggested that UDP-D-glucose assumes a strainless folded conformation in which the pyrimidine moiety is located in close proximity to the D-glucosyl unit and participates in the epimerase reaction. The assumption that the D-glucosyl nucleotides can assume such a conformation may be responsible for the ability of these compounds to undergo a large number of interconversions.

Wilson and Hogness (1964) found that extensively purified UDP-D-galactose 4-epimerase from *E. coli* contains 1 mole of tightly bound NAD per mole of enzyme. An absorption peak, almost identical in shape to that of NADH, appeared on addition of substrate to the enzyme. These results strongly support the proposed mechanism that an oxidation-reduction of the UDP hexoses presumably occurs at C-4 (Maxwell, 1957).

Besides the most commonly occurring C-4 epimerizations, other types have been reported in other positions (Roseman, 1962b). One is a 2-epimerization, shown in the following reaction:

$$\text{UDP-}N\text{-acetyl-D-glucosamine} \rightleftharpoons N\text{-acetylmannosamine} + \text{UDP}$$

It is not known whether UDP-acetylmannosamine is an intermediate in this reaction.

Another epimerization has been found to take place at C-5 in the conversion of UDP-D-glucuronic acid to UDP-L-iduronic acid (Jacobson and Davidson, 1963).

More complicated conversions, in which a change in configuration of several carbon atoms in the hexose unit takes place, lead to the formation of 6-deoxyhexoses. The first conversion of this type involving the transformation of GDP-D-mannose to GDP-L-fucose by enzymes from *Acetobacter aerogenes* was studied by Ginsburg (1960, 1961). The first step is an internal oxidation-reduction reaction, requiring NAD, in which the OH group at C-4 is converted to a keto group and the CH_2OH group to a CH_3 group. Subsequently, inversions take place at C-3 and C-5, which are supposedly occurring by an enediol transformation, and they produce a hypothetical intermediate. Reduction with NADPH at C-4 would result in GDP-L-fucose. These transformations are visualized by Ginsburg in Fig. 1.

In another case TDP-D-glucose is transformed to TDP-L-rhamnose by different microorganisms (Glaser and Kornfeld, 1961; Okazaki *et al.*, 1962; Pazur and Shuey, 1961). This transformation involves inversion of C-3, C-4, and C-5 plus reduction at C-6. A similar process occurs in plants involving the same steps but with UDP-D-glucose instead of TDP-D-glucose (Barber, 1963).

A reaction involving an inversion of C-3 and C-5 is postulated to take place in the formation of GDP-L-galactose from GDP-D-mannose (Su

TABLE I

INTERCONVERSION OF SUGAR NUCLEOTIDES[a]

Sugar in reactant	Reactions and positions		Sugar in product
	Epimerization	Other	
UDP-D-Glucose	4	—	D-Galactose
UDP-D-Glucose	—	Oxid. 6	D-Glucuronic acid
UDP-D-Glucose	3, 4, 5	Red. 6	L-Rhamnose
UDP-D-Glucuronic acid	4	—	D-Galacturonic acid
UDP-D-Glucuronic acid	5	—	L-Iduronic acid
UDP-D-Glucuronic acid	—	Decarboxylation	D-Xylose
UDP-D-Xylose	4	—	L-Arabinose
UDP-N-Acetyl-D-glucosamine	4	—	N-Acetyl-D-galactosamine
UDP-N-Acetyl-D-glucosamine	2	Hydrolysis	D-Mannosamine
UDP-N-Acetyl-D-glucosamine	—	+ Lactic acid	Acetylmuramic acid
Acetylmuramic acid	—	+ Amino acids	Acetylmuramic acid peptide
GDP-D-Mannose	3, 5	—	L-Galactose[b]
GDP-D-Mannose	3, 5	Red. 6	L-Fucose
GDP-D-Mannose	4	Red. 6	D-Talomethylose
GDP-D-Mannose	—	Red. 6	D-Rhamnose
GDP-D-Mannose	—	Oxid. 6	D-Mannuronic acid
GDP-D-Mannose	5	Red. 3, 6	Colitose
TDP-D-Glucose	3, 4, 5	Red. 6	L-Rhamnose
TDP-D-Glucose	4	—	D-Galactose
TPD-N-Acetyl-D-glucosamine	4	—	N-Acetyl-D-galactosamine
TDP-D-Glucose	?	Red. 4, 6 + acetylamino 4	4-Acetylamino 4,6-Dideoxyhexose
TDP-D-Glucose	?	Red. 3, 6	3-Acetamido 3,6-Dideoxyhexose
CDP-D-Glucose	2	Red. 3, 6	Tyvelose[b]
CDP-D-Glucose	4	Red. 3, 6	Abequose[b]
CDP-D-Glucose	4, 5	Red. 3, 6	Ascarylose

[a] Compiled by Leloir (1964b).

[b] Hypothetical.

and Hassid, 1962); and the synthesis of a 3,6-dideoxy-L-*xylo*-hexose (colitose) from GDP-D-mannose (Heath and Elbein, 1962) is assumed to involve a reduction at C-3 and C-6 and an inversion at the C-4 position.

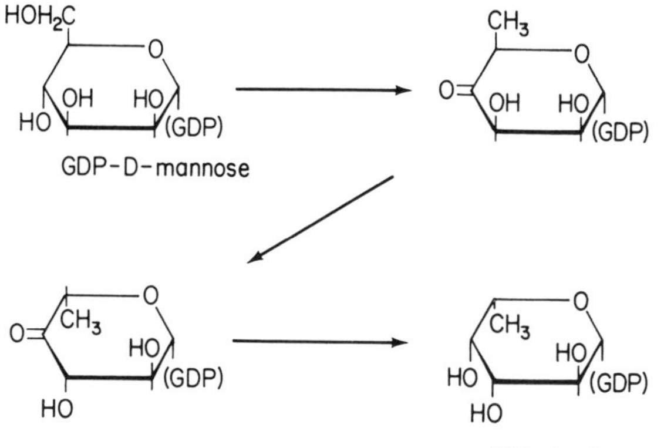

GDP-D-mannose

GDP-L-fucose

FIG. 1.   The transformation of GDP-D-mannose to GDP-L-fucose.

The interconversion reactions for which considerable evidence is available are listed in Table I.

DECARBOXYLATION

Neufeld *et al.* (1958) were the first to obtain a particulate preparation from *Phaseolus aureus* (mung bean) seedlings containing an enzyme capable of catalyzing the decarboxylation of UDP-D-glucuronic acid (UDPGA) to UDP-pentose, which consisted of a mixture of UDP-D-xylose and UDP-L-arabinose. This preparation also contained a UDP-xylose 4-epimerase which catalyzed the interconversion of the two pentose nucleotides and a UDPGA-4-epimerase capable of interconverting UDP-D-glucuronic and UDP-D-galacturonic acids. The possibility, therefore, remained that some of the UDP-L-arabinose might have been a decarboxylation product of UDP-D-galacturonic acid. Feingold *et al.* (1960) subsequently showed that the decarboxylase and UDP-xylose 4-epimerase could be extracted from the particulate preparation obtained from mung beans and other plants, with digitonin, leaving the UDPGA-4-epimerase in the particle, and that the initial product of decarboxylation of the UDP-D-glucuronic acid was UDP-D-xylose in which the pentose moiety retained the expected UDP-D-glucuronic acid configuration. No enzyme was present in the mung bean preparation capable of decarboxylating UDP-D-galacturonic acid to UDP-L-arabinose.

In a study of the properties of partially purified UDP-D-glucuronic acid decarboxylase from wheat germ, Castanera and Hassid (1965) found that no added cofactors were required for the activity of the enzyme. The enzyme showed a maximal activity between pH 6.0 and 6.8 Attempts to find a postulated 4-keto intermediate were not successful, and a dependence of enzyme activity on a protein-bound pyridine nucleotide could not be demonstrated.

Ankel and Feingold (1965) succeeded in purifying the wheat germ decarboxylase (UDPGA-carboxylase) 350-fold. They confirmed the previous results that UDP-D-xylose is the only sugar nucleotide formed by this enzyme from UDP-D-glucuronic acid. The purified enzyme has a pH optimum between 6.8 and 7.0, and the K_m of the UDP-D-glucuronic acid is about 3×10^{-4} M. The enzyme is neither activated by nicotinamide adenine dinucleotide (NAD) nor inhibited by NADH. However, NAD is released by wheat germ enzyme upon heat denaturation. In contrast, UDPGA-carboxylase obtained from the microorganism *Cryptococcus laurentii* (Ankel and Feingold, 1966) has an absolute requirement for NAD and is inhibited by NADH. Ankel and Feingold are of the opinion that the strong bond between NAD and wheat germ UDPGA-carboxylase indicates that this dinucleotide is necessary for enzyme activity. However, this cannot be stated with certainty until it is possible to inactivate the enzyme by removal of NAD and to restore activity by its addition.

SUCROSE

Cardini *et al.* (1955) and Leloir and Cardini (1955) found two enzymes in plants capable of synthesizing sucrose and sucrose phosphate according to the following two reactions:

$$\text{UDP-D-glucose} + \text{D-fructose} \rightleftharpoons \text{sucrose} + \text{UDP} \tag{1}$$

$$\text{UDP-D-glucose} + \text{D-fructose 6-phosphate} \rightleftharpoons \text{sucrose phosphate} + \text{UDP} \tag{2}$$

Reaction (1) in which sucrose is directly synthesized is freely reversible. The equilibrium constant of this reaction at pH 7.4 and 37°C was determined to be approximately 5, a value corresponding to a ΔF of -1000 cal (Cardini *et al.*, 1955). Using the known value of -6600 cal for the $\Delta F°$ of hydrolysis of sucrose (Barker and Hassid, 1951), the ΔF of hydrolysis of the α-D-glycosyl phosphate bond for UDP-D-glucose can be calculated to be -7600 cal.

Reaction (2), which results in the formation of sucrose phosphate, is catalyzed by another enzyme which utilizes D-fructose 6-phosphate as an acceptor instead of D-fructose. The equilibrium constant of this reaction was reported to be 3250 at 38°C and pH 7.5, indicating that the $\Delta F°$ of hydrolysis of the glycosidic bond of sucrose 6'-phosphate is only -2700 cal. It is surprising that the presence of the phosphate on the C-6 hydroxyl group of the D-fructofuranosyl moiety should cause such a large difference in $\Delta F°$ of hydrolysis of the disaccharide.

It should be noted that in reaction (1) the formation of sucrose involves incorporation of free D-fructose, which exists mainly in the pyranose configuration (about 80%), as D-fructofuranose. This conversion involves an additional several hundred calories. Since the hydroxyl group of C-6 of D-fructofuranose 6-phosphate is phosphorylated, thus stabilizing the furanose configuration, no such conversion need occur. This difference may partially account for the considerable difference in the ΔF values of the two reactions.

Experiments with a number of plants indicate that the enzyme which forms sucrose from UDP-D-glucose and D-fructose appears to be more prevalent than the one which is responsible for the formation of sucrose phosphate from the same sugar diphosphate nucleoside and D-fructose 6-phosphate. Sucrose phosphate is not readily obtainable from plants, as it is apparently hydrolyzed by a phosphatase to sucrose as soon as it is formed. However, Bird et al. (1965) found that when hexane-chloroform extracted tobacco leaf chloroplasts were used as an enzyme source with UDP-D-glucose and fructose 6-phosphate as substrates, sucrose 6-phosphate was formed. Haq and Hassid (1965) also showed that acetone-extracted chloroplasts from sugar cane leaves, in addition to forming sucrose from UDP-D-glucose and D-fructose, also utilized D-fructose 6-phosphate as an acceptor for the D-glucose, forming small amounts of sucrose phosphate. A phosphatase was also present which appeared to hydrolyze sucrose phosphate more readily than D-fructose 6-phosphate. Hatch (1964) also demonstrated the presence of enzymes that catalyze the synthesis and breakdown of sucrose phosphate from the stem and leaf tissue of sugar cane. Results of experiments in which ^{14}C-labeled D-glucose was supplied to plants have shown that the D-fructofuranosyl moiety of sucrose becomes highly labeled before any label appears in the free D-fructose pool, suggesting that the monosaccharide is not an intermediate in sucrose synthesis (Putman and Hassid, 1954). Furthermore, D-fructose 6-phosphate becomes labeled before sucrose, and small amounts of sucrose 6'-phosphate have also been detected among the labeled products (Buchanan, 1953; Bean et al., 1962). These results strongly indicate that sucrose 6'-phosphate is synthesized first and is sub-

sequently hydrolyzed to free sucrose. The results of Hatch (1964) lead
to the same conclusions. Such a pathway would be irreversible, because
of the hydrolytic step, and would account for the large accumulation of
sucrose in sugar beets, sugar cane, and some other plants.

Reaction (1) may serve an important function in degradation of sucrose. In spite of the fact that its equilibrium is in the direction of synthesis, complete breakdown of this disaccharide may occur if the resulting
UDP-D-glucose is used up in various other metabolic reactions.

RAFFINOSE

Sucrose in higher plants is often accompanied by higher molecular
weight oligosaccharides containing D-galactose units. The commonest of
these is the trisaccharide, raffinose, in which D-galactose is attached
through an α-glycosidic linkage to the C-6 position of the D-glucose
moiety of sucrose. Its constitution is therefore: O-α-D-galactopyranosyl-
$(1 \rightarrow 6)$-α-D-glucopyranosyl-β-D-fructofuranoside. Thus, it is logical to
assume that this sugar is formed from a nucleoside diphosphate-D-galac-
tose compound by a transfer of the D-galactosyl moiety to sucrose. However, attempts to synthesize raffinose in this way using enzymatic
preparations from germinated mung seedlings and other plants were not
successful. It appeared that if raffinose was formed, the germinated seedlings most probably contained glycosidases which degraded this trisaccharide.

Bourne et al. (1962) showed that raffinose could be synthesized by an
enzyme preparation from dormant broad bean (Vicia faba) seeds, using
a mixture of sucrose, α-D-galactose 1-phosphate, and uridine triphosphate
(UTP) as substrate. The dormant seeds apparently lacked active hydrolytic enzymes which interfered with the synthesis of raffinose. Using
UDP-D-galactose labeled with ^{14}C in the D-galactose moiety and sucrose
in the presence of an enzyme preparation from mature broad beans, a
direct transfer of D-galactose-^{14}C to sucrose could be effected resulting in
the production of raffinose (Pridham and Hassid, 1965). The amount of
[14]C-labeled D-galactose incorporated into the raffinose was 33 and 39%
after 1 and 2.5 hours, respectively.

Although the enzyme preparation was crude, the percentage of incorporation of label was relatively high, indicating that this mechanism
functions in maturing seeds. It is possible that D-galactose nucleoside
diphosphate derivatives with bases other than uridine are involved in
the synthesis of raffinose, but there is no information pertaining to this
point.

SYNTHESIS OF LACTOSE

The biosynthesis of lactose has previously been demonstrated to take place with particulate preparations from lactating guinea pig or bovine mammary glands (Watkins and Hassid, 1962) according to the following reaction:

$$\text{UDP-D-galactose} + \text{D-glucose} \xrightarrow[\text{transferase}]{\text{galactosyl}} \text{lactose} + \text{UDP}$$

Attempts to solubilize the preparations containing UDP-D-galactose D-glucose-β-4-galactosyl transferase were not successful. However, a soluble preparation was later obtained from bovine milk capable of synthesizing lactose from UDP-D-galactose and D-glucose by the same reaction (Babad and Hassid, 1964, 1965). Approximately 80% of the ^{14}C-labeled D-galactose can be incorporated into the lactose from the radioactive substrate by this preparation which has been purified 70-fold.

The enzyme appears to be specific for UDP-D-galactose and none of the ^{14}C-labeled D-galactosyl nucleotides containing bases other than uridine (guanosine, adenosine, cytidine, thymidine) can serve as substrate for the formation of lactose. The following compounds, which are listed in decreasing order, inhibit the activity of the enzyme: PP, ITP, UTP, UDP, P_i, UMP, TTP, and GTP.* No inhibition can be shown by ATP, CTP, or D-galactose. The pattern of enzyme inhibition appears to be in accord with the high enzyme affinity shown for UDP-D-galactose ($K_m = 5.0 \times 10^{-4} M$) and lower affinity shown for D-glucose ($K_m = 2.5 \times 10^{-2} M$).

α-D-Glucose 1-phosphate, α-D-galactose 1-phosphate, L-glucose, D-xylose, maltose, or α-D-methyl-D-glucoside will not act as an acceptor for the D-galactose moiety of UDP-D-galactose to form the corresponding oligosaccharides. However, N-acetyl-D-glucosamine is 25% as effective as D-glucose. The product appears to be O-β-D-galactosyl-N-acetyl-D-glucosamine. No reversal of the enzymatic reaction can be demonstrated when lactose and UDP are used as substrates for the formation of UDP-D-galactose and D-glucose.

The bovine milk lactose synthetase is activated by divalent cations. The enzyme shows maximum activation by Mn^{+2}. It has a temperature optimum of 42°C and a pH optimum of 7.5.

The existence of cellular material in milk appears to be the result of the disintegration of the glandular cells by enzymatic activity in the milk

---

* PP, pyrophosphate; ITP, iodine triphosphate; UTP, uridine triphosphate; UDP, uridine diphosphate; P_i, orthophosphate; UMP, uridine monophosphate; TTP, thymidine triphosphate; GTP, guanosine triphosphate.

during secretion. Apocrine secretion (decapitation of the apical portion of the alveolar cells) has been noted in the mammary glands during the secretory phase (Bloom and Fawcett, 1962; Mayer and Klein, 1961). The soluble lactose synthetase in milk can thus be presumed to have originated from the autolysis of the particulate enzyme which became part of the secretion of the mammary gland after disintegration of the alveolar cells.

The work of Wood and co-workers (Wood *et al.*, 1957, 1958, 1965; Hansen *et al.*, 1962) on lactose synthesis in the cow, or in cow udders, carried out *in vitro* agrees with that reported for cell-free preparation. Their experiments with ^{14}C-labeled sugars show that blood glucose is used directly for the formation of the glucose moiety of lactose, but is transformed to the galactosyl moiety only by way of hexose phosphate intermediates. All the enzymes required for the formation of UDP-galactose from glucose have been found in the mammary gland by a number of investigators (Smith and Mills, 1960; Maxwell *et al.*, 1955; Watkins and Hassid, 1962; Kittinger and Reithel, 1953).

CELLULOSE

It has been shown (Barber and Hassid, 1964) that mung beans (*Phaseolus aureus*) and peas contain an enzyme capable of forming ^{14}C-labeled guanosine diphosphate D-glucose (GDP-D-glucose) from guanosine triphosphate (GTP) and α-D-glucose 1-phosphate. Another enzyme (Elbein *et al.*, 1964; Barber *et al.*, 1964) was found to exist in rapidly grown root tissue of mung beans, peas, corn, squash, and string beans, which can utilize this radioactive sugar nucleotide as substrate for the formation of radioactive polysaccharide with chemical properties indistinguishable from those of natural cellulose. The cellulose-synthesizing enzyme is capable of transferring the activated D-glucose moiety from GDP-D-glucose-^{14}C to an unknown acceptor, forming the polysaccharide chain.

The enzyme system that polymerizes the D-glucose to cellulose shows a high degree of specificity for GDP-D-glucose. None of the ^{14}C-labeled glucosyl nucleotides containing bases other than guanosine (uridine, adenosine, cytidine, thymidine) serve as substrate for the formation of cellulose. At low enzyme concentration incorporation of radioactivity into cellulose is proportional to time and enzyme concentration over a 30-minute period. Analysis of the enzymatically synthesized compound shows that its chemical configuration is identical with that of cellulose. It has not been possible to separate the transferase activity from the endogenous acceptor. No stimulation of incorporation of D-glucose is observed upon addition of D-glucose, D-glucosamine, D-mannose, D-galactose, sucrose, cellobiose, soluble or insoluble cellodextrins, or swollen cellulose.

There is a pronounced stimulation of the incorporation of radioactivity from GDP-D-glucose-^{14}C into the insoluble material upon the addition of GDP-D-mannose, but this appears to involve the synthesis of polysaccharides other than cellulose.

When a suspension of the particulate enzyme is treated with twice its volume of a neutral saturated solution of $(NH_4)_2SO_4$, the particles lose their ability to catalyze the incorporation of radioactivity from GDP-D-glucose-^{14}C into cellulose. The activity can be restored by the addition of a boiled particle suspension to the reaction mixture or by the addition of any of the following cations: Co^{+2}, Mn^{+2}, Mg^{+2}, Zn^{+2} or Ca^{+2}. The optimal concentration of these cations is about 5×10^{-3} M.

The formation of cellulose in plants may be postulated to take place by a reaction in which guanosine diphosphate glucose is first formed as follows:

$$\text{Guanosine triphosphate} + \alpha\text{-D-glucose 1-phosphate} \xrightarrow[\hphantom{xxxxx}]{\text{pyrophosphorylase}}$$
$$\text{guanosine diphosphate D-glucose} + \text{pyrophosphate}$$

The polysaccharide is then formed by another enzyme (transferase), which catalyzes repetitive D-glucosyl transfers to an acceptor as shown by the following equation:

$$n(\text{Guanosine diphosphate D-glucose}) + \text{acceptor} \longrightarrow$$
$$\text{acceptor-}(\beta\text{-1,4-D-glucose})_n + n \text{ guanosine diphosphate}$$
$$(\text{cellulose})$$

PECTIN

The basic building unit of pectin, which is an important structural component of all higher plants, is known to be D-galactopyranosyluronic acid in which the linear skeleton of these units is connected by α-1,4-glycosidic linkages. The carboxyl groups of this compound are methylated to various degrees, and polygalacturonates are associated with other carbohydrates, mainly with D-galactan and L-araban (Beavan and Jones, 1947).

It has been previously shown (Neufeld and Feingold, 1961) that UDP-D-galacturonic acid exists in mung beans and that enzymes are present in this plant leading to the formation of this uronic acid nucleotide by the following pathway (Strominger and Mapson, 1957; Feingold et al., 1960):

$$\text{UDP-D-glucose} \xrightarrow{\text{dehydrogenase}} \text{UDP-D-glucuronic acid}$$
$$\text{epimerase} \quad \updownarrow$$
$$\text{UDP-D-galacturonic acid}$$

Furthermore, it has also been shown (Neufeld *et al.*, 1961) that a kinase is present in plants that catalyzes the formation of D-galacturonic acid 1-phosphate from D-galacturonic acid and ATP. UDP-D-Galacturonic acid is then formed from this uronic acid nucleotide and UTP by a pyrophosphorylase reaction. Thus, the same uronic acid nucleotide can be formed by an alternate mechanism. The sequence of these enzymatic reactions led to the hypothesis that UDP-D-galacturonic acid is a precursor of pectin. Recent experiments demonstrated this hypothesis to be correct.

It has been found (Villemez *et al.*, 1965) that a particulate preparation from mung bean (*Phaseolus aureus*) seedlings catalyzes the formation of radioactive polygalacturonic acid chain from UDP-D-galacturonic acid-^{14}C. The biosynthetic polygalacturonate could be completely hydrolyzed with *Penicillum chrysogenum* polygalacturonase to D-galacturonic acid-^{14}C. Partial degradation of this synthetic product with an exopolygalacturonic acid transeliminase produced radioactive unsaturated 4,5-digalacturonic acid. The action of this enzyme is known to be specific for the D-galacturonic acid chain. Approximately 65% of the labeled D-galacturonic acid from UDP-D-galacturonic acid-^{14}C could be incorporated into the polygalacturonic acid chain by this mung bean enzyme system.

Preliminary experiments indicate that the polygalacturonic acid chain is formed before methylation of the carboxyl groups occurs.

OBSERVATIONS ON THE SPECIFICITY OF SUGAR NUCLEOTIDE ENZYMES

The specificity of transglycosylases with regard to the particular base of the glycosyl nucleotide varies considerably. Thus, the transglycosylase from plants which produces cellulose is specific for GDP-D-glucose and shows a high degree of specificity. This transglycosylase will not form cellulose from D-glucose diphosphate nucleoside containing bases (uridine, adenosine, cytidine, thymidine) other than guanosine. Similarly, the soluble transglycosylase found in milk will catalyze the formation of lactose only from UDP-D-galactose and dUDP-D-galactose,* but not from ADP-D-galactose, GDP-D-galactose, CDP-D-galactose, or TDP-D-galactose.

The enzyme, glycogen synthetase, discovered by Leloir and Cardini

---

* dUDP, uridine diphosphate with deoxyribose for the sugar residue in place of ribose.

(1957) which synthesizes glycogen from UDP-D-glucose is not specific for this glycosyl nucleotide (Leloir, 1964a). This enzyme is also capable of synthesizing glycogen from ADP-D-glucose, but only at 50% of the rate obtained with UDP-D-glucose (Goldemberg, 1962). On the other hand, starch synthetase, which also utilizes UDP-D-glucose as substrate, will form starch from ADP-D-glucose at a rate which is ten times as rapid as that from UDP-D-glucose (de Fekete *et al.*, 1960). It is, therefore, obvious that these transglycosylases are not specific with regard to formation of polysaccharides containing α-D-glucose 1,4-linkages. Since ADP-D-glucose or a pyrophosphorylase which will synthesize this glucosyl nucleotide has not been found in animal tissues and since glycogen is formed from UDP-D-glucose at a higher rate than from ADP-D-glucose, it is most likely that this polysaccharide is formed *in vivo* from the UDP-D-glucose.

The situation pertaining to starch synthesis appears to be different. A pyrophosphorylase capable of synthesizing ADP-D-glucose from ATP and α-D-glucose 1-phosphate was found in wheat (Espada, 1962), and ATP-D-glucose was isolated from fresh maize seeds (Recondo *et al.*, 1963). An investigation by Kauss and Kandler (1962) of starch and sucrose synthesis from $^{14}CO_2$ in *Chlorella* revealed that the ADP-D-glucose pool was saturated earlier than the UDP-D-glucose pool and that starch took up ^{14}C earlier than sucrose. These experiments led them to conclude that *in vivo* ADP-D-glucose is involved in starch synthesis, whereas sucrose is synthesized from UDP-D-glucose. However, Leloir (1964a) is of the opinion that from "the scanty evidence available the answer is that both UPD-D-glucose and ADP-D-glucose are involved and probably in about equal proportions, because although UDP-D-glucose reacts more slowly (about one-tenth the rate) its concentration is higher (about 5–10 times). This would result in about the same rate of transfer." It is, therefore, likely that starch is synthesized *in vivo* from both sugar nucleotides.

A number of D-glucosyl derivatives, those of UDP, CDP, ADP, GDP, dTDP, and IDP,† and D-mannosyl derivatives of ATP, IDP, and GDP (Verachtert *et al.*, 1964) are synthesized from nucleosides triphosphates, and sugar 1-phosphates. All these glucosyl derivatives can also be synthesized by plant preparations (Barber and Hassid, 1964). As pointed out by Neufeld and Ginsburg (1965), the significance of these numerous phosphorylase activities that produce the various sugar diphosphate nucleosides is not clear. They cite the following examples: dTDP-D-glucose pyrophosphorylase from bacteria also inhibits dTDP-D-glucosamine pyro-

---

† dTDP, thymidine diphosphate with deoxyribose for the sugar residue in place of ribose; IDP, iodine diphosphate.

phosphorylase activity (Melo and Glaser, 1965); the assignment of a defi-
nite function to this enzyme is, therefore, not possible at this time.
Extracts of hog gastric mucosa catalyze the synthesis of dTDP-N-acetyl-
D-glucosamine and its epimerization to dTDP-N-acetyl D-galactosamine.
However, experiments *in vivo* do not indicate that these reactions have
any physiological significance (Kornfeld *et al.*, 1964).

Barber (1962) reported the presence of an enzyme in mung beans
(*Phaseolus aureus*) that will catalyze the transfer of L-rhamnosyl groups
from TDP-L-rhamnose to 3-quercetin-β-D-glucoside to form rutin. He subsequently found (Barber, 1963) that mung bean extracts could not synthesize TDP-L-rhamnose, but would synthesize UDP-L-rhamnose; both
nucleotides could be used by the glycosyl transferase to form rutin. It,
therefore, appears that although the glycosyl transferase has a rather low
degree of specificity, the physiological rhamnosyl donor is probably
UDP-L-rhamnose.

Lin (1965) showed the presence of the following sugar diphosphate
nucleosides in the marine brown alga, *Fucus gardneri* Silva: GDP-D-
mannose, GDP-D-mannuronic acid, GDP-L-guluronic acid, GDP-L-galactose, and a polymer of L-fucose. He demonstrated that the GDP-D-mannuronic acid is derived from GDP-D-mannose by a series of enzymatic
reactions, while the GDP-L-galactose and the L-fucose polymer are possible derivatives of the same D-mannose diphosphate nucleoside by known
enzymatic reactions. It is interesting to note that whereas the seaweed
polysaccharides (alginic acid and fucoidin) appear to be derived by a
series of various reactions from the common precursor, GDP-D-mannose,
most of the polysaccharide sugar constituents of higher plants, namely,
D-galactose, D-glucuronic and D-galacturonic acids, D-xylose, and L-arabi-
nose are derived from UDP-D-glucose (Hassid *et al.*, 1959; Leloir, 1964*b*).

REFERENCES

Ankel, A., and Feingold, D. S. (1965). *Biochemistry* **4**, 2468.
Ankel, A., and Feingold, D. S. (1966). *Biochemistry* **5**, 182.
Ayers, W. A. (1959). *J. Biol. Chem.* **234**, 2819.
Babad, H., and Hassid, W. Z. (1964). *J. Biol. Chem.* **239**, PC 947.
Babad, H., and Hassid, W. Z. (1965). *Science* **150**, 968.
Barber, G. A. (1962). *Biochemistry* **1**, 463.
Barber, G. A. (1963). *Arch. Biochem. Biophys.* **103**, 276.
Barber, G. A., and Hasid, W. Z. (1964). *Biochim. Biophys. Acta* **86**, 397.
Barber, G. A., Elbein, A. D., and Hassid, W. Z. (1964). *J. Biol. Chem.* **239**, 4056.
Barker, H. A., and Hassid, W. Z. (1951). *In* "Bacterial Physiology" (C. H. Werk-
    man and P. W. Wilson, eds.), p. 528. Academic Press, New York.

Bean, R. C., Barr, B. K., Welch, H. V., and Porter, G. G. (1962). *Arch. Biochem. Biophys.* **96**, 524.

Beavan, G. H., and Jones, J. K. N. (1947). *J. Chem. Soc.* p. 1218.

Bird, I. F., Porter, H. K., and Stocking, C. R. (1965). *Biochim. Biophys. Acta* **100**, 366.

Bloom, W., and Fawcett, D. W. (1962). "A Textbook of Histology" (8th Edition), p. 632. Saunders, Philadelphia, Pennsylvania.

Bourne, E. J., Pridham, J. B., and Walter, M. W. (1962). *Biochem. J.* **82**, 44P.

Buchanan, J. G. (1953). *Arch. Biochem. Biophys.* **44**, 140.

Cardini, C. E., Leloir, L. F., and Chiriboga, J. (1955). *J. Biol. Chem.* **214**, 149.

Castanera, E. G., and Hassid, W. Z. (1965). *Arch. Biochem. Biophys.* **110**, 462.

Cori, C. F., and Cori, G. T. (1936). *Proc. Exptl. Biol. Med.* **34**, 702.

Cori, G. T., and Cori, C. F. (1937). *Proc. Exptl. Biol. Med.* **36**, 119.

Cori, G. T., and Cori, C. F. (1940). *J. Biol. Chem.* **135**, 733.

Dedonder, R. A. (1960). *Bull. Soc. Chim. Biol.* **42**, 1748.

de Fekete, M. A. R., Leloir, L. F., and Cardini, C. E. (1960). *Nature* **187**, 918.

de Robichon-Szulmajster, H. (1961). *J. Mol. Biol.* **3**, 253.

Elbein, A. D., Barber, G. A., and Hassid, W. Z. (1964). *J. Am. Chem. Soc.* **86**, 309.

Espada, J. (1962). *J. Biol. Chem.* **237**, 3577.

Feingold, D. S., Neufeld, E. F., and Hassid, W. Z. (1960). *J. Biol. Chem.* **235**, 910.

Fitting, C., and Doudoroff, M. (1952). *J. Biol. Chem.* **199**, 153.

Ginsburg, V. (1960). *J. Biol. Chem.* **235**, 2196.

Ginsburg, V. (1961). *J. Biol. Chem.* **236**, 2389.

Glaser, L., and Kornfeld, S. (1961). *J. Biol. Chem.* **236**, 1795.

Goldemberg, S. H. (1962). *Biochim. Biophys. Acta* **56**, 357.

Hanes, C. S. (1940). *Proc. Roy. Soc.* (*London*) **B128**, 421.

Hanes, C. S. (1941). *Proc. Roy. Soc.* (*London*) **B129**, 174.

Hansen, R. G., Wood, H. G., Peeters, G. J., Jacobsen, B., and Wilken, J. (1962). *J. Biol. Chem.* **237**, 1037.

Haq, S., and Hassid, W. Z. (1965). *Plant Physiol.* **40**, 591.

Hassid, W. Z., and Neufeld, E. F. (1962). *In* "The Enzymes" (P. D. Boyer, H. Lardy, and K. Myrbäck, eds.), Vol. 6, p. 277. Academic Press, New York.

Hassid, W. Z., Doudoroff, M., and Barker, H. A. (1944). *J. Am. Chem. Soc.* **66**, 1416.

Hassid, W. Z., Neufeld, E. F., and Feingold, D. S. (1959). *Proc. Natl. Acad. Sci. U.S.* **45**, 905.

Hatch, M. D. (1964). *Biochem. J.* **93**, 521.

Heath, E. C., and Elbein, A. D. (1962). *Proc. Natl. Acad. Sci. U.S.* **48**, 1209.

Hestrin, S., Feingold, D. S., and Avigad, G. (1956). *Biochem. J.* **64**, 340.

Jacobson, B., and Davidson, E. A. (1963). *Biochim. Biophys. Acta* **73**, 145.

Kauss, H., and Kandler, O. (1962). *Z. Naturforsch.* **17b**, 858.

Kittinger, G. W., and Reithel, F. J. (1953). *J. Biol. Chem.* **205**, 527.

Mayer, G., and Klein, M. (1961). *In* "Milk: The Mammary Gland and Its Secretion," (Kon, S. K., and Cowie, A. T., eds.) Vol. I, p. 47. Academic Press, New York.

Kornfeld, R., Kornfeld, S., and Ginsburg, V. (1964). *Biochem. Biophys. Res. Commun.* **17**, 578.

Leloir, L. F. (1951). *Arch. Biochem.* **33**, 186.

Leloir, L. F. (1956). *Proc. Intern. Congr. Biochem., 3rd, Brussels, 1955* p. 151.

Leloir, L. F. (1964a). *Biochem. J.* **91**, 1.

Leloir, L. F. (1964b). *Proc. Intern. Congr. Biochem., 6th, New York, 1964* p. 15.

Leloir, L. F., and Cardini, C. E. (1955). *J. Biol. Chem.* **214**, 157.

Leloir, L. F., and Cardini, C. E. (1957). *J. Am. Chem. Soc.* **79**, 6340.

Lin, Tsau-Yen (1965). A study of nucleotide-linked uronic acids in plants. Ph.D. Thesis, University of California.

Lipmann, F. (1941). *Advan. Enzymol.* **1**, 99.

Marechal, L. R., and Goldemberg, S. H. (1963). *Biochem. Biophys. Res. Commun.* **13**, 106.

Maxwell, E. S. (1957). *J. Biol. Chem.* **229**, 139.

Maxwell, E. S., and de Robichon-Szulmajster, H. (1960). *J. Biol. Chem.* **235**, 308.

Maxwell, E. S., Kalckar, H. M., and Burton, R. M. (1955). *Biochim. Biophys. Acta* **18**, 444.

Maxwell, E. S., de Robichon-Szulmajster, H., and Kalckar, H. M. (1958). *Arch. Biochem. Biophys.* **78**, 407.

Melo, A., and Glaser, L. (1965). *J. Biol. Chem.* **240**, 398.

Munch-Petersen, A., Kalckar, H. M., Culoto, E., and Smith, E. E. B. (1953). *Nature* **172**, 1037.

Neufeld, E. F., and Feingold, D. S. (1961). *Biochim. Biophys. Acta* **53**, 589.

Neufeld, E. F., and Ginsburg, V. (1965). *Ann. Rev. Biochem.* **34**, 297.

Neufeld, E. F., and Hassid, W. Z. (1963). *Advan. Carbohydrate Chem.* **18**, 309.

Neufeld, E. F., Feingold, D. S., and Hassid, W. Z. (1958). *J. Am. Chem. Soc.* **80**, 4430.

Neufeld, E. F., Feingold, D. S., Ilves, S. M., Kessler, G., and Hassid, W. Z. (1961). *J. Biol. Chem.* **236**, 3102.

Nikaido, H. (1962). *Biochim. Biophys. Acta* **48**, 460.

Nikaido, H., and Jokura, K. (1961). *Biochem. Biophys. Res. Commun.* **6**, 304.

Okazaki, R., Okazaki, T., Strominger, J. L., and Michelson, M. A. (1962). *J. Biol. Chem.* **237**, 3014.

Park, J. T. (1952). *J. Biol. Chem.* **194**, 877, 885, 897.

Pazur, J. H., and Shuey, E. W. (1961). *J. Biol. Chem.* **236**, 1780.

Pridham, J. B., and Hassid, W. Z. (1965). *Plant Physiol.* **40**, 984.

Putman, E. W., and Hassid, W. Z. (1954). *J. Biol. Chem.* **207**, 885.

Recondo, E., Dankert, M., and Leloir, L. F. (1963). *Biochem. Biophys. Res. Commun.* **12**, 204.

Roseman, S. (1962a). *Proc. Natl. Acad. Sci. U.S.* **48**, 437.

Roseman, S. (1962b). *Federation Proc.* **21**, 1075.

Smith, E. E. B., and Mills, G. T. (1960). *Biochim. Biophys. Acta* **18**, 152.

Stacey, M., and Barker, S. A. (1960a). "Polysaccharides of Microorganisms," p. 136. Oxford Univ. Press (Clarendon), London and New York.

Stacey, M., and Barker, S. A. (1960b). "Polysaccharides of Microorganisms," p. 92. Oxford Univ. Press (Clarendon), London and New York.

Strominger, J. L., and Mapson, L. W. (1957). *Biochem. J.* **66**, 567.

Su, C. J., and Hassid, W. Z. (1962). *Biochemistry* **1**, 468.

Verachtert, H., Bass, S. T., and Hansen, R. G. (1964). *Biochem. Biophys. Res. Commun.* **15**, 158.

Villemez, C. L., Lin, T. Y., and Hassid, W. Z. (1965). *Proc. Natl. Acad. Sci. U.S.* **54**, 1626.

Watkins, W. M., and Hassid, W. Z. (1962). *J. Biol. Chem.* **237**, 1432.

Warren, L., and Blacklow, R. S. (1962). *Biochem. Biophys. Res. Commun.* **7**, 433.

Wiesmeyer, H., and Jourdian, E. (1961). *Anal. Biochem.* **2**, 281.

Wilson, D. B., and Hogness, D. S. (1964). *J. Biol. Chem.* **239**, 2469.

Wood, H. G., Shambye, P., and Peeters, G. J. (1957). *J. Biol. Chem.* **226**, 1023.

Wood, H. G., Joffe, S., Gillespie, R., Hansen, R. G., and Hardenbrook, H. (1958). *J. Biol. Chem.* **233**, 1264.

Wood, H. G., Peeters, G. J., Verbeke, R., Lauryssens, M., and Jacobson, B. (1965). *Biochem. J.* **96**, 607.

Nucleotides, Teichoic Acids, and Bacterial Cell Walls

James Baddiley

INTRODUCTION

It was with great pleasure that I accepted the honor of being invited to contribute to a volume dedicated to Fritz Lipmann, a man for whom I have the greatest respect both as a scientist and friend. In this chapter we intend to show how his theories on energy relationships and phosphate bonds influenced the work in my laboratory; in particular, it is hoped to illustrate the manner whereby events in one field of research can affect progress in others. The author asks to be forgiven for the occasional inclusion of a little personal biographical detail, as it would be difficult to give a logical account without reference to such matters.

At a time when space is such an important consideration in the publication of scientific journals and books it is rare that the opportunity arises for the publication of essays. This is unfortunate, because in an essay one can describe the circumstances leading to discoveries and discuss them freely in a historical context. Occasionally this is valuable, as it shows to others how quite weak analogies and distant relationships between research programs are sometimes important in directing effort along fruitful lines; thus it is possible to reveal how seemingly unrelated lines of work may have developed from each other through a logical process of reasoning. Essays are also valuable for the exposition of views rather than facts and conclusions; in this way it is possible to speculate, with the reasonable expectation that the author will be forgiven if he is shown later to be wrong.

When Lipmann's celebrated article appeared I was starting research with A. R. Todd, then at the University of Manchester. The aim at the

371

time was to attempt the first chemical synthesis of a nucleoside, and although the prospect of a synthesis of adenosine triphosphate (ATP) and other nucleotides was also an objective, much exploratory work on phosphorylation and the development of techniques for the synthesis, purification, and characterization of very labile pyrophosphate esters was required before progress could be made.

It would be incorrect to claim that the concept of the special energy characteristics of ATP and related compounds had a direct effect on the initial efforts toward a chemical synthesis of such nucleotides in Todd's laboratory, as the program had been started much earlier. Nevertheless, recognition of the importance of this class of compounds increased steadily and their true significance had been revealed by the time we had accomplished the first chemical synthesis of adenosine diphosphate (ADP) and ATP.

A consequence of this was that the chemists in Manchester and later in Cambridge developed an interest in biochemistry, particularly in intermediary metabolism and biosynthesis. This had a marked effect on the subsequent work of the department in Cambridge and of several individuals who moved later to other places. The result was the growth of a small but steadily increasing body of researchers who had a full formal chemical training but whose interests have been as much in biochemistry as they have been in organic chemistry. In my own case the stimulus was strengthened by a brief but most enjoyable and intellectually profitable period in Lipmann's laboratory in 1954, and although the researches described in this article are not directly concerned with the energetics of metabolic processes or biosynthesis, there is nevertheless a historical connection with the earlier work.

STUDIES ON NUCLEOTIDES

Lipmann's interests led him to study acylation reactions in cell-free systems, and one important result of this was the discovery of coenzyme A. Despite the considerable difficulty in working with small amounts of impure material he and his colleagues were able to show that the coenzyme was a derivative of pantothenic acid containing adenine, sulfur, and phosphate (Lipmann *et al.*, 1947). He visited Cambridge in 1949 and pointed out the need for a further chemical study of this compound. At that time I was about to move to the Lister Institute of Preventive Medicine in London and so the first project was a synthesis of the isomeric monophosphates and a cyclic phosphate of pantothenic acid. During this work close contact was maintained with the group in Boston and samples of natural and synthetic materials were freely exchanged. It was found that pantothenic acid 4'-phosphate was a degradation product of the coenzyme, and the location of one of the three phosphates was thus established (Baddiley and Thain, 1951a,b).

The discovery of coenzyme A was a landmark in biochemistry and its detailed structure aroused much interest. Work on it and related natural derivatives was pursued with vigor in a number of laboratories and significant contributors included Novelli, Snell, Kaplan, Cheldelin, Strong, Hoagland, and their many associates. A structure was proposed (Baddiley and Thain, 1951b), but the final detail, the location of the phosphomonoester group at the 3'- rather than the 2'-position, required the development of a novel enzymatic method (Wang et al., 1954). Confirmation of some of the structural features was obtained by a chemical synthesis of pantetheine 4'-phosphate (Baddiley and Thain, 1952, 1953) and a partial enzymatic synthesis of the coenzyme itself from this and ATP (Hoagland and Novelli, 1954; Levintow and Novelli, 1954).

In 1954 a joint investigation was made with Mathias, Hughes, and Pierpoint on the conversion of pantothenic acid into coenzyme A in *Lactobacillus arabinosus*. It was found that the organism readily produced pantothenic acid 4'-phosphate and it was suggested, contrary to views at the time, that the biosynthesis of the coenzyme proceeded through this phosphate (Pierpoint et al., 1955). This mechanism was established later as one of the main routes for the biosynthesis of coenzyme A (Brown, 1959). The isolation of pantothenic acid 4'-phosphate from extracts of the bacteria was made difficult by the presence of relatively large amounts of nucleotides, and during the development of suitable separation procedures a study of the nucleotides was undertaken. This almost casual investigation was a turning point and later developed into an extensive study of bacterial walls and problems of biosynthesis. It is noteworthy that when the study of the nucleotides was started effective chromatographic separation techniques were only recently available and had not been widely applied to bacterial nucleotides. In fact, no nucleotides containing cytosine, other than ribonucleic acid (RNA) itself, had been found in cell extracts. Consequently, the discovery of cytosine and cytidine in hydrolysates of our nucleotide mixture suggested that a more detailed examination would be profitable.

Fractionation of the nucleotides and careful study of the purified material led to the discovery of small amounts of two new cytidine derivatives, cytidine diphosphate (CDP)-glycerol (I) and CDP-ribitol

(II) (Baddiley *et al.*, 1956). This discovery was fundamental in the reasoning which culminated in the discovery of the teichoic acids, and it is noteworthy that had the work on the biosynthesis of coenzyme A been carried out a year later the discovery of the cytidine derivatives would probably not have been made. In the following year the presence of mono-, di-, and triphosphates of the four common ribonucleosides, including those of cytidine, was reported in a number of tissue extracts and the detection of cytidine in hydrolysates from the *Lactobacillus* might not have aroused our interest had it followed this report.

(I)   (II)

This is not the place to discuss the detailed evidence for the structure of the two nucleotides (for a review, see Baddiley and Buchanan, 1958). A feature of this work, however has been the close attention to details of stereochemistry of polyol phosphate residues in the nucleotides and polymers, as it was believed that, despite the difficulties in working on a very small scale, the results would be useful in later problems of their biosynthesis. The glycerol phosphate residue was shown to be the common L-glycerol 3-phosphate, but as the natural occurrence of ribitol phosphates had not been noted previously a special procedure had to be developed in order to show that CDP-ribitol was a derivative of D-ribitol 5-phosphate.

TEICHOIC ACIDS

From the structures of the nucleotides and from a general considera-tion of the function of nucleoside diphosphate sugars it seemed likely that the cytidine compounds were concerned in metabolic processes in-volving glycerol and ribitol phosphates. However, neither nucleotide could easily be fitted into any of the known or presumed intermediary processes of polyol or sugar phosphate metabolism, and an analogy was sought in the very recently discovered role of nucleotides in the biosynthesis of polysaccharides. It was argued that bacteria might produce polymers containing glycerol or ribitol phosphate residues and that the cytidine derivatives would thus be precursors, as uridine diphosphate (UDP)-glucose had been shown to be a precursor of starch. The correctness of this view was established by the demonstration that water-soluble polymers containing these residues occur in many bacteria (Armstrong *et al.*, 1958); however, a direct demonstration of the biosynthesis of the polymers from the nucleotides in a cell-free system from bacteria was achieved only recently. Thus, the history of the teichoic acids is unusual in that their discovery followed the discovery of their precursors. It is much commoner for precursors, usually present in only very small amounts under normal conditions, to be identified much later than the more abundant final products.

A possible place for the occurrence of these polymers was in the walls of bacteria, and examination of a number of different preparations revealed their presence in substantial amounts (up to 50% of the dry weight) in walls from many gram-positive bacteria. For this reason they were called teichoic acids (τειχδς = wall, Greek). It was shown later that they also occur elsewhere in the organisms and it could be argued that the name is somewhat misleading. If so, they are in good company because the nucleic acids, for example, are by no means confined to cell nuclei.

The occurrence, structure, biosynthesis, and location of teichoic acids have been active subjects of investigation for the last 5 years. Much has been published in these fields which have been reviewed in some detail elsewhere (Archibald and Baddiley, 1966); in this article attention will be directed to more general points. There are two types of teichoic acids, those containing ribitol and those containing glycerol. No other polyols are found but it now seems likely that both glycerol and ribitol may occur together in a teichoic acid from a species of *Streptomyces* (B. Bews, unpublished observations, 1966). In typical cases glycerol or ribitol units are joined together through phosphodiester linkages to form a chain, and sugars and D-alanine ester residues are attached to hydroxyl groups on the polyols. The general structures (III) and (IV) are typical of teichoic acids from many bacteria. Marked variations occur in the nature and number of glycosidic residues but so far only the sugars, glucose, N-acetylglucosamine, N-acetylgalactosamine, galactose, and possibly mannose, have been found in these compounds. On the other hand, both α- and β-glycosidic linkages and mono-, di-, or trisaccharide units may be present. Although preparations from a given strain of organism are usually reasonably constant in composition, variations in both the proportion of sugar residues and the ratio of α:β linkages have been noted. The sugar content is influenced to some extent by growth conditions and the composition of the medium, but the method of isolation can be important, i.e., until recently they were usually isolated by extraction from walls or cells with cold dilute trichloroacetic acid solution

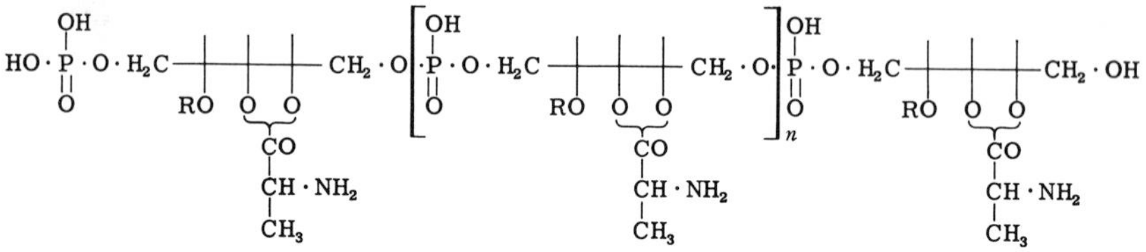

(III)

Bacillus subtilis wall (R = β-glucosyl; n = 7) (Armstrong *et al.*, 1961)

Staphylococcus aureus H (R = α- or β-*N*-acetylglucosaminyl; n = 6) (Baddiley *et al.*, 1962)

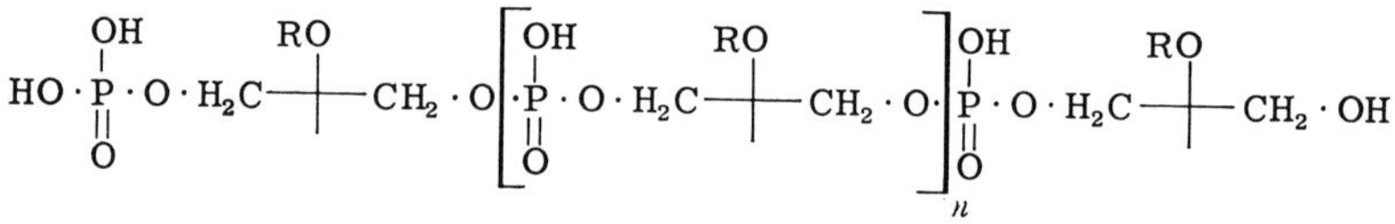

(IV)

Lactobacillus arabinosus membrane (R = α-glucosyl or alanine)
(Critchley *et al.*, 1962)

Staphylococcus lactis 7944 wall (R = α-*N*-acetylgalactosaminyl or alanine)
(Ellwood *et al.*, 1963)

Streptococcus faecium membrane (R = alanyl-α-kojibiosyl or kojitriosyl)
(Wicken and Baddiley, 1963)

and this can cause loss of sugar if acidic conditions are prolonged. Even so, wide variations in the number of sugar residues occur in teichoic acids from different organisms. In some cases the sugar content is high, e.g., in the group-specific teichoic acid from *Streptococcus faecium* (Group D) there is a trisaccharide on all or most of the glycerol residues, whereas others may contain little or no sugar.

It seems that regularity in structure differs in different cases. All ribitol teichoic acids have sugar substituents at the 4-position in D-ribitol 5-phosphate residues, and where the sugar:ribitol ratio is unity a highly regular structure is apparent. On the other hand, in a case where the sugar content is higher (*L. arabinosus*) (Archibald *et al.*, 1961*b*) it is not yet known whether mono- and diglycosyl substituents alternate regularly along the chain. Usually only one type of glycosidic linkage is found in a teichoic acid from a single strain of organism, but particularly in the case of strains of *Staphylococcus aureus* both α and β linkages can occur together. In this case a serological study (Torii *et al.*, 1964) has shown that the material is a mixture containing molecules in which all the glycosidic linkages have the α configuration and others which have only β linkages. In the glycerol teichoic acids examples have been found in which sugar residues occur regularly on each third glycerol and in others the distribution is more or less random.

In contrast to the structural diversity of the sugar residues, little variety occurs in the amino acid and in the position of the phosphate ester groups. In most cases the amino acid is entirely alanine and this is exclusively the D-isomer; exceptions are the polymer in a species of *Streptomyces* where succinic ester groups have been found (Naumova *et al.*, 1963) and the glycerol teichoic acid from a *Streptococcus* which contains, in addition to D-alanine, a very small proportion of L-lysine ester groups (Wicken and Baddiley, 1963). Occasionally teichoic acids lacking amino acids have been obtained, but it is not known whether loss of a small number of such groups occurred during isolation. The alanine ester residues are commonly attached through hydroxyl groups on the glycerol or ribitol, but more recently examples have been found in which sugar hydroxyl groups are esterified. A noteworthy feature of the alanine ester groups is their very great lability, particularly toward ammonia or hydroxylamine; however, in those cases where the alanine is attached to sugar rather than polyol the linkage is more stable.

In the ribitol teichoic acids phosphodiester groups join positions 1 and 5 in the ribitol of adjacent units. There are no exceptions so far to this rule; it has been shown, however, that in some of the pneumococcus capsular materials, which are structurally similar to teichoic acids, the phosphodiester linkages are between ribitol and a hydroxyl on a sugar residue attached to a neighboring ribitol. Most of the glycerol teichoic acids have phosphodiester groups joining positions 1 and 3 on glycerol, the sugar or alanine usually occupying position 2. Exceptions are known in which the sugar occupies position 1; in one of these phosphodiester groups join positions 2 and 3 on adjacent glycerol residues (A. J. Wicken, personal communication, 1966), whereas in the other cases it is not known whether the structure is similar or whether the linkages are between glycerol and a hydroxyl on the sugar of an adjacent unit. A particularly interesting exception is the polymer (V) from the walls of a strain of *Staphylococcus lactis*, where the sugar is joined through phosphate at its 1-position to glycerol (Archibald *et al.*, 1965).

$$CH_3$$
$$CH_2 \cdot O \cdot CO \cdot CH \cdot NH_2$$
$$O$$
$$OH \qquad OH$$
$$---O \qquad O \cdot P \cdot O \cdot H_2C$$
$$NHAc \quad O \quad HO$$
$$OH$$
$$CH_2 \cdot O \cdot P ---$$
$$O$$

(V)

Work on the detailed structure of teichoic acids was assisted considerably by knowledge of the chemistry of macromolecules containing phosphodiester and glycosidic linkages obtained during work on the nucleic acids. The similarities between teichoic and nucleic acids are many. Both are hydrolysed by acid and alkali through mechanisms involving the formation of intermediate cyclic phosphates where a hydroxyl adjacent to the phosphate ester group participates. Thus, most of the phosphodiester groups in a teichoic acid are hydrolysed by alkali to a mixture of isomeric phosphomonoesters, the process being analogous to the hydrolysis of ribonucleic acid (RNA) to isomeric nucleotides. Complete removal of phosphate from these products is easily achieved by the action of a phosphatase, a process leading to the formation of glycosides of glycerol or ribitol and which is similar to the dephosphorylation of nucleotides to give nucleosides. Another procedure with applications in nucleic acid chemistry has been used to demonstrate the presence of 1.3-linkages on glycerol; this involves successive treatment of the polymer with phosphomonoesterase, periodate, and phenylhydrazine in order to achieve a stepwise removal of glycerol phosphate residues from both ends of the chain. Although this procedure has been used mainly in phospholipid chemistry, it is related to the periodate-base method for stepwise degradation of oligonucleotides.

Two structural problems, the chain length of teichoic acids and the nature of their linkage to the rigid component (glycosaminopeptide) of the wall, have attracted some attention recently and these have been subjects of a certain amount of misunderstanding. Evidence for chain length of the ribitol phosphate polymers comes from two main sources, determination of the ratio of terminal phosphomonoester to total phosphate and a comparison of these values with those for the amount of terminal glycol group (by periodate oxidation to formaldehyde) at the other end of the molecule. Good agreement was obtained in the two independent determinations using purified material, and it was concluded that the molecules were homogeneous and of the sizes indicated in structure (III). However, some degradation by hydrolysis of phosphodiester groups would occur during extraction if acidic conditions were prolonged, and it has been suggested (Strominger and Ghuysen, 1963) that the native polymers are larger than we have claimed. On the other hand, the preparations examined earlier were almost certainly undegraded, as degradation by acid hydrolysis would proceed by a cyclic mechanism and this would give rise to discrepancies between values for phosphomonoester and for glycol end groups. Moreover, examination of chain length of polymer in the intact walls by determination of formaldehyde from periodate oxidation of walls and from hydrolysis of phosphomonoesters at pH 4 confirmed the original values (Hay et al., 1965). It has been found recently that quantitative extraction can be achieved at pH 7 with dilute solutions of phenylhydrazine or better dimethylhydrazine and these conditions cause no degradation. Material prepared in this way still has a chain length similar to that of teichoic acid prepared by other methods. Nevertheless, there is reason to believe that the reported chain lengths of some glycerol teichoic acids might be lower after isolation than they are in the walls themselves.

Although there has been discussion from time to time about the possible occurrence of covalent linkage between teichoic acids and the glycosaminopeptide in walls, little evidence for linkage has been available until recently. Suggestions that the amino groups of alanine ester residues are joined through peptide linkages to glycosaminopeptide have been shown to be incorrect (Archibald et al., 1961a), and it was not until enzymatically prepared soluble wall fractions had been examined that it became apparent that some form of covalent linkage must exist. As these soluble preparations contain no phosphomonoester groups it is concluded that the linkage involves the terminal phosphate in the teichoic acid chain (Ghuysen et al., 1965). However, the linkage is more labile toward acid than is a normal phosphodiester and on hydrolysis the phosphorus is retained by the teichoic acid, i.e., it does not hydrolyse through a cyclic phosphate mechanism. The linkage is also unstable toward alkali under moderate conditions and toward dilute dimethylhydrazine at pH 7. These properties are clearly not those of a normal phosphodiester, nor even one attached to the 1-position of a sugar residue, but would be consistent with a phosphoramidate involving the amino group at the 2-position of a reducing end of the glycosaminopeptide (VI) (Hay et al., 1965; Archibald and Baddiley,

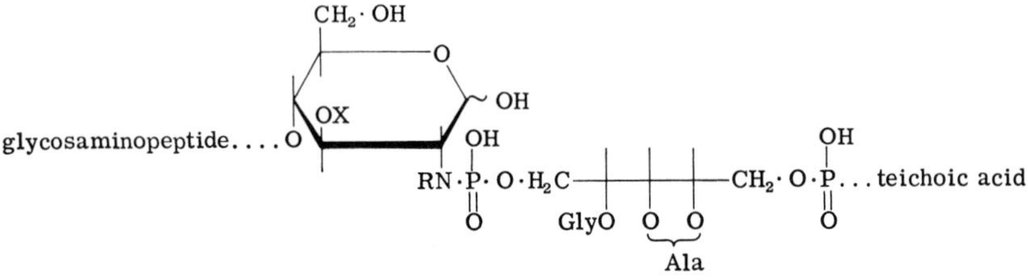

(VI)

X = H or peptide
Gly = sugar
R = H or $CH_3 \cdot CO$

1965). However, a phosphoramidate involving amide nitrogen of one of the peptide residues cannot be excluded, and the possibility that the linkage involves a pyrophosphate group is under consideration.

BIOSYNTHESIS AND FUNCTION OF TEICHOIC ACIDS

Increasing attention has been given to the biosynthesis, metabolism, properties, location, and function of this new group of natural polymers. Their discovery was based on certain assumptions about their biosynthesis, and the formation of the nucleotides from polyol phosphates was established at an early stage (Shaw, 1962). Only relatively recently has it been shown in cell-free systems that CDP-glycerol and CDP-ribitol donate their polyol phosphate residues to give a polymer chain (Burger and Glaser, 1964; Glaser, 1964). UDP-Sugar compounds are then able to donate sugar residues (Nathenson and Strominger, 1963) and it is assumed but not yet shown that the D-alanine-activating enzyme system (requiring ATP) donates the alanine ester residues (Baddiley and Neuhaus, 1960). Some of the details of the process are still obscure and there are indications that the biosynthesis of teichoic acids and glycosaminopeptides could be mutually interdependent. For example, the inhibition of biosynthesis of glycosaminopeptide caused by the action of penicillin is reflected in a simultaneous inhibition or interference in the formation of teichoic acid (Rogers and Garrett, 1963). Further developments in this field are awaited with interest. The unusual teichoic acid (V) is of particular interest, because in this case sugar residues, phosphate, and glycerol must be added to the growing polymer in successive and regular sequence. Moreover, the stereochemistry of the polymer indicates that if CDP-glycerol is a precursor then the glycerol phosphate unit donated must be represented by that one attached to the 4-position on the glucosamine; the other phosphate group attached to glycerol must originate elsewhere. It would be most interesting to know whether a nucleoside diphosphate N-acetylglucosamine donates amino sugar together with phosphate attached to its 1-position.

The walls of gram-positive bacteria often contain a high proportion of either the glycerol or ribitol polymers, but in some cases such compounds are absent. On the other hand, very nearly all bacteria examined possess a glycerol teichoic acid that can be sedimented by high-speed centrifugation of the supernatant from disrupted organisms. These so-called "intracellular" teichoic acids are always glycerol derivatives and are probably present in all gram-positive bacteria. They occur in amounts comparable with the wall compounds and so together account for a significant proportion (5–10%) of the weight of the dry organisms. Studies with protoplasts, using both chemical (Hay et al., 1963) and serological (Smith and Shattock, 1964; Shockman and Slade, 1964) techniques, indicate that they occur in the region between the wall and the protoplast membrane, attached at least in part to the membrane. For this reason we now call them "membrane teichoic acids."

Many teichoic acids are serologically active and often they constitute the group-specific components of bacteria. Consequently, their study has assisted in both taxonomy and the general understanding of the immunological properties of microorganisms, and progress has been made in relating their structural features with serological specificity. Nevertheless, these serological properties, although important and interesting, are unlikely to be related to the role of the polymers in the normal functioning of organisms. It does seem probable that they are essential, particularly in view of the widespread occurrence of membrane teichoic acids in gram-positive bacteria; and it is now recognized that the region of the membrane is of great importance in biosynthetic and metabolic activities as well as in transport and general ionic control. It could be argued, however, that the almost complete absence of reports of their occurrence in gram-negative bacteria suggests that they may be dispensable. This may be misleading, as aminoacyl phospholipids are abundant in such organisms and these might have a function comparable to the teichoic acids. It is also logical to assume that the energy required for the production and maintenance of substantial amounts of compounds containing large numbers of highly reactive groups would not be wasted by the cell.

Possible functions include the control of the passage of ions between the cell and the surrounding medium or the control of formation of the wall itself. Their role in ion regulation is suggested by their location and the structural arrangement of regularly alternating positive and negative charges. Such a role is also consistent with the admittedly inadequate knowledge of the amounts found in cells; gram-positive organisms containing large amounts of teichoic acids are particularly able to survive high salt concentrations in the medium (Archibald et al., 1961a). Another possibly significant observation is that the proportion of alanine ester to phosphorus in walls varies over a considerable range during the growth of a bacterial culture (N. B. Davey, unpublished observations, 1966), indicating a relationship between the proportion of positive to negative charge centers surrounding a cell and the age of the culture. This could explain the necessity for labile linkages between alanine and polyol in teichoic acids, i.e., there is a need for rapid removal of alanine as a means of adjustment of charge. Although teichoic acids exibit many similarities to aminoacyl-RNA, and their alanine residues have the same order of reactivity as the aminoacyl residue, it is unlikely that they have comparable functions. It seems more probable that this high reactivity is associated with a need for removal at short notice, and the lability of the linkage between teichoic acids and glycosaminopeptides may be associated with a similar requirement.

A function for these compounds in controlling the formation of the wall is difficult to discuss at present as it is entirely speculative. It may be, however, that the polymer molecules are highly oriented in the space between wall and membrane. This charged and oriented region would not only control the passage of ions but also of macromolecular compounds, e.g., partly formed glycosaminopeptide molecules synthesized in the membrane but to be cross-linked in situ on the wall structure. The membrane teichoic acid would provide an oriented matrix for directing the polymers into the physical structure of the wall. Whatever the purpose of this interesting class of compounds it is likely that their study will lead to an increased interest in the chemistry and biochemistry of those fascinating and most important areas, the membrane and the region between this and the bacterial wall.

Although much of what has been discussed in this article is rather far removed from the studies carried out by Lipmann on energy and phosphate bonds, it is possible to trace a logical connection between the two studies. In fact, their relationship is really closer that the historical development might suggest. The recognition of the central role of ATP in metabolism, and especially in processes of biosynthesis, is the basis of our present understanding of the function of nucleoside diphosphate sugars in the synthesis of polysaccharides. The connection between the latter topic and the cytidine diphosphate derivatives in bacteria has already been discussed. When the detailed mechanism of biosynthesis and the function of teichoic acids are more fully understood it will be clear that here again the concept of the high-energy bond occupies a key position in our understanding of biochemical processes.

REFERENCES

Archibald, A. R., and Baddiley, J. (1965). *Biochem. J.* **95**, 19c.

Archibald, A. R., and Baddiley, J. (1966). *Advan. Carbohydrate Chem.* **21**, in press.

Archibald, A. R., Armstrong, J. J., Baddiley, J., and Hay, J. B. (1961a). *Nature* **191**, 570.

Archibald, A. R., Baddiley, J., and Buchanan, J. G. (1961b). *Biochem. J.* **81**, 124.

Archibald, A. R., Baddiley, J., and Button, D. (1965). *Biochem. J.* **95**, 8c.

Armstrong, J. J., Baddiley, J., Buchanan, J. G., Carss, B., and Greenberg, G. R. (1958). *J. Chem. Soc.* p. 4344.

Armstrong, J. J., Baddiley, J., and Buchanan, J. G. (1961). *Biochem. J.* **80**, 254.

Baddiley, J., and Buchanan, J. G. (1958). *Quart. Rev. (London)* **12**, 152.

Baddiley, J., and Neuhaus, F. C. (1960). *Biochem. J.* **75**, 579.

Baddiley, J., and Thain, E. M. (1951a). *J. Chem. Soc.* p. 246.

Baddiley, J., and Thain, E. M. (1951b). *J. Chem. Soc.* p. 3421.

Baddiley, J., and Thain, E. M. (1952). *J. Chem. Soc.* p. 3783.

Baddiley, J., and Thain, E. M. (1953). *J. Chem. Soc.* p. 903.

Baddiley, J., Buchanan, J. G., Carss, B., Mathias, A. R., and Sanderson, A. R. (1956). *Biochem. J.* **64**, 599.

Baddiley, J., Buchanan, J. G., Martin, R. O., and RajBhandary, U. L. (1962). *Biochem.* **85**, 49.

Brown, G. M. (1959). *J. Biol. Chem.* **234**, 370.

Burger, M. M., and Glaser, L. (1964). *J. Biol. Chem.* **239**, 3168.

Critchley, P., Archibald, A. R., and Baddiley, J. (1962). *Biochem. J.* **85**, 420.

Ellwood, D. H., Kelemen, M. V., and Baddiley, J. (1963). *Biochem. J.* **86**, 213.

Ghuysen, J. M., Tipper, D. J., and Strominger, J. L. (1965). *Biochemistry* **4**, 474.

Glaser, L. (1964). *J. Biol. Chem.* **239**, 3178.

Hay, J. B., Wicken, A. J., and Baddiley, J. (1963). *Biochim. Biophys. Acta* **71**, 188.

Hay, J. B., Davey, N. B., Archibald, A. R., and Baddiley, J. (1965). *Biochem. J.* **94**, 7c.

Hoagland, M. B., and Novelli, G. D. (1954). *J. Biol. Chem.* **207**, 767.

Levintow, L., and Novelli, G. D. (1954). *J. Biol. Chem.* **207**, 761.

Lipmann, F., Kaplan, N. O., Novelli, G. D., Tuttle, L. C., and Guirard, B. M. (1947). *J. Biol. Chem.* **167**, 869.

Nathenson, S. G., and Strominger, J. L. (1963). *J. Biol. Chem.* **238**, 3161.

Naumova, I. B., Shabarova, Z. A., and Belozersky, A. N. (1963). *Dokl. Akad. Nauk. SSSR* **152**, 1471.

Pierpoint, W. S., Hughes, D. E., Baddiley, J., and Mathias, A. P. (1955). *Biochem. J.* **61**, 368.

Rogers, H. J., and Garrett, A. J. (1963). *Biochem. J.* **88**, 6P.

Shaw, D. R. D. (1962). *Biochem. J.* **82**, 297.

Shockman, G. D., and Slade, H. D. (1964). *J. Gen. Microbiol.* **37**, 297.

Smith, D. G., and Shattock, P. M. F. (1964). *J. Gen. Microbiol.* **34**, 165.

Strominger, J. L., and Ghuysen, J. M. (1963). *Biochem. Biophys. Res. Commun.* **12**, 418.

Torii, M., Kabat, E. A., and Bezer, A. E. (1964). *J. Exptl. Med.* **120**, 13.

Wang, T. P., Schuster, L., and Kaplan, N. O. (1954). *J. Biol. Chem.* **206**, 299.

Wicken, A. J., and Baddiley, J. (1963). *Biochem. J.* **87**, 54.

Metabolism of Poly-β-hydroxybutyrate in Bacteria

Michael Doudoroff

INTRODUCTION

The polymeric ester of D(—)-β-hydroxybutyric acid (PHB) is accumulated by diverse species of bacteria as their principal intracellular reserve of organic carbon. The excellent review on the subject of endogenous metabolism by Dawes and Ribbons (1964) summarizes the studies on PHB metabolism prior to 1964. Hence, in the present paper, only a brief review of the earlier work will be presented and a more detailed account will be given of more recent studies, with an emphasis on those initiated in our own laboratories.

GENERAL ASPECTS OF ENDOGENOUS PHB METABOLISM

A. OCCURRENCE AND FUNCTION OF INTRACELLULAR PHB

The storage of poly-β-hydroxybutyrate is not restricted to any particular morphological or physiological group of the true bacteria. It has been recorded in both gram-positive and gram-negative genera, in cocci as well as in bacilli, in both photosynthetic and aerobic types and in lithotrophs as well as in many organotrophs. The compound has not been detected in certain bacterial groups (e.g., the enterics, clostridia, corynebacteria, mycobacteria, and actinomycetes). Although polymer accumulation cannot apparently be used as a differential character for distinguishing among major bacterial taxa, there is no doubt that it will be an extremely useful taxonomic character at the generic or specific level as, for example, in the pseudomonads (Stanier *et al.*, 1966).

Aerobic bacteria use PHB as a substrate for the endogenous respiratory metabolism required for the provision of maintenance energy and, at least in some cases, as a carbon reserve for protein synthesis (Schlegel *et al.*, 1961; Doudoroff and Stanier, 1959). The endogenous utilization of accumulated PHB has been implicated in the process of sporulation in bacilli (Slepecky and Law, 1961; Buono *et al.*, 1965; Komineck and Halvorson, 1965). In the anaerobic photosynthetic bacteria, PHB can serve both as an electron donor for CO_2 reduction and as a source of carbon for protein synthesis in the absence of an organic substrate (Stanier *et al.*, 1959; Doudoroff and Stanier, 1959).

In cell free preparations, the biosynthesis of PHB has been shown to involve the condensation of hydroxybutyryl residues of D(—)-β-hydroxybutyryl-coenzyme A, which is presumably derived from acetoacetyl-coenzyme A that is produced in the metabolism of exogenous substrates (Merrick and Doudoroff, 1961). The endogenous breakdown of the polymer, on the other hand, may involve a complex hydrolytic enzyme system, which will be briefly described later and which does not function with purified PHB, but requires specially prepared intact polymer inclusions isolated from bacterial cells. The ultimate product of hydrolysis, β-hydroxybutyrate, is then oxidized to acetoacetate and metabolized via acetoacetyl-coenzyme A. Every PHB-storing bacterium that has been examined, has been found to contain high constitutive levels of NAD-linked β-hydroxybutyrate dehydrogenase.

COMPOSITION AND STRUCTURE OF PHB GRANULES

The polymer, which may constitute more than 50% of the total dry weight of bacterial cells, is stored in the cells in the form of microscopically visible sudanophilic granules. These granules can be isolated from disrupted cells by differential centrifugation and contain, in addition to PHB, small amounts of other lipids and protein (Williamson and Wilkinson, 1958). However, in all cases that have been examined, the isolated granules are no longer stainable with Sudan Black. In at least some cases, the granules also contain the enzyme required for PHB biosynthesis and either all or part of the enzyme system required for PHB hydrolysis (Merrick and Doudoroff, 1961, 1964). Merrick and Smith (personal communication, 1966) have analyzed enzymatically active polymer granules from *Bacillus megaterium* prepared by gradient centrifugation in glycerol (7–11 M) and fractionation in a polymer two-phase system of Hofsten and Baird (1962), containing w/w 5% dextran and 3.5% polyethylene glycol. The purified material contained 2.1 mg protein and 0.2 μmoles of phosphorus per 100 mg PHB. Phosphatidic acid accounted for 80% of the phosphorus content and no neutral lipid could be detected.

With the aid of the electron microscope, a thin membranelike coat surrounding the PHB core of such isolated granules has been demonstrated (Lundgren *et al.*, 1964) and it is presumably this coat that contains the protein and phospholipid. Electron micrographs of thin sections of some preparations of *Bacillus cereus* strongly suggest that the polymer inclusions are surrounded by a membranous envelope *in vivo* as well as *in vitro* (Pfister and Lundgren, 1964). Thin sections of *Lampropedia hyalina* prepared by Pangborn and Starr (personal communication, 1966) and of some strains of *Caulobacter* (Poindexter, 1964) also suggest the presence of a bounding membrane that is structurally less complex than the cell membrane. In some species, however, no evidence of such a membrane has yet been seen, even with highly refined preparative techniques. The evidence that cytoplasmic materials may adsorb on the PHB granules during cell disintegration will be discussed later and, for this reason, the morphology of the granules as observed in partially lyzed or otherwise mistreated cells should be interpreted with a certain amount of caution.

PROPERTIES OF PURIFIED PHB

The polymer contained in the granules can be extracted with chloroform, from which it can be precipitated by the addition of acetone, alcohol, or ether. The purified material from a variety of bacteria has essentially identical composition as indicated by X-ray and infrared analyses. The published and current studies of Alper *et al.* (1963), Lundgren *et al.* (1965), Okamura (1965), and Marchessault (personal communication, 1966) on the structure and properties of PHB have established that the crystalline conformation of the polymer has a twofold screw axis along the chain giving a right-hand helix stabilized by carbonyl-methyl interaction. The polymer crystals precipitated from chloroform have a "folded-chain" lamellar morphology. Electron micrographs of PHB granules isolated from bacterial cells suggest that the polymer contained in them also exists in crystalline form (Lundgren *et al.*, 1964).

The molecular weights of polymer samples from different bacterial species and even from different preparations of the same organism have been found to differ enormously, the recorded values ranging from 1000 to 256,000 (Lundgren *et al.*, 1965). Unfortunately, most preparations of PHB that have been analyzed were made from bacteria that had been treated with alkaline hypochlorite to destroy other cell constituents. This treatment is known to degrade the polymer chains (Peaud Lenoel and Kepes, 1952). In addition, the balance between biosynthetic and degradative reactions in the cells at the time of harvest may well affect the average molecular weight of the polymer. Further studies on carefully prepared and perhaps fractionated PHB from whole cells and from isolated granules of different bacteria might prove to be useful in elucidating the organization of the granules and the mode of action of the biosynthetic and hydrolytic enzymes associated with them.

Factors Influencing Endogenous PHB Metabolism

Both environmental conditions and the physiological state of the organism may determine the rate or extent of polymer synthesis and degradation in bacterial cells. The extrinsic factors that affect PHB biosynthesis include the availability of carbon and nitrogen sources, reducing power (as oxidizable organic or inorganic substrate), and energy (from photosynthesis or respiration). Highest yields of polymer can be obtained in media in which an excess of carbon and energy is available to the organism after the exhaustion of a nitrogen source. We have also observed that *Rhodospirillum rubrum* accumulates more polymer when its rate of growth is limited by the necessity of fixing atmospheric nitrogen than when ammonium salts are provided in the medium. As might be expected, in aerobic metabolism reduced organic substrates generally give greater polymer yields than do more oxidized ones. The same is true of anaerobic photosynthetic metabolism, except that compounds more reduced than PHB (e.g., butyrate) cannot be converted to PHB in the absence of a suitable electron acceptor, such as CO_2 (Stanier et al., 1959). With exogenous carbon sources more oxidized than PHB (e.g., acetate for *Rhodospirillum* and CO_2 for the hydrogen bacteria) molecular hydrogen may serve as the ultimate electron donor for their reduction to PHB. The source of ATP required for PHB synthesis can be derived from photophosphorylation or from oxidative phosphorylations associated with the oxidation of organic substrate or inorganic electron donors, such as H_2 or ferrous iron. The chemical configuration of the exogenous substrate may also greatly influence PHB production. In *R. rubrum*, which can store both glycogen and PHB as carbon reserves, substrates that can be readily converted to triose or hexose phosphates (e.g., lactate, pyruvate, malate, succinate, or CO_2) lead mainly to glycogen formation, whereas compounds that must be metabolized through either acetyl- or acetoacetyl coenzyme A (e.g., acetate, β-hydroxybutyrate, and butyrate) lead to polymer accumulation (Stanier et al., 1959). *Hydrogeno-*

monas eutropha, on the other hand, which apparently does not possess alternative carbon reserves, produces PHB from a variety of organic substrates as well as from CO_2.* In our studies with a variety of pseudomonads we have found that DL-β-hydroxybutyrate is a very good carbon source for the practical demonstration of PHB accumulation.

The intrinsic factors that may affect the *in vivo* accumulation of polymer have not been thoroughly analyzed. The relative rates of formation and oxidation of acetyl coenzyme A are undoubtedly important in determining the fraction of the substrate that will be converted to PHB. In the genus *Bacillus,* it has been found that under certain conditions of cultivation enzymes of the tricarboxylic acid cycle are repressed during the early phases of growth, but become functional in older cultures (Hanson *et al.,* 1963, 1964). This may account in part for the accumulation of polymer in cultures before sporulation and its later disappearance during sporulation (Slepecky and Law, 1961; Buono *et al.,* 1965). Kominek and Halvorson have also made the interesting observation that cultures of *B. cereus* growing exponentially in complex medium possess virtually no nicotinamide adenine dinucleotide-linked "acetoacetyl coenzyme A reductase" activity, but that this activity appears at the time that PHB is stored by the cells before sporulation. Unfortunately, many changes occur in the medium during growth and it is difficult to assess the factors responsible for the enzymatic alteration. In addition, it is not clear what enzyme is actually involved in the reduction of acetoacetyl coenzyme A and whether the immediate product is the D- or the L-hydroxybutyryl derivative. Preliminary experiments by Merrick (personal communication, 1966) suggest that in *R. rubrum* at least two enzymes, one of which is the L(+)-β-hydroxybutyryl coenzyme A dehydrogenase, may be involved in the interconversion of D-hydroxybutyryl and acetoacetyl coenzyme A.

The degradation of stored intracellular polymer, like its production, may be governed by extrinsic factors such as the availability of sources of nitrogen, carbon, and energy to the organism. The depletion of an exogenous carbon source leads to polymer decomposition and at least in two instances it has been shown that the provision of a nitrogen source increases the rate of polymer disappearance (Stanier *et al.,* 1959; Schlegel *et al.,* 1961). The rate of PHB consumption may also be dependent on the availability of a suitable electron acceptor and an energy source. For example, in media devoid of organic compounds the polymer

* The *Hydrogenomonas* strain 16, studied by Schlegel *et al.* (1961) and by Gottschalk (1965) has been identified by D. Davis in our laboratory as *H. eutropha.*

content of *R. rubrum* cells remains quite constant under anaerobic conditions in the dark, regardless of whether or not CO_2 and/or ammonium salts are provided. In the light, polymer disappearance in a nitrogen-free medium is negligible in the absence of CO_2, but considerable in its presence. Both PHB and CO_2 are converted mainly to carbohydrate in the latter case. In the presence of ammonium salts and CO_2 the rate of polymer degradation is increased and nitrogenous cell constituents are produced. Since the initial attack on the polymer appears to be of hydrolytic nature (Merrick and Doudoroff, 1964), it would seem that in this organism some internal control mechanisms must play a role in the mobilization of PHB reserves for endogenous metabolism. In contrast, the observation of Sierra and Gibbons (1962) that the rate of PHB hydrolysis in intact cells *Micrococcus halodenitrificans* is identical under aerobic and anaerobic conditions suggests that in this bacterium a similar internal control mechanism may be absent.

Because of the high molecular weight and insolubility of the polymer, it is difficult to visualize any control mechanisms that would simply depend on the molar concentration of PHB in the cells. Indeed, the absence or inefficiency of the control of biosynthetic reactions may account for the enormous accumulation of PHB that can be observed in some bacteria. In the continued absence of a nitrogen source, it is possible that polymer synthesis does eventually become impaired as a result of an unfavorable balance between the relative rates of destruction and resynthesis of an unstable enzyme. The control of polymer degradation in *R. rubrum*, on the other hand, appears to be fairly rigorous and to operate on the level of enzyme function. As will be seen in a subsequent section, the intracellular PHB-hydrolyzing enzyme system of this organism is quite complex and its functioning seems to depend on the integrity of the polymer-containing inclusions described earlier. The possibility that the production of depolymerizing enzymes is partially repressed during the active metabolism of exogenous substrates is also likely. We have observed that the specific activity of the total soluble depolymerizing enzyme system of *R. rubrum* is considerably lower in extracts prepared from cells that are producing polymer than in extracts of starved cells that have depleted their polymer reserves. A fair comparison is, however, difficult to make, since in extracts of polymer-rich cells a large fraction of such enzymes is associated with the PHB granules and comparable assays must be made after the polymer granules have undergone enzymatic digestion. It is impossible to determine how much of the enzymes may become inactive during this process.

ROLE OF PHB AS EXOGENOUS NUTRIENT

Because of its widespread occurrence and high concentration in bacterial cells, PHB is a relatively abundant organic constituent of the biosphere. As a consequence of the death and lysis of polymer-synthesizing bacteria, PHB must be constantly available as an extracellular nutrient for soil microorganisms. In view of the extreme insolubility of PHB and its occurrence in the form of granules, its utilization as an exogenous carbon source must depend on the ability of soil organisms to excrete extracellular esterases to effect its digestion. Furthermore, one would expect such esterases to be produced at least in small amounts constitutively, since it is hard to visualize how the polymer could penetrate the cells to act as an inducer. As a matter of fact, it is very simple to isolate from soil a variety of microorganisms (bacteria and fungi) that can grow with purified PHB as the sole source of carbon. All of these organisms produce exoenzymes and with one recorded exception (Chowdhury, 1963) the bacteria that have been examined produce the enzymes in media containing neither polymer nor the products of its digestion (Delafield *et al.*, 1965b).

A survey of a large number of strains of *Pseudomonas* and *Hydrogenomonas* in our laboratory has shown that, like the ability to synthesize polymer, the ability to use it as an exogenous substrate is a constant and useful taxonomic character. It is interesting to note that in these genera it has been found that every strain that can digest purified PHB can also store PHB as an intracellular reserve, although only a fraction of PHB accumulators can also use it as an extracellular nutrient. On the basis of this observation, one might postulate that PHB-digesting exoenzymes are a part of the intracellular system concerned with the metabolism of reserve materials that "leak" out of the cells. This probably is not the general case, since the one truly intracellular system that has been examined does not attack purified PHB. Furthermore, the high specific activity of the exoenzymes of *P. lemoignei* and of *"Pseudomonas sp."* indicates that in these organisms they are preferentially excreted and are not liberated by autolysis (Delafield *et al.*, 1965b; Chowdhury, 1963).

ENZYMATIC DEPOLYMERIZATION OF ENDOGENOUS PHB

Unfortunately, only one cell-free system concerned with the endogenous hydrolysis of PHB has been examined in some detail to date, and this is an artificial one in which soluble enzymes from *R. rubrum* have been used to digest polymer granules isolated from the asporogenous strain of *Bacillus megaterium* KM (Merrick and Doudoroff, 1964). The reason for this choice of enzyme and substrate was that neither organism alone could provide suitable materials for study. After cell disintegration, the polymer granules of *R. rubrum* undergo rapid self-digestion, even if they are separated from the soluble fraction of the extract. Both the biosynthetic and hydrolytic enzymes involved in PHB metabolism are associated with the granules and the depolymerizing enzymes become either activated or adsorbed on the PHB granules during cell breakage. The PHB granules of *B. megaterium* KM, on the other hand, contain little if any self-digesting activity, although they possess the biosynthetic enzymes. The stability of such granules is probably due to the virtual absence of depolymerase activity in the cells of this organism grown under the experimental conditions. The granules of *B. megaterium* are rapidly digested by soluble extracts of *R. rubrum*, especially if the extracts are prepared from cells that have been allowed to deplete their own polymer reserves by endogenous metabolism. Such extracts do not attack purified polymer, but require carefully prepared "native" PHB granules as substrate. The complete "depolymerase system" appears to consist of four components in addition to the PHB contained in the granules: (1) an extremely labile component associated with the *B. megaterium* granules, which is presumably also present in *R. rubrum* PHB inclusions; (2) a heat-stable proteinaceous "activator" in the *R. rubrum* extracts which is required for depolymerization; (3) a heat-labile "depolymerase" which is presumed to be the enzyme that hydrolyzes the polymer and which produces mainly monomer and small amounts of dimer; and (4) the dimer hydrolase which will be described in a later section, and which completes the digestion of residual dimer. The nature of the interaction between the first three components is not understood, and of these only the activator and depolymerase have yielded to purification procedures.

The factor that is associated with the "native" polymer granules of *B. megaterium* potentiates the combined action of the *R. rubrum* activator and depolymerase. This component is easily inactivated by a variety of physical and chemical treatments of the granules such as their close packing by centrifugation, freezing and thawing, exposure to heat, weak acids, certain detergents and antibiotics, and extensive digestion by trypsin. There is some reason to believe that the granule factor may be contained in the membranous coat surrounding these structures which has been discussed earlier. If such a coat does indeed exist in the intact cell, its function may well be involved in the regulation of polymer breakdown. Several lines of circumstantial evidence for the role of the membrane have been adduced. For example, treatments that make the granules resistant to digestion also alter the morphological appearance of the granules as visualized with the aid of the electron microscope (Merrick et al., 1965). Some characteristic changes are observed in the structure of the enveloping coat, which appears to be blistered or fragmented, and in the coalescent properties of the granules. Somewhat less convincing evidence is the fact that certain antibiotics that are known to affect cell membranes also interfere with depolymerization (Merrick, 1965). It is noteworthy that two of the antibiotics tested, polymyxin B and chlortetracycline, inhibit the digestion of the granules but not the biosynthetic enzymes associated with the particles. It would be interesting to test whether these compounds would inhibit the self-digestion of R. rubrum granules without affecting their biosynthetic enzymes.

The nature and role of the surface coat described in the PHB particles remain to be firmly established. The fact that isolated R. rubrum granules are relatively stable in vivo but not in vitro indicates that some control mechanism is lost during sonic disruption of the cells. Furthermore, isolated granules of B. megaterium, R. rubrum, and other species are not sudanophilic as are the in vivo inclusions, suggesting that a cytoplasmic outer layer of lipid may be lost during their preparation. Finally, we have shown that when polymer-depleted cells of R. rubrum, which contain large amounts of the soluble depolymerizing system, are sonicated together with polymer-rich cells of the same organism that contain very little if any soluble enzyme and the polymer granules are centrifuged out, some of the total soluble enzyme of the mixed preparation disappears. This indicates that at least some of the cytoplasmic proteins can be adsorbed on the granules in the process of cell disintegration.

The "activator" fraction of R. rubrum extracts is remarkably stable to heat, alkali, and acids (including trichloracetic). Purified preparations of it have been obtained that are homogeneous by electrophoretic analysis (Merrick, personal communication, 1966). Kinetic studies indicate that the action of the "activator" on the "native PHB granules" of B. megaterium must precede that of the depolymerase. No hydrolysis of either "native" or purified PHB has been observed with the activator fraction alone. Nor are any amino acids, peptides, lipids, or inorganic phosphate liberated in detectable amounts from the granules. Curiously, trypsin, which does digest some of the granule protein, is an effective substitute for the "activator," provided it is used in very low concentrations

(Merrick and Doudoroff, 1964). At high concentration or after prolonged incubation, trypsin has the opposite effect and destroys the susceptibility of the granules to digestion by either the purified depolymerase or the complete depolymerizing system of R. *rubrum*. It could be postulated that the function of trypsin is to liberate an activator from some constituent of the granules. Attempts to show the presence of such a factor in the soluble fraction of trypsin-treated granule preparations after centrifugation and the addition of ovomucoid have not been successful. Furthermore, if such an activator is indeed produced, its properties must be different from those of the R. *rubrum* activator, since the digestion of trypsin-treated granules by depolymerase is prevented by the addition of Tween 80. This detergent does not interfere with the depolymerization of granules exposed to R. *rubrum* activator either before or after the trypsin treatment.

The "depolymerase" fraction of the R. *rubrum* extracts is believed to be the enzyme which actually hydrolyzes the polymer. Unfortunately, no assay for it has yet been found which does not involve the complex system of "activated" PHB granules. β-Hydroxybutyrate is the main product of the hydrolysis of such granules throughout the course of polymer digestion. Between 15 and 20% of the PHB is converted, however, to an oligomer which cannot be further hydrolyzed by the depolymerase. This oligomer has recently been shown to be the dimeric ester of D-β-hydroxybutyric acid (Merrick, personal communication, 1966) and it is further hydrolyzed by the "dimer hydrolase" which will be described later.

ENZYMATIC HYDROLYSIS OF PURIFIED PHB AND OLIGOMERS

Very little information is available on the hydrolytic enzymes that attack purified PHB and oligomers of D(—)-hydroxybutyric acid. It is almost certain that a great variety of enzymes or enzyme systems will be found in different organisms. A cursory survey of a number of bacteria that can use PHB as an exogenous carbon source has already shown that the end products of extracellular PHB digestion may be β-hydroxybutyrate, the dimeric ester of the acid, and possibly higher oligomers (Delafield *et al.*, 1965*b*). The enzyme of one pseudomonad, characterized by Chowdhury (1963), is a rather nonspecific esterase that hydrolyzes PHB to its monomeric subunits. Another extracellular enzyme system studied in our laboratory produces mainly the dimer of D-β-hydroxybutyrate [3-D-(3'-D-hydroxybutanoyloxy) butanoate]. A systematic study of various exoenzymes may throw some light on the mechanism of intracellular PHB digestion.

I shall briefly review the present state of our knowledge of the extracellular PHB depolymerase system of *Pseudomonas lemoignei* and of two specific intracellular esterases that decompose the dimeric and trimeric esters of D(—)-β-hydroxybutyric acid. These esterases were partially purified from extracts of cells of *P. lemoignei* and *R. rubrum*, respectively. In the former organism, the intracellular enzyme is undoubtedly involved in the decomposition of hydroxybutyric dimer, which is the principal product of extracellular PHB digestion. It may also function in the final stages of the decomposition of intracellular PHB reserves which the bacterium accumulates. In *R. rubrum* the esterase is apparently concerned with the hydrolysis of the dimeric ester which is a minor product of the endogenous degradation of polymer by the complex depolymerase system that was described in the previous section. Studies on the enzymes of *P. lemoignei* were initiated by F. P. Delafield and continued by N. J. Palleroni, Keith E. Cooksey, C. J. Lusty, Rebecca Contopoulos, and M. Boll. The *R. rubrum* esterase has been investigated by J. M. Merrick and Chi Ing Yu, who have kindly supplied me with their unpublished data.

The Extracellular Depolymerase of *P. lemoignei*

The extracellular depolymerase system of *P. lemoignei* (Delafield *et al.*, 1965b; Lusty and Doudoroff, 1966) appears to be highly specific for PHB and does not attack the dimeric ester at an appreciable rate. The end products of polymer digestion are monomer and dimer, the former representing between 25 and 30% of the total hydroxybutyryl residues solubilized. Fractionation of the enzyme by electrophoresis or on carboxymethyl cellulose columns has revealed at least two components—one, referred to as Fraction A, eluting from CM cellulose with 0.01 M Tris buffer, pH 8.0, and the other, Fraction B, eluting with 0.1 M buffer of the same composition. Like the monomer-forming PHB hydrolase studied by Chowdhury (1963), the enzymes of *P. lemoignei* are basic proteins, but Fraction B has a greater electrophoretic mobility than Fraction A. They have very similar sedimentation constants and molecular weights. The two fractions are immunologically distinct, no cross-reactions having yet been observed with rabbit antisera prepared against either.

Both enzymes produce monomer and dimer as the only end products of PHB digestion, but these compounds appear in different ratios. Thus, Fraction A liberates only between 13 and 17% of the total hydroxybutyric residues as hydroxybutyrate. Fraction B, on the other hand, forms a considerable quantity of monomer (37–46%). Furthermore, in the early stages of digestion, Fraction A releases very little monomer (9–13%) and small amounts (9–15%) of the trimeric ester of hydroxybutyric acid, whereas Fraction B produces a larger amount of monomer (16–20%), the balance of the solubilized material being almost exclusively trimer. Both enzymes can hydrolyze trimer to yield equimolar quantities of monomer and dimer, but under the normal assay conditions Fraction A can do so in the presence of polymer, whereas Fraction B does not attack the trimer until the polymer has almost disappeared. This difference appears to be a reflection of the stronger adsorption of Fraction B than of Fraction A on the polymer surface. The available data do not allow any serious speculations on the question of whether the enzymes attack the polymeric molecule from the end of the chain or cleave it internally. Attempts to demonstrate the accumulation of any oligomers larger than the trimer during the course of PHB hydrolysis have been unsuccessful and the average molecular weight of partially digested polymer was found to approximate that of the initial substrate. This, however, does not rule out the possibility that during hydrolysis small amounts of insoluble polymeric esters of low molecular weight may be formed on the surface of the purified PHB granules and be preferentially decomposed by the enzyme.

Both fractions are inhibited by chelating agents, but Fraction B is far more susceptible to irreversible inactivation, particularly in the presence of its substrate. Although the addition of calcium seems to stabilize the enzymes in dilute solution, there is reason to believe that metal ions other than calcium may be involved in their activity. One further difference between the two enzymes is that Fraction B is strongly activated and somewhat protected by media of high ionic strength, whereas Fraction A is relatively unaffected by salt concentration.

Although the cells of *P. lemoignei* contain a fair amount of the depolymerase that is excreted into the medium (*ca.* 7% of the total activity in succinate cultures), a direct role of the enzyme in the digestion of intracellular PHB reserves of this organism is problematical.

"Dimer Hydrolases" of *P. lemoignei* and *R. rubrum*

The intracellular "dimer hydrolases" of *P. lemoignei* (Delafield *et al.*, 1965a) and *R. rubrum* (J. M. Merrick and C. I. Yu, personal communication, 1966) are both highly specific esterases which do not attack purified PHB, but which hydrolyze both the dimeric and the trimeric esters of D-β-hydroxybutyrate. Preparations of the enzyme from *R. rubrum* also show some depolymerizing activity with "native PHB granules" of *B. megaterium*, but this activity may be due to a contamination with the *R. rubrum* depolymerase already described. Neither one of the "dimer hydrolases" attacks the dimeric ester of L(+)-β-hydroxybutyric acid. There are some interesting differences in the stereospecificity of the enzymes of the two organisms. The principal specificity of the *P. lemoignei* enzyme is for the D(—) configuration of the oxybutanoate (CH₂—CHOR—CH₂—COOH) portion of its dimeric substrate. The L(+)-β-hydroxybutyryl and the butyryl (R) derivatives of D(—)-β-hydroxybutyrate are both attacked, though at lower rates than that for the natural dimer. The esterification of the carboxyl group of the dimer, as in its bromphenacyl derivative, does not prevent, however, the enzymatic cleavage of the bond between the hydroxybutyric moieties and one hydroxybutyrate is liberated. The principal specificity of the *R. rubrum* enzyme, on the other hand, appears to be for the D(—) configuration of the β-hydroxybutyryl (R) portion of the dimer. The L-hydroxybutyryl derivative of D-hydroxybutyrate is not attacked, whereas the D-hydroxybutyryl derivative of L-hydroxybutyrate is hydrolyzed relatively slowly. Ethyl-DL-β-hydroxybutyrate is not hydrolyzed. Another difference between the two enzymes is that the esterase of *P. lemoignei* hydrolyzes the trimeric ester of D-hydroxybutyrate very slowly, whereas the esterase of *R. rubrum* hydrolyzes the trimer at a rate at least three times greater than that for the dimer.

Unlike the extracellular PHB-hydrolyzing enzyme fractions described earlier, neither esterase is inhibited or inactivated by EDTA. All four enzymes are sensitive to inactivation by diisopropylfluorophosphate.

CONCLUSIONS AND PROSPECTS OF FUTURE STUDIES

The long lag between the discovery of PHB some 40 years ago by Lemoigne (1927) and the recently awakened interest of a number of microbiologists in this compound is partly attributable to the peculiar properties of the polymer that have led to its being overlooked or misidentified in my own and other early studies on oxidative and photosynthetic assimilation (Doudoroff and Stanier, 1959). Nor is the present work on the nature and metabolism of PHB progressing at a feverish pace for several obvious reasons. In the first place, being the simplest known biologically important polymer, PHB cannot carry any basic code for life (Spiegelman, personal communication, 1962). In the second place, although PHB is a good enough polymer to rate patent status for its manufacture (Baptist, 1962), it does not appear to be a likely competitor with synthetically produced materials. Finally, PHB does not occur in *Escherichia coli*, which automatically places it outside the frame of reference of many modern workers.

Neither our own nor related studies have so far shed much light on the basic problems concerning the biosynthesis and degradation of intracellular polymer. No experiments have been reported on the mechanism of PHB biosynthesis beyond the observation that isolated PHB granules contain a polymerizing enzyme that requires $D(-)$-hydroxybutyryl-coenzyme A. The occurrence and localization of this enzyme in polymer-depleted cells remains to be shown and the separation of the enzyme from the granules and its characterization remain to be attempted. The detailed enzymology of the formation of $D(-)$-hydroxybutyryl-coenzyme A from either the free acid or the acetoactyl, $L(+)$-β-hydroxybutyryl, and possibly crotonyl derivatives of coenzyme A has yet to be worked out. As has been pointed out, even the nature of the "acetoacetyl coenzyme A reductase" of *B. cereus* (Kominek and Halvorson, 1965) still is not clear.

The "artificial" depolymerizing system consisting of *R. rubrum* enzymes and *B. megaterium* PHB granules is far from being understood. The role of its various components in PHB hydrolysis must be elucidated before the possible involvement of these components in the regulation of polymer metabolism can be visualized. It is not even known whether or not enzymes or granules from other bacterial species can be substituted in this system. It can be hoped that eventually a more "natural" system will be investigated, possibly even in *B. megaterium* itself.

The problem of the extracellular digestion of purified polymer is far simpler and, hence, intrinsically less interesting than that of intracellular PHB metabolism. In our own laboratory, progress on this subject has been painfully slow mainly because of the technical diffculty of harvesting the relatively unstable enzymes from large volumes of medium. However, as happens in almost any intensive investigation, we have constantly encountered more problems than we have been able to solve and the very challenge of the technical obstacles has kept us from turning to greener pastures. It is to be hoped that these and similar studies with other PHB-digesting enzymes may eventually lead to a better understanding of the specificity, mode of action and structure of esterases, of the kinetics of interaction between soluble enzymes and completely insoluble substrates, and of the mechanism of enzyme excretion.

I do not pretend that the above review is concerned in any direct way with Fritz Lipmann's contribution to the biochemical concept of the "energy-rich bond." I merely wished to make my own small contribution to a volume honoring a man whom I consider to be one of the most inspiring scientists I know and whose friendship I value greatly. The rich human and intellectual bond that Lipmann has established with those of us who have had an opportunity to work with him is not measurable in calories, because it can perform work without ever being broken. The only direct connection between the subject of the present paper and Lipmann's research is the incidental fact that, some 16 years ago, I spent a memorable 2-month period in his laboratory as an apprentice to him and to my friend Earl Stadtman, in their experiments on the biosynthesis of acetoacetate (Stadtman *et al.*, 1951). As we have shown, this compound and its coenzyme A derivative are involved in the metabolism of poly-β-hydroxybutyric acid, which is the subject of this chapter.

REFERENCES

Alper, R., Lundgren, D. G., Marchessault, R. H., and Cote, W. A. (1963). *Biopolymers* 1, 545-556.

Baptist, J. N. (1962). U.S. Patents 3036959 and 3044942.

Buono, F. J., Lundgren, D. G., and Testa, R. T. (1965). *Bacteriol. Proc.* G137.

Chowdhury, A. A. (1963). *Arch. Mikrobiol.* 47, 167-200.

Dawes, E. A., and Ribbons, D. W. (1964). *Bacteriol. Rev.* 28, 126-149.

Delafield, F. P., Cooksey, K. E., and Duodoroff, M. (1965a). *J. Biol. Chem.* 240, 4023-4027.

Delafield, F. P., Doudoroff, M., Palleroni, N. J., Lusty, C. J., and Contopoulos, R. (1965b). *J. Bacteriol.* 90, 1455-1466.

Doudoroff, M., and Stanier, R. Y. (1959). *Nature* 183, 1440-1442.

Gottschalk, G. (1964). *Arch. Mikrobiol.* 47, 230-235.

Hanson, R. S., Srinivasan, V. R., and Halvorson, H. O. (1963). *J. Bacteriol.* 86, 45-50.

Hanson, R. S., Blishiarska, J., Arnaud, M., and Szulmajster, J. (1964). *Biochem. Biophys. Res. Commun.* 17, 690-695.

Hofsten, B. V., and Baird, O. D. (1962). *Biotechnol. Bioeng.* 4, 403.

Komineck, L. A., and Halvorson, H. O. (1965). *J. Bacteriol.* pp. 1251-1259.

Lemoigne, M. (1927). *Ann. Inst. Pasteur* 41, 148-165.

Lundgren, D. G., Pfister, R. M., and Merrick, J. M. (1964). *J. Gen. Microbiol.* 34, 441-446.

Lundgren, D. G., Alper, R., Schnaitman, C., and Marchessault, R. H. (1965). *J. Bacteriol.* 89, 245-251.

Lusty, C. J., and Doudoroff, M. (1966). *Proc. Natl. Acad. Sci. U.S.* (in press).

Merrick, J. M. (1965). *J. Bacteriol.* 90, 965-969.

Merrick, J. M., and Doudoroff, M. (1961). *Nature* 189, 890-892.

Merrick, J. M., and Doudoroff, M. (1964). *J. Bacteriol.* 88, 60-71.

Merrick, J. M., Lundgren, D. G., and Pfister, R. M. (1965). *J. Bacteriol.* **89**, 234-239.

Okamura, K. (1965). Master of Forestry Thesis, Syracuse University, Syracuse, New York.

Peaud Lenoel, C., and Kepes, A. (1952). *Bull. Soc. Chim. Biol.* **34**, 563-575.

Pfister, R. M., and Lundgren, D. G. (1964). *J. Bacteriol.* **88**, 1119-1129.

Poindexter, J. S. (1964). *Bacteriol. Rev.* **28**, 231-295.

Schlegel, H. G., Gottschalk, G., and von Bartha, R. (1961). *Nature* **191**, 463-465.

Sierra, G., and Gibbons, N. E. (1962). *Can. J. Microbiol.* **8**, 255-269.

Slepecky, R. A., and Law, J. H. (1961). *J. Bacteriol.* **82**, 37-42.

Stadtman, E. R., Doudoroff, M., and Lipmann, F., (1951). *J. Biol. Chem.* **191**, 377-382.

Stanier, R. Y., Duodoroff, M., Kunisawa, R., and Contopoulos, R. (1959). *Proc. Natl. Acad. Sci. U.S.* **45**, 1246-1260.

Stanier, R. Y., Palleroni, N. J., and Doudoroff, M. (1966). *J. Gen. Microbiol.* (in press).

Williamson, D. H., and Wilkinson, J. F. (1958). *J. Gen. Microbiol.* **19**, 198-209.

Studies on the Hydrolysis of Carbamyl Phosphates *

Charles M. Allen, Jr., Elliott Richelson and Mary Ellen Jones

The synthesis of carbamyl-P (carbamyl phosphate) from cyanic acid and phosphate dianion was first achieved in Dr. Lipmann's laboratory (Spector *et al.*, 1957). Preliminary studies there on the hydrolysis of carbamyl-P showed that below pH 6 (i.e., where the monoanion predominates) ammonium ion was produced, whereas above this pH cyanate was the major product (Jones and Lipmann, 1960). The detailed studies of the decomposition of carbamyl-P in water by Allen and Jones (1964)

$$(1)$$

demonstrated separate mechanisms for mono- and dianion decomposition. It was proposed on the basis of kinetic and isotopic $H_2^{18}O$ experiments that the decomposition of carbamyl-P monoanion proceeds by P—O bond cleavage with a monomolecular elimination of carbamic acid to form

* Supported by research grants from the National Science Foundation (B-3337), the National Institute of Health, Child Health and Human Development (HD-01244), the American Cancer Society IN 29, and a Public Health Service Fellowship (1962-64). Publication No. 443 from the Graduate Department of Biochemistry, Brandeis University, Waltham, Massachusetts.

401

monomeric metaphosphate which then reacts with H_2O to yield ortho-phosphate. The decomposition of the carbamyl-P dianion, however, leads to C—O bond cleavage and most likely proceeds by the monomolecular elimination shown below to yield cyanic acid and phosphate dianion.

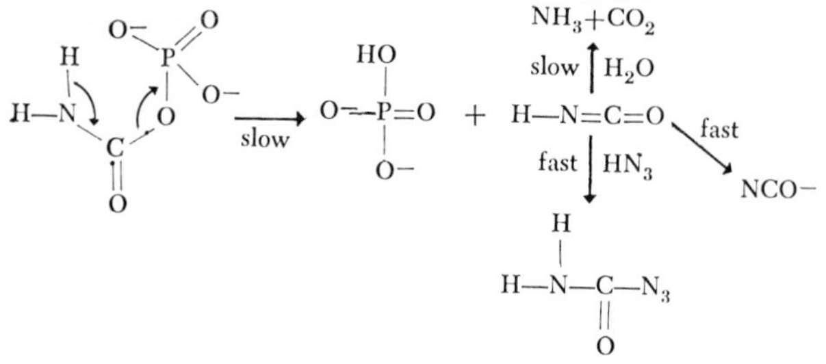

$$\tag{2}$$

The proposed mechanism for the hydrolysis of the monoanion of car-bamyl-P is analogous to that suggested by Di Sabato and Jencks (1961) for the hydrolysis of acetyl phosphate monoanion; however, the mechanism proposed for carbamyl-P dianion hydrolysis is not similar to that of acetyl phosphate dianion hydrolysis since it depends on the presence of an extractable hydrogen on the amide nitrogen and on the base strength of the secondary phosphate anion (Allen and Jones, 1964). It seemed of interest to examine the effect of replacement of a hydrogen atom of the amide nitrogen of carbamyl-P since it was possible that one might observe a change in the point of bond cleavage from the C—O bond to the P—O bond on nitrogen substitution.

The cyclic mechanism proposed for the decomposition of the dianion of carbamyl-P [Eq. (2)] was reexamined by observing the effect of divalent magnesium on the rates of dianion decomposition.

EXPERIMENTAL PROCEDURES

METHODS

The orthophosphate release during the decomposition of the carbamyl-P analogs was determined as previously described (Allen and Jones, 1964). The first-order rate constants were calculated by the method of least squares.

The isotope experiments which did not have added divalent magnesium were carried out as previously described by Allen and Jones (1964). In the experiments where magnesium was added the following modifications were made for isolation of the KH_2PO_4.

The buffered reaction mixture containing 0.22 mmole of carbamyl-P (90–92% pure), 0.017 mole of $MgCl_2 \cdot 6H_2O$ in 10 ml of $H_2^{18}O$ (1.575%) and 1.0 ml of appropriate buffer was brought to a volume of 50 ml to which was added 2–3 drops of methyl red indicator. (In control experiments, where Mg was omitted during incubation, $MgCl_2 \cdot 6H_2O$ was added before neutralization with base.) Then 2–3 ml of concentrated NH_4OH was added. The resulting precipitate was collected by centrifugation and dissolved in 25 ml of 1 N HCl. One drop of methyl red was then added and this solution neutralized again with NH_4OH. The solution was permitted to stand 15–30 minutes before collecting the precipitate by centrifugation. The precipitate was washed with 2 ml of 1 N NH_4OH, 5 ml of 95% ethanol and 5 ml of ethyl ether. Each precipitate was dissolved in 10 ml of H_2O and 0.4 ml of 1.0 N HCl. The pH was brought to 5.5 by the addition of 0.1 ml of 1.0 N KOH. This solution was placed on a Dowex 1-chloride column for chromatography. The phosphate was eluted from the column and isolated as previously described (Jones and Spector, 1960). The method for the incorporation of the phosphate oxygens into CO_2 for mass spectrographic analysis was that described by Williams and Hager (1958). The CO_2 collected was analyzed on a Consolidated 21-103C mass spectrometer.

MATERIALS

N-Phenyl carbamyl-P, N-tolyl carbamyl-P, and N-p-nitrophenyl carbamyl-P were prepared as the monotriethylamine salts by the reaction of equimolar concentrations of orthophosphoric acid, triethylamine, and the appropriate alkyl isocyanate in acetonitrile as solvent by the general procedure described by Cramer and Winter (1959). Reaction time was about 1 hour. The product crystallizes from solution. Small amounts of unreacted cyanate could be extracted from the isolated crystalline product by mixing the crystals with fresh acetonitrile while elevating the temperature of the mixture slightly above room temperature.

The N-methyl carbamyl-P was prepared as outlined above but was isolated as the dilithium salt by precipitation according to a modification of the method described by Spector et al. (1957), since this derivative does not crystallize in acetonitrile. After the N-methyl cyanate and the triethylammonium phosphate had reacted for 1 hour, the solvent, acetonitrile, was removed under vacuum to yield an oil. To 5 gm of this crude oily product was added 0.72 gm of LiOH dissolved in a minimal amount of water. The mixture was stirred well and then absolute ethanol (70 ml) was added. The volume of solution was then reduced by evaporation *in vacuo* until crystals appeared. The crystals were collected. Table I presents the carbon, hydrogen, and nitrogen analysis for each of these compounds.

TABLE I

CARBON, HYDROGEN, AND NITROGEN ANALYSES OF
CARBAMYL PHOSPHATE ANALOGS

Compound[b]	Experimental (%)[a]			Theoretical (%)		
	Carbon	Hydro-gen	Nitrogen	Carbon	Hydro-gen	Nitrogen
1. N-Phenyl car-bamyl-P ($C_{13}H_{23}O_5N_2P$)	49.24	7.30	8.78	49.05	7.28	8.80
2. N-Tolyl car-bamyl-P ($C_{14}H_{25}O_5N_2P$)	50.83	7.57	8.29	50.59	7.58	8.43
3. N-p-Nitrophenyl carbamyl-P ($C_{13}H_{22}O_7N_3P$)	42.84	6.14	11.71	42.97	6.10	11.57
4. N-Methyl car-bamyl-P ($C_2H_4O_5NLi_2 \cdot H_2O$)	13.51	3.45	7.50	13.00	3.24	7.57

[a] The experimental analysis was done by the Scandinavian Microanalytical Laboratory.

[b] Compounds 1, 2, and 3 are monotriethylamine salts; compound 4 is a dilithium salt with one water of hydration.

All other chemicals were of reagent grade unless otherwise noted. Water enriched with ^{18}O (1.575% ^{18}O) was obtained from the Weizmann Institute, Rehovoth, Israel.

RESULTS

STUDIES ON RATES OF HYDROLYSIS

The rate of decomposition of carbamyl-P was carried out in the presence and absence of divalent magnesium. The first-order rate constants for carbamyl-P decomposition in two buffered solutions at varying Mg^{2+} concentration are presented in Table II. Figure 1 presents the pH profile of the effect of added Mg^{2+} on the first-order rate constants in comparison to the uncatalyzed reaction. The evidence presented indicates that increasing Mg^{2+} has a marked effect on the rate of decomposition of the dianionic species and little effect on the monoanionic species.

In rate studies on the effect of monosubstitution at the nitrogen of

TABLE II
EFFECT OF Mg^{2+} ON THE DECOMPOSITION OF CARBAMYL-P^a

pH	[Mg^{2+}]	$k_{obs} \times 10^2$ min^{-1b}
0.06 M Maleate		
6.84	0.00	1.64
7.16	0.03	1.11
7.08	0.09	0.80
6.89	0.15	0.56
0.06 M Sulfate		
2.79	0.00	1.39
2.60	0.03	1.39
2.56	0.09	1.24
2.51	0.15	1.13

^{a} The concentration of carbamyl phosphate in each case is 0.001 M and the ionic strength of each reaction mixture is 0.6. Temperature, 37°C.

^{b} These first-order rate constants are taken from the data of Allen and Jones (1964).

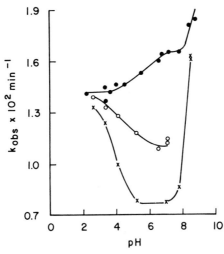

FIG. 1. Closed circles represent k_{obs} for carbamyl-P without added Mg. These data have been previously published (Allen and Jones, 1964). Open circles and crosses represent k_{obs} at 0.03 and 0.08 M Mg^{2+}, respectively. Various 0.06 M buffered solutions were used with a constant ionic strength of 0.6. These samples were incubated at 37°C.

carbamyl-P it was assumed that the pK's of the substituted carbamyl phosphates were not too different from those of carbamyl-P ($pK_1 = 1.1$, $pK_2 = 4.9$). We therefore chose pH 3.5 and 6.9 for the studies with the analogs and assumed that the major ionic species present would be the monoanion and dianion, respectively. Table III summarizes the rates of decomposition of the carbamyl-P analogs and compares them with those obtained by Di Sabato and Jencks (1961) for acetyl phosphate and

TABLE III

CONSTANTS FOR THE HYDROLYSIS OF THE MONO- AND DIANION
OF SUBSTITUTED ACYL PHOSPHATES[a]

X	$k_{obs} \times 10^2$ min^{-1} at 37°C	
	Monoanion	Dianion
H_2N—[b]	1.37[c]	1.60[d]
CH_3—HN—	0.45[c]	0.049[d]
		0.051[d]
C_6H_5—HN—	0.68[c]	0.51[d]
p CH_3—C_6H_4—HN—	0.56[c]	0.37[d]
p NO_2—C_6H_4—HN—	1.37[c]	2.69[d]
		2.77[d]
CH_3—[e]	1.3[f]	0.43[g]
C_6H_5—[e]	0.61[f]	0.31[g]
p CH_3—C_6H_4—[e]	0.57[f]	0.26[g]
p NO_2—C_6H_4—[e]	0.81[f]	2.8[g]

[a] X—CO_2—PO_3H_2 at 0.6 ionic strength.
[b] Data from Allen and Jones (1964).
[c] Buffer was potassium formate, pH = 3.40–3.53.
[d] Buffer was potassium maleate, pH = 6.45–6.72.
[e] Data from Di Sabato and Jencks (1961).
[f] Buffer was potassium formate, pH 2.7–3.1.
[g] Buffer was potassium phosphate, pH 6.9–7.5.

several benzyl phosphates. It can be seen that there is a striking similarity in the rates of hydrolysis of the carbamyl phosphates carrying a benzyl substituent on the nitrogen atom and the benzyl phosphates. Substitution of a single hydrogen atom of carbamyl-P with a methyl group slows the rate of hydrolysis of the mono- and dianion; this effect is very marked for the dianion where the rate is decreased by a factor of 30.

STUDIES OF THE MODE OF BOND CLEAVAGE

Magnesium ion had no effect on the point of bond cleavage of carbamyl-P, i.e., there is primarily P—O bond cleavage for the monoanion and C—O bond cleavage for the dianion (Table IV).

TABLE IV

P—O Bond Cleavage (%) for Carbamyl Phosphate Mono- and Dianion
in the Presence and Absence of 1.27 M MgCl$_2$

pH	Buffer (M)	Mg^{2+}	Atoms (%) excess ^{18}O in:		P—O Bond cleavage (%)
			H$_2$O	HOPO$_3$[a]	
3.01	0.15 Formate	+	1.07	0.205	77
3.57	0.16 Maleate	+	1.07	0.178	66.5
3.96	0.18 Formate	−	1.25	0.206	66
5.86	0.14 Maleate	+	1.07	0.054	20
6.00	0.18 Succinate	−	1.25	0.065	21

[a] Observed values were corrected for the small amount of orthophosphate present initially in carbamyl-P.

In contrast, the dianion of the substituted carbamyl phosphates appears to hydrolyze with primarily P—O bond cleavage as shown in Table V. As in the case of carbamyl-P monoanion hydrolysis, isotopic evidence for P—O bond cleavage was substantiated independently by the observation that methyl phosphate was formed during the methanolysis of the species which gave incorporation of ^{18}O in the isotopic experiments. For example, the methanolysis of the dianion of N-phenyl carbamyl-P (P—O bond cleavage) in 0.19 mole fraction methanol at pH 7.18 leads to 44%

TABLE V

P—O Bond Cleavage during the Hydrolysis of the Dianion of Carbamyl-P
and Various N-Substituted Carbamyl Phosphates in H$_2$^{18}O[a]

N-Substituent	pH	Atoms (%) excess ^{18}O in:		P—O Bond fission (%)
		Solvent	KH$_2$PO$_4$[b]	
H—	7.21	1.142	0.036	12.6
CH$_3$—	7.24[c]	1.142	0.246	86.0
	7.43	1.246	0.262	84.0
C$_6$H$_5$—	6.61[c]	1.142	0.233	81.5
p CH$_3$—C$_6$H$_4$—	6.59	1.257	0.246	78.7
p NO$_2$—C$_6$H$_4$—	6.53	1.246	0.313	101.0

[a] These experiments were carried out in 0.2 M maleate buffer, pH 7.1, 37°C, unless noted otherwise. The reaction mixture contained 2.5×10^{-4} mole of the carbamyl phosphate derivative which changed the pH as noted above. The error inherent in duplicate sample for the entire procedure, i.e., isolation, combustion and analysis of the orthophosphate samples is approximately ± 5%. (Allen and Jones, 1964).

[b] Observed values were corrected for the small amount of orthophosphate present initially in the solid carbamyl phosphate derivative.

[c] Maleate buffer used at 0.3 M.

of the total phosphate being found as methyl phosphate, whereas the dianion of carbamyl-P (C—O bond cleavage), under similar conditions, yields only 8.5% methyl phosphate.

DISCUSSION

Decomposition of Carbamyl-P Derivatives Bearing a Single Substituent on the N Atom

These studies show that replacement of a single hydrogen of the amide nitrogen of carbamyl phosphate with a methyl or aryl substituent changes the point of bond cleavage of the dianion from the C—O bond to the P—O bond. Steric factors do not seem to be involved.*

A comparison of the rates of hydrolysis of the mono- and dianionic species of the carbamyl phosphates bearing an aromatic group on the nitrogen atom is remarkably similar to the rates of hydrolysis of the similarly substituted benzyl phosphates as observed by Di Sabato and Jencks (1961), i.e., N-phenyl and N-p-nitrophenyl carbamyl-P have nearly the same rate of hydrolysis as benzyl and p-nitrobenzyl phosphate. If the similarity in the rates of the carbamyl-P bearing the aromatic substituent to the benzyl phosphates is not fortuitous it may mean that the dianion of these derivatives hydrolyzes as the dianion of acetyl phosphate (Di Sabato and Jencks, 1961), where the decomposition is facilitated by the repulsion of the leaving groups so that substitution with electron-withdrawing groups increases the rate of dianion hydrolysis. This simple comparison seems too facile since the amide nitrogen is interposed between the carbonyl group and the benzene ring.

It is difficult with the data collected here to make broad generalizations. For example, it is possible that the hydrolysis of these analogs is due to a direct reaction with water and does not proceed by an intramolecular decomposition. It has recently been reported that the 1-(N,N-dimethyl-carbamyl) pyrimidinium chloride is hydrolyzed by a nucleophilic attack of water (Johnson and Rumon, 1965).

The studies of Lapidot and Samuel (1964) on N,N-diethyl carbamyl-P seem to support an S_N1 mechanism for the hydrolysis of disubstituted carbamyl phosphate. It is of interest that the rates of hydrolysis of the mono- and dianion of N,N-diethyl carbamyl-P are one or two orders of magnitude slower than those of N-methyl carbamyl-P which, in turn, is hydrolyzed more slowly than carbamyl-P (see Table III).

---

* Pauling-Corey models of N-methyl and N-phenyl carbamyl-P show no steric hindrance.

To understand the hydrolysis of the monosubstituted carbamyl phosphates therefore requires that a number of conventional kinetic studies be undertaken. For the purpose of this Chapter, however, it seems fitting that substitution of carbamyl-P yields compounds which hydrolyze like acetyl phosphate or its derivatives.

MAGNESIUM ION EFFECTS

The solvolysis of phosphate compounds is usually catalyzed by the addition of metals [see discussion of Jencks (1962)]. However, the rate constant for the hydrolysis of the monoanion of carbamyl-P shows little effect of added magnesium, whereas the rate constant for the decomposition of the dianion of carbamyl-P shows a marked decrease in the presence of magnesium.

This observation is consistent with the mechanism proposed earlier (Allen and Jones, 1964) for the decomposition of the mono- and dianion of carbamyl-P. If the monoanion of carbamyl-P hydrolyzes by an intramolecular hydrogen transfer from the phosphate group to the carbonyl oxygen [see Eq. (1)], this reaction would not be expected to be affected by divalent metal ions since phosphate monoanions do not form strong complexes with Mg^{2+} ion (Greenwald et al., 1940). However, if the divalent phosphate group of carbamyl phosphate is more strongly chelated with divalent positive magnesium ion, the intramolecular transfer proposed for the decomposition of carbamyl-P dianion [see Eq. (2)] would be unlikely. A decrease in the rate of dianion hydrolysis would be expected and as observed this effect should be dependent on the magnesium concentration.

From the limited data presented here it is not possible to calculate a rate constant (if any) for the decomposition of the magnesium complex of the carbamyl-P dianion. However, a minimal value for the apparent binding constant (K_A) (at an ionic strength of 0.6) for the magnesium complex can be determined to be approximately 14.*

* Using the general equations (1a) and (2a) below:

$$k_{obs} = k_1 \, (\text{carbamyl-P}^{2-}{}_{equil.}) + k_2 \, (\text{Mg-carbamyl-P}) \tag{1a}$$

$$K_A = \frac{(\text{Mg-carbamyl-P})}{(\text{carbamyl-P}^{2-}{}_{equil.}) \, (\text{Mg}^{2+})} \tag{2a}$$

The terms ($\text{carbamyl-P}^{2-}{}_{equil.}$), (Mg-carbamyl-P), and k_{obs} represent the equilibrium concentrations of free carbamyl-P dianion, the magnesium complex of carbamyl-P dianion, and the observed rate of hydrolysis, respectively. Equation (3a) below can be obtained if Eq. (2a) is solved for both carbamyl-P$_{equil.}$ and Mg-carbamyl-P in

A K_A of this magnitude would assure that the minimal percentage of carbamyl-P dianion-magnesium complex in the oxygen isotope experiments was 95%. The isotope data indicate, therefore, that if the magnesium complex of the carbamyl-P dianion is decomposing, it cannot be proceeding by P—O bond cleavage to more than 20%. This figure is a maximal value for the percentage of P—O bond cleavage of the complex, since it has been shown that carbamyl-P decomposition at this pH also proceeds with about 20% P—O bond cleavage.

A situation analogous to the inhibitory effect of magnesium seen here has been observed in the effect of lithium on the glycine-catalyzed hydrolysis of acetyl phosphate (Kurz and Gutsche, 1960). In this general base-catalyzed reaction, the abstraction of a proton from the attacking glycine zwitterion by the dianionic phosphate moiety of acetyl phosphate is proposed. In the presence of lithium the second-order rate constant for the reaction decreases. Kurz and Gutsche (1960) suggested that the complexing of lithium with the phosphate moiety of acetyl phosphate decreased the effectiveness of the phosphate moiety as a general base catalyst.

BIOLOGICAL SIGNIFICANCE OF MAGNESIUM CHELATION

In vivo effects

The inhibitory effect of magnesium ion on the rate of hydrolysis of carbamyl-P dianion could be of some importance in a physiological system since it would lead to a stabilization of carbamy-P. The significance of this effect, however, would be highly dependent on the intracellular concentrations of magnesium ion and carbamyl-P, as well as the K_A for the formation of the complex. The lack of information on these unknowns makes it difficult to judge the physiological importance of a magnesium complex of carbamyl-P dianion at this time.

terms of the total carbamyl-P concentration and K_A. Substitution of these expressions into Eq. (1a) yields the rate expression below:

$$k_{obs} = \frac{k_1 + k_2 K_A (Mg^{2+})}{1 + K_A (Mg^{2+})} \qquad (3a)$$

In order to satisfy Eq. (3a) for the known values of k_1, k_{obs}, and (Mg^{2+}), K_A must have a minimal value of approximately 14 if $k_2 \lessgtr 0$. It would seem that the true value of K_A would be greater than 14, since the values for various phosphate dianions are generally much higher than this (Johnson, 1960).

Prebiological Synthesis of Carbamyl-P

The behavior of other carbamyl-P chelates may be of interest. Miller ·and Parris (1964) have shown that the addition of cyanate to hydroxyl apatite causes the formation of significant quantities of inorganic pyrophosphate near pH 6. This synthesis of inorganic pyrophosphate presumably occurs at the surface of the apatite since it is dependent on the presence of precipitated calcium phosphate (Beck and Orgel, 1965). Miller and Parris suggest that cyanate might be essential for pyrophosphate formation if it reacts with orthophosphate to yield carbamyl-P which then is attacked at the O—P bond by phosphate to yield carbamate and inorganic pyrophosphate.

If the calcium chelate of carbamyl-P dianion behaves as the magnesium chelate, it would be more stable than carbamyl-P, but would cleave predominantly at the C—O bond at pH 6.0. This raises the question of whether the pyrophosphate formation observed by Miller and Parris (1964) was brought about by a direct attack of orthophosphate on carbamyl-P (or calcium carbamyl-P) or if orthophosphate reacts with ionic metaphosphate formed on the decomposition of the small amounts of carbamyl-P monoanion present near pH 6.

The studies of Di Sabato and Jencks (1961) on the formation of pyrophosphate from acetyl phosphate seem pertinent. These authors have observed significant pyrophosphate formation with concentrated solutions (0.2–0.4 M) of acetyl phosphate in 7.3 M NaClO$_4$ (used to decrease the activity of water) but much smaller amounts of pyrophosphate formation were observed in water. The authors suggest that pyrophosphate formation is due to a reaction of phosphate with metaphosphate ion formed on the solvolysis of acetyl phosphate mono- or dianion. (In contrast to carbamyl-P or the magnesium chelate of carbamyl-P, where only the monoanion yields ionic metaphosphate both the mono- and dianion of acetyl phosphate undergo P—O bond cleavage to yield ionic metaphosphate.)

Miller and Parris (1964) found, in a single experiment, that the greatest yield of pyrophosphate occurred at pH 6.5 and that the yield was decreased at more acid and alkaline pH values. The catalysis of inorganic pyrophosphate formation by cyanate in the presence of apatite and its pH dependence would be expected to be extremely complex depending at least on the rates for formation of carbamyl-P (Jones and Lipmann, 1960), the stability of cyanate (below pH 6), and whether orthophosphate reacts directly with carbamyl-P (or its chelate) or indirectly with monomeric metaphosphate, the product of carbamyl-P monoanion hydrolysis. A study of pyrophosphate formation from carbamyl-P or calcium carbamyl-P would eliminate the factors concerned with carbamyl-P formation and would clarify the results of Miller and Parris (1961).

SUMMARY

The replacement of a single hydrogen of the amide nitrogen of carbamyl phosphate with a methyl group (or various benzyl groups) changes the point of bond cleavage for the dianion hydrolysis so that P—O bond cleavage is observed as it is for the dianion of other acyl phosphates, like acetyl phosphate. Substitution also affects the rate of hydrolysis. Magnesium ion has little effect on the hydrolysis of carbamyl phosphate monoanion but causes a marked decrease in the rate of dianion hydrolysis; the point of bond cleavage appears to remain the same for the magnesium chelate.

REFERENCES

Allen, C. M., Jr., and Jones, M. E. (1964). *Biochemistry* 3, 1238.
Beck, A., and Orgel, L. E. (1965). *Proc. Natl. Acad. Sci. U.S.* 54, 664.
Cramer, F., and Winter, M. (1959). *Chem. Ber.* 92, 2761.
Di Sabato, G., and Jencks, W. P. (1961). *J. Am. Chem. Soc.* 83, 440.
Greenwald, I., Redish, J., and Kibrick, A. C. (1940). *J. Biol. Chem.* 135, 65.
Jencks, W. P. (1962). *Brookhaven Symp. Biol.* BNL 738 (C-34) 15, 134.
Johnson, M. J. (1960). In *"The Enzymes"* (P. D. Boyer, H. A. Lardy, and K. Myrbäck, eds.), 2nd ed., Vol. 3, p. 416. Academic Press, New York.
Johnson, S. L., and Rumon, K. A. (1965). *J. Am. Chem. Soc.* 87, 4782.
Jones, M. E., and Lipmann, F. (1960). *Proc. Natl. Acad. Sci. U.S.* 46, 1194.
Jones, M. E., and Spector, L. (1960). *J. Biol. Chem.* 235, 2897.
Kurz, J. L., and Gutsche, C. D. (1960). *J. Am. Chem. Soc.* 82, 2175.
Lapidot, A., and Samuel, D. (1964). *J. Chem. Soc.* p. 1931.
Miller, S. L., and Parris, M. (1964). *Nature* 204, 1248.
Spector, L., Jones, M. E., and Lipmann, F. (1957). *Methods Enzymol.* 3, 653.
Williams, F. R., and Hager, L. P. (1958). *Science* 128, 1434.

Purification and Characterization of Nicotinate Phosphoribosyltransferase from Ehrlich Ascites Carcinoma Cells

R. Seifert, M. Kittler, and H. Hilz

INTRODUCTION

Observations in different laboratories have shown that the nicotinamide adenine dinucleotide content of tumor cells is lowered by the action of certain cytostatic compounds (cf. *1–5*). Under conditions of high dosage, a relative increase in nicotinate incorporation into the remaining DPN has been observed (*6*). X-Rays and ethylenimine derivatives in doses producing a partial inhibition of cell proliferation lead to an absolutely increased capacity of the treated cells to incorporate nicotinic acid into DPN (*7–9*) and also to an increase of DPNase (glycohydrolase E.C. 3.2.2.5) activity (*7–9, cf. 10*), indicating an increased DPN turnover. The opposite phenomenon—a decrease in nicotinate incorporation—is associated with supranormal DPN levels resulting from incubation with increasing concentrations of nicotinamide (*11*). Furthermore, there exists evidence that besides the Preiss-Handler pathway the Kornberg route for DPN synthesis in tumor cells probably functions to a considerable degree. From studies on the incorporation of nicotinamide into DPN under conditions of suppressed DPNase-catalyzed nicotinamide-DPN exchange (*12*) and the incorporation of labeled nicotinamide into NMN and DPN, respectively, under various conditions (*15*), two separable phosphoribosyltransferases appeared to be present in the cytoplasm, one specific for nicotinamide, the other for nicotinic acid (*12–14*).

It seemed of interest to analyze these enzymes at the starting point of the two routes for DPN synthesis, that may be subject to end-product inhibition. In this chapter we shall describe the purification and some characteristics of the (very unstable) enzyme nicotinate phosphoribosyltransferase (E.C. 2.4.2.11) from Ehrlich ascites carcinoma cells. Some properties of the corresponding nicotinamide enzyme (E.C. 2.4.2.12) are also reported.

EXPERIMENTAL PROCEDURE

MATERIALS

Nicotinic acid-^{3}H (specific activity 320 mc/mmole) and nicotinic acid-7-^{14}C (specific activity 27.9 mc/mmole) were obtained from the Radiochemical Center, Amersham, England.* ATP, ADP, AMP, UTP, NMN,† DPN, and TPN were obtained from Boehringer & Soehne GmbH., Mannheim, Germany; CTP, GTP, d-ATP, d-CTP, d-GTP, TTP, PRPP, pyridine-3-sulfonic acid, 3-acetylpyridine, nicotinonitrile, and nicotinyl hydroxamic acid from Nutritional Biochemical Corp., Cleveland, Ohio. Schleicher & Schüll paper 2043b, treated with HCl, was used in all chromatographic and electrophoretic separations. Nicotinamide, nicotinic acid, buffer substances, etc., were obtained from E. Merck, Darmstadt, Germany.

METHODS

Ehrlich ascites tumor cells were drawn from mice 6–7 days after transplantation, centrifuged at 500 $\times g$ and 4°C for 10 min, and extracted as described in the purification procedure (see below). Nicotinate phosphoribosyltransferase activity was measured by determining the rate of nicotinate mononucleotide formation from labeled nicotinate, using the chromatographic system C of Preiss and Handler (16, 17). The spots corresponding to DPN + d-DPN, NMN + N$_a$MN, N$_a$, and NAm were made visible under UV light by addition of carrier substances (0.5 μmole each of DPN and NMN, 2.5 or 0.5 μmoles each of N$_a$ and NAm before

---

* Abbreviations used in this chapter: AMP, adenosine monophosphate; ADP, adenosine diphosphate; ATP, adenosine triphosphate; UTP, uridine triphosphate; CTP, cytidine triphosphate; GTP, guanosine triphosphate; TTP, thymidine triphosphate; NMN, nicotinamide mononucleotide; DPN, diphosphopridine nucleotide (nicotinamide adenine dinucleotide, NAD) TPN, triphosphopyridine nucleotide (nicotinamide adenine dinucleotide phosphate, NADP); d-DPN, deamido-DPN; N$_a$MN, nicotinate mononucleotide; N$_a$, nicotinate; NAm, nicotinamide; PRPP, 5-phosphoribosyl-1-pyrophosphate.

† We thank Dr. H. U. Bergmeyer for a generous gift of NMN.

chromatography). The spots were cut out and either counted directly in dioxane scintillator or eluted with 1 ml of 0.1 N HCl and 0.25 ml of the eluate mixed with 20 ml of dioxane scintillator. With ^{3}H-labeled compounds, there was a 7.6-fold gain in counts on elution of the N_aMN spot and a 5.4-fold gain in the N_a spot.[*] The ^{14}C-labeled compounds gave only a 1.4-fold increase in counts upon elution. Nucleotides and nicotinic acid analogs were checked for purity by paper electrophoresis (18) and paper chromatography employing the systems used by Preiss and Handler (16, 17). The absence of myokinase activity was checked by incubating 2 µmoles ADP under standard conditions (see below) and analyzing the reaction mixture for ADP and ATP by electrophoresis (18). Protein determinations were made according to Warburg and Christian (19) or by the biuret method (20).

STANDARD ASSAY PROCEDURE

The solution to be assayed was prepared in the following manner: 0.1 µmoles Mg-PRPP; 0.85 µc ^{3}H-nicotinic acid (specific activity 320 mc/mmole); 1 µmole ATP; 1.8 µmoles MgCl$_2$; 15 µmoles potassium phosphate buffer, pH 7.3; and enzyme solution and water up to 0.3 ml. The sample was incubated for 180 min at 37°C; then the incubation was stopped by heating at 100°C for 1 min. After centrifugation, 20 or 40 µl was applied to paper and analyzed as described above. One unit is defined as that amount of enzyme which causes the formation of 1 nmole N_aMN under the above conditions.

ASSAY FOR NICOTINAMIDE PHOSPHORIBOSYLTRANSFERASE ACTIVITY

For this assay the following solution was prepared: 15 µmoles potassium phosphate buffer, pH 7.3; 0.1 µmole Mg-PRPP; 0.88 µc ^{14}C-nicotinamide (specific activity 10.7 mc/mmole); 1 µmole ATP; 1.8 µmoles MgCl$_2$; and enzyme solution and water up to 0.30 ml. The sample was incubated for 60 min at 37°C and incubation stopped by heating at 100°C for 1 min. After centrifugation, aliquots (20-40 µl) were chromatographed according to system C of Preiss and Handler (16, 17) and analyzed. One unit is defined as the amount of enzyme that causes the formation of 1 nmole NMN under the above conditions.

CONVERSION OF Mg-PRPP TO Na-PRPP

A solution of the Mg salt of PRPP was passed through a Dowex-50 Na column (200–400 mesh, 1.6 × 13 cm) and washed with a 3-fold volume

---

[*] Nicotinate is partially eluted from the paper by the scintillator mixture.

of water. The combined effluents were freeze-dried and taken up in a small volume of water. The PRPP content was estimated by the determination of acid-labile phosphate.

PREPARATION OF LABELED N_aMN

The solution was prepared as follows: 10 μmoles Mg-PRPP; 183 μmoles $MgCl_2$; 100 μmoles ATP; 1460 μmoles potassium phosphate buffer, pH 7.3; 50 μc ^{14}C-nicotinic acid (specific activity 27.9 mc/mmole); 24.2 ml of 105,000 $\times g$ supernatant of homogenate (see below); and water added to 30 ml. After incubating for 5 hr at 37°C the solution was inactivated by heating for 2 min at 100°C and cooled rapidly. After centrifugation (8500 $\times g$, 10 min) the cloudy supernatant was mixed with 1.3 ml of 70% $HClO_4$, centrifuged, and immediately neutralized with 4 N KOH to pH 6.0. The precipitate was removed by centrifugation. The heat-denatured protein residue was agitated with 15 ml of 3% $HClO_4$ and centrifuged. The supernatant was neutralized and combined with the main fraction; 49 ml of supernatant was chromatographed on a Dowex-1 formate column (200–400 mesh, 1.6 $\times$ 11 cm) according to the method of Preiss and Handler (17). The radioactive fractions were stirred with activated charcoal (4 mg/ml) for 25 min in the cold, sucked through a funnel with a sintered glass plate (G_4-Fritte), washed with cold water, and eluted with 200 ml of an isoamyl alcohol-water mixture (1/9, w/w) by stirring for 6 hour at 4°C. After removal of the charcoal by filtration (G_4-Fritte), the eluate was concentrated under reduced pressure at 27°C. Most activity was found in the fraction corresponding to N_aMN, which upon purification was about 95% pure. The yield was 85.2 nmoles N_aMN.

IDENTIFICATION OF REACTION PRODUCT

Reaction mixtures with crude homogenates or fractions obtained from acetone-dried cells always yielded two radioactive spots (in addition to the substrate nicotinic acid) corresponding to N_aMN and deamido-DPN. Yet, the removal of the particulate fraction abolished most of N_aMN adenylyltransferase activity (E.C. 2.7.7.1) which is present in the nucleoli (14, 21, 22). The purified fractions therefore catalyze the formation of a single radioactive product with labeled nicotinic acid as substrate. It has been identified as N_aMN on the following evidence. In the chromatographic systems of Preiss and Handler (17) as well as in paper electrophoresis methods (cf. 23) and chromatography on Dowex-1 formate columns (17), the product behaves like authentic N_aMN. Furthermore, isolation of the reaction product by chromatography on Dowex-1 formate columns and incubation with NMN adenylyltransferase purified from Ehrlich tumor cell nuclei resulted in a nearly quantitative conversion of the product to deamido-DPN (Table I).

TABLE I

CONVERSION OF THE REACTION PRODUCT TO DEAMIDO-DPN BY NMN
ADENYLYLTRANSFERASE PURIFIED FROM TUMOR CELLS[a]

Incubation	N_aMN (cpm)	d-DPN (cpm)
—	$67,900 \pm 510$	$3,860 \pm 1,720$
+	$15,230 \pm 3,200$	$58,540 \pm 1,970$

[a] Mean values from three single determinations. For further details see section on experimental procedure.

CONVERSION OF N_aMN TO DEAMIDO-DPN

The reaction mixture consisted of 5 µmoles ATP; 5 µmoles $MgCl_2$; 15 µmoles borate-acetate buffer, pH 6.0; 0.10 ml ^{14}C-N_aMN solution (92,300 cpm corresponding to 3.2 nmoles N_aMN, 95% pure); 0.05 ml NMN adenylyltransferase (0.06 units[*]); and water added to 0.30 ml. The mixture was incubated for 3 hr at 37°C. Samples were heated for 1 min at 100°C, and an aliquot (60 µl) was applied to chromatography paper and developed in ethanol-ammonium acetate solvent according to the method of Preiss and Handler (16). Strips (2×3 cm) were analyzed as described above.

PURIFICATION PROCEDURE

Step 1. Extraction

Packed tumor cells (21.7 ml) were lyzed by suspension in 195 ml of cold water for 10 min and homogenization with a tight-fitting Teflon-glass homogenizer until microscopic examination revealed that no unbroken cells ($< 1\%$) remained and that the nuclei were free of adhering cytoplasmic structures. The cell homogenate was centrifuged at 22,000 $\times g$ (20 min); the resulting supernatant was again spun at 60,000 $\times g$ (45 min) and 1 M potassium phosphate buffer, pH 6.35, was added to the 60,000 $\times g$ supernatant to give a final concentration of 0.2 M.

All subsequent steps were carried out in the cold and as rapidly as possible unless stated otherwise.

[*] The enzyme, kindly provided by Dr. K. Lorentz, was purified about 100-fold from Ehrlich tumor cells (24).

Step 2. *Ammonium Sulfate Fractionation*

In this step 74.4 ml of saturated (4°C) ammonium sulfate solution was added slowly to 222.5 ml of the 60,000 ×g supernatant, with continuous stirring (26% saturation). Fifteen minutes after the last addition, the suspension was centrifuged for 20 min at 22,000 ×g and the precipitate was discarded. To 296 ml of the supernatant, 108 ml of saturated (4°C) ammonium sulfate solution was added to yield 43% saturation. After 2 hr, the mixture was centrifuged again for 20 min at 22,000 ×g. The precipitate was dissolved in 15 ml of 0.2 M potassium phosphate buffer, pH 7.3.

Step 3. *Dialysis*

The fraction resulting from the purification in Step 2 was transferred into dialysis bags and dialyzed for 2 hr at 4°C against 3 liters of 0.005 M potassium phosphate buffer, pH 7.3, with internal mixing by an air bubble.

Step 4. *Acid Precipitation of Inactive Protein*

In this step 20.5 ml of the dialyzed fraction (16.1 mg protein/ml) were diluted (1:1) with 0.2 M potassium phosphate buffer, pH 7.3. To 41.0 ml of this dilution, 7.75 ml of 0.5 N acetic acid was added dropwise to give a final pH of 5.2. After 5 min, the mixture was centrifuged for 10 min at 40,000 ×g.

Step 5. *Removal of Inactive Protein by Alumina Gel Adsorption*

In this step 15.7 ml of aluminum hydroxide gel (14.8 mg/ml) was added to 40 ml of acid-precipitated supernatant. The solution was stirred for 5 min and centrifuged for 6 min at 1000 ×g. The supernatant constitutes the final fraction.

Step 3a. *Preparation of a Stable Intermediate Fraction*

To prepare a stable fraction, the dialyzed ammonium sulfate fraction (Step 3) was freeze-dried. This procedure usually results in a 70–80% loss in total activity. The sample then remains nearly constant for several weeks if kept over CaCl₂ at −20°C. To obtain a purer fraction, 37.75 mg of dried powder is taken up with 4.50 ml of 0.20 M phosphate buffer, pH 7.3, and stirred for 15 min. After centrifugation for 5 min at 4000 ×g the supernatant is further treated as described in Steps 4 and 5, respectively. The resulting purification is about the same as in the "direct" route. Because of the loss in total activity during drying, the final product has a lower specific activity than the enzyme prepared without interruption of purification.

Another stable form of the enzyme can be obtained if an acetone powder is prepared from whole tumor cells. Since attempts to purify the enzyme from this material have not been very successful, the experiments with such fractions are not included.

TABLE II

PURIFICATION OF NICOTINATE PHOSPHORIBOSYLTRANSFERASE

Fraction	Volume (ml)	Units	Yield (%)	Protein (mg)	Specific activity (units/mg protein)
Homogenate	187	401.1	—	3960	0.099
Supernatant, 60,000 $\times g$	180	974.9	—	1577	0.69
Ammonium sulfate-43	18.7	1569.3	100	396	3.96
Dialyzed	21.7	934.5	59	350	2.67
Acid-precipitated supernatant	43.7	702.8	45	198	3.55
Alumina gel supernatant	49.7	271.5	17	9.4	28.79

The purification procedure is summarized in Table II. With the exception of the dialyzed and dried ammonium sulfate fraction of Step 3a, none of the fractions is stable. Most activity is lost within 1–3 days. The final fraction exhibits a specific activity ca. 290 times that of the tumor cell homogenate. However, since removal of the particulate fractions and ammonium sulfate fractionation result in a nearly 4-fold increase in total activity, the true purification is about 70-fold.

RESULTS

LOCALIZATION AND PURIFICATION

The enzyme nicotinate phosphoribosyltransferase (N_aPRtransferase, E.C. 2.4.2.11) as well as nicotinamide phosphoribosyltransferase (NAm PRtransferase, E.C. 2.4.2.12) is localized in the cytoplasm of the tumor cells (Table III). It is unlikely that the enzyme leaks out of the nucleus since the nuclear fraction contains less enzyme than is to be expected from an equal distribution of the enzyme after lysis of the cells. On the other hand, neither NMN adenylyltransferase (E.C. 2.7.7.1) nor the nucleolar DPN glycohydrolase (E.C. 3.2.2.5) appears in the supernatant under the conditions of particle separation (14). The considerable increase in total activity after segregation of the particle fraction may be due to the concomitant removal of phosphatases or an inhibitor or both (cf. Tables II and III).

TABLE III

LOCALIZATION OF NICOTINATE PHOSPHORIBOSYLTRANSFERASE AND NICOTINAMIDE
PHOSPHORIBOSYLTRANSFERASE IN THE CYTOPLASM OF TUMOR CELLS[a]

Fraction	N_a PRtransferase (cpm)	NAm PRtransferase (cpm)
Homogenate	102,000	323,000
Cytoplasm		
Supernatant, 22,000 $\times g$	349,000	890,000
Supernatant, 105,000 $\times g$	344,000	700,000
Nuclei	<30	370
Nucleoli	<30	<40

[a] Values for 1 ml of packed cells analyzed under standard assay conditions with 0.8 μc ^{3}H-nicotinate and 0.8 μc ^{14}C-nicotinamide. In both assay mixtures, 0.6 μmole ribose-5-phosphate was included. The counts refer to noneluted N_aMN and NMN spots respectively. The preparation of nuclei and nucleoli can be found in detail in Ref. 14. Preparation of homogenate and supernatants is described in the section on purification procedure.

The enzyme nicotinate phosphoribosyltransferase is very unstable in solution. The only way to obtain a reasonable purification (∼ 70-fold) demands rapid purification without interruption as outlined above and summarized in Table II. A relatively stable preparation can be obtained, though with a 70–80% loss of activity, by freeze-drying the dialyzed ammonium sulfate fraction "Am. 43." The dry powder loses 5–20% of its activity per week when kept at −20°C.

KINETIC PROPERTIES

The enzyme at all stages of purification is stable for several hours under standard incubation conditions (Fig. 1D). The pH optimum lies below pH 7 (Fig. 1A). The enzyme depends on an adequate concentration of Mg^{2+} ions for full activity (Fig. 1B); Mg^{2+} can be partially replaced by Co^{2+} or Mn^{2+}, whereas Ca^{2+} inhibits the reaction (Table IV). The Michaelis constants for the reactants in the standard test are summarized in Table V. The dependency of these K_m values on the ATP concentration is discussed below.

SPECIFICITY FOR NICOTINIC ACID

The purified enzyme from Ehrlich tumor cells exhibits a similar specificity toward nicotinic acid as does the liver enzyme characterized by Imsande and Handler (25). Nicotinamide, freed of traces of nicotinic

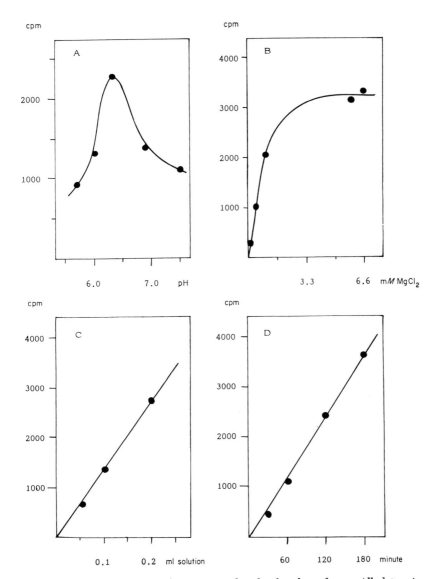

Fig. 1.   Kinetic properties of nicotinate phosphoribosyltransferase. All determinations were carried out with the final fraction (alumina gel supernatant) using ^{3}H-nicotinic acid as substrate. The counts per minute (cpm) refer to noneluted N_aMN spots (cf. section on experimental procedure). (A) pH-activity curve with phosphate buffers; (B) absolute requirement of the enzyme for Mg^{2+} ions; (C) and (D) Linearity of reaction with respect to time and enzyme concentration.

TABLE IV

SUBSTITUTION OF Mg^{2+} BY VARIOUS CATIONS IN NICOTINATE
PHOSPHORIBOSYLTRANSFERASE REACTION[a]

Cation	Activity	
(8.3 μmoles/ml)	cpm/sample	%
$MgCl_2$	$19,950 \pm 300$	100
$Co(NO_3)_2$	9750	49
$MnCl_2$	9000	45
$FeSO_4$	1370	7
$ZnCl_2$	990	5
$CaCl_2$	420	2
$CuSO_4$	<150	<1
$MgCl_2 + CaCl_2$	7530	38

[a] Incubation under standard conditions (cf. section on methods) with 0.20 ml of purified enzyme (alumina gel supernatant). The counts per minute (cpm) refer to HCl-eluted N_aMN spots (cf. section on experimental procedure).

TABLE V

MICHAELIS CONSTANTS UNDER STANDARD CONDITIONS[a]

Reactant	K_m
Nicotinate	7×10^{-7}
PRPP	3×10^{-5}
Mg^{2+}	9×10^{-4}
ATP	3×10^{-4}

[a] Approximate values deduced from three experiments analyzed by conventional procedures (26). Purified enzyme (alumina gel supernatant) was used throughout.

TABLE VI

INHIBITION OF N_aMN FORMATION BY NICOTINIC ACID ANALOGS[a]

Pyridine derivative added	Concentration (M)	Activity	
		cpm	%
None	—	$26,700 \pm 680$	100
Nicotinamide	1×10^{-4}	25,400	95
Nicotinamide	1×10^{-3}	22,400	84
Nicotinonitrile	1×10^{-3}	24,000	90
3-Acetylpyridine	1×10^{-3}	31,100	112
Nicotinylhydroxamate	1×10^{-3}	10,500	39
Pyridine-3-sulfonate	1×10^{-3}	5,710	21

[a] Determinations were carried out under standard conditions with 0.20 ml of alumina gel supernatant. The counts refer to HCl-eluted N_aMN spots (cf. section on methods). The compounds were added to the final concentrations as indicated. The different analogs were analyzed as described in the section on experimental procedure and proved to be chromatographically pure.

acid by passing the solution through a Dowex-1 formate column, has only a minor inhibitory effect even in a 100-fold excess (Table VI). However, concentrations above $10^{-2}\,M$ strongly inhibit the purified enzyme (cf. Fig. 5). Apparently, an acidic group attached to the pyridine ring is required in order to influence the enzyme at the $10^{-3}\,M$ level (Table VI). Thus, nicotinamide, nicotinonitrile, and 3-acetylpyridine at this concen-

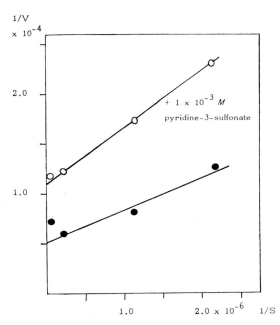

FIG. 2. Noncompetitive inhibition of nicotinate phosphoribosyltransferase by pyridine-3-sulfonate. Lineweaver-Burk plot (26) of experiments carried out with the final fraction (0.20 ml alumina gel supernatant) under standard conditions. ³H-nicotinic acid of the same specific activity (320 mc/mmole) was used throughout, with duplicate nonincubated controls for each concentration.

tration are practically without effect. On the other hand, nicotinylhydroxamate and pyridine-3-sulfonate exhibit a remarkable inhibition of the reaction. Surprisingly, the type of inhibition exhibited by the sulfonic acid analog is not competitive (Fig. 2). This effect may be connected with the allosteric influences on the enzyme (see below).

Additional support for the specificity of the enzyme comes from the nearly quantitative removal of the enzyme nicotinamide phosphoribosyltransferase in the course of purification (Table VII) and from the fact

TABLE VII
SEPARATION OF NICOTINATE PHOSPHORIBOSYLTRANSFERASE FROM
NICOTINAMIDE PHOSPHORIBOSYLTRANSFERASE[a]

	Nicotinate PRtransferase		Nicotinamide PRtransferase	
Fraction	Units	Specific activity	Units	Specific activity
Homogenate	109.9	0.11	20.4	0.02
Supernatant, 60,000 ×g	432.2	0.84	87.2	0.17
Ammonium sulfate-43	370.0	2.65	9.0	0.06
Alumina gel supernatant	73.8	28.78	0.1	0.06

[a] Purification procedure was exactly as described, starting with 6.00 ml of packed tumor cells. For analytical details see section on experimental procedure.

that nicotinic acid in a 30-fold excess over nicotinamide does not interfere with NMN formation (and vice versa).

ALLOSTERIC PROPERTIES OF NICOTINATE PHOSPHORIBOSYLTRANSFERASE

Activation by ATP and Other Nucleotides

In contrast to the enzyme from liver (cf. 25) the nicotinate transferase from tumor cells has an absolute requirement for ATP under standard conditions (Table VIII). The apparent K_m value under these conditions is 3×10^{-4} (Table V).

TABLE VIII
INFLUENCE OF VARIOUS NUCLEOTIDES ON NICOTINATE
PHOSPHORIBOSYLTRANSFERASE[a]

Nucleotide (3.3 μmoles/ml)	Activity	
	cpm/sample	%
ATP	3510 ± 90	100
ADP	1330	38
AMP	<30	<1
CTP	2930	83
GTP	1910	54
UTP	550	16
d-ATP	2110	60
d-CTP	1500	43
d-GTP	750	21
d-TTP	310	9
—	<15	<1

[a] Incubation under standard conditions (cf. section on methods) with 0.19 mg of purified enzyme (alumina gel supernatant). Counts per minute (cpm) values refer to noneluted N_aMN spots (cf. section on experimental procedure). The nucleotides were added in place of ATP.

Adenosine triphosphate seems to have allosteric properties with respect to PRPP and nicotinate (Figs. 3 and 4). Increasing the concentration of PRPP in the absence of ATP leads to an obvious activity optimum with PRPP concentrations twenty times higher than those in the presence of ATP (Fig. 3). It can be deduced from these experiments that ATP influences the K_m value of the enzyme for PRPP, as well as its maximal

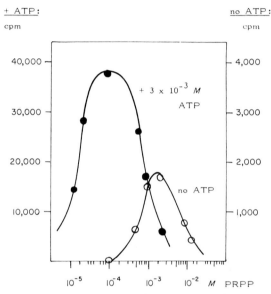

Fig. 3. Influence of ATP on the PRPP dependency of N_aMN formation. All determinations were carried out under standard conditions except for nicotinic acid and PRPP; ^{14}C-nicotinic acid (0.5 µc = 18 nmoles) instead of nicotinic acid and Na-PRPP instead of Mg-PRPP were used. The values correlate to 0.2 mg of protein from the final fraction (alumina gel supernatant).

velocity. The inhibition of the substrate at the higher concentration range and its "transfer" to lower ranges by ATP points to a specific effect.

A more complicated situation is indicated by the results obtained by increasing the concentration of nicotinate. As shown in Fig. 4, the optimal concentration of nicotinate in the presence of saturating ATP levels ($3 \times 10^{-3} M$) is 0.8×10^{-5}–$3 \times 10^{-5} M$. Decreasing the ATP level to $2 \times 10^{-4} M$ considerably changes the activity-concentration curve of the substrate indicating the overlapping of two enzyme forms. In the absence of ATP, nicotinate must be added in high concentrations in order to obtain a reasonable activity.

The sigmoidal curves for PRPP and nicotinate point to an allosteric phenomenon for the ATP-enzyme interaction, although it has not yet been possible to isolate two forms of the enzyme.

The concept of an allosteric ATP effect is further supported by experiments which show that ATP does not act merely as a stabilizer for the

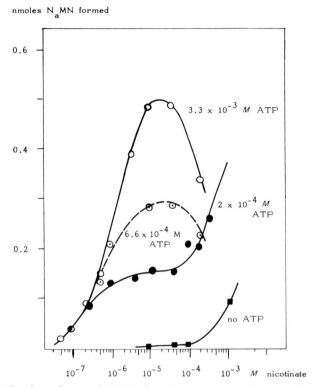

FIG. 4. The dependency of $N_a MN$ formation on nicotinate concentration under various ATP levels. Determinations were made under standard conditions with alumina gel supernatant as enzyme source. ^{3}H-labeled nicotinic acid was used throughout with carrier nicotinic acid where needed and with nonincubated controls. Factors for conversion of counts per minute (cpm) into nmoles are listed in the section on experimental procedure.

enzyme. Preincubation with or without ATP does not change the final activity.

The enzyme is not very specific for ATP (Table VIII). To give reasonable binding to the presumably allosteric site at least one pyrophosphate group is necessary. The pyrimidine nucleotide CTP with its amino group in a position comparable to the adenines is nearly as effective as ATP itself. In contrast, the purine nucleotide GTP which has the amino group in the "wrong" position is considerably less active. Also, the ribose moiety has a remarkable influence, because all deoxyribonucleotides are about half as effective as the corresponding ribonucleotides.

In contrast to the enzyme from liver, nicotinate transferase from tumor cells is not stimulated by inorganic phosphate, but partially inhibited by it. Certainly, the degree of inhibition is less than that with nicotinamide transferase (cf. *13*).

Inhibition by Pyridine Coenzymes

The enzyme during all purification stages is inhibited by pyridine co-enzymes at concentrations between 10^{-3} and $10^{-2} M$ (Table IX and

TABLE IX

INHIBITION OF NICOTINATE PHOSPHORIBOSYLTRANSFERASE
BY PYRIDINE COENZYMES[a]

Pyridine derivative added	Concentration (M)	Activity (cpm)	Inhibition (%)
None		5820 ± 160	0
DPN	3.3×10^{-3}	3820	34
TPN	3.3×10^{-3}	3970	32
DPNH	3.3×10^{-3}	2470	58
TPNH	3.3×10^{-3}	2760	53
NMN	3.3×10^{-3}	2620	55
d-DPN	2.1×10^{-3}	<40	>99

[a] The experiments were performed in duplicate or quadruplicate with the alumina gel supernatant fraction (0.20 ml) under standard conditions using ^{14}C-nicotinic acid (0.5 µc) as substrate. Mean values were obtained from noneluted paper counting (cf. section on experimental procedure).

Fig. 5). The reduced forms seem to be somewhat more effective, whereas deamido-DPN clearly exceeds all other coenzymes. As shown in Fig. 5, these effects are distinct from the probably unspecific response of the enzyme to high nicotinamide concentrations.

NICOTINATE PHOSPHORIBOSYLTRANSFERASE AND N_aMN PHOSPHATASE

Recently, Nakamura and co-workers postulated a reversible conversion of the liver nicotinate transferase into a phosphatase in the absence of ATP (*27*). With purified enzyme from tumor cells, we could not detect any significant N_aMN degradation to the N_a riboside or to free nicotinate caused by the omission of ATP in the reaction mixture (Table X). Even

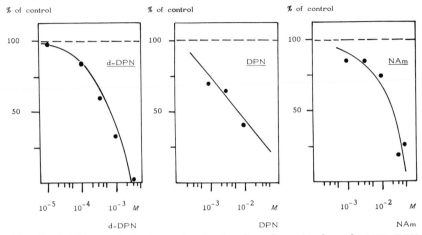

Fɪɢ. 5.   Inhibition of nicotinate phosphoribosyltransferase by deamido-DPN, DPN and nicotinamide. Determinations were carried out with the final fraction (alumina gel supernatant) under standard conditions.

TABLE X

Fᴀɪʟᴜʀᴇ ᴏꜰ Pᴜʀɪꜰɪᴇᴅ Nɪᴄᴏᴛɪɴᴀᴛᴇ Pʜᴏꜱᴘʜᴏʀɪʙᴏꜱʏʟᴛʀᴀɴꜱꜰᴇʀᴀꜱᴇ ᴛᴏ Aᴄᴛ ᴀꜱ ᴀ
Pʜᴏꜱᴘʜᴀᴛᴀꜱᴇ ɪɴ Aʙꜱᴇɴᴄᴇ ᴏꜰ ATP[a]

		With incubation (cpm)		
Compounds	No incubation (cpm)	+ ATP	−ATP	Δ ∓ ATP
Homogenate				
$N_a MN + NMN$	14,190	8,802	14,856	—
d-DPN + DPN	409	5,920	426	—
N_a Riboside	201	234	354	+120
N_a	535	657	678	+ 21
Ammonium sulfate-43 dialyzed fraction				
$N_a MN + NMN$	14,145	12,110	12,040	—
d-DPN + DPN	589	3,810	2,890	—
N_a Riboside	243	203	244	+ 41
N_a	289	308	457	+149
Alumina gel supernatant				
$N_a MN + NMN$	13,006	11,824	11,890	—
d-DPN + DPN	746	1,920	1,270	—
N_a Riboside	210	250	240	− 10
N_a	140	124	124	± 0

[a] Incubation with 0.20 ml of homogenate, 0.20 ml of ammonium sulfate-43 dialyzed fraction, and 0.20 ml of alumina gel supernatant under conditions as described in the section on experimental procedure.

in crude homogenates, the conversion of labeled N_aMN to the riboside or nicotinate is negligible. This could be due to the presence of ATP in the homogenate, since there is a significant conversion of N_aMN to deamido-DPN in the samples which do not contain added ATP. Also, there is some formation of nicotinate with the ammonium sulfate-43 fraction if ATP is omitted. Except for a slight formation of d-DPN, none of these reactions can be observed with the final enzyme preparation.

DISCUSSION

The purified nicotinate phosphoribosyltransferase of Ehrlich ascites tumor cells has many similarities to the enzyme from liver characterized by Handler and co-workers (17, 25, 28): the localization in the cytoplasm, the very low K_m value for nicotinate, the specificity for nicotinate, the requirement for Mg^{2+} ions, and the nonidentity with nicotinamide transferase. Nevertheless, there are several features in which the enzyme from tumors differs from the transferase in liver. It has an absolute requirement for ATP at low concentrations of PRPP and nicotinate. Apparently, ATP has allosteric properties in this system changing both K_m and V_{max} for PRPP. Similar effects are seen with nicotinate. No N_aMN phosphatase activity of the enzyme could be observed in absence of ATP, as postulated by Nakamura and co-workers (27) for the enzyme from liver.

Another interesting aspect of the enzyme from tumor cells is its inhibition by the pyridine coenzymes DPN, TPN, and the corresponding reduced forms. It has not yet been determined whether this inhibition is also based on an allosteric property of the enzyme. Certainly, the inhibition by DPN would fit in well with the general scheme of end-product inhibition. However, the concentrations required for an effective retardation of the reaction are somewhat high compared to the DPN level in tumor cells (0.35–0.55 μmole/ml packed cells). Whether this is also true concerning deamido-DPN has not yet been established. None the less, the general concept of feedback inhibition operative at the nicotinate transferase level gains support from experiments with intact tumor cells. Incubation of cells with increasing concentrations of nicotinamide leads to a concomitant rise in DPN content and a fall in nicotinate incorporation into DPN.*

---

* Unpublished observations (1966). The effect on nicotinate incorporation cannot be explained by an isotope dilution effect through intracellular deamidation of nicotinamide. Control experiments reveal a complete lack of NAm deamidation in normal tumor cells incubated under the same conditions.

SUMMARY

A nicotinate phosphoribosyltransferase has been purified approximately 70-fold from Ehrlich ascites tumor cells. It is practically free of nicotinamide phosphoribosyltransferase. The enzyme has an absolute requirement for ATP at low concentrations of substrates, which can be partially substituted by other ribonucleotides and deoxyribonucleotides having an amino group in the pyrimidine ring. Inorganic phosphate is slightly inhibitory; DPN, TPN, the reduced forms thereof, and especially deamido-DPN seem to exhibit a feedback inhibition. No N_aMN phosphatase activity could be detected in the purified enzyme preparation upon omission of ATP.

ACKNOWLEDGMENTS

We thank Mr. G. Jarmers for providing tumor cells. This work was supported by grants of the Deutsche Forschungsgemeinschaft.

REFERENCES

1. Roitt, J. B., *Biochem. J.* **63**, 300 (1956).
2. Holzer, H., Glogner, P., and Sedlmayr, G., *Biochem. Z.* **330**, 59 (1958).
3. Maass, H., Höhne, G., Künkel, H. A., and Rathgen, G. H., *Z. Naturforsch.* **12b**, 553 (1957).
4. Weitzel, G., Buddecke, E., and Schneider, F., *Z. Physiol. Chem.* **323**, 211 (1961).
5. Hilz, H., Hubmann, B., Oldekop, M., Scholz, M., and Gossler, M. v., *Biochem. Z.* **336**, 62 (1962).
6. Hilz, H., Hlavica, P., and Bertram, B., *Biochem. Z.* **338**, 283 (1963).
7. Hilz, H., Rüter, J., Oldekop, M., and Wüppen, I., *Life Sci.* **4**, 765 (1965).
8. Erbe, W., Preiss, J., Seifert, R., and Hilz, H., *Biochem. Biophys. Res. Commun.*, **23**, 392 (1966).
9. Rüter, J., Vachek, H., Oldekop, M., Wüppen, I., and Hilz, H., *Biochem. Z.* **344**, 153 (1966).
10. Green, S., and Bodanski, O., *J. Biol. Chem.* **240**, 2574 (1965).
11. Hilz, H., Erbe, W., and Preiss, J., *Z. Klin. Chem.* **3**, 7 (1965).
12. Grunicke, H., Liersch, M., Richter, E., and Holzer, H., *Z. Klin. Chem.* **3**, 7 (1965).
13. Dietrich, L. S., Fuller, L., Yero, L. I., and Martinez, L., *Nature* **208**, 347 (1965).
14. Königk, E., Preiss, J., Kittler, M., and Hilz, H., *Z. Klin. Chem.* **3**, 9 (1965).
15. Seifert, R., unpublished experiments, 1966.
16. Imsande, J., Preiss, J., and Handler, P., *Methods Enzymol.* **6**, 345 (1963).
17. Preiss, J., and Handler, P., *J. Biol. Chem.* **233**, 488 (1958).
18. Hilz, H., and Lipmann, F., *Proc. Natl. Acad. Sci. U.S.* **41**, 880 (1955).
19. Warburg, O., and Christian, W., *Biochem. Z.* **310**, 384 (1942).
20. Weichselbaum, T. E., *Am. J. Clin. Pathol.* **10**, 40 (1946).
21. Kaufmann, E., Traub, A., and Ginzburg-Tietz, Y., *Israel J. Chem.* **2**, 252 (1964).
22. Siebert, G., and Busch, H., *Z. Klin. Chem.* **3**, 13 (1965).
23. Nishizuka, Y., and Hayaishi, O., *J. Biol. Chem.* **238**, 3369 (1963).

24. Lorentz, K., and Hilz, H., unpublished experiments, 1966.
25. Imsande, J., and Handler, P., *J. Biol. Chem.* **236**, 525 (1961).
26. Lineweaver, H., and Burk, D., *J. Am. Chem. Soc.* **56**, 658 (1934).
27. Nakamura, S., Nishizuka, Y., and Hayaishi, O., *J. Biol. Chem.* **239**, PC2717 (1964).
28. Preiss, J., and Handler, P., *J. Biol. Chem.* **233**, 493 (1958).

Biochemical Aspects of Membrane Function

Eugene P. Kennedy

The decade beginning in 1940 ushered in a new era in biology, an era in which the attack on fundamental problems of cell physiology became the most exciting and dramatic development in contemporary science. The introduction of new and powerful physicochemical methods, particularly the isotope tracer technique and chromatography in all of its myriad forms, was of course absolutely essential to this development of biology, but in retrospect it appears that the crystallization at just that time of new concepts of bioenergetics was also of crucial importance. These new views were clearly formulated in the classic paper of Lipmann (1941), the publication of which is honored by the present anniversary volume. At about the same time, Kalckar (1941) also arrived at similar ideas, and the publication of his review added to the impact on the biochemical community.

Dynamic biochemistry during the period 1920–1940 was marked by efforts to discover the chemical basis of the principal energy-yielding processes in living cells. This phase came to a climax in the 1930's with the elucidation of the central reactions of glycolysis by Warburg and the formulation of the tricarboxylic acid cycle by Krebs. It is a striking fact that in 1940, although the chemical framework of these primary exergonic processes was understood, nothing was known about the biosynthesis of any of the major constituents of living cells. Lipmann recognized that the central role of adenosine triphosphate (ATP) and other energy-rich phosphates in the chemical and energetic coupling of energy-requiring to energy-releasing processes provided the key to the experimental study of biosynthetic reactions, and now 25 years later, the biosynthesis of all major classes of cellular substances—carbohydrates, lipids, proteins and nucleic acids—has been worked out at least in outline and often in considerable detail.

In his paper (1941), Lipmann also considered the energetics of active transport across membranes and pointed out that here also the coupling of such an endergonic process to the utilization of ATP is to be expected. Twenty-five years later, however, in sharp contrast to the progress in our understanding of biosynthesis, very little has yet been learned about the biochemical basis of the specific transport of substances across cell membranes in general or about active transport in particular. Why has this problem, recognized as a central one in cell biology, proved so refractory? In part, at least, the answer may lie in the difficulty of applying chemical methods to a problem in which cellular topology plays such a large part. The cytoplasmic membrane of the living cell is in effect a boundary which delineates rather sharply the transition between two phases, the living substance and the outer milieu. The methodology which has proved so successful in studying problems of biosynthesis can be summarized in the maxim: extract and purify. This approach unfortunately necessarily involves disruption of cellular architecture and the disappearance of that distinction between cytoplasm and the surrounding medium which is the heart of the transport problem. One solution of this dilemma, which will be discussed in a later section of this paper, is to develop methods of recognizing and labeling components of transport systems *while still in the living cell* which may make it possible to isolate and study them after disruption of the cell.

Recognition of the vital role played by the cytoplasmic membrane not only in modulating the passage of metabolites into and out of the cell, but also as the possible site of action of drugs and hormones, and in cell growth and cell division, has greatly stimulated work on biochemical aspects of membrane function in recent years. Many aspects of this work have been discussed in recent reviews (Hoffman, 1964; Kleinzeller and Kotyk, 1961). This paper will be concerned principally with recent work on the biochemical aspects of the lactose transport system in *Escherichia coli*.

THE β-GALACTOSIDE TRANSPORT SYSTEM
OF *ESCHERICHIA COLI*

The brilliant contributions of workers at the Institut Pasteur (Cohen and Monod, 1957; Kepes and Cohen, 1962) have demonstrated that lactose (like many other hydrophilic substances) does not enter cells of *E. coli* by a process of free diffusion, but rather that transport of lactose into the cell is mediated by a highly specific, genetically controlled transport system. Evidence for the existence of such transport systems for sugars was implicit in the earlier work of Doudoroff (1951) and his collaborators and of others, but it remained for Monod and his collaborators to provide the decisive genetic and kinetic evidence for such systems in bacteria.

The term permease was coined by the Parisian workers to describe these bacterial transport systems. The introduction of this term has been vigorously contested on the grounds that such a designation is appropriate only for an enzyme, and no enzyme has yet been demonstrated to catalyze a reaction required for the transport of β-galactosides. There is, however, clear evidence that a specific *protein* is involved in β-galactoside transport (Kepes and Cohen, 1962).

In the original definition of *permease* (Rickenberg, *et al.*, 1956) this designation was applied to the entire transport system: "Nous définirons une perméase comme étant un système de nature protéinique assurant le transfert catalytique d'un substrat à travers une barrière osmotique cellulaire, possédant les propriétés de spécificité stérique et cinétique d'activité d'un enzyme, mais distinct et indépendant des enzymes assurant le métabolism proprement dit du substrat. Cette définition ne préjuge pas du mécanisme d'action des perméases, mais elle implique deux hypothèses essentielle:

"a) Que le transfert perméasique comporte la formation transitoire d'un complex spécifique entre la proteine de la perméase et le substrat;

"b) Que le permease est un système *fonctionnellement spécialisé* n'intervenant pas dans le métabolisme intracellulaire proprement dit."

It is clear that the word permease as originally defined is the designation of a *system* and in this sense is analogous to designations such as *galactozymase*, formerly applied to the entire complex of enzymes involved in the fermentation of a sugar. However, the term permease has been widely used in the literature to designate, not only the entire system, but also the specific, as yet hypothetical enzyme postulated by Monod and his collaborators to play an essential role in lactose transport. This substitution of the part for the whole has been the source of very real confusion, since it has carried the implication that the transport system consists of a single protein, coded by the y gene in the *lac* operon. Such usage is clearly at variance with the original definition of the term and may have hindered progress in this field by masking the possible degree of biochemical complexity of the system.

A related conceptual difficulty arises from ambiguity in the operational basis of tests designed to measure "permease." Such tests are usually devised on the basis of one of the four manifestations of the activity of the system, listed by Kepes and Cohen (1962).

"Galactoside permease has been defined as an entity different from and independent of β-galactosidase, that is essential for (1) growth on lactose as carbon source, (2) hydrolysis of o-nitrophenyl-β-D-galactoside (ONPG) at a high rate *in vivo*, (3) inducibility of the synthesis of β-galactosidase with low concentrations of inducer (with simultaneous induction of the permease itself), and (4) accumulation of large amounts of gratuitous inducers, i.e., non-metabolizable β-galactosides or thio-galactosides."

It seems likely that tests based on the *accumulation* of galactosides [(3) and (4) listed above] may involve a different set of reactions from tests based on the rate of hydrolysis of ONPG by intact cells. Under ordinary conditions, a large excess of β-galactosidase is present in fully induced wild-type cells. Thus, the rate of *entry* of the substrate into the cell, mediated by the transport system, is indeed the rate-limiting factor for the hydrolysis of ONPG by intact cells. In contrast, *accumulation* of unaltered galactoside to levels higher than that in the external medium requires not only the entry of the substrate in the cell, but also a coupled system of reactions dependent upon a continuous supply of metabolic energy. The biochemical nature of the coupled accumulation system is at present quite unknown, but probably involves several enzymatic steps. Evidence that uncoupling of the energy-requiring reactions has little or no effect on the rate of hydrolysis of ONPG by intact cells will be discussed in a later section of this paper. It would appear hazardous to assume that estimations of permease function based on assays requiring accumulation of substrate are equivalent to those involving only the mediated entry of substrate into the cell.

BIOCHEMICAL MODELS OF THE β-GALACTOSIDE TRANSPORT SYSTEM

In the early biochemical model of the β-galactoside transport system proposed by Cohen and Monod (1957) the specific permease was as-signed the role of an enzyme catalyzing the accumulation of galactosides within the cell. The exit of β-galactosides from the cell was suggested to be an independent reaction, not involving the specific permease. The rate of exit according to this formulation is a function of the intracel-lular concentration of β-galactosides (or more accurately the difference between the intracellular and extracellular concentrations) and thus the accumulation process reaches a steady state when the rate of exit becomes equal to the rate of entry.

Evidence was soon obtained to suggest that the simple "pump vs. leak" mechanism envisaged in the first models of the system is inadequate to explain all the experimental facts. It became clear that the exit of β-galactoside from the cell in the case of the lactose transport system, and the exit of galactose in the closely related galactose transport system, must be specifically mediated processes and not the result of nonspecific leakage (Kepes, 1960). The rate of exit of galactosides from the cell is much lower in strains lacking the transport system, certain inhibitors of the accumulation system also slow down exit, and the temperature coefficient for the exit reaction is higher than one would expect for leakage by simple diffusion.

The Permease Model of Kepes

A more detailed model, attempting to take account of these findings, was proposed by Kepes (1960) and is shown in Fig. 1. Some features

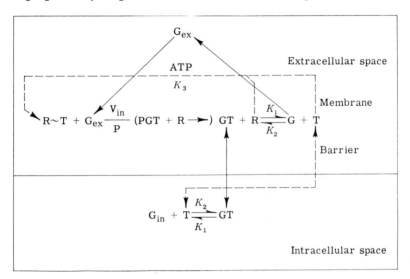

Fig. 1. Model of the permease system according to Kepes (1960).

of this model appear in revised form in the scheme suggested by Koch (1964).

In the Kepes model, the permease is represented as an enzyme P which catalyzes a reaction between R-T, an activated *transporteur*, and

G_{ex}, a molecule of galactoside in the medium [Eq. (1)]. The reaction is

$$R\text{-}T + G_{ex} \xrightarrow{\quad P \quad} G\text{-}T + R \tag{1}$$

postulated to be virtually irreversible and to be rate-making for the entire process. The compound G-T is thought to have physicochemical properties permitting it to pass the membrane barrier, and it is in this form that the sugar enters the cell.

The postulation of T, the *transporteur* component of the transport system, arises from studies of the interaction of glucose (and of other carbohydrates) with the β-galactoside transport system. For example, the addition of glucose to cells previously loaded with thiomethylgalactoside leads to the expulsion of the galactoside. This has been interpreted as a result of competition between the glucose permease and the β-galactoside permease for a common *transporteur* (Koch, 1964; Kepes, 1960). Another line of evidence brought forward to support the idea of the *transporteur* common to several carbohydrate transport systems arises from the experiments of Egan and Morse (1965). These workers have isolated pleiotropic mutants of *Staphylococcus aureus* in which the ability of the organism to transport several carbohydrates appears to be blocked by a single mutation, leading to the suggestion that the defect is in the synthesis of the common *transporteur*. Alternative explanations of these findings in terms of other models are possible, however, and will be discussed below.

Perhaps the most serious difficulty in the model shown in Fig. 1 is in the enzymatic role ascribed to P, the permease. According to Kepes, the permease-mediated entry of galactoside into the cell requires the expenditure of metabolic energy. The reaction $R\text{-}T + G \rightarrow GT + R$ is considered to be practically irreversible, i.e., proceeds with considerable release of free energy. It has long been recognized that metabolic poisons such as azide and dinitrophenol which uncouple oxidative phosphorylation, the major source of energy for aerobic cells, completely prevent the *accumulation* of β-galactosides. However, the effect on mediated *entry*, when the over-all rate of hydrolysis of ONPG by intact cells is measured, is much less. Kepes (1961) recognized this difficulty and suggested that transport in such cases might be dependent upon residual ATP synthesis, not blocked by agents such as sodium azide. This explanation does not seem very convincing since the inhibition of accumulation is apparently complete. Much more striking evidence to indicate that the permease-mediated entry of β-galactosides into the cell is not dependent upon metabolic energy comes from recent experiments of Luria and his collaborators (Fields *et al.*, 1966). These workers have studied the effect of colicins E_1 and K on β-galactoside transport in *E. coli*. These colicins completely block energy-dependent reactions, such as the biosynthesis of proteins and nucleic acids, by interfering with ATP generation or utilization in some unknown manner. Under conditions in which energy-dependent processes are completely blocked, there is no significant effect on the rate of hydrolysis of ONPG by intact cells.

If it is accepted that the permease-mediated entry of galactosides into the cell does not require the expenditure of metabolic energy, then it is very difficult to ascribe any enzymatic function to the permease. Such an enzyme presumably must catalyze the making (or breaking) of covalent bonds, and it is not easy to visualize a cycle in which covalent bonds are made and broken without a continuous expenditure of energy. Furthermore, extensive and ingenious efforts in many laboratories have failed to demonstrate an enzymatic reaction associated with the presence of the permease. For a time, it was suggested that the enzyme thiogalactoside transacetylase might be such an enzyme. This enzyme catalyzes the following reaction:[*]

$$\text{Acetyl CoA} + \text{galactoside} \rightarrow \text{6-O-acetylgalactoside} + \text{CoA} \qquad (2)$$

However, it is now clear that this enzyme is not involved in β-galactoside transport. In the first place, the pattern of specificity of this enzyme, as studied *in vitro*, does not reflect the specificity of the transport system. Indeed, the affinity of the enzyme for all galactosides yet studied is so low, as pointed out by Zabin (1963), that the possibility must be considered that the enzyme carries out some quite different function in the living cell. Furthermore, mutants may be isolated, blocked in transport, but still possessing the transacetylase, or as recently shown by Beckwith (1966) lacking the transacetylase but with unimpaired transport function.

Membrane Protein Model of Galactoside Transport

As pointed out by Kepes in his recent review (1964), it has proved very difficult to work out the biochemical basis of lactose transport in *E. coli* in spite of the great advantages to the biochemist of the fund of available genetic and kinetic information concerning this system. It therefore appeared worthwhile to attempt to reformulate the problem to

[*] Acetyl CoA, acetyl coenzyme A.

determine if other models could be devised which would explain the presently available experimental evidence and suggest new lines of experimental approach. It need hardly be said that the value of any such formulation is a function of its usefulness as a guide for further experiment. One such model that we have found useful is shown in Fig. 2.

In this model, two processes are sharply distinguished: (a) the facilitated entrance of β-galactosides into the cell and (b) after entry, the accumulation of the galactosides against a concentration gradient. Process (b) requires metabolic energy and is abolished by metabolic poisons, such as dinitrophenol and azide, which essentially do not affect process (a).

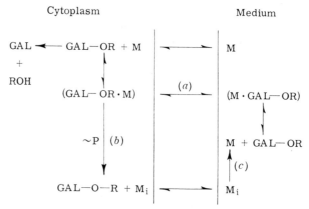

Fig. 2. Simplified working model of the β-galactoside transport system.

According to the model, a molecule of β-galactoside in the medium combines with a component M, a specific protein localized in the membrane, on the exterior surface of the membrane, and passes through the membrane as a β-galactoside–M complex [reaction (a) of Fig. 2]. The combination of the β-galactoside with the protein M is simply of the Michaelis-Menten type and does not involve the catalysis by the protein of the formation of any covalent bond. On the inner surface of the membrane the complex may simply dissociate, and if it can be hydrolyzed by the enzyme β-galactosidase, the continuous breakdown of galactoside may lead to a substantial flow of galactoside from the medium into the cell. This is the process, independent of metabolic energy, which takes place when the hydrolysis of ONPG is measured in intact cells poisoned with azide. Alternatively, if sources of metabolic energy are at hand, the M protein may be converted to an altered form M_i, with a greatly reduced affinity for galactosides [reaction (b)]. M_i moves back through the membrane to the exterior surface, where it is reconverted to the active form M in reaction (c) which does not require coupled metabolic energy.

Salient features of this model are the following.

1. The facilitated entry of the β-galactoside into the cell mediated by the specific membrane protein does not require metabolic energy. This accounts for the finding, mentioned above, that the mediated entry of ONPG into intact cells does not depend upon coupled metabolic energy.

2. The M protein need not be an enzyme; rather, the possibility must be considered that it may be a *substrate* in reaction (b).

3. The expenditure of metabolic energy takes place on the inner surface of the membrane and has the effect of reducing the affinity of the M protein for the galactoside. Accumulation is the result of a reduced rate of exit. This view is strikingly supported by the recent work of Winkler and Wilson (1965) and previous findings of Koch (1964), as well as the studies of Rotman and Guzman (1961) on the closely related galactose transport system in *E. coli*.

4. The retention of accumulated galactosides requires the continuous expenditure of energy. The M protein mediates both the exit and the entrance of β-galactosides in reaction (a) and thus will act to equilibrate the internal and external pool of galactoside in the absence of reaction (b). It has been known from the early investigations of Rickenberg *et al.* (1956) that dinitrophenol not only blocks the accumulation of thiogalactosides, but when added to cells already loaded with thiogalactoside causes the prompt release of the internal galactoside.

5. The model does not require the *transporteur* component which is a central feature of the model of Kepes (1960) and of Koch (1964). The evidence for such a component is quite indirect, and it is not at all clear just what the chemical nature of the postulated *transporteur* may be. If one accepts the view that mediated entry of galactosides does not require metabolic energy, then an activated *transporteur* with the function suggested in the Kepes model becomes inadmissable, as pointed out above. Since it has not been ruled out that the competitive effect of other sugars on β-galactoside transport may be related to the metabolism of these sugars, it would appear that the more economical hypothesis, not involving the postulation of additional entities, may be preferable. An alternative explanation for the finding of pleiotropic transport mutants such as those of Egan and Morse (1965) is also afforded by the model in Fig. 2. If, for example, reactions (b) and (c) are catalyzed by enzymes with a similar general function in several carbohydrate transport systems,

mutations in the genes controlling such enzymes might well be pleiotropic.

IDENTIFICATION OF THE MEMBRANE PROTEIN COMPONENT OF THE β-GALACTOSIDE TRANSPORT SYSTEM

Formulation of the problem in terms of the model shown in Fig. 2 suggested two useful guide lines for experiments aimed at the identification of the essential component M. First, since this protein need not be an enzyme, it should be recognized on the basis of some stoichiometric principle, such as isotopic labeling. Second, the model suggests that the rate of ONPG hydrolysis by intact cells containing an excess of β-galactosidase and poisoned with azide should be directly dependent upon the amount of functional M protein. Combining these two principles led us to search for inhibitors of the process of ONPG hydrolysis in intact cells, of the type which acts by irreversible attachment to protein, thus opening the way for labeling of the M protein. This approach has the great advantage that the labeling can be carried out in the intact cell and can be related directly to the transport process.

Experiments along these lines led to the finding (Fox and Kennedy, 1965) that some essential component of the transport system reacts with the sulfhydryl reagent N-ethylmaleimide under conditions in which neither β-galactosidase nor thiogalactoside transacetylase will react with this inhibitor. Furthermore, it could be shown that the N-ethylmaleimide-sensitive component possesses a high and specific affinity for certain galactosides, such as thiodigalactoside, and has other properties required of the M protein in the model. When the protein is combined with thiodigalactoside, it is protected from reaction with N-ethylmaleimide. Exploitation of this fortunate circumstance led to the development of methods for the specific labeling and partial purification of the M protein (Fox and Kennedy, 1965). It also serves as the basis for a direct chemical test for the M protein in cell-free fractions. Such fractions are first incubated with *unlabeled* N-ethylmaleimide in the presence of thiodigalactoside. The M protein is specifically protected by the thiodigalactoside, but other proteins react with the unlabeled reagent, greatly reducing the background in the subsequent reaction with labeled N-ethylmaleimide. The protective agent and the unlabeled N-ethylmaleimide are then removed. Aliquots of the fraction are then tested for the capacity to react with radioactive N-ethylmaleimide in the presence and in the absence of thiodigalactoside. The observed difference in protein-bound radioactivity is a direct measure of the amount of M protein (Fox and Kennedy, 1965).

GENETIC CONTROL OF THE M PROTEIN

With the aid of this chemical test, it has been possible to examine a number of mutant strains of *E. coli* for the presence of the M protein. The protein is a product of the *lac* operon as shown by the fact that uninduced wild-type cells do not contain significant amounts of the protein, which however appears upon induction. Strains, such as ML 308, with i^- genotype, contain the M protein constitutively. A number of y^- mutants have been tested and found to lack the M protein, either before or after induction. These include a number of mutants kindly made available by Drs. Jacob and Malamy, with mutations accurately mapped in the y region. This correlation of the presence of M protein with y gene was strongly reinforced by the finding that $z^-\ y^+\ a^+$ and $z^+\ y^+\ a^-$ strains contain the M protein. As mentioned above, the a^- strains (isolated by Beckwith) have a lesion that deletes part of the a gene and all of the *lac* region distal to it. Since these acetylaceless mutants show no impairment either in the facilitated entry of galactosides into the cell, as measured by ONPG hydrolysis in intact cells, or in accumulation, it is clear that only two proteins of the *lac* operon, β-galactosidase and the M protein, are involved in these processes.

POSSIBLE MECHANISMS OF FUNCTION OF THE M PROTEIN

The model shown in Fig. 2 appears to offer a rather satisfactory explanation for the facilitated entry of β-galactosides into the cell. However, the role of the M protein in the accumulation process, that is to say in the active transport of β-galactosides, remains obscure.

In general, models of active transport may be divided into two types. The first of these involves some set of reactions in which the substrate to be transported undergoes a cycle of transformations. Suggestions that hexokinase is involved in the active transport of glucose may represent perhaps the earliest versions of this model. In general, it would appear that no convincing evidence has been obtained that the active transport of lactose involves phosphorylation and dephosphorylation of any similar cyclic transformations of the substrate.

The second general model for transport postulates that it is the carrier which undergoes a cyclic series of transformations, rather than the substrate. The role of the carrier here would be fundamentally analogous to hemoglobin in the transport of oxygen. Hemoglobin is a highly specific carrier protein, but not an enzyme in the strict sense of the word. It is of interest in this regard that in the physiological function of this carrier protein, a transformation of the carrier molecule, its reaction with hydrogen ions at regions of lower pH in the venous capillary bed, markedly lowers the affinity of the carrier for oxygen, causing an "unloading" of the substrate which is of great physiological importance. The M protein, then, is roughly analogous to hemoglobin in its presumptive function, rather than to hexokinase. Presumably, however, the transformation of the M protein in reaction (b) is not simply a reaction with hydrogen ion.

The most obvious kind of energy-linked transformation might be phosphorylation of the M protein at the expense perhaps of ATP. However, this is by no means the sole type of reaction which could bring about accumulation. Any change in the conformation of the protein, such as dissociation into subunits, which would reduce its affinity for galactosides, would fulfill the requirements of the model.

Further experiments aimed at working out the steps involved in process (b) and (c) may well utilize the genetic, as well as the biochemical approach. If it were to prove possible to isolate mutants blocked in reactions (b) or (c), the biochemical analysis of such strains might shed light on the nature of the accumulation process.

The problem now appears to have reached a point in which the application of the principles of bioenergetics laid down by Lipmann 25 years ago is crucially important. One may only hope that in another 25 years an understanding in terms of those principles of this and other transport systems will be achieved.

ACKNOWLEDGMENT

Work in this laboratory on the β-galactoside transport system has been carried out in collaboration with Miss Marilynn Rumley, Drs. J. R. Carter, Jr., C. F. Fox, and A. R. Tarlov and has been supported by grants from the Life Insurance Medical Research Fund and the National Institute of Neurological Diseases and Blindness NB-02946.

REFERENCES

Beckwith, J. R. (1966). In press.
Cohen, G. N., and Monod, J. (1957). Bacteriol. Rev. 21, 169.
Doudoroff, M. (1951). In "Phosphorus Metabolism" (W. D. McElroy and B. Glass, eds.), Vol. I, pp. 42-48. Johns Hopkins Press, Baltimore, Maryland.
Egan, J. B., and Morse, M. L. (1965). Biochim. Biophys. Acta 97, 310.
Fields, K. L., Ruby, R. H., and Luria, S. E. (1966). Federation Proc. 25, XX.

Fox, C. F., and Kennedy, E. P. (1965). *Proc. Natl. Acad. Sci. U.S.* **54**, 891.

Hoffman, J. H., ed. (1964). "The Cellular Functions of Membrane Transport." Prentice-Hall, Englewood Cliffs, New Jersey.

Kalckar, H. M. (1941). *Chem. Rev.* **28**, 71.

Kepes, A. (1960). *Biochim. Biophys. Acta* **40**, 70.

Kepes, A. (1961). *Colloq. Ges. Physiol. Chem., 1960* **12**, 100-111.

Kepes, A. (1964). *In* "The Cellular Functions of Membrane Transport" (J. H. Hoffman, ed.), pp. 155-169. Prentice-Hall, Englewood Cliffs, New Jersey.

Kepes, A., and Cohen, G. N. (1962). *In* "The Bacteria" (I. C. Gunsalus and R. Stanier, eds.), Vol. IV, pp. 179-221. Academic Press, New York.

Kleinzeller, A., and Kotyk, A., eds. (1961). "Membrane Transport and Metabolism." Academic Press, New York.

Koch, A. L. (1964). *Biochim. Biophys. Acta* **79**, 177.

Lipmann, F. (1941). *Advan. Enzymol.* **1**, 99.

Rickenberg, H. W., Cohen, G. N., Burrin, G., and Monod, J. (1956). *Ann. Inst. Pasteur* **91**, 829.

Rotman, B., and Guzman, R. (1961). *Pathol. Biol.* **9**, 806.

Winkler, H. H., and Wilson, T. H. (1965). *Federation Proc.* **24**, 352.

Zabin, I. (1963). *Federation Proc.* **22**, 27.

Regulation of Enzyme and Coenzyme Levels*

Nathan O. Kaplan

Fritz Lipmann's interest in bioenergetics has extended beyond the mechanisms involved in the synthesis and utilization of high-energy bonds to the factors regulating the synthesis of molecules, both large and small, in the intact cell. During the course of my association with Lipmann, an interest was stimulated in the possible mechanism by which the cellular concentrations of enzymes and coenzymes are controlled. In this particular field little direct experimental data are as yet available. The present paper relates some of my thinking in this area which has evolved through the years since leaving the Lipmann laboratory.†

An interesting feature of all living cells is the consistency of levels of enzyme and coenzyme in a given cell. Table I gives the concentrations of a number of coenzymes in rat liver. The levels can be correlated roughly with the dietary requirement of the vitamin moiety present in the co-enzyme. For example, the amount of nicotinamide or pantotheine essential for growth and maintenance of an animal is some 10,000 to 100,000 times greater than the amount of vitamin B_{12} required. A correlation can also be obtained between the levels of coenzyme and the concentrations of enzymes with which a particular coenzyme is associated. Hence, the total number of DPN- and TPN-linked enzymes or coenzyme A-requiring enzymes are found in liver in much greater concentrations than vitamin B_{12} coenzyme or folic acid-linked proteins. Enzymes using pyridoxal phos-

* Publication No. 433, from the Graduate Department of Biochemistry, Brandeis University, Waltham, Massachusetts.

† The following abbreviations are used in this chapter: AMP, adenosine mono-phosphate; ADP, adenosine diphosphate; ATP, adenosine triphosphate; CoA, coenzyme A; DPN, diphosphopyridine nucleotide (NAD); AcPyDPN, acetylpyridine DPN; DPNH, reduced DPN; AcPyDPNH, reduced acetylpyridine DPN; TPN, triphospho-pyridine nucleotide (NADP); TPNH, reduced TPN; FAD, flavin adenine dinucleo-tide; LDH, lactic dehydrogenase.

phate, thiamine pyrophosphate, and the flavin nucleotides are present in intermediate amounts. Table II shows the distribution of several of the coenzymes in a number of different rat tissues. It is noteworthy that skeletal muscle contains much smaller amounts of TPN or coenzyme A as compared to liver. This correlates to the fact that there are only a small number of TPN or coenzyme A-linked enzymes in skeletal muscle. On the other hand, the total levels of DPN and DPNH in skeletal muscle are comparable to those found in liver. The relatively high concentration of the diphosphopyridine nucleotides can be related to the high concentra-

TABLE I
COENZYME LEVELS IN RAT LIVER

Pyridine coenzyme	Concentration (μmoles/gm of wet weight)
DPN + DPNH	0.88 ⎱ 1.17
TPN + TPNH	0.29 ⎰
Coenzyme A	0.42
FAD	0.0700
Thiamine pyrophosphate	0.0350
Pyridoxal phosphate	0.0074
Vitamin B_{12} coenzyme	0.00012

TABLE II
COENZYME DISTRIBUTION IN DIFFERENT RAT TISSUES

Tissue	DPN + DPNH	TPN + TPNH	CoA	TPP
Liver	0.88	0.29	0.42	0.035
Heart	0.74	0.064	0.130	0.015
Brain	0.35	0.003	0.084	0.004
Skeletal muscle	0.64	0.013	0.012	0.002
Adrenal	0.73	0.18	0.272	—

tions of the three dehydrogenases (glyceraldehyde phosphate, lactate, and α-glycerol phosphate). The data available strongly suggest that the level of coenzyme is directly related to the concentration of enzyme of which the coenzyme is a cofactor. It seems reasonable to assume that regulation of coenzyme levels depends on the relative rates of synthesis and breakdown of the apoenzymes. Furthermore, as will be discussed below, there may be a reciprocal relationship—that is, the level of enzyme may depend on the amount of available coenzyme.

The turnover of coenzymes may be partly attributable to the dissociation of the coenzyme from the holoenzyme complex. There is, in fact, a relatively good correlation between the level of coenzyme and its relative rate of dissociation. For example, it is well known that enzymes containing vitamin B_{12} coenzyme are difficult to resolve, and only under quite strenuous conditions can the coenzyme be dissociated. In contrast, the pyridine nucleotides and coenzyme A are, in general, relatively easy to dissociate from their respective enzymes.

An interesting example of coenzyme turnover was studied a number of years ago in our laboratory. We found that when nicotinamide was injected into mice, a large increase in liver DPN was observed (see Fig. 1)

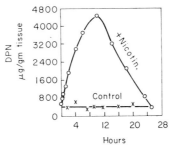

FIG. 1. Effect of nicotinamide administration on oxidized pyridine nucleotides from the liver. Mice were injected with 500 mg per kilogram of nicotinamide (1–3).

(1–3). Similar increases have been observed in dogs and rats (4, 5). As illustrated in Fig. 1, the maximum increase occurs 8-10 hours after the administration of nicotinamide; this rise is followed by a rapid decrease in the level of pyridine nucleotides. The final level obtained is similar to that present before the injection of the vitamin. In some strains of mice the DPN concentration can be elevated 20-fold. Examination of the acid-soluble fraction of the liver from the nicotinamide-injected mice shows an increase in the total ribose and adenine levels which, roughly, parallels the increase in total pyridine nucleotides (see Table III). There is also

TABLE III

CHANGE IN SOME ACID-SOLUBLE CONSTITUENTS OF MOUSE LIVER
FOLLOWING THE ADMINISTRATION OF NICOTINAMIDE[a]

Constituent	Concentration (μmoles/gm of wet weight)	
	Control	Nicotinamide-injected
DPN	0.79	5.74
Total nicotinamide	0.73	5.99
Adenine	3.8	8.4
Ribose	12.9	20.4
Total phosphate	48.2	59.4

[a] After Shuster et al. (9).

some increase in total acid-soluble phosphate. The level of adenosine triphosphate remains unchanged. The increase in ribose and adenine levels is the result of *de novo* synthesis. It thus appears that the injection of nicotinamide leads to an increase in the rate of formation of ATP from newly formed adenine and ribose. These changes are best explained if one postulates that any decrease in ATP leads to a stimulation of ribose and purine synthesis; this would imply that the level of the adenylic acid system (ATP, ADP, and AMP) regulates the synthesis of both ribose and adenine. The decrease in ATP results from the incorporation of the adenylic acid moiety into DPN.

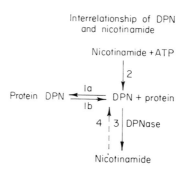

Fig. 2. Reactions (1a) and (1b) represent the reversible dissociation of DPN with the various DPN-linked enzymes. Reactions (2) represents the over-all reaction in the conversion of nicotinamide to DPN. Reaction (3) represents the hydrolytic cleavage of DPN, and reaction (4) denotes the inhibition of this reaction by nicotinamide.

The scheme generally recognized as the pathway by which nicotinamide is converted to DPN is summarized in the following reactions:

$$\text{Nicotinamide} \rightarrow \text{nicotinic acid}^\circ$$
$$\text{P-Ribose pyrophosphate} + \text{nicotinic acid} \rightarrow \text{nicotinic acid mononucleotide} + \text{PP}_i$$
$$\text{Nicotinic acid mononucleotide} + \text{ATP} \rightarrow \text{nicotinic acid DPN} + \text{PP}_i$$
$$\text{Nicotinic acid DPN} + \text{ATP} + \text{glutamine} \rightarrow \text{DPN} + \text{ADP} + \text{glutamic acid}$$

To account for the rise and decrease in DPN after injection of nicotinamide, we offer the following explanation which is given in schematic form in Fig. 2. Injection of nicotinamide leads to a rise in both blood and liver nicotinamide (6, 7). Nicotinamide inhibits the action of DPNase on the nicotinamide riboside linkage of DPN by the exchange mechanism described several years ago (8). Hence, the presence of free nicotinamide

° It is possible that deamination of the nicotinamide moiety occurs at the mononucleotide level rather than at the free base.

in the liver will tend to favor an increase in DPN by blocking the hydrolysis of the coenzyme. As indicated in Fig. 2, the presence of nicotinamide leads to newly synthesized DPN by the pathway outlined in reactions (1) to (4). Therefore, the rise in DPN is a result of the formation of new DPN combined with an inhibition of DPNase, which allows the DPN concentration to build up. As soon as the free nicotinamide in the liver is exhausted, there is a rapid drop in the level of DPN, since the hydrolytic action of the DPNase becomes unhindered. That the scheme in Fig. 2 is essentially correct is suggested by the fact that there is no significant change in the levels of enzymes concerned with the synthesis or degradation of DPN.

It is noteworthy that the DPN levels off at essentially the same concentration as existed before the administration of nicotinamide. The DPNase has a low activity on enzyme-bound DPN and this may be an important factor in the regulation of the level of DPN. As a corollary to this fact, one must assume that most of the pyridine nucleotides exist in the cell bound to protein, and this would imply that the concentration of coenzyme is determined by the total amount of pyridine nucleotide-linked enzymes. Normally there must be some dissociation of the bound DPN into the free form, which can then be attacked by the DPNase. The constant loss of DPN by the hydrolytic action of the DPNase suggested that some synthesis of DPN also occurs under conditions where large quantities of nicotinamide are not available by injection. This has been ascertained by the administration of labeled substances (i.e., ribose, adenine) other than nicotinamide (9).[*] Hence, the requirement of the vitamin in the diet of a mature animal probably is caused by the loss of DPN through the hydrolytic action of the DPNase on the *unbound coenzyme*. Although it has not yet been definitely established experimentally, it appears very likely that the excess DPN found in liver after injection of nicotinamide is *not* bound to protein.

Administration of reserpine maintains the elevated level of DPN in liver resulting from administration of nicotinamide (10); this has been attributed to a prolonged increase in both blood and liver nicotinamide (6, 7). Hypophysectomy also promotes changes similar to those observed with reserpine chlorpromazine and related compounds (5, 11). The changes in hypophysectomy may reflect lack of adrenocorticotropic and

---

[*] Injection of tracer amounts of C^{14}-labeled nicotinamide into mice leads to the interposition of the labeled pyridine moiety into DPN. However, the incorporation is largely caused by the exchange reaction promoted by the DPNase.

thyrotropic secretion (11). The level of blood nicotinamide, therefore, must be a critical factor in determining the concentration of pyridine nucleotides in liver. Further evidence indicating a rapid turnover of DPN in liver is suggested by the marked fall in this coenzyme after injection of azoserine.

Some general conclusions can be drawn from the work on the regulation of DPN with respect to mechanisms controlling the concentration of coenzymes in animal cells. Not only are the enzymes involved in synthesis important in maintaining a given level of coenzyme but the hydrolytic enzymes also play an important role in homeostasis. In addition, the concentration of various enzymes which interact with the coenzyme must also be considered in an appreciation of regulatory mechanisms.

"Feedback" inhibition, although possibly a factor in regulating the synthetic pathway, cannot be the only phenomenon accounting for maintenance of the steady-state concentrations of coenzymes in animal cells. The enzymes involved in coenzyme hydrolysis also must be important factors. The mature animal cell apparently does not lose its capacity to synthesize coenzymes, but the level is controlled by the splitting of any excess that is produced. This excess is related to the level of holoenzyme present in the cell. If the specific hydrolytic enzymes were not present, there would be an abnormal accumulation of one coenzyme within the cell, since most coenzymes cannot penetrate out of an animal cell. For example, in the case of nicotinamide injection, if DPNase was not present, there could be an abnormal permanent accumulation of the coenzyme which could be toxic to the cell. These points indicate that "turnover" of coenzymes in animal cells is an important physiological phenomenon that may not take place in bacteria.

Studies on orotic acid injection in rats may have some relationship to the views presented above. Administration of orotic acid has been found to decrease the levels of acid-soluble adenine and pyridine nucleotides, which are concomitant with the increase in uridine nucleotides (12–14). Orotic acid also prevents the rise in DPN after injection of nicotinamide. Windmuller and Spaeth have found that orotic acid stimulates hepatic purine biosynthesis; this is apparently caused by a release of feedback inhibition caused by the decrease in purine nucleotide level (15). The mechanism by which orotic acid depresses the total purine nucleotides is as yet not clear.

There have been many reports in the literature implying that coenzymes or small molecules prevent their inactivation by various agents or environmental conditions. The stabilizing effect is quite remarkable.

TABLE IV
EFFECT OF NUCLEOTIDES ON INACTIVATION OF CHICKEN H_4 LDH[a]

Additions	Concentration (M)	Activity (%) lost after incubation for 10 min	
		6 M urea	3.8 M LiCl
None	—	90	48
AMP	10^{-3}	90	45
DPN	10^{-3}	80	34
AcPyDPN	10^{-3}	62	10
DPNH	10^{-3}	55	22
AcPyDPNH	10^{-3}	28	0
DPN	1.4×10^{-5}	90	46
AcPyDPN	1.4×10^{-5}	78	30
DPNH	1.4×10^{-5}	74	43
AcPyDPNH	1.4×10^{-5}	42	3

[a] After Di Sabato and Kaplan (19).

Table IV illustrates the action of coenzymes in protecting against the action of denaturing agents (16–19).

The presence of a specific coenzyme also lowers the rate of cleavage of a given enzyme by proteases (20–22). It seems reasonable to assume from this type of *in vitro* result that the level of an enzyme may depend on the presence of a coenzyme, since the cathepsins may act only on the apoenzyme. Hence a decrease in coenzyme brought about by a vitamin deficiency may result in a diminution in the level of apoenzyme. Although data relative to this particular phenomenon are somewhat scarce, it may well be that enzymes that have a higher rate of dissociation with a given cofactor decrease at a more rapid rate in vitamin deficiency than enzymes having the same cofactor but with smaller dissociation constants. Such a difference has been observed with pyridoxal phosphate-dependent enzymes in pyridoxal-deficient animals (23). It is interesting that in duck-lings with nicotinamide deficiency the pyridine nucleotides are lowered much more markedly in the soluble part of the cell than in the mitochondrial (Table V). One might predict a greater rate of turnover of a given

TABLE V
TOTAL LIVER PYRIDINE NUCLEOTIDES IN NICOTINAMIDE-DEFICIENT DUCKS[a]

Type of bird	Number of birds	Fresh liver (μg/gm)	
		Soluble	Mitochondrial
Normal	8	480 ± 22	180 ± 17
Nicotinamide-deficient	7	216 ± 42	162 ± 28

[a] N. O. Kaplan and M. M. Ciotti, unpublished observations.

enzyme during a vitamin deficiency owing to an increased rate of break-down of the enzyme.

The intimate relationship between the coenzyme and enzyme concentration is illustrated by the important contributions of Glock and McLean (24) on changes in mammary tissues during lactation. As shown in Fig. 3 there is a striking increase in glucose-6-phosphate dehydrogenase as well as a significant rise in 6-phosphogluconic dehydrogenase following the onset of lactation. There is a precipitous decrease in these enzymes during involution. These changes are paralleled by changes in the total TPN concentration and, in particular, the reduced form. We have made a

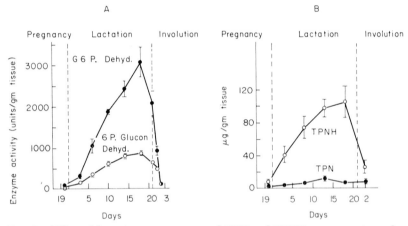

Fig. 3.   Effect of lactation on enzymes and TPN and TPNH concentrations of rat mammary gland (24).

precursory examination of the data of Glock and McLean based on what is known about the turnover and molecular weights of the two "shunt" enzymes and also assuming that for every 35,000 molecular weight units in the enzymes, one mole of TPN or TPNH is bound. From such very rough values we have found two to three newly formed moles of TPN or TPNH per 35,000 units of glucose-6-phosphate dehydrogenase and phosphogluconic acid dehydrogenase synthesized. It may be of value, from the above results, to attempt to correlate changes in enzyme and coenzyme concentrations to ascertain the validity of the suggested hypothesis.

Another possible role of coenzymes and substrates may be as "directional" agents in promoting the formation of enzymatically active structures. It has become increasingly apparent that many enzymes in their active conformation exist in polymeric form. Considerable discussion has arisen whether subunits of an enzyme made on a polysome spontaneously combine to form polymers or whether environmental and other factors may be involved in the association. *In vitro* studies on the reassociation of subunits imply the credibility of such a possibility.

The H-type lactic dehydrogenase, as well as other enzymes, can be converted into its tetrameric form after dissociation in either urea, guanidine, or lithium chloride (25). This is accomplished by dilution or dialysis by the particular denaturing reagent. It has been observed that addition of DPNH will greatly accelerate the rate and amount of active en-

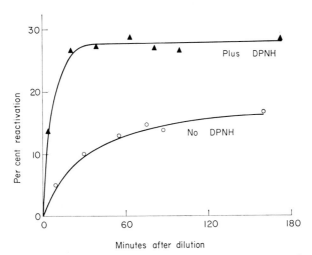

FIG. 4. Effect of DPNH on reassociation of chicken H_4 LDH after treatment with guanidine (25).

zyme after treatment with the above-mentioned denaturing agents (see Fig. 4). From the data available at present, it is not possible unambiguously to conclude that the action of coenzyme is to promote aggregation or to direct the subunits into conformations, which are enzymatically active. During the course of these investigations, an enzymatically active intermediate was detected which had catalytic and physical properties different from those of the native lactic dehydrogenase. When the coenzyme is present, this intermediate is undetectable. Hence, the coenzyme may be significant in orienting the subunits into a thermodynamically stable structure with properties similar to those of the native undissociated enzyme

Conformational changes evidenced by coenzyme are also suggested by the recent report of Levy *et al.* (*26*) on glucose-6-phosphate dehydrogenase. These authors believe that this enzyme is in its catalytically active form when it is present as a unit of molecular weight 135,000. There appear to be two forms of the enzyme; one has low catalytic activity, but can be converted to a more active form in the presence of low levels of TPN. This activation appears to result from a conformational change. Experiments of this type further suggest the role of the coenzymes in stabilizing the functional structures of enzymes.

Recent studies by Dr. Sandra Blethen in our laboratory with arginine kinase are of some interest with regard to the importance of small molecules in promoting the formation of the catalytically active structure of an enzyme. She has found that this enzyme, which consists of a single polypeptide chain, is inactivated in urea. If the urea is diluted out, an abnormal disulfide bond is formed, and no enzymatic activity ensues. (There are no disulfide bridges in the native enzyme.) Apparently during the refolding of the protein on dilution, the disulfide arises. Addition of reducing agents such as mercaptoethanol to this urea-treated enzyme results in a rapid recovery of the enzyme activity. If arginine is added to the dilution mixture, considerable activity is also regained even in the absence of the reducing agents. However, once the disulfide structure is formed, arginine is without effect, and only the reducing agents will promote a restoration of catalytic activity. One can interpret such experiments as indicating that the substrate (or coenzyme), by binding to the unfolded polypeptide chain, helps to direct the enzyme into a conformation which is catalytically active. This thereby suggests that one sequence may give several possible permanent structures. These multiple structures *may* or *may* not be catalytically active (*27*).

One can speculate about the action of small molecules in controlling the rate of synthesis of enzymes. It is possible that in the synthesis of a protein on a polysome the protein remains in an unfolded or inactive state, until small molecules or certain environmental conditions promote the release of the nascent protein from the polysomes. The formation of the "proper" disulfide bonds in molecules such as insulin and lysozyme have already led to a search for enzymes that might promote the generation of biologically active structures (*28*).

One might assume that the nascent enzyme remains on the polysome in the absence of the factors promoting the release of the protein. Hence, a decrease in the concentration of a coenzyme may also decrease the synthesis of an enzyme. At present we know little of the intimate mechanisms involved in the turnover of enzymes in animal cells and the effect of small molecules on this turnover. The data, however, already at hand, suggest that the coenzymes (or substrates) play an important role in permitting the functional configuration of the enzyme to be formed—be it by directing the attainment of a proper conformation in a monomeric enzyme or by allowing the proper association of subunits. Regulation of enzyme synthesis may be a reflection of changes in relative rates of enzyme turnover; and it seems a reasonably good guess that the turnovers of coenzyme and enzymes are closely dependent phenomena.

REFERENCES

1. Kaplan, N. O., Goldin, A., Humphreys, S. R., Ciotti, M. M., and Stolzenbach, F. E. *J. Biol. Chem.* **219**, 287 (1956).
2. Kaplan, N. O., in "The Enzymes" (P. Boyer, H. Lardy, and K. Myrbäck, eds.), Vol. III, pp. 160-165. Academic Press, New York, 1960.
3. Kaplan, N. O., in "Metabolic Pathways" (D. Greenberg, ed.), Vol. II, p. 627. Academic Press, New York, 1961.
4. Bonsignore, A., and Ricci, C. *Farm. Sci. Tec.* **4**, 300 (1949).
5. Greengard, P., Quinn, G. P., and Landrau, M. A. *Biochim. Biophys. Acta* **47**, 614 (1961).
6. Greengard, P., Kalinsky, H., and Petrack, B. *Biochim. Biophys. Acta* **52**, 408 (1961).
7. Ricci, C., and Pallini, V. *Biochem. Biophys. Res. Commun.* **17**, 34 (1964).
8. Zatman, L. J., Kaplan, N. O., and Colowick, S. P. *J. Biol. Chem.* **200**, 197 (1953).
9. Shuster, L., Langan, T. A., Jr., Kaplan, N. O., and Goldin, A. *Nature* **182**, 512 (1958).
10. Burton, R. M., Kaplan, N. O., Goldin, A., Leitenberg, M., Humphreys, S. R., and Sodd, M. A. *Science* **127**, 30 (1958).
11. Greengard, P., Quinn, G. P., and Reid, M. B. *J. Biol. Chem.* **239**, 1887 (1964).
12. Euler, von L. H., Rubin, R. J., and Handschumacher, R. E. *J. Biol. Chem.* **238**, 2464 (1963).
13. Rajalakshmi, A., Sarma, D. S. R., and Sarma, P. S. *Indian J. Exptl. Biol.* **1**, 63 (1963).
14. Windmuller, H. *J. Nutrition* **85**, 221 (1965).
15. Windmuller, H. G., and Spaeth, R. E. *J. Biol. Chem.* **240**, 4398 (1965).
16. Grisolia, S. *Physiol. Rev.* **44**, 657 (1964).
17. Burton, K. *Biochem. J.* **48**, 458 (1951).
18. Srere, P. A. *J. Biol. Chem.* **241**, 2157 (1966).
19. Di Sabato, G., and Kaplan, N. O. *J. Biol. Chem.* **240**, 1072 (1964).
20. McKay, R. H., and Kaplan, N. O. *Biochim. Biophys. Acta* **52**, 156 (1961).
21. Allison, W. S., and Kaplan, N. O. *Biochemistry* **3**, 1792 (1964).
22. Okunuki, K. *Advan. Enzymol.* **23**, 29 (1961).
23. Fasella, P. M., personal communication.
24. Glock, G. E., and McLean, P. *Proc. Roy. Soc. (London)* **B149**, 354 (1958).
25. Chilson, O. P., Kitto, G. B., and Kaplan, N. O. *Proc. Natl. Acad. Sci. U.S.* **53**, 1006 (1965); Chilson, O. P., Kitto, G. B., Pudles, J., and Kaplan, N. O. *J. Biol. Chem.* **241**, 2431 (1966).

26. Levy, H. R., Raineri, R. R., and Nevaldine, B. H. *J. Biol. Chem.*, **241**, 2181 (1966).
27. Kitto, G. B., Wassarman, P., and Kaplan, N. O. *Proc. Natl. Acad. Sci. U.S.* **56**, August (1966).
28. Goldberger, R. F., Epstein, C. J., and Anfinsen, C. B. *J. Biol. Chem.* **239**, 1406 (1964).

Leloir Coenzymes, Cell Membranes, and Protein Synthesis[*]

Morris Soodak

> Chemical reactions occurring in living cells are part of cell procedures. A procedure implies purpose and design, and to approach the understanding of cell procedures their purposefulness has to be taken into consideration.[†]
>
> Fritz Lipmann

> Nature does not employ all figures, but only certain ones of those which are possible; and of these, the determination is not to be fetched from the brain or proved *a priori*, but obtained by experiments and observations.[**]
>
> (Author unknown and prior to about 1707)

This chapter, largely speculative in nature, is concerned with coenzymes and enzymes and with proteins and lipoproteins and their role in the organized living cell. It is written from the point of view of a chemical biologist rather than from that of a biochemist.

The following group of hypotheses or concepts will be developed herein.

1. Glycoproteins are obligatory intermediates in protein synthesis.

2. "Cytotaxis," as defined by Sonneborn (*1*), can be explained by sug-

---

[*] This is Publication No. 463 from the Graduate Department of Biochemistry, Brandeis University, Waltham, Massachusetts.

This work was supported by grants from the National Science Foundation, the National Institutes of Health, the American Cancer Society, and the Medical Foundation of Boston.

[†] Advances in Enzymology **1**, 148 (1941).

[**] From W. M. Clark "Topics in Physical Chemistry" 1948, p. 89. The Williams and Wilkins Company, Baltimore.

gesting that the "primary" primers for the synthesis of macromolecules are proteins built into the membrane structures of the cell.

3. Membrane transport is probably a countercurrent distribution phenomenon and involves a "flip-flop" mechanism for the halves of the unit membrane.

4. An important function for the "unaccounted for" deoxyribonucleic acid (DNA) is to program a sequential release of precursors for Leloir coenzymes.

5. While "building in" implies that a template determines the order of the building blocks, "building on" is the addition of substances on to the "built-in" backbone and does not involve the necessity of a template.

The central idea which led to the accumulation of much of the material of this article stems from the reports of Leloir and associates (2) concerning the isolation of uridine diphosphate glucose (UDPG) (1949–1950) and the papers of Park and Johnson (3) in which UDP-N-acetylmuramic acid pentapeptide was reported (1950). An interesting generalization was formulated, namely, that all the component bases of ribonucleic acid (RNA) and DNA would eventually be shown to be a part of a Leloir coenzyme with special transfer function. The review articles in 1964 of Leloir (4) and Ginsburg (5) indicate that more than sixty such coenzymes are known.

In 1952 the present author made the following comment (6): "If one looks at the gene as providing purine and pyrimidine bases leading to the formation of coenzymes, one can think of many examples of how genes could control certain enzymatic processes. We know of the importance of the adenine nucleotides and the new coenzymes described by Leloir, including the uridine diphosphate glucose and guanine diphosphate mannose."

In 1955 (7), the following comments were made: "Green's 'trace substance-enzyme thesis' (1941) boils down to the view that enzyme catalysis is the only rational explanation of how a trace of some substance can produce profound biological effects. In the light of the five lines of evidence stated and in the light of the 'trace substance-enzyme thesis,' the hypothesis is put forward stating that all the derivative bases of the nucleic acids are components of coenzymes of the usual size, and that the nucleic acids themselves, or polynucleotides derived from them may also be coenzymes. It is further postulated that one of the major roles of both the ribonucleic and deoxyribonucleic acids is to serve as coenzymes or as source material for coenzyme formation. This precursor material may be as polynucleotides, nucleotides, nucleosides, the bases, ribose phosphates, or even as inorganic phosphate. An ordered release of coenzymes or precursors for coenzyme synthesis at certain times in the life cycle of the cell would determine the rate, the concentration, and the time of formation of coenzymes. These factors would in turn control the rate, the concentration, and the time of appearance of cellular substances, be they other coenzymes, proteins, lipids, or carbohydrates. It is postulated that in this manner the nucleic acids act as important controlling influences in the numerous biosynthetic processes occurring in the cell.

"Most of the theories concerning the action of nucleic acids involve a nucleic acid template mechanism for protein synthesis. That nucleic acids may also push protein synthesis to completion, or act as a source of energy, or provide material for coenzyme synthesis, has also been suggested. The theory proposed here is essentially not a new idea, but represents a change of emphasis based on a biochemical approach. The suggestion that the nucleic acids may act mainly as coenzymes or coenzyme precursors opens up a broader horizon for investigation."

It is of interest, for the sake of maintaining a proper chronology, to quote from a publication of Stacey (8) in 1953. "Few proteins are free from some content of carbohydrate residue, and thus by suitable cautious treatment most proteins could give rise to a mucoprotein fragment. It could well be that this prosthetic group is somehow connected with the enzyme which synthesizes protein."

GLYCOPROTEINS, PROTEIN POLYSACCHARIDES, PROTEIN POLYNUCLEOTIDES, AND "CYTOTAXIS"

The large number of glycoproteins and their widespread distribution has been apparent for some time. That this implied a special significance was also apparent. Why synthesize a protein, which is problem enough, and then add a glycoid unit?

Two sets of facts point up one aspect of the significance of this class of protein. (1) Almost all the proteins in human sera are glycoproteins, except possibly albumin. Almost all of these proteins are made by the liver or plasma cells. (2) Almost all the proteins in the chicken egg are glycoproteins. The egg has only 1% carbohydrate and all of it is present in glycoproteins. It is obvious that all these proteins have been secreted by cells. One function for the glycoid unit, therefore, is concerned with insuring the release of these proteins. In a recent essay Eylar (9) has mustered evidence for this thesis.

Myoglobin, a typical intracellular protein, is in all probability a glycoprotein.* "In the interpretation of the 2 Å sperm whale myoglobin Fourier map, it was found that the electron density in the space between two molecules, but adjacent to threonine residues, could be interpreted as attached sugar-rings" (25a). Preliminary experiments with horse heart myoglobin (Pentex, recrystallized twice) indicate the presence of ca. 1 μmole of hexosamine per μmole of myoglobin (25b).

Although glycoproteins definitely occur in plants (10) and animals (11), there is enough evidence to indicate their presence in lower forms. In a chapter entitled, "Distribution of Amino Sugars in Microorganisms, Plants, and Invertebrates," Sharon [cf. (11)] indicates the multiplicity of amino sugars in nature. Glucose oxidase from *Aspergillus niger* is a glycoprotein (12), as is the chloroperoxidase of *Chaldariomyces fumago* (13). Histoplasmin, the culture filtrate from mycelial growths of *Histoplasma capsulatum* contains several glycoproteins (14). *Trichomonas foetus*, a paramecium, contains a number of glycoproteins (15). Colicine K from *Shigella sonii* is a glycoprotein (16), and T2 phage contains glucosamine (17).

The following enzymes are known to be glycoproteins: glucose oxidase, chloroperoxidase, horseradish peroxidase (18), Japanese radish peroxidase (19), ribonuclease B (20), α-amylase (A. oryzae) (21), γ-glutamyl transpeptidase (22), sulfatase of ox liver (23), L-amino acid oxidase (snake venom), and (DPNase) from *Bacillis subtilis* (25).†

The widespread occurrence of the sialic acid group (26), its presence on the cell membranes of a wide variety of cells (27), its role in viral attachment, its presence at the nonreducing end of glycoid units of glycoproteins and the blood group substances (28), the mild conditions for its hydrolysis [both chemical (29) and enzymatic (30)], and the availability of good and sensitive methods for its determination have made it the subject of many studies and has served as a stimulus for advances in the glycoprotein field. On the evolutionary level a recent review by Aaronson and Hutner entitled "Biochemical Markers and Microbial Phylogeny" summarizes much of the data available on the sialic acids (31).

Grant and Simkin (1965) have written an excellent article entitled

---

* "A better designation might be those proteins having at least one mole of hexose or hexosamine per mole of protein." (R. J. Winzler *In* "The Plasma Proteins," (E. W. Putnam, ed.) Vol. 1, p. 311. Academic Press, New York and London (1960).

† In the several cases studied, the removal of all or part of the glycoid moiety had no effect on enzyme activity (i.e., as for RNase A and B).—The microheterogeniety of some glycoproteins is due to the variable composition of their glycoid unit.

"Structure and Biosynthesis of Carbohydrate-Polypeptide Polymers" (32). Schmid has reviewed methods for the isolation, purification, and analysis of glycoproteins (33). Spiro (1963) describes the occurrence, structure, and function of the glycoproteins from a biological viewpoint (34). Gottschalk and Graham (1966) review "The Basic Structure of Glycoproteins" (35) [see also Neuberger (35a)]. The metabolism of the glycoproteins has been reviewed by Winzler (1965) (35b). Gottschalk has edited an excellent book entitled "Glycoproteins—Their Composition, Structure, and Function" (1966) (35c).

Protein Polysaccharides and Protein Polynucleotides

It is now known that the following polysaccharide compounds exist covalently linked to protein as protein-polysaccharide substances (36, 37): hyaluronic acid (38), chondroitinsulfuric acid (39), heparin (36), keratosulfate (36), amylopectin (40), glycogen (41), and chitin (42).

Telser and co-workers (1964) have studied the biosynthesis of the chondroitinsulfate complex (44). The summary of their paper reads as follows: "A preparation of minced embryonic chicken cartilage catalyzes the *in vitro* incorporation of serine-C^{14}, acetate-C^{14}, and inorganic sulfate-S^{35} into chondroitin sulfuric acid. Puromycin inhibits the incorporation of all three compounds into polysaccharide: serine > sulfate > acetate. 6-Diazo-5-oxonorleucine also inhibits the incorporation of all three compounds into polysaccharide: acetate > sulfate > serine. The inhibition by 6-diazo-5-oxonorleucine is reduced by addition of glucosamine. Puromycin has no inhibitory effect on nucleotide hexosamine biosynthesis and neither puromycin nor 6 diazo-5-oxonorleucine has a marked effect on the incorporation of hexosamine into polysaccharide, catalyzed by a cell-free system.

"These observations are consistent with a biosynthetic mechanism which involves addition of carbohydrate units to preformed protein to yield a protein-polysaccharide complex."

In 1951 Dorfman set out to study hyaluronic acid synthesis in *Streptococcus haemolyticus* A. The work with these streptococci culminated in the observations of Markovitz and Dorfman (1962) (45), which indicated that 99% of the hyaluronic acid-synthesizing enzyme responsible for the net synthesis of hyaluronic acid from UDPG and UDP-glucuronic acid in the cell-free system was bound to the cell membrane. Another very interesting observation that they made was that a primer was not needed, but by the use of ^{14}C-labeled membrane-bound enzyme and nonlabeled nucleotides they demonstrated that less than 1% of the polysaccharide was derived from the enzyme. These results did not rule out a primer, but if it existed it was below the level of detection by the available methods. This work pointed out what may be considered two important guidelines. It set a pattern for heteropolysaccharide synthesis in general, namely, that enzymes which are involved in such synthesis are membrane-bound. Second, since no external primer need be added, one may make the assumption that the primer is membrane-bound and is actually a part of the structure of the membrane. The release of the hyaluronic acid would involve a hydrolase present in the membrane.

Evidence for an analogous primer for lypopolysaccharide synthesis in mutant strains of *Salmonella* was adduced by Nikaido (*43*). Lipopolysaccharide synthesis also involves membrane-bound enzymes and primers (*43, 43a*).

Evidence for the existence of protein-polynucleotide-like substances (i.e. amino acids covalently bound) has also been documented for RNA (*46*) and DNA (*48*). Baylis believes that repression and derepression have to do with the covalently linked amino acids.

The protein portions of these substances make up a small percentage of the molecular weight and are probably the "primary" or "membrane-bound primers" within the cell. The structure of chondroitin sulfate mucoprotein deduced by Marler and Davidson (*39*) may serve as a model for these substances. These primers are part of the structure of the cell membranes and are probably located on the inside of the cell membrane. The molecular weight of the protein portion of these compounds is in the range of 10,000 to 20,000, and this is suggested to be the average size of a typical protein in the unit membranes of the cell. Corroborating evidence can be gleaned from recent work on myelin (*49*) and on the glycoproteins of the fat globule membranes of milk (*49a*). It is further suggested that the typical cistron codes for a protein of this molecular size.

Cytotaxis has been defined by Sonneborn (*1*) as the "ordering and arranging of new cell structure under the influence of pre-existing cell structure. The place and orientation of the assembly of genic products is also determined by pre-existing assemblies of molecules and structures. The picture that emerges is no less deterministic or molecular than self-assembly, but is fuller and truer: there is more than 'self' to the mechanism of assembly; it includes pre-existing and independently modifiable assembly." It is suggested that cytotaxis may be explained by the fact that the appropriate primers are built into the existing structures as described above.

THE BIOSYNTHESIS OF PROTEINS VIA GLYCOPROTEINS

In 1964 Sarcione reported on the biosynthesis of glycoproteins by perfused rat liver in a paper entitled "The Initial Subcellular Site of Incorporation of Hexoses into Liver Protein" (50). He showed that this site for ^{14}C-labeled galactose was "into the deoxycholate-soluble fraction of the microsomes and essentially no incorporation into the rat ribosomal protein fraction was observed." This was in obvious contrast to results with ^{3}H-labeled leucine, which was, of course, found initially in the ribosomes. He then adds that "The striking difference in the patterns of an amino acid and hexose incorporation is interpreted to indicate that hexose or hexose-containing oligosaccharides are incorporated into completed peptide chains subsequent to polypeptide synthesis by the ribosome rather than during synthesis of the growing peptide chain. Since the membraneous component of the microsomes accounted for essentially all of the incorporated hexose radioactivity, these data strongly suggest that the membranes of the endoplasmic reticulum are the actual site of covalent linkage of hexoses to the completed peptide chains."

In July, 1964 the hypothesis concerning glycoproteins as intermediates in protein synthesis was formulated, and essentially it read:

One of the important unanswered problems in protein synthesis is that of the release of the completed polypeptide from the ribosomal surface, so that a new round of synthesis can occur. Enough evidence exists in the literature to suggest that, in almost all instances from *Escherichia coli* to mammals, as well as in plants, glycoproteins are obligatory intermediates in protein synthesis. The covalent addition of oligosaccharide moieties to the polypeptide forms the "handle" by which the protein is removed from the ribosomal surface. Recent evidence (50) indicates that the glycoid units are synthesized in the lipoprotein membranes of the endoplasmic reticulum. The glycoid units are probably transferred to the completed polypeptide of the adjacent ribosome attached to the membrane. Thus, glycoproteins would be the "nascent proteins" (51).

In order to synthesize the glycoid moieties of thyroglobulin or some of the serum glycoproteins, the following Leloir coenzymes are required: U, UDP galactose and UDP-*N*-acetylglucosamide; G, GDP mannose and GDP fucose; C, CMP sialic acid; and A, ADPG. Thus, A, U, G, and C are necessary for the synthesis of glycoproteins. Therefore, in addition to the three known types of RNA needed for polypeptide synthesis, namely messenger RNA, transfer RNA, and ribosomal RNA, each of the four bases of RNA plays a special role as part of a glycosyl transfer coenzyme.

It seems significant that, of the enzymes contained in the lysosomes (52), the following seven enzymes, acid phosphatase, β-galactosidase, α-glucosidase, α-mannosidase, β-acetylaminodeoxyglucosidase, β-glucuronidase, and cathepsin would seem to be involved in the turnover of phosphoglycoproteins. The acid ribonuclease and acid deoxyribonuclease could conceivably be concerned with supplying precursor materials for Leloir coenzyme synthesis.

Hers has shown that the lysosomal α-glucosidase is necessary for the normal turnover of glycogen (53).

Later in 1964, Sarcione and associates showed similar results when glucosamine (54) was used in place of galactose. Sarcione and Carmody (1966) have recently described "a cell-free system containing the deoxycholate-soluble fraction of microsomes and ribosomes obtained from rat liver which catalyzes incorporation of D-galactose, from UDP-galactose, into protein" (55). In their discussion they state: "It should be emphasized however, that this observation does not imply that ribosomes are the site of galactose incorporation into glycoproteins *in vivo*. Based on previous conclusions that *in vivo*, hexoses and hexosamine are incorporated into completed polypeptide chains during their migration through the membranes of the endoplasmic reticulum, it can be predicted that any proteins remaining bound to ribosomes isolated *in vitro* would be incompletely glycosylated."

Similar experiments are now being carried out with thyroid tissue (56, 57). The thyroid synthesizes thyroglobulin which is an iodinated glycoprotein. The sequence of formation of the component parts has been shown to be (1) the synthesis of the polypeptide portion, followed by (2) the addition of the glycoid moieties, and finally (3) the iodination of protein-bound tyrosines (58).

P. N. Campbell (59) were probably the first to make a systematic study in search of net synthesis of albumin in a cell-free system from rat liver. This work indicated that the intact microsomal fraction was necessary for such a synthesis. In 1965, Ganoza and colleagues showed that the microsomal fraction from mouse liver could synthesize several complete proteins (60). These were identified by immunoelectrophoresis. This year, Redman *et al.* demonstrated the synthesis and transfer of amylase in pigeon pancreatic microsomes which has been summarized as follows. "Taken together, our results support the conclusion that protein newly synthesized for export by attached ribosomes is unidirectionally released across the membrane of the endoplasmic reticulum into the cisternal space. They also indicate that the system *in vitro* contains the mechanism involved in the transfer and release of such proteins" (*61*).

Hemoglobin synthesis in the reticulocyte also seems to involve membrane-bound ribosomes (*62*).

THE SCHEME FOR THE BIOSYNTHESIS OF PROTEINS (VIA GLYCOPROTEINS) (*63*)

The polypeptide is assembled on membrane-bound polysomes containing mRNA. Because the polypeptide is held by hydrophobic bonds [Woese *et al.* (*64*)], it cannot leave the enzyme-forming site. It is necessary to "spot weld" on a glycoid unit at some position along the protein. This permits the protein to leave its hydrophobic attachment at one significant point which allows the beginning of the folding process which will result in the globular protein. If the glycoprotein is meant for export, it will "flip-flop" into the cisternae and travel to the Golgi apparatus where it will be packaged for leaving the cell. If, on the other hand, it must stay in the cell, the proteins must have most of their glycoid moieties removed by carbohydrases. The lysosomes contain the required enzymes, but the lysosomes also contain the cathepsins. Associated with the enzyme-forming sites, however, there may be lysosomes which do not contain the cathepsins or part of the membrane may contain the required hydrolases. The protein now depleted in glycoid content can no longer leave the cell. The sequential removal of the monosaccharide units is analogous to removal of the N-formylmethionine, followed by alanine, and then serine as is the case at the end terminal of proteins in *E. coli* [Adams and Capecchi (*65*)].

CELL MEMBRANES AND PROTEIN SYNTHESIS

Certainly it is of extreme importance to know whether a substance is in or out of the cell. One must distinguish between being in or out of the cell, the mitochondrion, the chloroplast, etc. The "in-ness" or "out-ness" is determined by the various cell membranes which are lipoprotein in nature.

Robertson, Stoeckenius, and others have unequivocally proved that the Danielli-Davson model for the "unit membrane" holds up essentially unchanged (*66*). Recent electron microscopy evidence has indicated that the inner and outer protein layers are different, and other evidence has indicated that the outer layer is more mucoprotein or glycoprotein in nature. The proteins of the membranes may best be described as being lipoglycophosphoproteins (66a). Since parts of the proteins which make up the membranes contain probably both helical and randomly coiled sections, both hydrophilic and hydrophobic areas add to the diversity of parameters of solubility available. Thiol groups are also found at the surface of the cell (66b).

It is quite interesting to note how little attention has been paid to the prebiotic evolution of the membranes of the cell. And yet, it is certainly one of the most important problems facing the spontaneous generation of life. In fact, one might well say that there can be no life without a limiting membrane. Just as a molecule of DNA is dead outside of a cell, so are viruses dead, because they are not surrounded by membranes of the usual type found in cells. The establishment of a *milieu interieure* has been of prime importance (63).

Once the lipoprotein membranes were formed, a new phase for chemical reactivity was made available within the cell. The establishment of a hydrophobic phase, be it only 40 Å in size, made possible a situation of extreme interest. One could go from an aqueous to a nonaqueous phase and back to the aqueous medium. This is one way to insure a flow of substances through the cell. The significance of this possibility cannot be overemphasized, for this is probably a key trick in the superb bag of tricks which is the cell.

The protein-forming sites of the cell are comprised of membrane-bound ribosomes, not free ribosomes and not free membranes. It is the rough endoplasmic membrane which is the protein-forming site. That this is indeed the case is clearly indicated by the histological characteristics of tissues busily engaged in making protein. Just as the original correlations made by Brachet (1941) and Caspersson (1941) concerning basophilia (RNA) and protein synthesis have proved fruitful, so the fact that the rough endoplasmic reticulum is related to protein synthesis must be strictly observed. In 1957, Loftfield (67) wrote a review article on protein synthesis which is still pertinent today. He wrote concerning the membrane problem: "Palade's systematic examination of forty mammalian cell types has revealed that all but mature red blood cells contain these dense particles associated in some degree with the membranes (Palade, 1955). Some granules may exist unattached to membranes, and the number of granules varies with the cell type, being lowest in the cytoplasm of granulocytes and seminal epithelia, highest in rapidly proliferating cells and glandular cells. In cell types showing intense basophilia (acinar cells of pancreas, mammary and salivary glands) almost all of the particles appear to be attached to the membranes."

Siekevitz (68) was the first to report a cell-free system capable of amino acid incorporation. The system was further resolved in 1954 by Zamecnik and Keller (69). They showed that the microsomes in the presence of a soluble fraction could, in the presence of adenosine triphosphate (ATP) incorporate amino acids. In the next 3 years further important clarifications were contributed by this laboratory at Massachusetts General Hospital and are reviewed by Hoagland (70). Schweet and associates contributed the cell-free system from reticulocytes in 1958 (70a). The next big step was that of Lamborg and Zamecnik (71). In 1960 they developed such a system for *E. coli*. In the summer of 1961, Nirenberg announced his polyU experiments.

Over the past years it had become apparent that something was wrong. Only a few cases of the synthesis of a complete protein could be demonstrated, and with difficulty. A few voices in the desert were heard. Hendler (1962) concerned with his work on protein synthesis in hen's oviduct "pointed to the basic and general importance of a cellular membrane in the process of normal characteristic protein synthesis" (72). Godson *et al.* (73), Schlessinger (73a), and Hendler *et al.* (73b) have shown by careful work that many of the ribosomes of bacteria are membrane-bound. For some bacteria an extensive system of internal membranes have been demonstrated (Salton, (73c)).

Novelli and Eisenstadt (74) first reported on the synthesis of β-galactosidase by a cell-free system from *E. coli* in 1960. At about the same time Nisman first described his work with a preparation consisting of digiton in treated spheroplasts. Nisman and Pelmont (75) have reviewed the problem of *de novo* protein synthesis through the first half of 1964. The membrane preparation of Nisman is a complex system containing ribosomes, extraribosomal RNA, and DNA. It can consistently make both constitutive and inducible enzymes.

It should be mentioned that for the rat, Pitot and his co-workers have presented a model to explain the deranged metabolic patterns of tumors. Their model states that "a primary defect in the structural mosaic of the endoplasmic reticulum of the liver cell could explain much of the data." They suggest that the steroid hormones also work at this level (75a).

THE LYSOSOMES—THEIR FUNCTION AND BACTERIAL "EQUIVALENT" IN *E. coli*

de Duve first demonstrated the lysosomal fraction of the cell in 1955 (76). He has recently reviewed the structure, properties, and what is thought to be the function of this fraction (77). The Pathology Symposium on "Lysosomes" held at the meeting of the Federation of American Societies for Experimental Biology in 1964 provides an excellent review of the subject (77a). Novikoff in 1963 said of the lysosomes: "Under normal conditions they may play important roles in organismic physiology as well as cell physiology" (77b).

The thesis of the present hypothesis is that the lysosomal enzymes are intimately involved in protein synthesis. That these organelles are universally distributed in the animal kingdom has been clearly demonstrated. It is suggested that *E. coli* contains a corresponding system of enzymes. The enzymes located in the space between the cell membrane and the cell wall may be analogous lysosomal constituents (deDuve 77). The enzymes contained in this compartment have been studied by the following groups: Neu and Heppel (78), Malamy and Horecker (79), and Melo and Glaser (80). These enzymes include a ribonuclease (RNase) (78), an alkaline phosphatase (79), a cyclic phosphodiesterase (78), a 5'-nucleotidase (78), an acid phosphatase most active as an α-aldose-1-phosphatase (78), and a series of nucleotide diphosphate hexose pyrophosphatases (80). Melo and Glaser point out that their demonstrated nucleotide diphosphate pyrophosphatases, "Together with the 5'-nucleotidase and the α-aldose-1-phosphate phosphatase described previously provided a mechanism for the complete breakdown of nucleotide diphosphate sugars to the corresponding monosaccharide and nucleoside, both of which can penetrate the cell membrane." It is significant that although the mammalian lysosomes contain a series of carbohydrases capable of splitting glycoid units manufactured from Leloir coenzymes, what appear to be the lysosomal enzymes of *E. coli* destroy the Leloir coenzymes themselves. It is obvious that one must cross-check the various specificities of these two groups of enzymes.

Melo and Glaser continue their discussion in this manner.

"The nucleotide diphosphate sugar pyrophosphatases described in this communication are clearly distinct from the nucleotide diphosphate pyrophosphorylases, since they do not require inorganic phosphate and attempts to demonstrate the formation of UDP and ADP by carrying out the reaction in the presence of excess pyruvic kinase and lactic dehydrogenase have been unsuccessful.

"It seems unlikely that the function of the nucleotide diphosphate sugar pyrophosphatases is to hydrolyze exogenously supplied nucleotide diphosphate sugars. It appears much more likely that they function to hydrolyse excess nucleotides, preventing nucleotide accumulation in the cell. This mechanism is an alternative to feedback inhibition, for those nucleotides, whose hydrolysis products are readily metabolizable as has been discussed previously. For enzymes described in this communication, a mechanism must also be provided for bringing together the enzymes and the substrate across the cell membrane."

It would seem that the flip-flop mechanism for membrane transport described below could serve to bring enzyme and substrate together.

It is of interest that these hydrolytic enzymes must be activated by heating a homogenate at 56°C. The uninhibited enzymes exist in the space between the membrane and the cell wall, but the inhibitor stays within the sphereoplast. This necessity for activation by heat is reminiscent of the DPNase first demonstrated by Swartz et al. (81). The recent work of Coval (82) with B. subtilis enzyme indicates that the amino acid compositions of the enzyme and the inhibitor are very similar. It would be most interesting if the situation were analogous to that of RNase A and RNase B. This DPNase is a glycoprotein (25).

The analogy between the so-called "lysosomes" of E. coli and those of the mammals may not be too tightly drawn. But what is obvious is that the Leloir coenzymes are intimately involved in protein synthesis in both instances.

The evidence of Nisman indicates that in order for his system to make protein there must be a concomitant synthesis of RNA (75). The RNase found in the "lysosomal compartment" (78) would seem to be involved in the breakdown of this RNA, which should be mRNA in character, and this situation might well account for the rapid turnover of mRNA in E. coli [see Kivity-Vogel and Elson (83)].

A PROPOSAL FOR A MECHANISM OF MEMBRANE TRANSPORT

This mechanism may be called the flip-flop mechanism or the counter-current distribution mechanism. The idea for the proposal is derived from the following observations made by Gregory and Craig in working out the design of their apparatus (84).

Although 25–50 inversion cycles, through 30° above and below the horizontal, are sufficient to attain complete equilibrium between the phases, more vigorous shaking does not insure equilibration. It is at the make and break of the increased interfacial area that the substance in question crosses the interface. It seems quite logical that the cell membrane should work in much the same manner, a flip-flop of the two halves of the unit membrane. The mechanism implies that for part of the time the outer surface of the cell is lipid in character, and for the rest of the time it is lipoglycophosphoprotein in nature. The most thermodynamically stable form is that of the standard Davson-Danielli model. That is the model that one sees in the electron microscope. Subunits of the membrane probably flip-flop dynamically at all times. Of interest in this connection is the fact that the myelin sheath, originally derived from Schwann cell membranes which admittedly contain a higher lipid content than normal cell membranes, is proteolipid in nature (85). This may well indicate a reversal of the unit membrane structure.

In membrane transport terminology one may say that in 1% of the membrane there are "pores" which allow K^+ transport. According to the proposed mechanism this would imply that in only 1% of all the unit membranes making up the cell surface does one find an inner membrane protein and an outer membrane protein of the proper specificity for the passage of a K^+ ion.

THE STORAGE PROBLEM

There are two basic types of storage: bulk and ordered. Storage of glycogen and fat are obvious examples of bulk. DNA in most instances is an example of ordered, informational storage. Proteins are also stored in the sense that one can fast for 6 months. Here is an example of ordered bulk. There are examples also of DNA being stored. In *Helix pomatia*, at one stage of development, one finds a thirtyfold excess over the diploid number in the nucleus of the salivary glands. As development proceeds, this excess disappears (86). It is worthwhile to recall the experiments of Geiger and Yamasaki with perfused cat brain (87). They showed that the previous requirement for including a liver in the perfusion system to prevent degeneration of the brain could be replaced by including uridine and cytidine in the perfusate. These experiments indicate that although the capacity to make purines is not limiting, the perfused brain cannot maintain an adequate synthesis of pyrimidines. Here, then, one may ask whether this may not also be a matter of insufficient storage of pyrimidines [Mandel, 1964 (88)].

If one looks carefully one finds that even DNA can turn over under proper conditions, in bacteria (89), plants (90), insects (91), and possibly even in mammals (92).

The nonrandom array of the genes in T4 phage has been beautifully demonstrated by Epstein and associates (93). In higher forms the complexity of the programming must be much greater.

If one cares to cite theoretical arguments, the DNA in man can conceivably code for 1×10^6 proteins. A likely value for the actual number involved probably lies below 1×10^5 [Haldane (94)] and may be nearer 20,000. If one assumes the latter figure to be valid, there is a fiftyfold excess of DNA. (One might mention that the weight of DNA in a rat liver cell is equal to the entire weight of an *E. coli* cell.) There should be other functions for this very large excess. It has been suggested that in the higher forms, where a more complex order of programming is involved in embryogenesis, etc., this excess DNA orders the assembly of yet another type of RNA, whose ultimate function is to service as a source of Leloir coenzymes.

The recent work of Scott (95) and his group with a rapidly turning-over RNA species found in the nucleus of ascites cells seems particularly pertinent. This RNA fraction comprises 5% of the RNA of the cell and 60% of it turns over in 1 hour. The composition, as determined from specific activities of the isolated nucleotides, is roughly UMP, 40 parts; GMP, 30; AMP, 20; and CMP, 10 parts (96). The G/C ratio is 3, and the U/A ratio is 2. The $G + U$ content of this RNA is the highest ever described and is an exception to the Chargaff rule that the 6-keto bases should equal the 6-NH_2 bases. It seems significant that the order $U > G > C$ approximates the requirement for sugar moieties for glycoprotein synthesis via the Leloir coenzymes. A logical function for this RNA would be for the RNA to give up its bases in some exonuclease reaction and yield an ordered sequence of bases for Leloir coenzyme synthesis. It may be recalled that the nucleus is a major site for the synthesis of both Leloir coenzymes and pyridine nucleotide coenzymes. In a recent paper Wykes and Smellie (97) report: "The results described above demonstrate that the microsomal fraction of Lanschutz ascites-tumor cells catalyzes the independent incorporation into polyribonucleotides of AMP, GMP, CMP, and UMP residues from the corresponding ribonucleoside triphosphates. The reaction is promoted by the addition of RNA and not DNA, is inhibited by ribonuclease but not by deoxyribonuclease or actinomycin D, requires Mg^{2+} rather than Mn^{2+} ions and is inhibited to some extent by the addition of the three complementary ribonucleoside 5'-triphosphates." These homopolymers would also serve as storage molecules or may indeed have another more specific function. Seaman working with Spiegelman made similar observations with a membrane preparation from *E. coli* in the late 1950's (98).

The problem of the biosynthesis of DNA is still an intriguing one. Kornberg and his associates have worked hard and beautifully for many years on their highly purified DNA polymerase. The failure of these preparations to manufacture biologically active DNA molecules is not surprising, since both the enzyme and primer were too highly purified. Ganesan and Lederberg (99) in their paper entitled "A Cell-Membrane Bound Fraction of Bacterial DNA" conclude: "From the above observations, the most plausible explanation is that membrane cell wall is the site of DNA synthesis in bacteria." This later finding, plus the fact that DNA synthesis is exquisitely dependent upon previous protein synthesis (100) brings one back to the membrane-bound primer concept. Most RNA synthesis also depends on protein synthesis. "The fact that a number of protein synthetic inhibitors can exert the same inhibitory effect suggests that these drugs are interfering with an RNA synthetic system which is coupled to a protein synthetic system in such a way that the rate of the later governs the rate of the former" [Martin, 1966 (101); see also De Kloet, 1966 (47)].*

"BUILD IN" VERSUS "BUILD ON"

The principle of building on was first unequivocally demonstrated by Kornberg and associates (102). They showed that the glycosyl residues on the 5-hydroxymethylcytosine groups of T-even phages were added after the backbone polynucleotide was assembled from the nucleoside triphosphates. There is an ever expanding list of such reactions: the sulfate of chondroitin sulfuric acid (103), the synthesis of protein polysaccharides, lipopolysaccharides, and glycolipids, the glycoid of glycoproteins, the iodine of thyroglobulin (104), the hydroxyls of hydroxyproline of collagen (105), methylation to the odd bases in nucleic acids (109). The acetyl group at the N-terminal end of many proteins (106), and the covalent "sewing up" of subunits to form the fibrin clot (107). The "backbone" of these molecules are coded for (i.e., the building in process); the building on is carried out later. [At a low molecular weight level, it has been shown that lecithin can be formed from phosphatidyl ethanolamine (108).]

The coded information for the basic subunit is genetically determined. The structure of the basic subunit is such that the build-on enzyme can recognize a part of its structure as a substrate for adding on the necessary moiety. Although it is true that the build-on enzyme is coded for, one build-on enzyme can act on many different substrate molecules. The number of basic subunits may thus be kept to a minimum.

* S. Spiegelman's recent work deals with a special viral RNA system.

EPILOGUE

Biochemistry is the study of the chemistry of biologically related compounds and systems. Chemical biology is the biology derived, guided, and based on the study of these chemical substances and their properties. There is a fundamental difference in viewpoint.

To the chemical biologist the fundamental unit of study is first, foremost, and always the cell. The cell is alive. The substances in the cell are dead. Any structure within the cell is only significant as a part in understanding the whole. In essence this is the organismic approach. This also implies that every substance in the cell is "the" most important.

Biochemists have come a long way since Buchner in 1897 demonstrated that a cell-free extract of yeast could ferment alcohol. They now know of thousands of enzymes, substrates, and reactions that are found in cells. They have been hard at work breaking down the cell to its component parts. This work is, of course, absolutely essential to an understanding of the whole. The time has come, however, when even to understand the chemistry of the situation, let alone the biology, it is necessary to start putting the pieces back together.

ACKNOWLEDGMENT

I wish to thank Drs. H. M. Kalcker, H. Linschitz, W. P. Jencks, Mrs. Marie Sacks, and F. J. Kull for their help in preparing the final manuscript.

REFERENCES

1. Sonneborn, T. M. *Proc. Natl. Acad. Sci. U.S.* **51**, 915 (1964).
2. Caputto, R., Leloir, L. F., Trucco, R. E., Cardini, C. E., and Paladine, A. C. *J. Biol. Chem.* **179**, 497 (1949); Caputto, R., Leloir, L. F., Cardini, C. E., and Paladini, A. C. *J. Biol. Chem.* **184**, 333 (1950).
3. Park, J. T., and Johnson, M. J. *J. Biol. Chem.* **179**, 585 (1949); Park, J. T. *Federation Proc.* **9**, 213 (1950).
4. Leloir, L. F. *Proc. 6th Intern. Congr. Biochem., New York, 1964* pp. 15-29 (1964).
5. Ginsburg, V. *Advan. Enzymol.* **26**, 35 (1964).
6. Soodak, M. *in* "Phosphorus Metabolism" (W. D. McElroy and B. Glass, eds.), p. 439. Johns Hopkins Press, Baltimore, Maryland, 1952.
7. Soodak, M. *J. Cellular Comp. Physiol.* **47** (Suppl. 1), 111 (1956).
8. Stacey, M. *Discussions Faraday Soc.* **13**, 245 (1953).
9. E. H. Eylar, *J. Theoret. Biol.* **10**, 89 (1966).
10. Pusztai, A. *Biochem. J.* **94**, 604 (1965); Kocourek, J., Jiráček, V., Tictiá, M., Buchbaucrová, V., and Faltejsková, J. *Proc. 6th Intern. Congr. Biochem., New York, 1964* Vol. II, p. 99 (1964); Liener, I. E., Ramachandramurthy, P., and Takahashi, T. *Federation Proc.* **25**, Abstract 3475 (1966).

11. Jeanloz, R. W., and Balazs, E. A. eds. "The Amino Sugars," Vol. IIA. Academic Press, New York, 1965.
12. Pazur, J. H., and Kleppe, K. *Proc. 6th Intern. Congr. Biochem., New York, 1964* Vol. II, p. 149 (1964); Pazur, J. H., Kleppe, K., and Ball, E. M. *Arch. Biochem. Biophys.* **103**, 515 (1963); Swoboda, B. E. P., and Massey, V. *J. Biol. Chem.* **240**, 2209 (1965).
13. Morris, D. R., and Hager, L. P. *J. Biol. Chem.* **241**, 1763 (1966).
14. Hermans, P. E., O'Connell, E. J., and Markowitz, H. *Proc. 6th Intern. Congr. Biochem., New York, 1964* Vol. II, p. 78 (1964).
15. Feinberg, J. G., and Morgan, W. T. J. *Brit. J. Exptl. Pathol.* **34**, 104 (1953).
16. Hinsdill, H. D., and Goebel, W. F. *Proc. 6th Intern. Congr. Biochem., New York, 1964* Vol. II, p. 81 (1964).
17. Sarkar, N., Sarkar, S., and Kozloff, L. M. *Biochemistry* **3**, 511 (1964).
18. Theørell, H., and Åkeson, A. *Arkiv Kemi Mineral. Biol.* **16a**, 1 (1943).
19. Morita, Y., and Kameda, K. *Mem. Res. Inst. Food Sci. Kyoto Univ.* **14**, 49 (1958); Morita, Y., and Kameda, K. *Bull. Agr. Chem. Soc. Japan* **23**, 28 (1959).
20. Plummer, T. H., Jr., and Hirs, C. H. W. *J. Biol. Chem.* **238**, 1396 (1963).
21. Tsugita, A., and Akabori, S. *J. Biochem. (Tokyo)* **46**, 695 (1959).
22. Orlowski, M., and Meister, A. *J. Biol. Chem.* **240**, 238 (1965).
23. Nichol, L. W., and Roy, A. B. *Biochemistry* **4**, 386 (1965).
24. Wellner, D. *Biochemistry* **5**, 1585 (1966).
25. Soodak, M., Kaplan, N. O., and Everse, J. unpublished observations.
25a. Watson, H. C. personal communication.
25b. Soodak, M. unpublished observations.
26. Gottschalk, A. "The Chemistry and Biology of Sialic Acids and Related Substances." Cambridge Univ. Press, London and New York, 1960.
27. Eylar, E. H., Madoff, M., Brody, O., and Oncley, J. *J. Biol. Chem.* **237**, 1992 (1962); Glaeser, R., Todd, P., and Richmond, J. *Federation Proc.* **25**, Abstract 3226 (1966).
28. Kabat, E. A. "Blood Group Substances." Academic Press, New York, 1956; Watkins, W. M. *Science* **152**, 172 (1966).
29. Warren, L. *J. Biol. Chem.* **234**, 1971 (1959).
30. Eylar, E. H., and Jeanloz, R. W. *J. Biol. Chem.* **237**, 1021 (1962).
31. Aaronson, S., and Hutner, S. H. *Quart. Rev. Biol.* **41**, 13 (1966).
32. Grant, P. T., and Simkin, J. L. *Ann. Rept.* **61**, 491 (1964).
33. Schmid, K. *Chimia (Aarau)* **18**, 321 (1964).
34. Spiro, R. G. *New Engl. J. Med.* **269**, 566, 616 (1963).
35. Gottschalk, A., and Graham, E. R. B. *in* "The Proteins" (H. Neurath, ed.), Vol. 4, p. 96. Academic Press, New York, 1966.
35a. Neuberger, A. *Proc. 6th Intern. Congr. Biochem., New York, 1964* Vol. II, p. 55 (1964).
35b. Winzler, R. *Clin. Chem.* **11**, 339 (1965).
35c. Gottshalk, A. (ed.) "Glycoproteins" Elsevier, Amsterdam (1966).
36. Schiller, S. *Ann. Rev. Physiol.* **28**, 137 (1966).
37. *Federation Proc.* **25**, 939 (1966).
38. Hamerman, D., Rojkind, M., and Sandson, J. *Federation Proc.* **25**, 1040 (1966).

39. Partridge, S. M. *Federation Proc.* **25**, 994 (1966); Marler, E., and Davidson, E. *Proc. Natl. Acad. Sci.* **54**, 648 (1965).

40. Erlander, S. R., Tobin, R., and Dimler, R. J. *Proc. 6th Intern. Congr. Biochem., New York, 1964* Vol. VI, p. 28 (1964).

41. Petrova, A. N. *Proc. 6th Intern. Congr. Biochem., New York, 1964* Vol. VI, p. 87 (1964); Sie, H. -G., and Fishman, W. H. *Proc. 6th Intern. Congr. Biochem., New York, 1964* Vol. VI, p. 108 (1964); Tata, J. R. *Biochem. J.* **90**, 284 (1964); Maley, F., McGarrahan, J. F., and Del Giacco, R. *Biochem. Biophys. Res. Commun.* **23**, 85 (1966); Deman, J. C. H., and Blok, A. P. R. *J. Histochem. Cytochem.* **14**, 135 (1966).

42. Lipke, H., and Graves, B. *Federation Proc.* **25**, Abstract 2915 (1966).

43. Nikaido, H. *Proc. Natl. Acad. Sci. U.S.* **48**, 1542 (1962).

43a. Osborn, M. J., Rosen, S. M., Rothfield, L., Zeleznick, L. D., and Horecker, B. L. *Science* **145**, 783 (1964).

44. Telser, A., Robinson, H. C., and Dorfman, A. *Proc. Natl. Acad. Sci. U.S.* **54**, 912 (1965).

45. Markovitz, A., and Dorfman, A. *J. Biol. Chem.* **237**, 273 (1962).

46. Kull, F. J., Maloof, F., and Soodak, M. *Federation Proc.* **24**, Abstract 1965 (1965); Hall, R. H. *Biochemistry* **3**, 769 (1964).

47. De Kloet, S. R. *Biochem. J.* **99**, 566 (1966).

48. Salser, J. S., and Balis, M. E. *Federation Proc.* **25**, Abstract 3358 (1966); Holoubek, V. *Federation Proc.* **25**, Abstract 3327 (1966); Balis, M. E., Salser, and Elder, A. *Nature* **203**, 1170 (1964); Bendich, A. and Rosenkranz, H. S. *in* "Progress in Nucleic Acids," (J. M. Davidson and W. E. Cohen, eds.), Vol. 1, p. 219. Academic Press, New York, 1963; Levine, L. and Van Vanakis, H. *in* "Antibodies to Biologically Active Molecules" Pergamon Press, Oxford and London, in press.

49. Autilio, L. *Federation Proc.* **25**, Abstract 3250 (1966); Lees, M. B. *Federation Proc.* **25**, Abstract 3271 (1966); Kies, M. W., Bier, C. J., Alvord, E. C., Kaku, J., and Hruby, S. *Federation Proc.* **25**, Abstract 3415 (1966).

49a. Brunner, J. R. *Abstr. 152nd Meeting Am. Chem. Soc.* No. C86, New York (1966).

50. Sarcione, E. J. *J. Biol. Chem.* **239**, 1686 (1964).

51. Straub, F. B. *Advan. Enzymol.* **26**, 89 (1964).

52. de Duve, C. *J. Theoret. Biol.* **6**, 33 (1964).

53. Hers, H. G. *Advan. Metab. Disorders* **1**, 2 (1964).

54. Sarcione, E. J., Bohne, M., and Leahy, M. *Biochemistry* **3**, 1973 (1964).

55. Sarcione, E. J., and Carmody, P. J. *Biochem. Biophys. Res. Commun.* **22**, 689 (1966).

56. Bouchilloux S., and Cheftel, C. *Biochem. Biophys. Res. Commun.* **23**, 305 (1966).

57. Strycharz, W. A., Kull, F. J., and Soodak, M. Work in progress.

58. Spiro, R. G., and Spiro, M. J. *J. Biol. Chem.* **241**, 1271 (1966).

59. Sargent, J. R., and Campbell, P. N. *Biochem. J.* **96**, 134 (1965).

60. Ganoza, M. C., Williams, C. A., and Lipmann, F. *Proc. Natl. Acad. Sci. U.S.* **53**, 619, 622 (1965).

61. Redman, C. M., Siekevitz, P., and Palade, G. E. *J. Biol. Chem.* **241**, 1150 (1966).

62. Schulman, H. personal communication.
63. Soodak, M. *J. Cellular Comp. Physiol.* **66** (Suppl. 1), 180 (1965).
64. Woese, C. R., Dugre, D. H., Saxinger, W. C., and Dugre, S. A. *Proc. Natl. Acad. Sci. U.S.* **55**, 966 (1966).
65. Adams, J. M., and Capecchi, M. R. *Proc. Natl. Acad. Sci. U.S.* **55**, 147 (1966); Capecchi, M. R. *Proc. Natl. Acad. Sci. U.S.* **55**, 1517 (1966).
66. Robertson, J. D. *Progr. Biophys. Biophys. Chem.* **10**, 343 (1960); Stoeckenius, W. *Proc. 6th Intern. Congr. Biochem., New York, 1964* Vol. VIII, p. S1, (1964); Vandenheuvel, F. A. *J. Am. Oil Chemists' Soc.* **42**, 481 (1965); Van Deenen, L. L. M. *J. Am. Oil Chemists' Soc.* **43**, 296 (1966).
66a. Emmelot, P., Bos, C. J., Benedetti, E. L., and Rumke, P. *Biochim. Biophys. Acta* **90**, 126 (1964).
66b. Vanstevenick, J., Weed, R. I., and Rothstein, A. *J. Gen. Physiol.* **48**, 617 (1965).
67. Loftfield, R. B. *Progr. Biophys. Biophys. Chem.* **8**, 347 (1957).
68. Siekevitz, P. *J. Biol. Chem.* **145**, 549 (1962).
69. Zamecnik, P. C., and Keller, E. B. *J. Biol. Chem.* **209**, 337 (1954).
70. Hoagland, M. B. *in* "The Nucleic Acids" (E. Chargaff and J. M. Davidson, eds.), p. 349. Academic Press, New York, 1960.
70a. Schweet, R., Lamfrom, H., and Allen, E. *Proc. Natl. Acad. Sci.* **44**, 1029 (1958).
71. Lamborg, M. F., and Zamecnik, P. C. *Biochim. Biophys. Acta* **42**, 206 (1960).
72. Hendler, R. W. *Nature* **193**, 821 (1962); Hendler, R. W. *Biochim. Biophys. Acta* **74**, 659, 667 (1963).
73. Godson, G. N., Hunter, G. D., and Butler, J. A. V. *Biochem. J.* **81**, 59 (1961).
73a. Schlessinger, D. *J. Mol. Biol.* **7**, 569 (1963).
73b. Tani, J., and Hendler, R. W. *Biochim. Biophys. Acta* **80**, 279 (1964); Hendler, R. W., and Tani, J. *Biochim. Biophys. Acta* **80**, 294 (1964); Hendler, R. W., Banfield, W. G., Tani, J., and Kuff, E. L. *Biochim. Biophys. Acta* **80**, 307 (1964).
73c. Salton, M. R. J. "The Bacterial Cell Wall." Elsevier, Amsterdam, 1964.
74. Novelli, G. D., and Eisenstadt, J. M. *in* "Informational Macromolecules" (H. T. Vogel, V. Bryson, and J. O. Lampen, eds.), p. 301. Academic Press, New York, 1963.
75. Nisman, B., and Pelmont, J. *Progr. Nucleic Acid Res.* **3**, 236 (1964).
75a. Pitot, H. C., Cho, Y. S., Lamar, C., Jr., and Peraino, C. *J. Cellular Comp. Physiol.* **66** (Suppl. 1), 163 (1965); Pitot, H. C. *Perspectives Biol. Med.* **8**, 50 (1964).
76. de Duve, C., Pressman, B. C., Gianetto, R., Wattiaux, R., and Appelmann, F. *Biochem. J.* **60**, 604 (1955).
77. de Duve, C., and Wattiaux, R. *Ann. Rev. Physiol.* **28**, 435 (1966).
77a. *Federation Proc.* **23**, 1009 (1964).
77b. Novikoff, A. B. *Biol. Bull.* **125**, 358 (1963).
78. Neu, H. C., and Heppel, L. A. *J. Biol. Chem.* **239**, 3893 (1964); Neu, H. C., and Heppel, L. A. *J. Biol. Chem.* **240**, 3685 (1965).
79. Malamy, M. H., and Horecker, B. L. *Biochemistry* **3**, 1889 (1964).
80. Melo, A., and Glaser, L. *Biochem. Biophys. Res. Commun.* **22**, 524 (1966).

81. Swartz, M., Kaplan, N. O., and Lamborg, M. F. *J. Biol. Chem.* **232**, 1051 (1958).
82. Coval, M. L. *Federation Proc.* **23**, 159 (1964).
83. Kivity-Vogel, T., and Elson, D. I. E. G. 7, Memo 360 (1966).
84. Gregory, J. D., and Craig, L. C. *Ann. N.Y. Acad. Sci.* **53**, 1015 (1951).
85. Folch, J., and Lees, M. *J. Biol. Chem.* **191**, 807 (1951).
86. Leuchtenberger, C., and Schrader, F. *Proc. Natl. Acad. Sci. U.S.* **38**, 99 (1952).
87. Geiger, A., and Yamasaki, S. *J. Neurochem.* **1**, 93 (1956).
88. Mandel, P. *Progr. Nucleic Acid Res.* **3**, 299 (1964).
89. Contois, D. E., and Seymour, W. F. K. *Biochem. Biophys. Res. Commun.* **16**, 124 (1964).
90. Sampson, M., Katoh, A., Hotta, Y., and Stern, H. *Proc. Natl. Acad. Sci. U.S.* **50**, 459 (1963).
91. Lang, C. A., and Meins, F., Jr. *Proc. Natl. Acad. Sci. U.S.* **55**, 1525 (1966).
92. Roels, H. *Intern. Rev. Cytol.* **19**, 1 (1966).
93. Epstein, R. H., Bolle, A., Steinberg, C. M., Kellenberger, E., Boy de la Tour, E., Chevally, R., Edgar, R. S., Susman, M., Derhardt, G. H., and Lielausis, A. *Cold Spring Harbor Symp. Quant. Biol.* **28**, 375 (1963).
94. Haldane, J. B. S. "The Biochemistry of Genetics," p. 106. Allen & Unwin, London, 1954.
95. Scott, F., Kaltreider, H. B., Boeker, F. A., and Taft, E. B. *Federation Proc.* **23**, Abstract 405 (1964).
96. Scott, J. F. personal communication.
97. Wykes, J. R., and Smellie, R. M. S. *Biochem. J.* **99**, 347 (1966).
98. Seaman, E. Ph.D. Thesis, University of Illinois, Urbana, Illinois, 1960.
99. Ganesan, A. T., and Lederberg, J. *Biochem. Biophys. Res. Commun.* **18**, 824 (1965).
100. Billen, D., and Hewitt, R. Information Exchange Group No. 7, Memo 358 (1966); Cohen, S. S., *Ann. Rev. Biochem.* **32**, 83 (1963).
101. Martin, E. M. Information Exchange Group No. 7, Memo 352 (1966).
102. Kornberg, A., Zimmerman, S. B., Kornberg, S. R., and Josse, J. *Proc. Natl. Acad. Sci. U.S.* **45**, (1959).
103. D'Abramo, F., and Lipmann, F. *Biochim. Biophys. Acta* **25**, 211 (1957).
104. Maloof, F., Sato, G., and Soodak, M. *Medicine* **43**, 375 (1964); Taurog, A., and Howells, E. M. *Federation Proc.* **23**, 149 (1964); Goldberg, I. H., Seed, R. W., Schneider, A. B., and Sellin, H. G. *Federation Proc.* **23**, 434 (1964).
105. Udenfriend, S. *Science* **152**, 1335 (1966).
106. Marchis-Mouren, G., and Lipmann, F. *Proc. Natl. Acad. Sci. U.S.* **53**, 1147 (1965).
107. Lorand, L. *Federation Proc.* **24**, 784 (1965); Laki, K. *Federation Proc.* **24**, 794 (1965).
108. Bremer, J., and Greenberg, D. M. *Biochim. Biophys. Acta* **46**, 205 (1961); Gibson, K. D., Wilson, J. D., and Udenfriend, S. *J. Biol. Chem.* **236**, 673 (1961).
109. Feissner, E. and Borek, E. *Proc. Natl. Acad. Sci. U.S.* **48**, 1199 (1962).

Topical Subject Index

A

ADP, *see* Adenosine diphosphate

ATP, *see* Adenosine triphosphate

Acetoacetyl coenzyme A, synthesis of, 48

Acetyl coenzyme A

acetyl transfer function of, 44-48

growth of *C. kluyveri* and, 49-51

thioalkyl transfer function of, 49

Acetylcholine

analogs of, comparative potencies, 160

role in excitable cell membranes, 145-149

sulfur and selenium isologs of, of choline, and related compounds, 164-166

transformation into local anaesthetics, 161-164

modifications of chemical structures during, 162(T)

Acetylcholine esterase, ACh-receptor and, 155-158

Acetylcholine-receptor, 149-171

acetylcholinesterase and, 155-158

determination of dissociation constants with, 153-155

monocellular electroplax preparation, 149-153

protein of, conformational changes, 158-161

Active acetate, 185

Adenosine diphosphate, concentration in mouse jejunum, 122(T)

Adenosinetriphosphatases (ATPases), oxidative phosphorylation and, 6-7

Adenosine triphosphate

concentration in mouse jejunum, 122(T)

effect on uptake and phosphorylation of 2-deoxyglucose in muscle, 136-137

formation, reductive glycine deamination and, 51 ff

growth and, 21-23

Ambenonium derivatives, dissociation constants of, 157(T)

Amino acids, *see also* individual compounds

fermentations of, 51-55

γ-Aminobutyrate, fermentation of, 53-55

Aminothiazole, inhibition of thiamine biosynthesis by, 344-347

B

Bacteria, *see also* individual bacteria

anaerobic, energy metabolism of, 39-62

effect of starving and refeeding on polysome structure in, 205-206

poly-β-hydroxybutyrate metabolism in, 385-400

occurrence and function of intracellular poly-β-hydroxybutyrate, 385-386

Bark

decayed by white-rot fungi, analysis of, 318(T)

holocellulose and cellulose content of, 320(T)

Benzoquinonium derivatives, dissociation constants of, 157(T)

Biological systems

axioms on nature of, 87-88

disappearance of nonfunctional characters, 88-90

multiple uses of basic units, 90-91

Biology

developmental, genetic regulation and, 316-317

theoretical concepts in, 83-95

origin of, 86-87

present standing, 85 ff

C

Carbamyl phosphates

hydrolysis, effect of magnesium ions on, 409-410